CIVIL ENGINEERING AND ENERGY-ENVIRONMENT
VOLUME 1

Civil Engineering and Energy-Environment focuses on the research of civil engineering, environment resources and energy materials. This proceedings gathers the most cutting-edge research and achievements, aiming to provide scholars and engineers with preferable research direction and engineering solution as reference. Subjects in this proceedings include:

- Engineering Structure
- Environmental Protection Materials
- Architectural Environment
- Environment Resources
- Energy Storage
- Building Electrical Engineering

The works of this proceedings will promote development of civil engineering and environment engineering. Thereby, promote scientific information interchange between scholars from top universities, research centers and high-tech enterprises working all around the world.

PROCEEDINGS OF THE 4TH INTERNATIONAL CONFERENCE ON CIVIL ENGINEERING, ENVIRONMENT RESOURCES AND ENERGY MATERIALS (CCESEM 2022), SANYA, CHINA, 21–23 OCTOBER 2022

Civil Engineering and Energy-Environment Volume 1

Edited by

Qingfei Gao
Department of Bridge and Tunnel Engineering, School of Transportation Science and Engineering, Harbin Institute of Technology, China

Zhenhua Duan
Department of Structural Engineering, Tongji University, China

CRC Press is an imprint of the
Taylor & Francis Group, an **informa** business

A BALKEMA BOOK

First published 2023
by CRC Press/Balkema
4 Park Square, Milton Park, Abingdon, Oxon, OX14 4RN
e-mail: enquiries@taylorandfrancis.com
www.routledge.com – www.taylorandfrancis.com

CRC Press/Balkema is an imprint of the Taylor & Francis Group, an informa business

© 2023 selection and editorial matter, Qingfei Gao & Zhenhua Duan; individual chapters, the contributors

The right of Qingfei Gao & Zhenhua Duan to be identified as the authors of the editorial material, and of the authors for their individual chapters, has been asserted in accordance with sections 77 and 78 of the Copyright, Designs and Patents Act 1988.

All rights reserved. No part of this book may be reprinted or reproduced or utilised in any form or by any electronic, mechanical, or other means, now known or hereafter invented, including photocopying and recording, or in any information storage or retrieval system, without permission in writing from the publishers.

Although all care is taken to ensure integrity and the quality of this publication and the information herein, no responsibility is assumed by the publishers nor the author for any damage to the property or persons as a result of operation or use of this publication and/or the information contained herein.

Library of Congress Cataloging-in-Publication Data
A catalog record has been requested for this book

SET
ISBN: 978-1-032-44029-3 (hbk)
ISBN: 978-1-032-44033-0 (pbk)

Volume 1
ISBN: 978-1-032-56057-1 (hbk)
ISBN: 978-1-032-56058-8 (pbk)
ISBN: 978-1-003-43364-4 (ebk)
DOI: 10.1201/9781003433644

Volume 2
ISBN: 978-1-032-56059-5 (hbk)
ISBN: 978-1-032-56061-8 (pbk)
ISBN: 978-1-003-43365-1 (ebk)
DOI: 10.1201/9781003433651

Typeset in Times New Roman
by MPS Limited, Chennai, India

Table of Contents

Preface   xv
Committee Members   xvii

VOLUME 1

Civil structure repair and seismic technology

PyroSim-Based exterior wall fire prevention design for northern high-rise buildings *Yansheng Song & Zhenping Ba*	3
Study on burst pressure of corroded pipelines under axial force and bending moment *Tong Xu, Yuchao Yang, Shuai Feng & Feng Liu*	9
Research on mechanical characteristics of lining structure of shallow-buried multi-arch tunnel without middle drift *Chengye Jiang*	18
Analysis of influence of asymmetric zoned excavation on response variation of foundation pit engineering *Yongguo Yan & Junxing Luo*	25
Study on the effect of the moisture content change on resilient modulus of subgrade soils *Yuanzhong Chen, Fan Li, Yangyang Lu & Dan Hang*	33
Ground penetrating radar and light dynamic penetration test-based analysis and evaluation technology for existing railway subgrade *Yuanshui Cheng, Cui Du, Lijun Wang, Taifeng Li, Lyuzhou Lyu, Jingyu Liu & Xingang Zhang*	39
Evaluation of Acropolis of Athens under earthquake excitation and a proposal for roof restoration *Haohuan Xu, Xiaotao Shang, Chelsey Tao & Zhiqian Fang*	48
Design and implementation of BIM + prefabricated building platform based on Unreal Engine 4 *Bei Wu, Chenjie Zou, Binyan Ye, Xingyou Liu & Yanru Yang*	67
Study on tensile mechanical properties of steel strand considering the damage *Shilong Gao, Yachao Hu, Xiaobin Zhang & Feng Liu*	76
Research on fine management of engineering projects based on BIM5D technology *Bei Wu, Yuhe Zhao, Xiang Ou, Yun Bai & Ziyi Zhang*	91
Research on waterproofing performance optimization of cabinet panels based on DOE experimental design *Mengbing Li & Zhao Wang*	100

Research on reinforcement technology of unstable rock slopes 108
Renjie Wu, Zheng Li, Tao Hu, Wengang Zhang, Shilong Xiao, Dengsui Zhang, Chengwu Ming, Jianhua Huang, Zhangcan Kuang & Juan Pang

Study on natural frequency of damage position of implicit glass curtain wall 117
Chongge Wang, Meng Zhang, Yubiao Liu & Hui Li

Dynamic monitoring of citrus spatial distribution in Guilin based on GEE 123
Zhigang Qin, Haotian You, Tingting Gan & Xu Tang

Design and study of a steel truss arch bridge 134
Shui-Ping Fang, Jin-Liang Qiu, Fang Huang & Shuang Wang

Deformation analysis of inclined bar under vertical tensile 141
Enyang Zhu, Shengjie Wang, Yan Li, Fang Fang, Bowen Li & Zhitong Pei

Application analysis of BIM technology in building safety design 146
Bei Wu, Yunfan Peng, Yanmin Li, Menghui Qiao, Zongli Hu & Xinglan Nie

Application of modern surveying technology in the digital mine 156
Xiaoping Shi

Research on robustness of space steel frames against progressive collapse based on component method 162
Zheng Tan, Weihui Zhong & Yingzhao Qiu

Research on identification of key factors of construction quality based on AHP-DEMATEL method 169
Zhao Cheng & Meng Li

A study on space-time evolution of landscape patterns of building lands in eco-friendly areas—Taking Dongting Lake as an example 176
Zhiyong Tang, Jingtong Lv, Fuqiang Huang & Suting Zhang

Microwave heating removal and laboratory evaluation of pavement markings 190
Xiaoyong Zou, Wenxiu Wu, Yonglin Hu, Jing Liu & Lei Dong, Biao Zhang & Dapeng Li

Research on prefabricated buildings cost management based on value chain theory 197
Ting Cao & Tingting Liu

Shape and size effect on compressive strength of rammed earth 203
Tiegang Zhou, Dong Li, Wei Tan & Hui Tao

Research on safety planning technology of water projects construction 211
Qian Fu, Hui Tan, Xue Leng & Meng Ting Huang

Construction technology of bored pile in geotechnical engineering based on energy-saving concept 218
Chunbo Yin, Yongge Hou & Zehao Hou

Earthquake hazard analysis and safety evaluation of East African Rift Valley 225
Yan Yu & Xin Zhang

Modelling one-dimensional compression on structured soils considering time effects 232
Enyang Zhu, Yukun Chen, Xiyang Li, Chongqing Xu & Zhenghao Zhang

Research on the application of green building design based on BIM technology *Bei Wu, Yihan Cheng, Ya Dang, Yunfan Peng, Wen Zhao & Zhijun Ouyang*	237
Experimental study on slag improvement in a power shield tunnel in Xi'an *Jie Liu, Xuanrong Zheng & Jiahui Qi*	246
Experimental study on the effect of particle grade on the compressive strength of rammed earth *Tiegang Zhou, Mengyi Li & Wei Tan & Kan Hu*	253
Temperature sensitivity analysis of long-span arch bridge cable hoisting construction *Jiashou Dao, Qinghua Yang, Yonglaing Yu & Hongfei Zhuang*	261
Green building analysis and energy-saving and low-carbon transformation of existing buildings based on green building standards *Bei Wu, Fujie Liu & Lingkun Jing*	269
Research on zoning design method of high embankment slope with rigid foundation *Junlong Hu, Yao Xie, Jing Wang & Deyong Wang*	277
Evaluation of the construction effect of the Three-North Shelterbelt in Chaoyang City, China *Hongge Li*	285
Research and analysis of the distribution of greenhouses in Jiangsu Province *Jikun Zhao & Chaowei Deng*	297

Biomaterial equipment and metallurgical engineering

Analysis on mechanical properties of prefabricated pipe laying with fabricated machine-made sand concrete *Hua Mao, Fang Geng, Suna Bai, Zhipeng Xiong, Jipeng Tang, Xiangyang Fang, Tao Qin & Bingran Shao*	321
Research on key technologies and standards of waste plastics recycling in China *Yanxin Gao, Shuang Ding, Dongfeng Gao, Yi Zhu & Rui Zhang*	328
N-doping porous carbon with CoP loading for hydrogen evolution reaction *Yuelong Xu, Shasha Wang & Zhi Tian*	335
Discussion on shear strength parameters of rock mass *Yong Yang, Wen Fan, Zhangjian Xu, Zhihai Zhao & Haifeng Zhang*	341
Simulation of typical odor of automotive materials *Yalin Liu, Chen Cui, Siwei Zheng, Ke Wang, Jiayong Fu, Yi Zheng & Xiaojing Zhu*	351
Risk identification and evolution analysis of comprehensive urban river management based on WBS - RBS - ISM *Guofa Li, Liu Yang, Shutian Li, Xin Wang & Yan Li*	357
A novel method of synthesizing high thermal stability of $Ce_{0.37}Zr_{0.53}(LaY)_{0.10}O_2$ by introducing sulfate ligands *Zheng Zhao, Yongqi Zhang, Yongke Hou, Meisheng Cui, Weixin Zhao, Qingping Zhang, Juanyu Yang, Zongyu Feng & Xiaowei Huang*	364

Effect of different dosing of fly ash and silica fume on the mechanical properties of coral concrete *Wei Liu*	370
Research on QC achievement problems and countermeasures of water project safety production based on high-quality development *Qian Fu, Hui Tan, Zhenyu Bai & Mengting Huang*	378
Simulation research on fire emergency evacuation based on Pathfinder *Bei Wu, Zhen Ma, Yuhe Zhao, Ming Wang & Yunjun Yang*	386
Stress state study of atmospheric pressure storage tanks with corrosion defects *Lijian Zhou, Donglin Zhu, Shouye Dong & Xinjie Yu*	393
Experimental study on comprehensive recovery of bismuth smelting slag by hydrometallurgy *Tengyue Gao, Guangsheng Li, Xingfu Zhu & Qiang Ji*	403
Aluminate-based flocculant from fly ash for dye wastewater treatment with flue gas neutralization *Guoqiang Zhong, Zhaohui Ren, Haixin Zheng, Jinyun Xu, Minjing Li, Di Zhao, Xudong Hu, Xiangyin Cheng, Jianing Guo, Guanwei Yao, Chunming Zheng & Xiaohong Sun*	409
Study on the mechanical characteristics of red-bed mudstone in Southwest China under point load and uniaxial compression and tensile *Yao Cui, Siyu Qi, Pengyu Zhu, Rui Wang & Yongneng Feng*	415
Numerical analysis of beach sediment dredging under different artificial sand laying schemes *Xiaodong An, Bin Zhou, Tao Gao, Haiwen Fan, Hongchang Hua & Tingting Cui*	424
Preparation and evaluation of gels for conformance control of high temperature and high salinity reservoirs *Hongbin Guo, Jijiang Ge & Longjie Li*	431
Application research and technology development of cryogenic energy storage materials *Fan Yang, Chao Zhang, Bochao Zhang, Xi Zhong & Cong Zhen*	439
Multi-layered micro/nano filters for efficient air filtration *Wenhua Ma, Huan Qi, Yongmeng Zhang, Minggang Lin & Chuyang Zhang*	446
Is the NOx tax optimal? – Evidence from Inner Mongolia *Xinjiletu Yang, Zijie Qu, Weihong Han & Yanli Yang*	453
Study on strain characteristics of Zhoushan marine soft clay under continuous variable frequency cyclic loading *Jiajie Chen, Feng Xiong & Jinbao Wang*	465
Research on method for establishing standard system on green production and consumption in China *Yanxin Gao, Shuang Ding, Dongfeng Gao, Yi Zhu & Rui Zhang*	471

Study on grouting parameters and properties of grouting reinforced soil of ultra-fine Portland cement and normal Portland cement   477
Fan Chen, Wei Ouyang, Zhongmeng Guo, Yanhua Gao, Haoran Pang, Yingxin Ma, Liangtao Zhu, Kun Wang, Liangcai Di & Bangqing Xia

Research on the economic and environmental impacts of photovoltaic power generation systems in rural Tibet   487
Jiapeng Lu

Application of iron tailing waste rock aggregate to produce prefabricated laminated plate in construction engineering   499
Chi Zhang, Binbin Li, Zhangmiao Li, Junqian Peng, Tiejun Liu

Challenges and opportunities for recycling waste photovoltaic modules   508
Guochen Zhao

Reconstruction method of vertical seawall based on ecological engineering concept   517
Biao Zhou, Zijian Guo, Qi Hang & Ying Jiang

Application of time series augmented reality model to underwater topographic change of riprap   525
Ya Wen

Preliminary analysis of Rectisol and Selexol (NHD) in pre-combustion carbon capture technology   532
Guochen Zhao

Status and countermeasures of cadmium pollution in soil   538
Baodan Yang, Shuang Cui, Xiuju Sun, Weijun Qi & Xinyue Liu

Research process on alkaline regulation and solidification regulation of red mud   544
Dongmei Yan, Shuai Zou, Maoli Yang, Jing Yang, Mingyuan Dou & Qing Feng

Research progress in dispersion stability of nanolubricant additives   551
Ting Li, Junmiao Wu, Zhipeng Zhang, Rui Wang, Qianqian Zou & Yulan Tang

Modeling rock deformation and breaking considering the initial compaction stage   556
Ben Wang

Research on influencing factors of compressive strength of fly ash-based geopolymer mortar new building structure materials   563
Chao Li, Jianhua Li, Xueyong Xu & Lele Yu

Description of strain softening curve by relative referring   571
Enyang Zhu, Yinxi Ma, Jiaying Wang, Yangbo Li & Yuqi Zhang

Author index   577

Preface

The International Conference on Civil Engineering, Environment Resources and Energy Materials is a leading conference held annually. It aims at building an international platform for the communication and academic exchange among participants from various fields related to civil engineering, environment resources and energy materials. Here, scholars, experts, and researchers are welcomed and encouraged to share their research progress and inspirations. It is a great opportunity to promote academic communication and collaboration worldwide.

This volume contains the papers presented at the 2022 4th International Conference on Civil Engineering, Environment Resources and Energy Materials (CCESEM 2022), held during October 21st–23rd, 2022 in Sanya, China (virtual form). Under the influence of COVID-19 and for the safety concern of all participants, we decided to hold it as a virtual conference which is also effective and convenient for academic exchange and communication. Everyone interested in this field were welcomed to join the online conference and to give comments and raise questions to the speeches and presentations.

The online conference was composed of keynote speeches, oral presentations, and online Q&A discussion, attracting 200 individuals from all over the world. We have invited three sophisticated professors to perform keynote speeches. Among them, Prof. Zhenhua Duan from Tongji University deliver a keynote speech on Early-age Properties of 3D Printed Concrete with Recycled Coarse Aggregate. In his research, a preparation method of 3D printed concrete (3DPC) is proposed based on the secondary mixing of fine aggregate commercial concrete at the construction site. This study investigated the effect of different materials, including cement, metakaolin (MK), and cellulose ether (HPMC) on the workability, rheological properties and density of fine aggregate commercial concrete and the early-age properties of 3DPC, including the extrudability and fresh compressive strength, were studied. All keynote speakers made brilliant speeches and share their unique experience and insights, and here we are hoping the pandemic soon come to an end and we could see each other face to face next year.

CCESEM 2022 received a great many submissions in the areas of civil engineering, environment resources and energy materials. Each submission was reviewed by at least two review experts and the committee picked out some excellent papers that are included in the proceedings, including but not limited to the following topics: Wind Power, Diagnosis and Sensing Systems, Structural Engineering, Plant Protection, Semiconductor Technology, New Energy Materials, etc.

On behalf of the Conference Organizing Committee, we would like to thank the Program Committee members and external reviewers for their hard work in reviewing and selecting papers. And we would like to acknowledge all of those who have supported CCESEM 2022. In particular, our special thanks go to the CRC Press. Hopefully, all participants and other interested readers can benefit scientifically from the proceedings and find it rewarding in the process.

The Committee of CCESEM 2022

Committee Members

Co-Chairman
Prof. Yingbo Ji, *North China University of Technology (NCUT), China*

Program Committee Chairman
A. Prof. Qingfei Gao, *Harbin Institute of Technology, China*

Organizing Committee Chairman
Prof. Jingzhou Lu, *Yantai University, China*

Publication Chair
A. Prof. Zhenhua Duan, *Tongji University, China*

Program Committees
Prof. Songlin Zhang, *Northwest Normal University, China*
Prof. Hui-Mi Hsu, *National Dong Hwa University, Taiwan, China*
Prof. Guangliang Feng, *Chinese Academy of Sciences, China*
A. Prof. Jui-Pin Wang, *National Central University, Taiwan, China*
A. Prof. Zawawi Bin Daud, *University Tun Hussein Onn Malaysia, Malaysia*
A. Prof. Leszek Chybowski, *Maritime University of Szczecin, Poland*
Prof. Haluk Akgün, *Middle East Technical University, Turkey*
Prof. Salvatore Grasso, *University of Catania, Italy*
Prof. Víctor Yepes, *Universitat Politècnica de València, Spain*

Organizing Committees
Prof. Chunzhen Qiao, *North China University of Technology, China*
Prof. Wei Song, *North China University of Technology, China*
Prof. Kamel Khlaef Jaber Al Zboon, *Al-Balqa Applied University, Jordanian*
A. Prof. Md. Naimul Haque, *East West University, Bangladesh*
A. Prof. Damian Pietrusiak, *Wroclaw University of Science and Technolog, Poland*
A. Prof. Supriya Mohanty, *Indian Institute of Technology, India*
A. Prof. Luigi Palizzolo, *University of Palermo, Italy*
Dr. Samia Hachemi, *University of Biskra, Algeria*

Civil structure repair and seismic technology

PyroSim-Based exterior wall fire prevention design for northern high-rise buildings

Yansheng Song* & Zhenping Ba
School of Civil Engineering, Shenyang Jianzhu University, Shenyang, China

ABSTRACT: In recent years, high-rise building fires occurred frequently in our country. If a fire happens, it will cause a lot of casualties and property loss. It is very necessary to study high-rise building fires for fire organizations. In this paper, fire simulation software PyroSim is used to simulate the external wall fire of an 11-story small high-rise in Heilongjiang Province. According to the layout of the fire isolation belt, six working conditions are set. The time of fire spread to the top floor of a residential building under different fire barrier arrangements was studied. The results show that the time of flame spreading to the top layer can be extended by 140.3% by arranging the "fire isolation layer" in the middle-and-lower part and the middle-and-upper part. The reasonable setting of the fire isolation layer compared with the conventional isolation belt, the fire resistance effect is more obvious. The combination of "fire isolation layer" in the lower and upper parts of the building can not only ensure safety but also control the cost

1 INTRODUCTION

With the continuous advancement of the Chinese urbanization process, there are more and more high-rise buildings in China, and the problem of a high-rise building fire is not allowed to ignore. Eric *et al.* conducted a building physical fire test, and by comparing and analyzing the results of physical fire and simulated fire, they obtained the differences between software simulation and physical fire. Zhao Yongfeng *et al.* obtained the change of the main direction of fire spread with time through numerical simulation of fire spread in the external wall insulation system of high-rise residential buildings. In this paper, a fire isolation belt or centralized fire prevention materials in the outer wall of high-rise buildings that are laid into the "fire isolation layer" is set, which is a barrier to prevent the longitudinal spread of fire "barrier" and avoid the formation of fire through the outer wall. This paper uses PyroSim fire simulation software to the fire isolation layer in high-rise buildings related research. Different fire isolation layer combination method has different fire retardant effect, and a basis for high-rise building fire prevention program design is provided.

2 THE NUMERICAL MODEL

This paper takes an 11-story high-rise residence as the model. Its height is 3 m, its total height is 33m, and its window size is set as 1.5m × 1.8m. The simulation grid area set in this paper only covers the area to be studied, which can meet the requirements of simulation accuracy and save simulation time. The simulated area is a common exterior wall location, the grid size

---

*Corresponding Author: ceyssong@sjzu.edu.cn

is 5m × 8m × 36m, and the grid cell size is 0.25m × 0.25m. For Pyrosim modeling, the location of the fire source is selected at the bottom level near the corner. The combustion reaction was set as polyurethane combustion, the area of the ignition source was set as 1m², the power of the ignition source was set as 6MW, and the type of the ignition source was the growth type of the fire, i.e., T2 growth fire, and the growth coefficient α of the ignition source was 0.04689. The ambient temperature is set to 20°C, the natural wind is set to 0.3m/s, and the background ambient pressure is set to 1.01325 × 102mPa. The model is shown in Figure 1.

The model exterior wall insulation inner layer is extruded polystyrene board (XPS), and rock wool, XPS as insulation material, and rock wool material is used as "fire isolation layer" and fire isolation belt. The combustion performance grade of XPS is B1, the combustion grade of rock wool material is A, and the height of the fire isolation belt is set to 300mm. The outer layer is a protective layer constructed by mortar material. The protective layer of mortar covers the entire thermal insulation material, and there is no cavity between the mortar, thermal insulation material, and the wall. The thickness of XPS and rock wool is set to 100mm, the thickness of outer mortar is set to 15mm in the first layer, and the thickness of other floors is set to 10mm. The combustion performance parameters mainly include the heat release rate (HRR) and ignition point of XPS. The heat release rate (HRR) of the insulation material extruded polystyrene board is set as 300kW /m2, and the ignition point is set as 360°C. The physical parameters of the three materials are shown in Table 1.

Figure 1. Architectural model.

Table 1. Thermal physical properties of building material.

Material name	Density kg/m³	Thermal conductivity W/(m·k)	Specific heat capacity J/(kg·K)
XPS	25	0.03	5346.4
Rock wool	150	0.04	750
Mortar	1600	0.81	1050

3 FIRE SIMULATION AND RESULT ANALYSIS

3.1 *Working condition setting*

In this paper, different isolation layers and belts are added to the floors to prevent and control the spread of fire in external walls. Different arrangements and combination layouts from less to more are taken for the fire isolation layer layout. In this paper, a total of 6 working conditions are set. Six working conditions are set, and the specific working conditions are shown in Table 2.

Table 2. Setting of fire prevention measures.

Scene number	Insulation material	Fireproof material	Protective layer	Fire isolation belt	Fire isolation layer
Condition 1	XPS	Rock wool	mortar	No barriers	No barriers
Condition 2	XPS	Rock wool	mortar	Each layer is set	No barriers
Condition 3	XPS	Rock wool	mortar	Each layer is set	Sixth floors
Condition 4	XPS	Rock wool	mortar	Each layer is set	The sixth and seventh floors
Condition 5	XPS	Rock wool	mortar	Each layer is set	The fourth and eighth floors
Condition 6	XPS	Rock wool	mortar	Each layer is set	4th, 5th, 8th, 9th floors

3.2 Simulation results of each working condition

3.2.1 Condition 1

Because the fire point is at the corner of the building, with the chimney effect, the fire is more fierce, and the flame spreads quickly in the absence of isolation measures. When the fire simulation time is 718S, the flames spread to the top floor. The simulation results are shown in Figure 2.

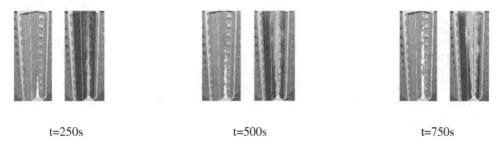

t=250s   t=500s   t=750s

Figure 2. Simulation results of working condition 1.

3.2.2 Condition 2

Each layer sets an isolation belt, and during the process of flame spreading by layers of the isolation barrier, isolation belts to the original insulation system as a whole "cut" into multiple areas, interrupting the continuity of insulation materials and slowing down the fire longitudinal spread speed. The time was 830s when the fire reached the top floor. Compared with working condition 1, the isolation zone extends the fire spreading time by 112s, which is 15.6%. Because the flame has a chimney effect in the corner, the flame barrier effect is not obvious when only the isolation belt is set. The simulation results are shown in Figure 3.

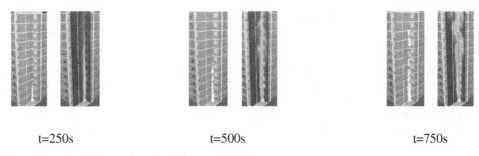

t=250s   t=500s   t=750s

Figure 3. Simulation results of working condition 2.

3.2.3 Condition 3

Since the isolation layer is set in the middle of the model, it is consistent with working condition 2 before the fire reaches the isolation layer. At 500s, the flame spreads to the bottom of the isolation layer, and the flame slows down in the isolation layer. However, due to the chimney effect, the fire resistance effect of the isolation layer is limited, and the fire reaches the top layer at 880s. Compared with working condition 1, the isolation zone extends the fire spreading time by 162S, 22.6%. The simulation results are shown in Figure 4.

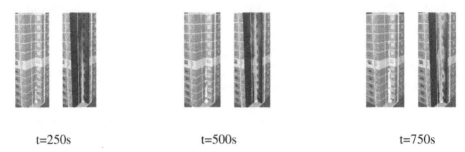

t=250s   t=500s   t=750s

Figure 4. Simulation results of working condition 3.

3.2.4 Condition 4

Two isolation layers are continuously set in the middle of the model. Before the fire reaches the isolation layer, it is consistent with working condition 3. Under the action of fire resistance of two layers of isolation layer, the time of flame crossing the isolation layer increases, and the fire resistance effect is obvious by setting two layers of isolation layer continuously. The fire reached the top floor at 1256S. Compared with working condition 1, the isolation zone extends the fire spreading time by 538s, which is 75.2%. The simulation results are shown in Figure 5.

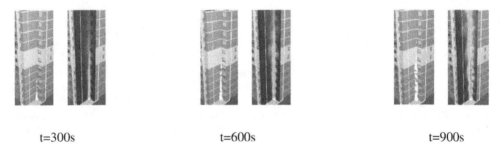

t=300s   t=600s   t=900s

Figure 5. Simulation results of working condition 4.

3.2.5 Condition 5

One layer of isolation layer is set in the lower part and upper part of the model, respectively. The flame is delayed by the isolation layer every time it reaches the isolation layer, but the effect is not as good as the continuous setting of two layers of isolation layers, so it can be concluded that the continuous setting of the isolation layer has a better effect. The fire reached the top floor at 1029S. Compared with working condition 1, the isolation zone extends the fire spreading time by 311s, which is 43.4%. The simulation results are shown in Figure 6.

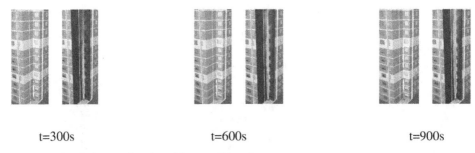

t=300s　　　　　　　　t=600s　　　　　　　　t=900s

Figure 6.　Simulation results of working condition 5.

3.2.6 *Condition 6*

Two isolation layers are respectively set in the middle and upper part of the model. Each time the flame reaches the isolation layer, it will be effectively blocked, and the effect of the isolation layer is very obvious. At 1723S, the fire reached the top floor. Compared with working condition 1, the isolation zone extended the fire spreading time by 1005s, which was 140.3%. The simulation results are shown in Figure 7.

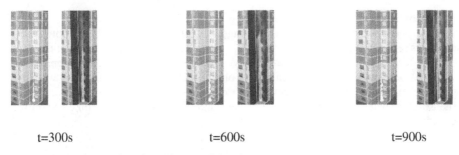

t=300s　　　　　　　　t=600s　　　　　　　　t=900s

Figure 7.　Simulation results of working condition 6.

3.3 *Comparative analysis of simulation results of each working condition*

Based on the simulation analysis of six working conditions, the following results can be obtained: The heating curve of the 11th layer is shown in Figure 3.3.1. By comparing the temperature curves of different working conditions, it can be concluded that the isolation zone of each layer has a certain effect on delaying the fire, but the effect is limited. The continuous setting of the isolation layer has an obvious effect on delaying fire, and the more continuous setting of the isolation layer is, the better the effect is. The time of fire reaching the roof in working condition 4 is 376s longer than that in working condition 3, which is 52.6% longer. In the upper and lower part of the building, two consecutive layers of isolation belts are set, and the fire prevention effect is very good. In general, the layout scheme of the isolation belt in working condition 6 is the best. In the case of a certain area of the isolation belt, the reasonable arrangement of the isolation layer is used to maximize the fire resistance ability of the isolation belt, which has a certain fire resistance ability and controls the cost. The temperature time history curve is shown in Figure 8.

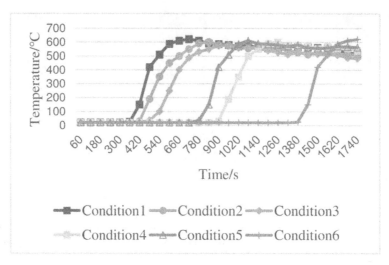

Figure 8. Temperature time history curve

4 CONCLUSION

The exterior insulation materials of buildings in northern China are mostly combustible materials. The phenomenon of piling garbage and other debris at the bottom corner of buildings is relatively common, which has the risk of outdoor and external wall fire, and the chimney effect exists at the corner, and the vertical spread of fire is faster. Compared with the conventional method of only setting an isolation belt, the effect of fire resistance is more obvious. The reasonable arrangement of the isolation layer can maximize the fire resistance of the isolation belt under a certain area of the isolation layer, to meet both cost control and safety requirements.

REFERENCES

Alexandra Bystrom, Xudong Cheng, Uif Wickstrom & Milan Veljkovic (2012). Full-scale Experiment and Numerical Studies on Compartment Fire Under Low Ambient Temperature. *J. Building and Environment*, 51: 255–262.
Bo W. (2003) Mechanical Properties of Reinforced Concrete Structures after Fire. *Science Press*.
Eric Guillaume, Virginie Dréan, Bertrand Girardin, Faiz Benameur, Maxime Koohkan and Talal Fateh. (2020). Reconstruction of Grenfell Tower fire. Part 3–Numerical Simulation of the Grenfell Tower Disaster: Contribution to the Understanding of the Fire Propagation and Behavior During the Vertical Fire Spread. *J. Fire and Materials*, 44 (1).
Yansheng Song, Yongxu Pan, Gang Zhao. (2021) Study on Mechanical Properties of Concrete Frame Structures Under Fire. *Journal of Shenyang Jianzhu University (natural science edition)*, 2021, 37 (01): 77–85.
Youbo Huang. (2017) Building Fire Simulation Engineering Software: PyroSim from Beginner to Master. *Beijing: Chemical Industry Press.*
Zijun L. (2017) Research on Fire Control Technology of Exterior Wall of High-rise Building Based on FDS. *Shenyang*: Dissertation of Shenyang Jianzhu University, 38–42.
Zuo Q.L., Wang Y.J. and Li J.S. (2018). Safety Performance of Exterior Wall Insulation Material Based on Large Security Concept. *J. IOP Conference Series: Materials Science and Engineering*, 359 (1).

Study on burst pressure of corroded pipelines under axial force and bending moment

Tong Xu, Yuchao Yang, Shuai Feng & Feng Liu*
Shandong Key Laboratory of Disaster Prevention and Mitigation in Civil Engineering, Shandong University of Science and Technology, Qingdao, Shandong, China

ABSTRACT: Based on the ductile damage theory of metal materials, the burst pressure of corroded pipelines under the joint action of axial force and bending moment is systematically studied using fluid cavity simulation technology. The trajectory of pipe failure caused by burst pressure was established for pipes with different corrosion characteristics by considering the coupling effect of medium properties, pressure value, external axial force, and bending moment simultaneously. The numerical simulation results verified by the experimental data show that the ductility damage model can overcome the shortcoming of the existing analysis methods, which take the maximum strain as the failure characteristic, in order to truly reflect the burst phenomenon and the ultimate bearing capacity of the pipeline. The change in the value and direction of the axial force and bending moment will change the limit value of the burst pressure of the corroded pipeline. Among them, the axial force and bending moment, which produce pressure at the defect have the greatest influence on the burst pressure. In addition, the burst pressure of corroded pipelines is strongly dependent on the size of pipelines and defects, but the depth of defects is the decisive factor affecting the degree of pressure reduction caused by corrosion. This paper expands the load environment of the burst pressure variation of corroded pipelines and provides a technical route and preliminary conclusion for a deeper understanding of the burst pressure of pipelines under real service conditions.

1 INTRODUCTION

At the beginning of the design of marine or land transportation pipelines, only the influence of internal pressure is considered, and the influence of external loads, such as axial force and bending moment, is ignored (Liu *et al.* 2009). For the former, the external load may be caused by the free fall caused by the impact of seawater flow on the pipeline or the excessive span of the pipeline. For the latter, the external load may be caused by seismic activities, foundation subsidence, and landslides. These external loads have a certain impact on the burst pressure of the pipeline.

Researchers (Lasebikan & Akisanya 2014; Liu *et al.* 2009; Roy *et al.* 1997; Taylor *et al.* 2015) used finite element simulation technology and similar model experiment technology to reduce the bearing capacity of pipelines under external loads. Oh *et al.* (2008, 2009) proposed that the shape of defects has a great impact on the plastic limit load of pipelines under axial and bending loads. Mondal (2018) proposed that for corroded pipelines, it is impossible to simulate the impact of corrosion cracking and crack propagation on the pressure-bearing capacity of pipelines by using standard finite element modeling technology.

Mondal *et al.* (2019) studied the corroded pipeline subjected to axial force and bending moment load and established the failure track of corroded pipelines under the joint action of

---
*Corresponding Author: feng.liu@sdust.edu.cn

axial force and bending moment with the ultimate strength criterion as the failure criterion. They also proposed that when DNV-RP-F101 (2015) considered the impact of axial force and bending moment on the burst pressure of corroded pipelines, the value of the influence coefficient H_1 added to the model of corroded pipelines without axial force and bending moment load in the case of longitudinal stress $\sigma_L<0.25\sigma_u$ was much higher than the actual value, which was a conservative prediction of this situation by DNV-RP-F101 (2015).

Yi Shuai *et al.* (2022) further optimized and modified the finite element simulation of Mondal *et al.* (2019) and developed a new prediction model. This model has higher accuracy than traditional models. In addition, Yi Shuai *et al.* (2021) carried out a detailed simulation study on the impact of defect width on the burst pressure of corroded pipelines, which is not considered in the specifications, and proposed that the impact of defect width on the burst pressure of corroded pipelines depends on the defect depth.

Currently, the developed prediction models are based on the ultimate tensile strength or yield strength of materials, without considering the stress state of corroded pipelines after reaching the ultimate tensile strength. According to the damage mechanics, this paper defines the ductile damage of materials and uses the finite element simulation technology of a fluid chamber to realize the whole process of the burst of corroded pipelines.

2 ESTABLISHMENT AND VERIFICATION OF THE FINITE ELEMENT MODEL

2.1 *Modeling*

ABAQUS dynamic analysis module is used for model calculation. The cavity made of shell element simulates the pipe and the plugs at both ends of the pipe in the experiment. The shell element uses the four-node continuous element (S4R element). This model can well simulate the real boundary conditions of corroded pipelines in the laboratory. This paper adopts the treatment method of Mondal *et al.* (2019) for pipeline defects – the simplified rectangular corrosion shape commonly considered in pipeline design codes.

Using the finite element fluid cavity technology, the cavity is defined by specifying the surfaces around the cavity and associated with a node called the cavity reference node. The fluid cavity model can be used to simulate a liquid-filled or gas-filled structure, such as filling a pipe with water. However, the fluid cavity model is only applicable to the case where the pressure and temperature of the fluid in a specific cavity are uniform at any time point and cannot analyze the impact of the medium in the pipe on the pipe wall.

In the process of analysis, stress concentration will occur at the defective part. In addition, to reduce the calculation amount, this paper adopts the non-uniform grid. As shown in Figure 1, the grid size of the defective part is 3 mm, and the grid size of the non-defective part is 26 mm. Five integral points are selected in the thickness direction of the shell element at

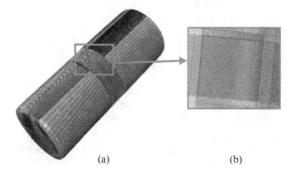

(a)   (b)

Figure 1. ABAQUS finite element model. (a) Corroded pipe (b) Local defects.

the non-defective part, and three integral points are selected in the thickness direction of the shell element at the defective part. The "plug" elements at both ends of the pipeline are constrained, so the poor mesh quality at these two places does not affect the calculation results.

2.2 Verify the finite element model

The experiments and simulations are used to verify the feasibility of the finite element model with real experimental data. The materials and sizes of corroded pipelines are selected from the articles of Oh et al. (2007), as shown in Tables 1 and 2.

The stress curve of the most unfavorable point of corroded pipelines under internal pressure is drawn in Figure 2. The red solid line indicates that the ultimate tensile strength of pipeline material is 563.8 MPa, and the black virtual solid line indicates that the internal pressure value measured by simulation when reaching the ultimate tensile strength is 24.09

Table 1. Material parameter data used in the material model (Oh et al. 2007).

Property	Value
Density, ρ (kN/m^3)	7850
Modulus of Elasticity, E (GPa)	210.7
Poisson's Ratio, v	0.30
Yield Strength, σ_Y (MPa)	464.5
Ultimate Tensile Strength, σ_U (MPa)	563.8

Table 2. Corroded pipe model dimensions (Oh et al. 2007).

Parameter	Value
Pipe Diameter, D (mm)	762
Wall Thickness, t (mm)	17.5
Defect Depth, d (mm)	8.75
Defect Length, l (mm)	100
Defect Width, w (mm)	50

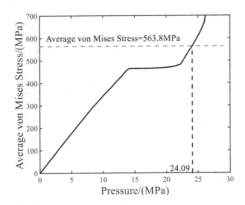

Figure 2. Burst pressure of finite element model.

MPa, which has an error of 0.864% (0.21 Mpa) with the experimental value of 24.3 MPa in the article of Oh *et al.* (2007). The finite element model used in this paper can better simulate the real experimental conditions of corroded pipelines in the experiment.

3 INFLUENCE OF AXIAL FORCE AND BENDING MOMENT ON BURST PRESSURE OF CORRODED PIPELINES

In this paper, the pipe model with isotropic hardening plasticity and ductile damage is used to simulate the nonlinear response of the pipe (Roy *et al.* 1997). Figure 3 shows the true stress-strain curve of the material, and Table 3 shows the material parameters of the pipe model. The nonlinear stress-strain data are input into the finite element model in the form of connected piecewise straight lines, and the ductile damage parameter values are input. The burst point of the pipe model (the disappearance of the model elements or the cracking between the elements) is taken as the failure pressure of pipes.

The iterative method of numerical simulation and experiment is used to determine the ductile damage parameters. Through the comparison between experiments and finite element simulation, the constitutive relationship of materials is parameterized, and multiple sets of parameter data are obtained. The particle swarm optimization algorithm in MATLAB is used to calculate the optimal solution of the data obtained, thus obtaining multiple sets of ductile damage parameter values of materials under various complex stresses. As shown in Figure 4, each group of parameters corresponds to the stress-strain state of the material under one or more stresses. In this paper, multiple sets of parameter values are selected to ensure that the ductile damage parameters meet the needs of finite element simulation.

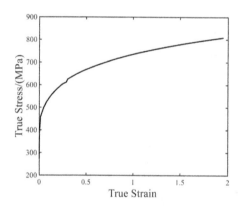

Figure 3. True stress-strain curve.

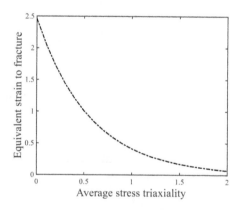

Figure 4. Evolution of equivalent strain on damage initiation along with stress triaxiality.

Table 3. Material parameter data used in the material model.

Property	Value
Density, ρ (kN/m^3)	7800
Modulus of Elasticity, E (GPa)	210
Poisson's Ratio, v	0.30
Yield Strength, σ_Y (MPa)	300
Ultimate Tensile Strength, σ_U (MPa)	480

Table 4. Corroded pipe model dimensions (Liu et al. 2009).

Parameter	Value
Pipe Diameter, D (mm)	203.2
Wall Thickness, t (mm)	8.2
Defect Depth, d (mm)	4.1
Defect Length, l (mm)	65.6
Defect Width, w (mm)	65.5

Four working conditions (Mondal & Dhar 2019) are studied: the axial pressure, the axial tension, the closing bending moment (axial compressive stress at the pipe defect), and the opening bending moment (axial tensile stress at the pipe defect). The axial pressure and axial tension of 200 kN, then the closing bending moment and opening bending moment of 20 kN·m are respectively used, and the dimensions of corroded pipes are shown in Table 4 (Liu et al. 2009).

According to the deformation diagram of the simulation results (as shown in Figure 5(a)), the first place where the pipe is damaged is the edge of the defect parallel to the pipe axis, that is, the long edge of the defect, and then it is gradually "torn" along the pipe axis. As shown in Figure 5(b), in the experiment, the damage to the corroded pipe is distributed along the axial direction of the pipe, which indicates that when the pipeline is damaged, its circumferential stress dominates. The simulation results are consistent with the failure mechanism shown in the experimental results.

As shown in Figure 6, the axial pressure and closing bending moment make the corroded pipeline enter the yield stage under a smaller internal pressure. In the area from the ultimate

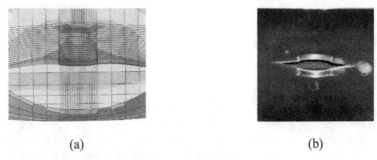

Figure 5. Burst deformation diagram of corroded pipelines. (a) Failure in simulation (b) Failure in the experiment (Oh et al. 2007).

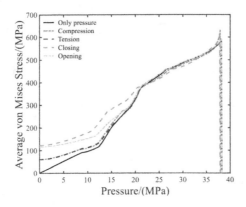

Figure 6. Influence of axial force and bending moment on burst pressure of corroded pipelines.

tensile strength to the pipe failure, the influence of axial pressure and closing bending moment is not great, but the axial pressure and closing bending moment can advance the burst pressure of corroded pipelines. This is because the axial pressure and closing bending moment generate the axial compressive stress at the defect, which increases the circumferential stress at the defect of pipelines. The axial tension and opening bending moment generate the axial tensile stress at the defect, which will have a certain impact on the failure of corroded pipelines, but the influence of axial tension and opening bending moment is smaller than that of axial pressure and closing bending moment. This paper will further analyze the impact of different combinations of axial pressure and closing moment on the burst pressure of corroded pipelines and draw the interaction diagram.

4 FACTORS AFFECTING BURST PRESSURE OF CORRODED PIPELINES

This paper studies the influence of different defect sizes and pipe diameters on the pressure-bearing capacity of pipelines. The research content is divided into the influence of defect depth on the pressure-bearing capacity of pipelines, the influence of defect area on the pressure-bearing capacity of pipelines, and the influence of pipe diameter on the pressure-bearing capacity of pipelines. The defect area is divided into two controllable variables: defect width and defect length. In this paper, the bending moment and axial force applied when the pipe burst in the simulation results are normalized. The internal pressure bearing capacity Po, the bending moment bearing capacity Mo and the axial bearing capacity Fo of the corroded pipeline are calculated by using the simulation results of the finite element model under a single load. In order to obtain the bending moment bearing capacity and axial bearing capacity of corroded pipelines, all of them are simulated by applying bending moment or axial force to the corroded pipe model filled with incompressible media, and the next research models are all defective pipe models filled with incompressible media.

4.1 4 Defect depths

This paper studies the influence of two defect depths on the bearing capacity of pipelines. One model has a defect depth of 4.2 mm ($d/t = 0.5$), and the other model has a defect depth of 1.64 mm ($d/t = 0.2$). Both pipe models apply the same axial pressure ($F = 200$ kN).

As shown in Figure 7, the corroded pipeline with shallow defects needs a larger bending moment or internal pressure to burst than the corroded pipeline with deep defects, but under the action of low axial force and low bending moment, the burst pressure of deep defect

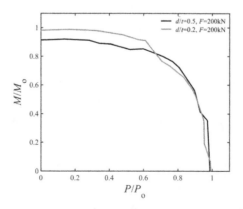

Figure 7. Effect of defect depth on the failure of corroded pipelines.

pipeline decreases faster than that of shallow defect pipeline. Therefore, the influence of defect depth needs to be considered in establishing the failure track of the corroded pipeline.

4.2 Defect area

The influence of three different defect areas on the bearing capacity of the pipeline is studied. Three defect area models are designed, all of which apply the same axial pressure ($F = 200$ kN).

As shown in Figure 8, the failure trajectories of the three corroded pipelines are approximately the same, and the downward trend of the bearing capacity of pipelines with different defect areas is the same, which indicates that the influence of defect area, defect width, and defect length on the failure of corroded pipelines can be ignored. When studying the bearing capacity of corroded pipelines, the fixed defect area, defect width, and defect length can be selected.

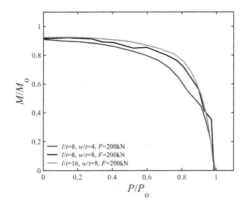

Figure 8.   Effect of defect area on the failure of corroded pipelines.

4.3 Pipe diameter

The influence of two pipe diameters on the bearing capacity of pipelines is studied. Two corroded pipe model sizes are designed, as shown in Table 5. All of them are applied with the same axial pressure ($F = 200$ kN).

As shown in Figure 9, the decreasing trend of the bearing capacity of corroded pipelines with different diameters under the same load is consistent. The change in the pipe diameter will affect the bearing capacity of pipelines, but will not affect the changing trend of the bearing capacity of pipelines. In the next study of this paper, the influence of pipe diameter will not be considered, and only the unified diameter value will be selected for simulation.

Table 5.   Two corroded pipe model sizes.

Parameter	Pipe "A"	Pipe "B"
Pipe Diameter, D (mm)	203.2	416.4
Wall Thickness, t (mm)	8.2	8.2
Defect Depth, d (mm)	4.1	4.1
Defect Length, l (mm)	65.6	65.6
Defect Width, w (mm)	65.6	65.6

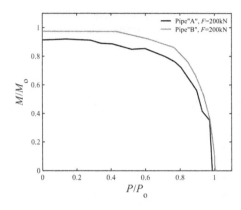

Figure 9. Effect of pipe diameter on the failure of corroded pipelines.

5 FAILURE TRACK OF CORRODED PIPELINES

According to the simulation results in this paper, two kinds of defects with different depths (d/t = 0.2, d/t = 0.5) are designed to establish the failure track of corroded pipelines. Four different axial forces were applied to the corroded pipelines of each defect depth, the failure trajectories of the corroded pipelines under different axial forces were obtained, and the interaction diagrams were established.

As shown in Figures 10–11, the greater the axial force on the corroded pipeline, the greater the decrease in the burst pressure and bending moment bearing capacity of the pipeline. Moreover, the influence of axial force on the bending moment bearing capacity of the corroded pipeline is greater than that on the burst pressure of the corroded pipeline. As shown in Figure 11, the low axial pressure improves the bending moment bearing capacity of corroded pipes to a certain extent but reduces the burst pressure of corroded pipelines.

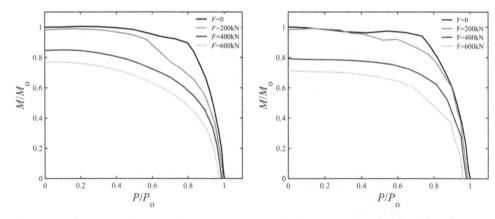

Figure 10. Interaction diagram of corroded pipelines with defect depth of 0.2.

Figure 11. Interaction diagram of corroded pipelines with defect depth of 0.5.

6 CONCLUSION

Based on the results and discussions presented above, the conclusions are obtained as below:

1. The finite element model adopted in this paper can well simulate the real bursting of corroded pipelines. The finite element model finally appears in the burst phenomenon (the element disappears). When the external load generates axial pressure at the defect, the pressure-bearing capacity of the corroded pipeline decreases the most.
2. The interaction diagram established in this paper has a certain reference value for predicting the burst pressure of corroded pipelines under the same axial force and bending moment.
3. The depth of defects greatly impacts the bearing capacity and bending resistance of corroded pipelines. When analyzing the impact of defect size on the bearing capacity of corroded pipelines, it is necessary to focus on the depth of defects.

ACKNOWLEDGMENTS

The financial support for this study was provided by the National Natural Science Foundation of China (52078283).

REFERENCES

As D N V. Corroded pipelines[R]. DNV-RP-F101, 2015.

Lasebikan B.A and Akisanya A.R. Burst Pressure of Super Duplex Stainless Steel Pipes Subject to Combined Axial Tension, Internal Pressure, and Elevated Temperature. *International Journal of Pressure Vessels and Piping*, 2014, 119: 62–68.

Liu J., Chauhan V., Ng P. et al. *Remaining Strength of Corroded Pipe Under Secondary (biaxial) Loading*. GL Industrial Services UK Ltd, 2009.

Mondal B.C., Dhar A.S. Burst Pressure of Corroded Pipelines Considering Combined Axial Forces and Bending Moments. *Engineering Structures*, 2019, 186: 43–51.

Mondal B.C. *Remaining Strength Assessment of Deteriorating Energy Pipelines*. Memorial University of Newfoundland, 2018.

Oh C.K, Kim Y.J, Baek J.H. et al. Ductile Failure Analysis of API X65 Pipes with Notch-type Defects Using a Local Fracture Criterion. *International Journal of Pressure Vessels and Piping*, 2007, 84(8): 512–525.

Oh C.K., Kim Y.J., Kim J.S. et al. Yield Locus for Circumferential Part-through Surface Cracked Pipes Under Combined Pressure and Bending. *Engineering Fracture Mechanics*, 2008, 75(8): 2175–2190.

Oh C.K, Kim Y.J., Park C.Y. Effects of Local Wall Thinning on Net-section Limit Loads for Pipes Under Combined Pressure and Bending. *Nuclear Engineering and Design*, 2009, 239(2): 261–273.

Roy S., Grigory S., Smith M. et al. Numerical Simulations of Full-scale Corroded Pipe Tests with Combined Loading. 1997.

Shuai Y., Wang X.H., Cheng Y.F. Buckling Resistance of an X80 Steel Pipeline at Corrosion Defect Under Bending Moment. *Journal of Natural Gas Science and Engineering*, 2021, 93: 104016.

Shuai Y., Zhang X., Feng C. et al. A Novel Model for Prediction of Burst Capacity of Corroded Pipelines Subjected to Combined Loads of Bending Moment and Axial Compression. *International Journal of Pressure Vessels and Piping*, 2022: 104621.

Taylor N., Clubb G., Matheson I. *The Effect of Bending and Axial Compression on Pipeline Burst Capacity* [C]//SPE Offshore Europe Conference and Exhibition. OnePetro, 2015.

Civil Engineering and Energy-Environment – Gao & Duan (Eds)
© 2023 the Author(s), ISBN 978-1-032-56057-1

Research on mechanical characteristics of lining structure of shallow-buried multi-arch tunnel without middle drift

Chengye Jiang*
State Key Laboratory of Geomechanics and Geotechnical Engineering, Institute of Rock and Soil Mechanics, Chinese Academy of Sciences, Wuhan, China
University of Chinese Academy of Sciences, Beijing, China

ABSTRACT: Multi-arch tunnel without middle drift is a new type of tunnel structure. At present, the mechanical characteristics of the lining structure are not clear. An improved pressure calculation method considering the excavation sequence of two tunnels is compared with the existing standard method. The load-structure method is used to conduct the numerical analysis of the lining structure under two load modes. The main conclusions are as follows: (1) the surrounding rock pressure value of the first tunnel calculated by the improved calculation method is larger than that of the standard method, but the surrounding rock pressure value of the second tunnel is smaller; (2) the internal force amplitude of the lining structure under the two load modes has little difference, but the distribution form has a great difference, it is suggested that the lining structure of the two tunnels should be designed asymmetrically; (3) the lining structure safety performance of the first tunnel is not fully considered, especially the inner arch shoulder area when the existing standard method is used in the design. Research results can provide a certain reference for the support structure design for the multi-arch tunnel without middle drift.

1 INTRODUCTION

With the implementation of a national western development strategy in China, the construction of highway tunnels in the southwest area has achieved great development in recent years. To overcome the disadvantages of the traditional multi-arch tunnel, such as cumbersome construction procedure, narrow construction working face, and easy water leakage in lining structure, the multi-arch tunnel with the elimination of the central guide hole is widely used in the construction of road tunnels in Yunnan province. It replaces the traditional middle partition wall with the two tunnels' first layer of support to avoid the construction of the central drift, which has the significant advantages of accelerating the construction schedule and having the lower cost of construction (Tang *et al.* 1958). The structural form is shown in Figure 1. However, because the few existing engineering projects and the different geological conditions of surrounding rocks are not the same, it is more blind to adopt the experience analogy method in structural design, and the lining cracking phenomenon exists in the existing engineering (Wang *et al.* 2019). Therefore, it is an urgent engineering problem to explore the mechanical behaviors of multi-arch tunnel lining structures without the central guide hole.

The load-structure method is one of the research methods to analyze the mechanical characteristics of tunnel lining structure, which is widely accepted in the field of tunnel engineering because of its convenience for engineering applications. The key to this method is to determine the surrounding rock pressure applied to the supporting structure. Based on the load-structure

*Corresponding Author: jiangchengye19@mails.ucas.ac.cn

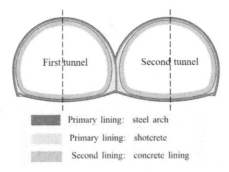

Figure 1. Schematic diagram for the multi-arch tunnel without middle drift.

method, Li et al. (2010) explored the mechanical features of loess tunnel lining under standard loads and measured loads. Li et al. (2009) optimized the parameters of the design for undersea tunnel lining structure. Xiao et al. (2018) studied the design method of the initial supporting structure of the tunnel. However, there are few pieces of research focusing on the mechanical characteristics of the lining structure of the multi-arch tunnel without the central drift.

In this study, the surrounding rock load mode obtained by the previous research work is compared with the standard method. And based on the load structure method, the mechanical properties of the lining structure were carried out by numerical analysis. Besides, the similarities and differences of the force characteristics under the two load modes are compared, which can give a certain theoretical basis for the structural design and optimization of the multi-arch tunnel without the construction of the central drift.

2 VALUE OF SURROUNDING ROCK PRESSURE

2.1 *Surrounding rock pressure action mode of the standard method*

In the specification, the load action mode for the double-arch tunnel under a shallow burial depth can be expressed by using Figure 2. This method does not consider the sequential excavation sequence of the two tunnels, and the load action mode of the surrounding rock is symmetrically distributed (JTG/T D70, 2010), in which the upper uniform load q is calculated as follows:

$$q = \gamma h_1 \left(1 - \frac{h_1 \lambda \tan\theta}{2B_t}\right) \quad (1)$$

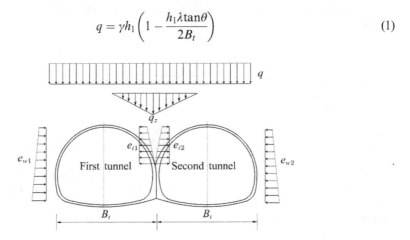

Figure 2. The action mode of surrounding rock pressure in the standard.

where γ is the bulk density of surrounding rock; h_1 is the thickness of the overlying rock mass of the tunnel; λ is the lateral pressure factor; B_t is the excavation span of a single cavern; θ is an empirical value, which depends on the friction angle of the rock mass.

2.2 Surrounding rock pressure action mode of the improved method

Considering the sequential excavation sequence of the two tunnels (Tang et al. 1958), the load distribution mode of surrounding rock can be obtained as shown in Figure 3. The calculation expressions q_1 and q_2 of the two tunnels are expressed by using Eq. (2) and Eq. (3), respectively, and the calculation expression of the lateral pressure e_i can be expressed by using Eq. (4).

$$q_1 = \gamma h_1 \left[1 + \frac{h_1 \lambda (\tan\varphi_0 - \tan\theta)}{2B_t} \right] \quad (2)$$

$$q_2 = \gamma h_1 \left[1 - \frac{h_1 \lambda (\tan\varphi_0 + \tan\theta)}{2B_t} \right] \quad (3)$$

$$e_i = \lambda \gamma h_i \quad (4)$$

where h_i is the distance from any point to the horizontal ground, and other symbols and meanings are the same as mentioned before.

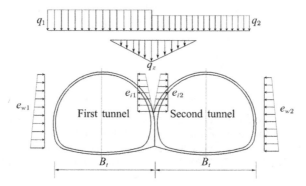

Figure 3. Schematic diagram of surrounding rock pressure distribution mode of the improved method.

3 CALCULATION OF LOAD STRUCTURE MODEL

3.1 Load calculation

The value of the pressure obtained by the above two methods is shown in Table 1. When calculating the pressure, the surrounding rock grade is set as V, and the buried depth is set as 10 m. As seen from the table, the pressure value calculated by the standard method is between that of the first tunnel and the second tunnel obtained by the improved method. Therefore, the current standard method fails to reflect the asymmetry of the pressure on the two tunnel support structures. In addition, according to the current standard method, the structural design underestimates the pressure on the support structure of the first tunnel, which may result in unsafe structural designs.

Table 1. Value of the acting load under two methods.

Rock Mass Grade	Buried Depth of Tunnel/ $h_1(m)$	Bulk Density of Surrounding Rock/ $\gamma(kN \cdot m^{-3})$	Calculate Friction Angle/φ_0	The Lateral Pressure Coefficient.25/λ	Standard Method q/kpa	Improved Method q_1/kpa q_2/kpa
V	10	20	45	0.22	191	209　173

3.2 Internal force calculation and comparative analysis of lining structure

3.2.1 Comparison of lining structure internal forces

Based on the load structure model, MIDAS-GTS finite element program was adopted to calculate the lining structure internal forces under two load modes. The lining structure is simulated by the beam element, and the formation reaction is simulated by the radial spring element, which only considers its compression. The thickness of the lining structure and middle wall are set as 0.5 m and 1 m, respectively. The elastic modulus was set as 33 GPa, the Poisson's ratio was set as 0.2, and the elastic reaction coefficient generated by the surrounding rock was set as 200 MPa/m. In addition, taking into account the load shared by the initial support and referring to relevant specifications, the proportion of the load on the secondary lining is set as 80%. The internal forces of the lining structure under the two calculated modes are shown in Figures 4 and 5, respectively. As can be seen from Figures 4 and 5 that:

1. The maximum positive and negative bending moments under the standard method appear at the lap position of the two tunnels and the inner arch foot of the first tunnel,

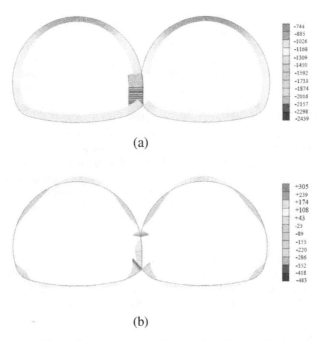

Figure 4. Lining internal force diagram under loading mode of the standard method. (a) Axial force (unit: kN) (b) Bending moment (unit: kN·m).

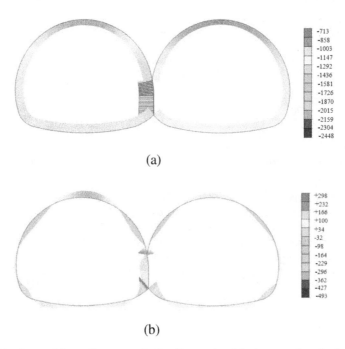

Figure 5. Lining internal force diagram under loading mode of the improved method. (a) Axial force (unit: kN) (b) Bending moment (unit: kN·m).

which are 305 and −483 kN·m, respectively. The lining structure is all in a compressed state with a maximum value of 2439 kN at the position of the middle partition wall. In addition, compared with the loading mode of the improved method, the internal force distribution of the lining structure of the two tunnels is more symmetrical.
2. The maximum positive and negative bending moments of the lining structure under the improved method also appear at the lap position of the two tunnels and the inner arch foot of the first tunnel, which are 298 and −493 kN·m, respectively. The lining structure is all in a compressed state with a maximum value of 2448 kN at the position of the middle partition wall all in a compression state. Compared with the loading mode of the standard method, the magnitude of internal forces, including bending moments and axial forces, is slightly increased. However, due to the asymmetric load, the magnitude of internal forces generated on the first tunnel supporting structure is obviously bigger than that on the second tunnel.

3.2.2 Safety coefficient comparison of key parts

When conducting the safety inspection on tunnel lining, the eccentricity coefficient and safety coefficient must satisfy the demands of the relevant specifications (JTG/T D70, 2010). The eccentricity calculation formula can be expressed as follows:

$$e_0 = M/N \tag{5}$$

where N and M are the axial force and the bending moment of the lining structure, respectively.

When the section eccentricity $e_0 \leq 0.2h$ (small eccentricity), the bearing capacity should be checked according to the requirements of compressive strength. The calculation formula is as follows:

$$KN \leq \varphi \alpha R_a bh \qquad (6)$$

where K is the safety coefficient; φ is equal to 1.0; α is the influence coefficient of axial force eccentricity, $\alpha = 1 - 1.5e_0/h$; R_a is the compressive strength of concrete. b, h are the width and thickness of the lining structure, respectively.

When the eccentricity $e_0 \geq 0.2h$ (large eccentricity), the judgment criteria depend on the tensile strength. The calculation formula can be expressed as follows:

$$KN \leq \varphi \frac{1.75 R_l bh}{\frac{6e_0}{h} - 1} \qquad (7)$$

where R_l is the ultimate tensile strength of the lining structure.

The axial force and bending moment values of each key point under the two calculation methods are extracted, and the comparison diagram of the safety coefficient is shown in Figure 6. It is clearly evident that:

1. In general, the safety coefficient of the first tunnel obtained by the standard method is greater than that obtained by the improved method, and the opposite is correct for the second tunnel.
2. Compared with the standard method, the safety coefficient of the 4# calculation point obtained by the improved loading mode has the largest amplitude of decrease, and its value is the smallest, which indicates that the standard method overestimated the security of the area near the 4# point.
3. Under the improved loading mode, the lining structure safety coefficient of the second tunnel has a large safety surplus, so it is suggested that the first and second tunnels adopt unequal thickness structure design.

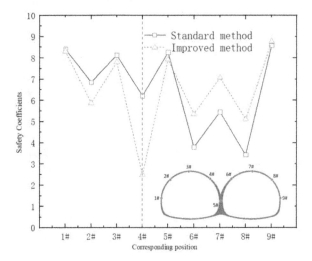

Figure 6. Comparison diagram of safety coefficient.

4 CONCLUSION

1. Compared with the loading mode of the standard method, the load acting on the first tunnel increased, but the opposite is true for the second tunnel. In general, the pressure distribution is in a biased situation in which the pressure acting on the first tunnel supporting structure is greater than that acting on the second tunnel.
2. The internal force amplitude of the lining structure under the two load modes has little difference, but the distribution form has a great difference.
3. Compared with the loading mode of the standard method, the lining structure safety coefficient of the first tunnel calculated by the improved method is reduced, and with the inside spandrel area getting the largest reduction, the safety coefficient of the second tunnel is increased. It is suggested that different parameters should be adopted in the structural design of the two tunnels.

ACKNOWLEDGEMENTS

We are very grateful for the financial support from the Traffic Science and Technology Project of Yunnan Province [(2019)79].

REFERENCES

Li Pengfei, Zhang Dingli, Wang Mengshu, et al. Mechanical properties of lining structure and its cross-section shape optimization of the subsea tunnel. *China Railway Science*, 2009, 30(3): 51–56.

Li Pengfei, Zhang Dingli, Zhao Yong, et al. Study of Mechanical Characteristics of the Secondary Lining of Large-section Loess Tunnel. *Chinese Journal of Rock Mechanics and Engineering*, 2010, 29(8): 1690–1696.

Tang Hua, Jiang Chengye, Deng Qin, et al. Calculation of Pressure on the Shallow-buried Double-arch Tunnel Without Middle Drift. *KSCE Journal of Civil Engineering*. DOI:10.1007/s12205-022-1958-4

The Professional Standards Compilation Group of the People's Republic of China. *JTG/T D70— 2010 Guidelines for Design of Highway Tunnel* Beijing: China Communications Press, 2010.

Wang Jianhong, Chen Wei, Shen Dong, et al. Cracking Analysis and Structural Optimization of the Lining of the Multi-arch Tunnel Without Middle Drift. *Journal of Highway and Transportation Research and Development*, 2019, 36(6): 79–85, 111.

Xiao Mingqing, Wang Shaofeng, Chen Libao, et al. Research on the Design Method of Primary Support of Tunnel Based on the Load Structure Method. *Journal of Railway Engineering Society*, 2018, 35(4):60–64.

Civil Engineering and Energy-Environment – Gao & Duan (Eds)
© 2023 the Author(s), ISBN 978-1-032-56057-1

Analysis of influence of asymmetric zoned excavation on response variation of foundation pit engineering

Yongguo Yan & Junxing Luo*
CCCC Fourth Harbor Engineering Institute Co., Ltd, Guangzhou, China
CCCC Key Lab of Environmental Protection & Safety in Foundation Engineering of Transportation, Guangzhou, China

ABSTRACT: Based on the reasonable calculation parameters of an actual engineering inversion, Midas GTS is used to establish a three-dimensional numerical model of asymmetric zoned excavation, and the effect of zoned excavation sequence on the horizontal displacement of the enclosure structure and the axial force of the support members is studied and analyzed. The results show that: for a certain side of the foundation pit, the horizontal displacement into the pit can be controlled by the excavation sequence of the middle area first, then the surrounding area, first the far area, and then the near area. The axial force of the main support beam member and the axial stress of the main support slab member show an increasing trend as a whole with the zoned excavation, and at the end of each layer of soil excavation, the support internal force in basin excavation is slightly larger than that in island excavation. The axial force of the supporting beam members near the external corner of the foundation pit shows a variation law of first increase and then decrease or first decrease and then increase with the zoned excavation.

1 INTRODUCTION

In recent years, deep and large foundation pits have become the mainstream in urban construction, and the deformation control of foundation pits is the focus of attention, and zoned excavation is an effective deformation control method. Zoned excavation is to use the space-time effect of the foundation pit to control the deformation of the foundation pit by dividing the large foundation pit into several small foundation pits. Although this method increases the construction process and engineering period, it has an obvious effect on controlling the deformation of the foundation pit and can ensure the safety of the foundation pit and surrounding important structures (Shen *et al.* 2019; Xie *et al.* 2017; Zhang & Li 2012).

Some scholars have conducted useful discussions on the impact of zoned excavation of foundation pits on supporting structures. Huang *et al.* (2015) analyzed the influence of large-scale foundation pit-zoned excavation on the vertical and horizontal deformation of adjacent subway stations and shield tunnels through measured data. Huang *et al.* (2015) used a numerical calculation method to analyze the influence of partition width and partition excavation sequence on the diaphragm wall and soil deformation behind the wall on one side of the protected structure during the zoned excavation of deep and large foundation pits. Lin *et al.* (2016) analyzed the effect of zoned excavation of a super deep foundation pit on the vertical displacement of the top of the diaphragm wall based on the on-site monitoring results. Shen (2017) used ABAQUS to analyze the time-varying laws of mechanical effects

*Corresponding Author: ljunxing@cccc4.com

DOI: 10.1201/9781003433644-4

such as the displacement of the enclosure structure and the internal force of the support caused by the zoned excavation of a deep and large foundation pit. Xu (2020) studied the interaction characteristics of the deformation of the first and the latter excavation area by analyzing the monitoring data of the lateral deformation of the diaphragm wall and the supporting axial force caused by the zoned excavation of a deep foundation pit.

At present, there are many studies on the zoned excavation of foundation pits (Wang 2021), but zoned excavation has little influence on the deformation of the beam-slab bracing system. Based on a foundation pit project using a beam-slab bracing structure, this paper designs the excavation zones and sequences according to island excavation (that is, surrounding first and then middle) and basin excavation (that is, middle first and then surrounding), and establishes a three-dimensional numerical model of asymmetric zoned excavation, analyzes the excavation sequence and analyzes the horizontal displacement of the enclosure structure and the axial force of the supporting members (main supporting beams, connecting beams, supporting slab, etc.). The law of response effect caused by the asymmetric zoned excavation of the foundation pit is obtained.

2 MODELING

2.1 Modeling method and consistency verification

Firstly, the actual project is modeled, the model parameters are inverted according to the measured data, and the reasonable modeling method and calculation parameters are obtained.

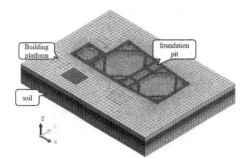

Figure 1. Finite element model of a foundation pit project.

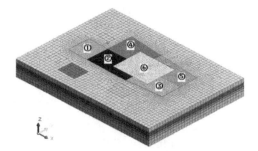

Figure 2. Finite element model of the asymmetric excavation.

The foundation pit has a total length of 270 m, a width of 128 m, and a depth of 14.7 m. The soil adopts solid elements, and the 1 m-thick diaphragm wall adopts plate elements. The internal support dimensions of the first and second reinforced concrete are 0.8 m × 1.0 m and 1.0 m × 1.2 m, respectively, and the slab thickness is 0.25 m.

The soil parameters are shown in Table 1. The modified Mohr-Coulomb constitutive is adopted. The remaining materials are steel and reinforced concrete, all of which adopt elastic constitutive. Unit weight is 78.5 kN/m^3 and 25.0 kN/m^3, poisson's ratio is 0.3 and 0.2, and the elastic modulus is 200 GPa and 30 GPa, respectively. The surrounding buildings shall consider the equivalent load of 20~50 kPa.

It can be seen from Figure 3 that the simulation results are consistent with the distribution law of the field-measured data. Compared with the actual measurement, the maximum

Table 1. Model parameters.

Soil	γ (kN·m^{-3})	c (kPa)	φ (°)	E_{50}^{ref} (MPa)	E_{oed}^{ref} (MPa)	E_{ur}^{ref} (MPa)	Thickness (m)
Fill	18.0	8	5	10	10	50	1.5
Clay	18.0	5	3	15	15	75	10.1
Silty Clay	20.0	11	9	15	15	75	3.1
Fully Weathered	19.5	10	15	18	18	90	8.0
Strong Weathered	21.0	28	36	36	36	180	5.0
Medium Weathered	25.8	100	30	50	50	250	6.0
Micro-Weathered	26.4	150	35	100	100	500	16.3

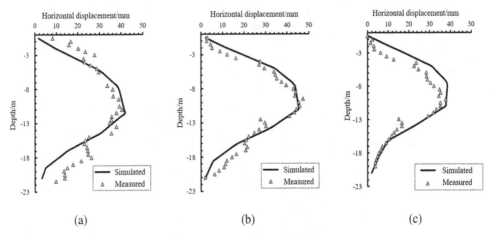

Figure 3. Measured and simulated values of diaphragm wall.

simulated displacement deviates from 0.56% to 3.69%, indicating that the modeling method and calculation parameters are accurate and reasonable.

2.2 Asymmetric partitioned excavation conditions

The zoned excavation sequence is shown in Table 2, and the calculation model is shown in Figure 2.

3 CALCULATION RESULTS AND ANALYSIS

3.1 Horizontal displacement of diaphragm wall

Considering that the horizontal displacement curves of each measuring point in different plans are similar when excavating to the bottom of the pit, and only the values are different, this paper takes measuring point A of plan 1 as an example for analysis and discussion. It can be seen from Figure 4 that the first three processes in the first layer of soil excavation basically do not affect the displacement of the diaphragm wall, and the maximum value is about 0.68 mm. When the soil in area ④ was excavated, the maximum horizontal displacement suddenly increased to 30.73 mm, and after the first layer of soil was excavated, the maximum horizontal displacement was 33.6 mm. Similarly, the maximum horizontal displacement of the second layer of soil increased suddenly to 43.21mm after the soil in the area ④ was excavated. In general, the diaphragm wall increased significantly twice during the

Table 2. Asymmetric excavation calculation conditions.

Working Condition	Plan 1	Plan 2	Plan 3	Plan 4
Initial Condition	Initial stress field analysis: simulate the real stress field and reset the displacement			
Initial Working Process	Construction site connecting wall and column structure, excavation of 1.5m thick top-soil			
Process 1	Build of the first support beam + the first support slab + capping beam			
	Excavate the first layer of soil ①area			
Process 2~6	Excavate 1st layer of soil area: ②→③→④→⑤→⑥	Excavate 1st layer of soil area: ④→⑤→②→③→⑥	Excavate 1st layer of soil area: ⑥→②→③→④→⑤	Excavate 1st layer of soil area: ⑥→④→⑤→②→③
Process 7	Build of the second support beam + the second support slab + waling			
	Excavate the second layer of soil ①area			
Process 8~12	Excavate 2nd layer of soil area: ②→③→④→⑤→⑥	Excavate 2nd layer of soil area: ④→⑤→②→③→⑥	Excavate 2nd layer of soil area: ⑥→②→③→④→⑤	Excavate 2nd layer of soil area: ⑥→④→⑤→②→③

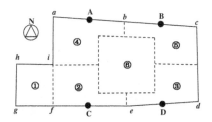

Figure 4. Measurement point of horizontal displacement of diaphragm wall.

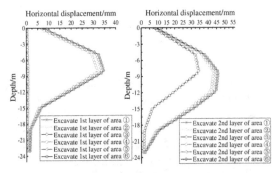

Figure 5. Development process of horizontal displacement curve of measuring point A in Plan 1.

Table 3. The maximum horizontal displacement of the ground connecting wall under different excavation conditions.

Working Condition	Horizontal Displacement of Measuring Point/mm			
	A	B	C	D
Plan 1	45.91	37.60	43.01	44.83
Plan 2	49.82	41.59	38.79	40.51
Plan 3	44.26	35.77	45.75	48.32
Plan 4	53.40	45.78	37.04	38.47
Overall Excavation	47.22	39.83	39.56	41.80

whole process, both of which occurred after the soil excavation in area ④. It can be seen from this that the displacement of the diaphragm wall is affected by the sequence of excavation of the adjacent soil. The more lag in the excavation sequence of the soil mass inside the diaphragm wall, the more the soil acting as back pressure can weaken the stress release effect caused by the excavation of the distant soil mass, and the more it can control the deformation of the diaphragm wall.

As shown in Table 3, compared with the overall excavation, the displacement of point A in Plan 1 is reduced by 1.31 mm, and the displacement of point C is increased by 3.45 mm, the displacement of the diaphragm walls on the north and south sides to the center of the foundation pit is different, excavating the soil in the pit on the south side first. And the back pressure soil in the reserved pit on the north side is beneficial to reduce the displacement of the diaphragm wall on the north side, which is caused by the different effects of stress release caused by soil excavation.

Compared with the overall excavation, the maximum horizontal displacement of points A and B in Plan 1 is reduced by 1.30 mm and 2.23 mm, respectively, and the maximum horizontal displacement of points A and B in Plan 3 is reduced by 2.95 mm and 4.06 mm, respectively. It shows that compared with island excavation, basin excavation can reduce the displacement of the diaphragm wall and increase the displacement of the diaphragm wall first. The reason is that before excavating the soil at points A and B, the basin excavation excavates the soil in the areas ②, ③, and ⑥, while the island excavation only excavates the soil in the areas ② and ③. The stress release range caused by the excavation is large, which causes a large displacement of the north diaphragm wall into the pit. In general, for the enclosure structure on one side of the foundation pit, the horizontal displacement into the pit can be controlled (reduced) through the excavation sequence of the middle first, then the surrounding area, and the far area first and then the near area.

3.2 *Response of the internal support system*

It can be seen from Figure 6 that the main support beam members show a growing trend as a whole with the excavation. At the end of the excavation of the first layer of soil, the axial forces of ZC1-1 in Plans 1 to 4 are 3899.5 kN, 3772.6 kN, 4185.1 kN, and 3979.2 kN, respectively. At the end of the excavation of the second layer of soil, the axial forces of ZC1-1 in Plans 1 to 4 are 5082.3 kN, 4899.5 kN, 5252.4 kN, and 5174.7 kN, respectively. It can be seen that at the end of each layer of soil excavation, the axial force of the main support is slightly larger than that of the island excavation in the basin excavation, which is greater than 5.20%.

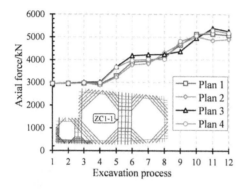

Figure 6. The axial force of the first main support beam ZC1-1.

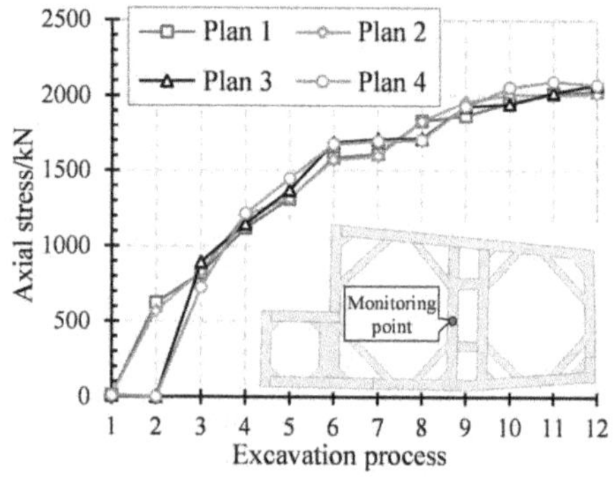

Figure 7. Axial stress of the first main support slab.

It can be seen from Figure 7 that the axial stress of the main support slab shows an increasing trend as a whole with the excavation. After the second support is installed, the axial stress of the first support slab increases slowly. The average axial stress corresponding to basin excavation and island excavation are 2074.9 kPa and 2024.3 kPa, respectively. It can be seen that for the same excavation method, the partitioned excavation has little effect on the stress of the support beam and the slab, while different excavation methods have a greater impact on the stress of the support beam and the slab. In general, the axial stress of the support slab and the axial force of the support beam change synergistically during the zoned excavation process.

Taking the main supporting connecting beam ZC1-2 as an example (as shown in Figure 8), the axial force of the soil mass in Area ④ in Plan 1 decreases from 1125.9 kN to 881.6 kN after excavation, and that in Area ② in Plan 2 decreases from 1249.2 kN to 944.3 kN after excavation. The axial force of the soil mass in Area ④ and Area ② in Plans 3 and 4 also decreases after excavation, and the supporting axial force changes little before excavation. It can be seen from this that when the soil mass on one side of the brace is completely excavated, due to the development trend of lateral deformation of the brace, the lateral connecting beam support tends to be tensioned, reducing the axial force of the connecting beam support. However, when the soil mass on one side is partially excavated, the effect of lateral deformation caused by the release of soil excavation stress is weak, and the axial force of the connecting beam support does not change significantly.

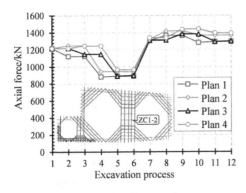 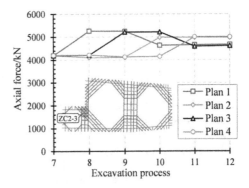

Figure 8. Axial force of the first main support connecting beam ZC1-2.

Figure 9. The axial force of the second support ZC2-3 at the external corner.

From the amplitude of axial force, in the excavation of the first layer of soil, the average reduction percentage of the axial force caused by the excavation of all the soil on the side of the support to the support of ZC1-2 is 22.8%, and the reduction percentage of the axial force in the excavation of the second layer of soil is 4.9% on average. It can be seen that after the erection of the second support, the axial force of the first support connecting beam is less affected by the excavation in different zones. In addition, in the process of zoned excavation of the same layer of soil, the axial force of the connecting beam support will decrease significantly, but it has little change after a reduction.

As shown in Figure 9, for the support ZC2-3 located near the outer corner of the foundation pit, affected by the sequence of soil excavation, the axial force of the support beam is redistributed, showing a law of first increase and then decrease or first decrease and then increase. For example, in Plan 1, the axial force of the supporting beam members has a development trend of increasing first and then decreasing. The increase in the axial force is due to the excavation of the soil in the second area, the ground connecting wall in the hi section has more displacement into the pit, and the support bears more load of the enclosure structure. At this time, the axial force increases from 4195.4 kN to 5257.8 kN. The reduction of the axial force is due to the excavation of the soil in the ④ area, the deformation of the ground connecting the wall in the ai section into the pit, and the original compressive and deformed supports tend to be in tension, which reduces the axial force from 5251.7 kN to 4636.7 kN. In Plan 2, since area ④ is excavated first and area 2 is excavated later, the axial force shows the opposite variation law. In addition, the support axial force during the partition excavation process will be larger than the support axial force after the excavation. For example, in Plan 1, the maximum axial force of ZC2-3 is 5257.8 kN during excavation and 4671.7 kN after excavation. To sum up, it can be seen that the soil in the side pit of the ground connection wall with the same length direction as that of the support beam is excavated first, and the change of the support axial force in the process of zoning excavation can be used to decrease first and then increase, in order to avoid the situation that the axial force increases sharply and exceeds the design value.

4 CONCLUSION

1. The more lag in the excavation sequence of the soil mass inside the diaphragm wall, the weaker the stress release effect caused by the excavation of the distant soil mass, and the better the deformation of the diaphragm wall can be controlled. For the enclosure

structure on one side of the foundation pit, the horizontal displacement into the pit can be controlled by the excavation sequence of the middle first, then the surrounding area, the far area first and then the near area.
2. With the continuous excavation of the partitions, the axial force of the main support beam and the slab shows an increasing development trend as a whole, and at the end of each layer of soil excavation, the support internal force in the basin excavation is slightly larger than that in island excavation. When the excavation of the soil on one side of the support is completed, the axial force of the connecting support will be greatly reduced, and there will be little change after the large reduction.
3. The axial force of the supporting beam near the external corner of the foundation pit shows a variation law of first increase and then decrease or first decrease and then increase with the zoned excavation. During construction, the soil in the pit with the same length direction as the support beam can be excavated first, taking advantage of the tendency of the support axial force to decrease first and then increase during the excavation process, in order to avoid the situation that the axial force increases sharply and exceeds the design value.

REFERENCES

Huang P., Chen H. and Zhang Q. (2015) Influence of Zonal Excavation of Large Foundation Pits on Adjacent Subways. *Engineering Investigation*. 43(08): 15–20.
Huang P., Liu G.B. and Huo R.K. (2015) Analysis of Excavation Parameters of Foundation Pit Zones in Soft Soil Areas. *Journal of Central South University (Natural Science Edition)*. 46(10): 3859–3864.
Lin Z.J., Zhang X.C., Zhao B. et al. (2016) Influence of Zonal Excavation of Super Deep Foundation Pit in Soft Soil Area on the Vertical Displacement of Underground Diaphragm Wall. *Tianjin Construction Technology*. 26(05):3–7 + 12.
Shen W., Shen R. and Sun L.W. (2019) Measured Analysis of the Impact of Subdivisional Excavation of Ultra-deep Foundation Pits on the Side Subway. *Chinese Journal of Underground Space and Engineering*. 15(S1): 354–360.
Shen Y.T. (2017) Numerical Simulation of Mechanical Effects of Subdivisional Excavation of Deep and Large Foundation Pits in Soft Soil Areas. *Chinese Journal of Hydraulic and Architectural Engineering*. 15(06):23–27.
Wang S.Y. (2021) Influence of Zoning Excavation of Foundation Pit on Adjacent Subway Stations. *Engineering Investigation*. 49(06): 14–18.
Xie W., Lu K.L., Zhu D.Y. (2017) Monitoring and Numerical Simulation of Subdivision Excavation of Subway Deep Foundation Pit. *Journal of Changjiang Academy of Sciences*. 34(12):106–110 + 121.
Xu J. (2020) Analysis of the Mutual Influence of the Deformation of Each Zone of the Zone Excavation Foundation Pit. *China Municipal Engineering*. (02):112–114 + 137.
Zhang S.N. and Li S.Y. (2012) Numerical Analysis of the Influence of Deep Foundation Pit Zoning Excavation. *Low-temperature Building Technology*. 34(12): 113–115.

Study on the effect of the moisture content change on resilient modulus of subgrade soils

Yuanzhong Chen & Fan Li
Shenzhen Gongming Water Supply and Storage Engineering Management, Shenzhen, China

Yangyang Lu*
Department of Geotechnical Engineering, Nanjing Hydraulic Research Institute, Nanjing, China

Dan Hang
Jiangsu Flood Control and Emergency Drill Center, Nanjing, China

ABSTRACT: The moisture content of subgrade soil always fluctuates during the service period. To accurately evaluate the safety of the road subgrade, it is necessary to study the effect of the moisture content change on the resilient modulus of the subgrade soil. In this study, dynamic triaxial tests on a kind of subgrade soil near the Gongming reservoir were conducted to study the influence of moisture content change on the elastic modulus of the subgrade soil. The results show that repeated shear will damage the soil structure; therefore, the resilient modulus gradually decreases with increased deviatoric stress. While the confining pressure limits the lateral deformation of the subgrade soil under cyclic deviator stress, thereby improving the resilience modulus of the subgrade soil. When the water content increases, the migration and penetration of water weaken the force between the particles in the subgrade soil and destroy the overall structure, decreasing its resilience modulus.

1 INTRODUCTION

Subgrade soils are generally compacted near their optimum moisture content in road engineering, and the relative compaction degree shall not be less than 95%. However, the moisture content of the subgrade soil gradually rises to the optimal moisture content wet side during the service period, and it fluctuates within a certain range of the optimal moisture content wet side with the changing climate (Kim & Kim 2007; Uzan 1998). The change in the water content affects the physical and mechanical properties of the subgrade soil and further affects the normal use of the road.

The elastic modulus (M_R) of the subgrade soil, referring to the ratio of the stress and its corresponding elastic strain, is an important index to characterize the elastic deformation of subgrade soil under the action of traffic dynamic load, and is also a key parameter to predict fatigue cracking of pavement structure and design the thickness of subgrade structure layer (Bassani *et al.* 2015; Liu *et al.* 2021). At present, the subgrade design method based on MR of the subgrade soil has been widely used (Bilodeau *et al.* 2016; Leung *et al.* 2013; Sadrossadat *et al.* 2016). However, previous studies have only explored the influence of soil type, compactness, stress level, and loading frequency on M_R of the subgrade soil at the optimal moisture content (Fedakar *et al.* 2022; George *et al.* 2009; Kumar & George 2018;

*Corresponding Author: yylu@nhri.cn

Liu *et al.* 2019; Li & Selig 1994), and have not yet discussed the influence of moisture content change on the MR. Therefore, dynamic triaxial tests on a kind of subgrade soil near the Gongming reservoir were conducted to study the influence of moisture content change on M_R in this study.

2 DYNAMIC TRIAXIAL TESTS

After the decomposed plants and stones are removed from the subgrade clay taken from the area near the No. 4 dam body of Gongming reservoir in Shenzhen, China, it is air dried and ground through a 2 mm sieve to remove large particles. The basic properties of the clay are summarized in Table 1. In the clay, the sand accounts for 52.4%, the powder accounts for 23.7%, and the clay account for 23.9% measured by the particle analysis tests. The clay with the optimal moisture content (14.3%) and the maximum dry density (1.86 g/cm3) is divided into three layers and statically compacted in oedometer rings 61.8 mm in diameter and 20 mm in height. After each layer is compacted, the surface is roughened with a geotechnical knife to ensure that no fault occurs between layers. The prepared sample is immediately pushed out of the mold, wrapped with fresh-keeping film, and placed in a sealed box for 24 h to achieve water balance before conducting the dynamic triaxial tests.

Table 1. The permeability coefficient of different materials of the dam.

Liquid Limit (%)	Plastic Limit (%)	Specific Gravity	Maximum Dry Density (g/cm^3)	Optimum Water Content (%)
16.2	30.9	2.69	14.3	1.86

Four moisture contents w (15.0%, 15.7%, 16.4%, and 14.3%) are chosen to investigate the influence of moisture content change on the resilience modulus of the subgrade soil, and three confining pressures σ_c (30 kPa, 45 kPa, and 60 kPa) are set in dynamic triaxial tests. The loading waveform used in the tests is a half-sine wave. The loading frequency of the sine wave is 1 Hz, in which the holding time is 0.1 s and the intermittent time is 0.9 s. To eliminate the possible bad contact between the end of the sample and the instrument, 1000 repeated loads are first applied under the confining pressure of 30 kPa and the deviatoric stress of 50 kPa. Then, it is cycled 100 times under the combined load of each loading level, and the average rebound deformation ε_R of the last five cycles is recorded to calculate the resilient modulus M_R of the sample. The resilient modulus M_R is determined as

$$M_R = \frac{\sigma_d}{\varepsilon_R} \quad (1)$$

where σ_d is the deviatoric stress.

3 TEST RESULTS AND ANALYSIS

Figure 1 shows the relationship between the resilient modulus and the deviatoric stress under the four water contents. The resilient modulus gradually decreases with the increase of deviatoric stress under all confining pressures and water contents.

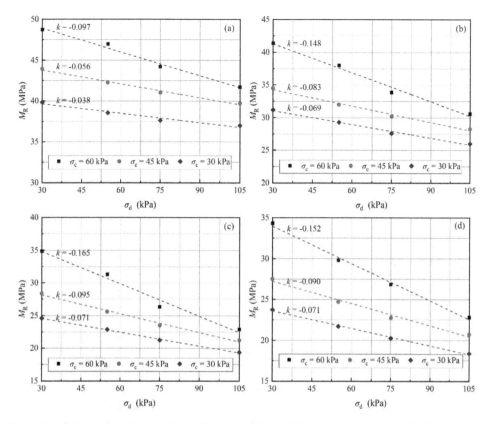

Figure 1. Relationships between the resilience modulus and deviatoric stress under the four water contents: (a) w = 14.3%; (b) w = 15.0%; (c) w = 15.7% and (d) w = 16.4%.

Generally, deviator stress has two opposite effects on the resilience modulus of the soil. On the one hand, the soil structure is damaged by repeated shear, reducing the resilience modulus. On the other hand, the soil is gradually compacted during the shear process, leading to an increase in the resilience modulus. When the soil structure is weak, the attenuation effect of the elastic modulus caused by repeated shear is greater than the enhancement effect of the elastic modulus caused by compaction, which occurs in this study, resulting in the decrease of the elastic modulus. It also can be seen from Figure 1 that the attenuation of resilience modulus with deviator stress can be approximately fitted by a straight line, and the slope of the straight line slightly decreases with the increase of the confining pressure under each water content. With the increase of water content, the slope of the straight line under the same confining pressure gradually decreases and then becomes stable.

Figure 2 presents the relationship between the resilient modulus and confining pressures under the four water contents. The resilient modulus gradually increases with the increase of confining pressure under all levels of deviatoric stress and water content. This is because confining pressures limit the lateral deformation of the soil under the action of cyclic deviatoric stress, thereby reducing the axial strain of the soil and improving the overall stiffness of the sample. The resilient modulus can also be approximated by a straight line with the increase of the confining pressure. Under the same water content, the slope of the

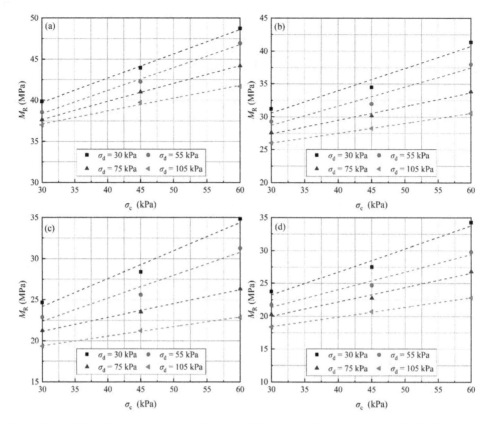

Figure 2. Relationships between the resilience modulus and confining pressure under the four water contents: (a) w = 14.3%; (b) w = 15.0%; (c) w = 15.7% and (d) w = 16.4%.

straight-line decreases with the increase of the deviatoric stress. The decrease is related to the shear failure effect of the deviatoric stress. The larger the deviator stress, the stronger the failure effect of the specimen, and the less the confining restraint effect of confining pressure on the soil.

Figure 3 presents the relationship between the resilient modulus and the water content. At σ_c = 60 kPa, there is a phenomenon that the resilience modulus of the sample in the high-water content section slightly increases with the increase of the water content, but the resilience modulus generally shows a downward trend with the increase of the water content. With the increase of moisture content in the humidification process, the decline of resilience modulus tends to be gentle, while between the last two levels of moisture content, the attenuation of resilience modulus is not obvious enough or even increases inversely. In the humidification process, because the migration and infiltration of water weaken the force between particles in the sample and damage the overall structure of the sample, resulting in the decrease of its resilience modulus, the resilience modulus of the sample will not decrease all the time in the same amplitude, but gradually decrease to stabilize in the exponential decay mode. Therefore, there is certainly critical moisture content. When the humidification moisture content is greater than this value, the attenuation of the modulus of resilience is not obvious.

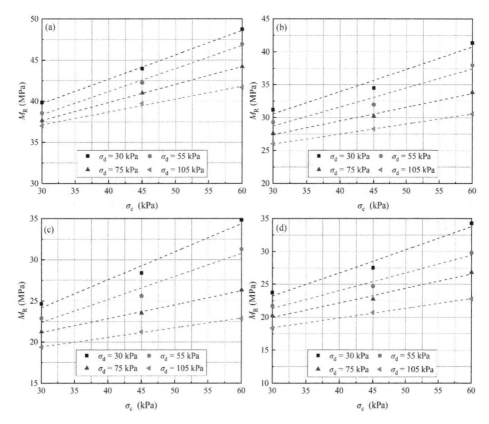

Figure 3. Relationships between resilience modulus and moisture content at different confining pressures: (a) σc = 30 kPa; (b) σc = 45 kPa and (c) σc = 60 kPa.

4 CONCLUSION

It was shown that using data from dynamic triaxial tests on the subgrade soil, the resilient modulus gradually decreases with the increase of deviatoric stress, while increasing with the increase of the confining pressures. As the force between the particles in the subgrade soil is weakened and its overall structure is destroyed by the migration and penetration of water, the resilient modulus of the subgrade soil decreases with the increase of the water content.

REFERENCES

Bassani M., Khosravifar S., Goulias D.G. et al. (2015) Long-term Resilient and Permanent Deformation Behavior of Controlled Low-Strength Materials for pavement Applications. *Transp. Geotechnics*, 2: 108–118.

Bilodeau J.P., Plamondon C.O., Doré G. (2016) Estimation of Resilient Modulus of Unbound Granular Materials Used as Pavement Base: Combined Effect of Grain-size Distribution and Aggregate Source Frictional Properties. *Mater. Struct.*, 49(10): 4363–4373.

Fedakar H.I., Rutherford C.J. and Cetin B. (2022) Effect of Principal Stress Rotation on Deformation Behavior of Dense Sand-clay Mixtures. *Road Mater. Pavement.*, 23(9): 2035–2056.

George V., Rao N. and Shivashankar R. (2009) Effect of Soil Parameters on Dynamic Cone Penetration Indices of Laterite Sub-Grade Soils From India. *Geotech. Geol. Eng.*, 27(4): 585–593.

Kim D. and Kim J.R. (2007) Resilient Behavior of Compacted Subgrade Soils Under the Repeated Triaxial Test. *Constr. Build. Mater.*, 21(7): 1470–1479.

Kumar A., George V. (2018) Effect of Soil Parameters on Resilient Modulus Using Cyclic Tri-Axial Tests on Lateritic Subgrade Soils from Dakshina Kannada, India. *Geotech. Geol. Eng.*, 36(6): 3987–4000.

Leung G.L.M., Wong A.W.G. and Wang Y.H. (2013) Prediction of Resilient Modulus of Compacted Saprolitic Soils by CBR Approach for Road Pavement Subgrade: A Re-examination. *Int. J. Pavement Eng.*, 14(4): 403–417.

Li D. and Selig E.T. (1994) Resilient Modulus for Fine-grained Subgrade Soils. *J. Geotech. Eng.*, 1994, 120(6): 939–957.

Liu S.H., Liao J., Bong T.T. et al. (2021) Repeated Loading of Soil Bag-reinforced Road Subgrade. *Geosynth. Int.*, 28(2): 113–124.

Liu X., Zhang X., Wang H. et al. (2019) Laboratory Testing and Analysis of Dynamic and Static Resilient Modulus of Subgrade Soil Under Various Influencing Factors. *Constr. Build. Mater.*, 195: 178–186.

Sadrossadat E., Heidaripanah A., Osouli S. (2016) Prediction of the Resilient Modulus of Flexible Pavement Subgrade Soils Using Adaptive Neuro-fuzzy Inference Systems. *Constr. Build. Mater.*, 123: 235–247.

Uzan J. (1998) Characterization of Clayey Subgrade Materials for the Mechanistic Design of Flexible Pavements. *Transp. Res. Rec.*, 1629(1): 189–196.

Ground penetrating radar and light dynamic penetration test-based analysis and evaluation technology for existing railway subgrade

Yuanshui Cheng*, Cui Du, Lijun Wang & Taifeng Li
Railway Engineering Research Institute, China Academy of Railway Sciences Corporation Limited, Beijing, China

Lyuzhou Lyu
School of Energy and Environmental Engineering, University of Science and Technology Beijing, China

Jingyu Liu & Xingang Zhang
Railway Engineering Research Institute, China Academy of Railway Sciences Corporation Limited, Beijing, China

ABSTRACT: The existing railways were built many years ago, and the poor subgrade filler tends to lead to insufficient bearing capacity of subgrade beds, so it is necessary to investigate the subgrade condition during the reconstruction and upgrading of existing railways. When evaluating the existing railway subgrade, we should focus on its bearing capacity. The onboard ground penetrating radar can quickly detect and evaluate the subgrade bed diseases and their distribution, subgrade surface deformation, subgrade bed moisture content, and track bed thickness of the whole line. Selecting and determining the key sections for the test and evaluation of subgrade bearing capacity based on the radar test results will save great effort. Given the characteristics of existing lines and the enforceability of test methods, this paper has proposed a comprehensive analysis and evaluation technology for railway subgrade conditions based on the onboard ground penetrating radar rapid test and in-situ bearing capacity light dynamic penetration test. This test method has important application value for testing and evaluating the subgrade of existing lines and is worthy of promotion.

1 INTRODUCTION

An early-built existing railway is located in the Yellow River flood plain, where a thicker Quaternary stratum occurs. The foundation settlement of the railway is stable after years of operation. The soil in this region is mainly composed of silty sand and fine sand, with low clay content, and the filler tends to be subject to flushing and mud-pumping. With the upgrading and reconstruction of the line (Yan 2016) and the increase of axle load and traffic volume, the dynamic load level and the number of repeated actions of the subgrade bed will also increase correspondingly. The increase in traffic density and train formation length will also increase the number of continuous actions. The increase of cumulative pore moisture pressure of the subgrade bed will decrease the subgrade strength. This phenomenon is particularly obvious for the filler adopted in this railway subgrade, so the subgrade bed, including the subgrade bed of low embankment, shall be systematically evaluated to ensure the requirements of railway operation after reconstruction.

---

*Corresponding Author: cyszxyd1980@163.com

Combined with the evaluation needs of the existing railway subgrade, the subgrade, especially its bearing capacity, was evaluated (Qin *et al.* 2016). According to the characteristics of this existing line and the enforceability of the test method, the continuous general survey with onboard ground penetrating radar and a local ground survey was adopted in combination. The onboard ground penetrating radar was adopted to rapidly test and evaluate the whole line, mainly the subgrade bed diseases and their distribution, the subgrade surface deformation, the subgrade bed moisture content, the track bed thickness, etc. According to the radar test results, representative characteristic sections were selected for the light dynamic penetration test of the subgrade bearing capacity (Yang & Zhou 2002), and the specific values of the subgrade bearing capacity of the characteristic construction site were obtained to analyze and evaluate the subgrade condition comprehensively. This method has important reference significance in evaluating the subgrade condition of other existing railways.

2 ONBOARD GEOLOGICAL RADAR TEST

2.1 *Introduction to the test method*

The onboard ground penetrating radar system is a high-speed test system developed in recent years (Li 2013; Liu *et al.* 2008). It is mainly applied in the comprehensive evaluation of railway subgrade structure, the flatness of the subgrade bed, the contamination degree of the track bed, and the moisture content of the track bed and subgrade bed. Based on the multi-channel high-speed ground penetrating radar, this system comprises a doppler high-speed coding radar, an environmental recorder, a data acquisition, an analyzing and processing system, etc. It can continuously test the underground distribution of objects, and has the advantages of quick, continuous, nondestructive, high-resolution, and real-time display (Dong 2014), with a test speed of up to 80 to 100 km/h, basically not or rarely affecting normal railway transportation.

Taking the propagation law of electromagnetic waves in lossy media as the theoretical basis, the railway subgrade test utilizes the radar transmitting antenna to propagate high-frequency and wide-band short-pulse electromagnetic waves into the railway subgrade. When propagating in the subgrade media, the electromagnetic waves will be reflected and transmitted at different media interfaces (Liu 2006), and the reflected electromagnetic waves will be received by the receiving antenna to form subgrade radar test data. The depth of the subgrade structural layer, the contamination degree of the track bed, and the moisture content of the subgrade can be judged by calculating the two-way travel time, amplitude, spectrum, instantaneous power, phase shift, and other

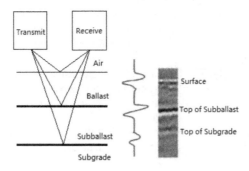

Figure 1. Working principle diagram of on-board ground penetrating radar system.

characteristic values of electromagnetic waves in the media. Please refer to Figure 1 for its working principle.

2.2 *Radar test results*

2.2.1 *Abnormal condition*

After processing and analyzing relevant data of the geological radar profile collected on site, a total of 27 abnormal subgrade sections were identified, with diseases of large subsidence and deformation of the subgrade, high moisture content of the track bed and subgrade bed, serious contamination of track bed, and mud pumping, among which high moisture content of the track bed and subgrade bed and serious contamination of the track bed are the main problems. Please refer to Table 1 for the details of the abnormal conditions.

1) Larger subgrade deformation: In this test, the subgrade with a deformation larger than 10 cm was taken as the identification basis for larger subgrade deformation. This type of abnormality is caused by a locally uncompacted subgrade, whose strength and bearing capacity cannot meet the requirements. Under the action of the overlaying load, the

Table 1. Statistics of line abnormalities.

S/N	Starting Mileage	Ending Mileage	Length	Type of Abnormalities
1	K3 + 729	K3 + 783	54	The slightly larger moisture content of the subgrade
2	K4 + 101	K4 + 204	103	The slightly larger moisture content of the subgrade
3	K4 + 975	K5 + 038	63	The larger moisture content of subgrade
4	K9 + 803	K9 + 863	60	Existence of ballast grooves
5	K10 + 391	K10 + 486	95	The larger moisture content of track bed and subgrade bed
6	K11 + 063	K11 + 160	97	Serious track bed contamination
7	K11 + 899	K12 + 129	230	The larger moisture content of track bed and subgrade bed, and serious track bed contamination
8	K12 + 129	K12 + 361	232	Serious mixing of ballast and soil
9	K12 + 971	K13 + 235	264	The larger moisture content of track bed and subgrade bed
10	K13 + 591	K14 + 556	965	The larger moisture content of subgrade, serious track bed contamination, and mud-pumping phenomena existing in the station yard.
11	K15 + 050	K15 + 325	275	The larger moisture content of track bed and subgrade bed, and serious track bed contamination
12	K17 + 128	K17 + 390	262	The larger moisture content of track bed and subgrade bed, and serious track bed contamination
13	K17 + 805	K18 + 196	391	Serious track bed contamination
14	K18 + 393	K18 + 708	315	The larger moisture content of track bed and subgrade bed, and serious track bed contamination
15	K19 + 416	K19 + 747	331	The larger moisture content of the subgrade bed
16	K20 + 000	K20 + 384	384	The larger moisture content of the subgrade bed and the serious mixing of ballast and soil
17	K21 + 050	K21 + 600	550	The larger moisture content of the subgrade bed
18	K22 + 053	K22 + 266	213	The larger moisture content of track bed and subgrade bed, and serious track bed contamination
19	K23 + 539	K23 + 884	345	Serious mixing of ballast and soil
20	K25 + 622	K25 + 931	309	The larger moisture content of the subgrade bed
21	K26 + 105	K26 + 163	58	The larger moisture content of track bed and subgrade bed
22	K27 + 796	K28 + 158	362	The larger moisture content of the subgrade bed
23	K28 + 348	K28 + 471	123	The larger moisture content of the subgrade bed
24	K28 + 595	K28 + 663	68	The larger moisture content of the subgrade bed
25	K28 + 745	K28 + 854	109	The larger moisture content of the subgrade bed
26	K29 + 062	K29 + 253	191	Mud-pumping of subgrade
27	K30 + 345	K31 + 000	655	The larger moisture content of track bed and subgrade bed

subgrade will settle locally. This abnormality is presented as obvious bending and sinking of the phase axis reflected by the surface layer of the subgrade bed or the interruption and discontinuity of the phase axis on the radar profile. Sometimes it is intermittent. For example, when the ballast and soil are seriously mixed, the phase axis may disappear. Please refer to Figure 2 for the typical radar profile.

2) Larger moisture content: Moisture is a major cause of railway subgrade diseases. The dielectric constant of water is 81, the dielectric constant of ballast is 6 to 8, and the relative dielectric constant of air is 1. When there is moisture in the subgrade, its relative dielectric constant, reflection coefficient, propagation speed of the electromagnetic wave, reflection amplitude, polarity, spectrum, phase, and other factors will change. The existence of moisture will present low-frequency, strong amplitude, and high-energy reflection, sometimes multiple reflections, on the radar profile. On the color radar profile, it will present low-frequency, strong amplitude, and high-energy radar images. The larger the moisture content, the greater the reflection ability. Please refer to Figure 3 for the typical radar profile for the subgrade with larger moisture content.

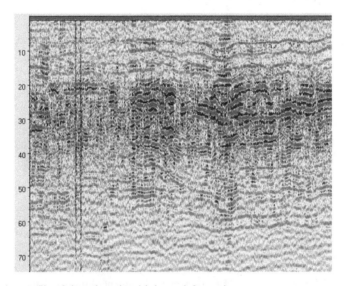

Figure 2. Radar profile of the subgrade with large deformation.

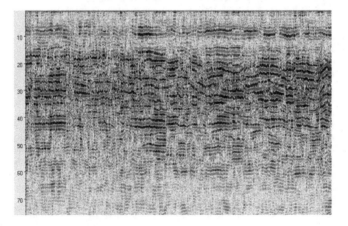

Figure 3. Radar profile of the subgrade with larger moisture content.

2.2.2 Track bed thickness

The average track bed thickness of this line is 0.66 m, wherein the track bed with a thickness of small than 0.50 m accounts for 1.11% of the line, 0.51 to 0.60 m accounts for 13.2%, 0.61 to 0.70 m accounts for 62.14%, 0.71 to 0.80 m accounts for 19.39%, and 0.80 m above accounts for 4.12%. According to the tested track bed thickness, the track bed thickness in this section is relatively uniform, and the surface layer of the subgrade bed is relatively flat, indicating that the bearing capacity of the subgrade in this section is relatively balanced. Please refer to Figure 4 for the thickness distribution of the whole track bed.

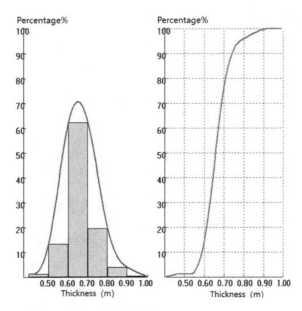

Figure 4. Distribution diagram of track bed thickness.

3 SUBGRADE BEARING CAPACITY TEST

The radar test results show that six representative sections (K4 + 400 to K4 + 900, K9 + 00 to K9 + 500, K15 + 000 to K15 + 500, K17 + 000 to K17 + 500, K23 + 000 to K23 + 500, and K27 + 500 to K28 + 000) were selected for a light dynamic penetration field test (Zhang & Zuo 2006). Tests were carried out at 2 to 3 test points in each section. To improve its resolution to the stratum, the blows/10 cm penetration was adopted, and this number of blows was expanded by three times as the characteristic value of the number of blows at a depth of 30 cm to calculate the bearing capacity. The light dynamic penetration tests were carried out at a total of 16 test points. To avoid affecting the driving and other factors, the field tests were generally arranged at the ballast foot close to the railway sleeper. During the test, the tests were imposed on the soil subgrade after excavating the cover hard shell layer.

During the previous tests on existing lines and this test, it was found that there was a hard-shell layer with a thickness of about 100 mm to 300 mm on the surface of most existing subgrade beds, and the bearing capacity of this layer was different, but generally high, usually above 180 kPa. This layer was formed under the action of long-term train and environmental load. The filler under this layer is mostly in poor condition, and there are soft and weak intercalations in some parts. Based on a large number of light dynamic penetration test data of existing lines, the China Academy of Railway Sciences proposed the technical requirement curve of light dynamic penetration reconstruction for the existing line subgrade bed in the "Research on Comprehensive Subgrade Evaluation and Reinforcement Technology for Speed-up of Existing Lines" (RERI, CARS 2005). This technical requirement curve is to unify the elevations of all light dynamic penetration tests to the top surface of the track in consideration of the differences in the track bed thickness of the existing lines. It was obtained by drawing the left envelope of most of the penetration curves at good subgrade beds.

Given the specific situations and operation status of this line and the test experience on existing lines, the above idea was adopted to evaluate the subgrade of this line. Considering the actual track bed thickness and field test situation of this line (the hard-shell layer at the ballast foot was excavated to carry out the test), the part below 1 m on the technical requirement curve was taken as the technical requirement curve for evaluating the subgrade bearing capacity.

This line belongs to the National Railway Class II single-track electrified railway, with a maximum running speed of 120 km/h, and mainly adopts SS4 locomotives. According to the empirical formula of dynamic load on subgrade surface:

$$\sigma_{dl} = 0.26 \times P \times (1 + 0.003v) \quad \text{(kPa)}$$

where, P is the locomotive axle weight, 230 kN for the SS4 locomotive; v is the driving speed, km/h.

According to the report "Research on Comprehensive Subgrade Evaluation and Reinforcement Technology for Speed-up of Existing Lines," 220 kN was taken as the locomotive axle weight, and the technical requirements curve for evaluation of the subgrade bearing capacity of this line, which mainly adopts SS4 locomotive, was derived in direct proportion, as shown in Figure 5.

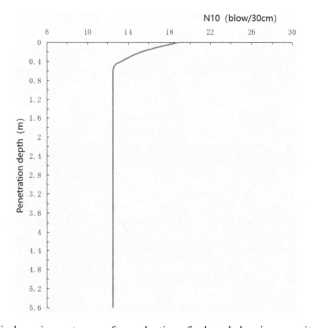

Figure 5. Technical requirements curve for evaluation of subgrade bearing capacity.

Table 2. Proportion of the stratum represented by N_{10} (Blow/30 cm) in the penetrated stratum (%).

Mileage Location	Blow Counts/Bearing Capacity			Penetration Depth (m)
	<15/ ($\sigma 0$<100 KPa)	15 to 20/ ($\sigma 0$ 100 to 140 kPa)	>20/ ($\sigma 0$ >140 KPa)	
K4 + 840	16.3	25.6	58.1	4.3
K4 + 960	18.2	29.5	52.3	4.4
K9 + 600	13.2	13.2	73.7	3.8
K9 + 700	2.0	18.4	79.6	4.9
K10 + 000	23.3	11.6	65.1	4.3
K15 + 230	2.3	30.2	67.4	4.3
K15 + 450	20.6	20.6	58.8	3.4
K17 + 400	16.3	30.6	53.1	4.9
K17 + 550	7.7	40.4	51.9	5.2
K17 + 750	1.9	23.1	75.0	5.2
K23 + 100	5.3	26.3	68.4	3.8
K23 + 300	0.0	16.2	83.8	3.7
K23 + 500	0.0	0.0	100.0	2.6
K28 + 100	0.0	4.5	95.5	4.4
K28 + 300	11.8	35.3	52.9	3.4
K28 + 480	0.0	14.0	86.0	4.3
Whole section	8.7	22.0	69.3	

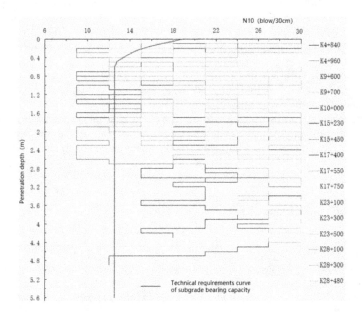

Figure 6. Light dynamic penetration of subgrade and its technical requirements curve.

Please refer to Table 2 for the proportion of the stratum bearing capacity represented by N_{10} at each test point on site, and refer to Figure 6 for the penetration curve and the technical requirements curve of subgrade bearing capacity at each test point.

It can be seen from Table 2 that, at all test points, about 8.7% of the stratum have a bearing capacity of less than 100 kPa, and about 69.3% have a bearing capacity of 140 kPa or above. It can be seen from Figure 6 that, in general, the basic bearing capacity of about 10.5% of the stratum in the whole test section does not meet the requirements of the technical curve of subgrade bearing capacity, that is, the bearing capacity of the most stratum at all test points on the line meets the requirements of the technology curve, and the bearing capacity is generally high.

4 CONCLUSIONS

1. The test results of onboard geological radar show that this line has few subgrade diseases, but there are some sections with larger subgrade moisture content and serious track bed contamination. The track bed of the line is relatively thick, with an average thickness of 0.66 m. The subgrade bed is relatively flat, and the subgrade bearing capacity is relatively balanced.
2. The light dynamic penetration test showed that the stratum with a basic subgrade bearing capacity of fewer than 100 kPa accounts for about 8.7% of the tested stratum in the whole section, indicating that there is a soft and weak intercalated layer in the subgrade of this section, and the stratum with a basic subgrade bearing capacity reaching or exceeding 140 kPa accounts for about 69.3% of the tested stratum in the whole section.
3. According to the analysis of technical requirements for bearing capacity, the bearing capacity of a small part of the subgrade in this section is relatively low, and the bearing capacity of most parts is high, which can meet the technical requirements curve of the subgrade bed of the 120 km/h existing line proposed in the "Research on Subgrade Comprehensive Evaluation and Reinforcement Technology for Speed-up of Existing Lines."
4. The sections with subgrade diseases and insufficient bearing capacity shall be reinforced to improve the stability of the subgrade bed, and the maintenance of the line shall be strengthened to ensure driving safety.
5. The comprehensive railway subgrade analysis and evaluation technology and method based on onboard ground penetrating radar rapid test and in-situ bearing capacity light dynamic penetration test have important application value for the test and evaluation of the existing line subgrade.

REFERENCES

Dong P. Application of Geological Radar in Engineering Geophysical Exploration of Subgrade Cavity Diseases of Existing Railways. *Subgrade Engineering*, 2014 (3): 172–174.

Li W. Application of On-board Ground Penetrating Radar in the General Survey of Subgrade Quality of New Railway. *Subgrade Engineering*, 2013 (6): 32–34.

Liu J. Application of Ground Penetrating Radar Technology in Existing Railway Lines. *Railway Architecture*, 2006 (10): 77–78.

Liu J., Zhang Q.L., Ma W.B. Application of Ground Penetrating Radar Technology in Evaluating the Status and Development of Existing Railway Subgrade. *Railway Architecture*, 2008 (1): 52–54.

Qin J.Y., Wang S., Diao X.H. Application of Light Dynamic Penetration in Speed-raising of Existing Railway Lines. *Geotechnical Foundation*, 2016, 24 (3): 27–29.

Railway Engineering Research Institute, China Academy of Railway Sciences Corporation Limited (RERI, CARS). *Research on Comprehensive Evaluation and Reinforcement Technology of Speed-up Subgrade of*

Existing Lines. Beijing: Railway Construction Research Institute of China Academy of Railway Sciences Group Co., Ltd., 2005.

Yan Z.J. Treatment Measures for Subgrade and Subgrade Bed Diseases of Ordinary-speed Railway. *Inner Mongolia Science and Technology and Economy*, 2016 (9): 65–69

Yang X.A., Zhou Q. Research on Railway Subgrade Diseases and Dynamic Penetration Test. *Journal of China University of Mining and Technology*, 2002, 31 (4): 358–362.

Zhang T. and Zuo D.Y. Application of Dynamic Penetration in Subgrade Compactness Test. *Subgrade Engineering*, 2006 (6): 140–141.

Evaluation of Acropolis of Athens under earthquake excitation and a proposal for roof restoration

Haohuan Xu*
School of Civil and Environmental Engineering, Georgia Institute of Technology, Atlanta, GA, USA

Xiaotao Shang
Saint James School, Hagerstown, MD, USA

Chelsey Tao
China Shanghai American School Pudong Campus, Shanghai, China

Zhiqian Fang
Shanghai Southwest Weiyu Middle School, Shanghai, China

ABSTRACT: As a milestone of human civilization, the Acropolis of Athens withstood natural disasters for thousands of years until its destruction by human factors. In this study, the dynamic properties of a model similar to that of the Parthenon were determined through its natural frequency and harmonic response with the results refined through ANSYS finite element analysis. An Earthquake was simulated on the response spectrum on ANSYS. Two meshes are adopted in this study. One is the default mesh. The second is the refiner mesh on significant components based on inspection from the first trial. The independent mesh study verifies that the obtained results are reasonable because the output deformations and stresses from two models with different mesh are similar to each other. Due to the destruction caused by a blast during the war in the 17th century, Parthenon is incomplete: the roof is gone and some columns are broken. Therefore, a renovation plan was proposed to add the original roof in fiber-reinforced polymer (FRP) for its lightweight and chemical stability. The static properties of the new model with added structures were determined through ANSYS static structure. The simulation results demonstrate an understanding of the original structure of the Parthenon, the model's response to an earthquake, and the viability of restoring a roof of synthetic material. Based on those analyses, columns, especially corner columns, are the weakest components of the structure. For future maintenance, it is necessary to take care of the columns for better protection of this ancient structure. The restoration of the roof with FRP is not feasible because of potential secondary damage to Parthenon.

1 INTRODUCTION

This study aims to analyze the Parthenon's stability in natural environments and seismic activity. The software ANSYS will be used to conduct finite element analysis and reach a conclusion by analyzing natural frequency, harmonic response, response spectrum, static structural, transient analysis, and explicit dynamics.

---

*Corresponding Author: hxu451@gatech.edu

The Parthenon, one of the most iconic monuments in the Acropolis of Athens, remains a historically and culturally significant structure in the world today. The Acropolis of Athens, meaning "high city" or "city in the air," symbolizes the civilization and classic art of Ancient Greece (Armstrong 2022). The structure of the Parthenon was chosen due to its stunning complex, universal symbol, and seismic resistance.

The construction of the Parthenon started in 447 B.C., ordered by the Greek Statesman Pericles. The two architects, Ictinus and Callicrates, built the structure, and the sculptor Phidias was responsible for designing this Doric-styled temple (AE. T. 2018) (Woodford 2008). The Parthenon made almost entirely of Pentelic marble, is separated into four zones: the crepida, the colonnade, the entablature, and the roof. Measured from the top layer of the step, the dimension of the base is 69.54 by 30.89 meters. Above the floor, the Parthenon has forty-six outer and nineteen inner pillars (Parthenon 2022). The average height of the pillars is 10.43 meters, and the average approximate diameter is 1.93 meters. Each of these columns is made of around eleven drums or sections that do not have the same size (iPedia 2022). The Parthenon is purposely made to be a structure from the base with imperfect angles to produce a straight and perfect frame for the human eye from a distance. This structure's careful design and construction, including the columns and marble slab sections, allowed the Parthenon to stand for centuries (Chrysopoulos 2022). The building was known and studied for its resistance to the abundant earthquake activities around Greece.

Greece has many natural disasters, including seismic activity, acid rain, and pollution, which can corrupt and damage many historical monuments and structures (A. P. 2022). Within these natural activities, earthquakes are one of the most common phenomena (Greece 2022). The country's location on the border of Africa and Eurasia contributes to its high seismic activity. However, even with the frequent earthquakes in the Acropolis, the Parthenon was never severely damaged, and the building remained stable until 1687. This year, during the Morean War, the Parthenon was severely damaged and destroyed by the impact of an explosion during the bombarding of the Venetian army (Kyriakos 2017). A cannonball struck the structure's interior, where the Ottomans stored gunpowder (Pollard & Pollard 2018). After this event, the restoration of the Parthenon is still being investigated and improved.

The focus of this study will be on the dynamic analysis and response spectrum of the Parthenon by using ANSYS. A Mesh independence study will be performed to verify our outputs; the verified results from the finite element analysis can be used to conclude the stability of the structure and can be used for future restoration proposals.

Greece has many natural disasters, including seismic activity, acid rain, and pollution, that can corrupt and damage many historical monuments and structures (A. P. 2022). Within these natural activities, earthquakes are one of the most common phenomena (Greece 2022). The country's location on the border of Africa and Eurasia contributes to its high seismic activity. However, even with the frequent earthquakes in the Acropolis, the Parthenon was never severely damaged, and the building remained stable until 1687. This year, during the Morean War, the Parthenon was severely damaged and destroyed by the impact of an explosion during the bombarding of the Venetian army (Kyriakos 2017). A cannonball struck the structure's interior, where the Ottomans stored gunpowder (Pollard, J., Pollard 2018). After this event, the restoration of the Parthenon is still being investigated and improved.

2 METHODOLOGY

A rough model of the original Parthenon is created in SolidWorks, consisting of 38 outer columns (13 in length and 8 in width), a roof, and a base. The inside of the Parthenon, authentically a temple containing a statue of Athena, is simplified to a solid cuboid in the model. The roof and the base are 69.5 meters in length and 31 meters in width. The 38 columns, 1.93 meters in diameter and 10.43 meters tall, are identical in the model. Figure 1 below shows the geometry inserted into Ansys that would be analyzed.

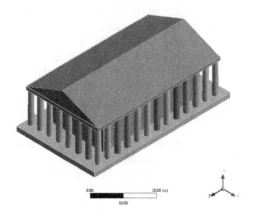

Figure 1. Geometry of structure.

The Parthenon was mainly constructed of Pentelic Marble and limestone. The columns, the roof, the entablature, and the chamber are all modeled by using Pentelic Marble in our simulation. The platform under columns, however, is modeled as limestone based on a real structure. As an ANSYS built-in material, limestone is 2.71 g/cm³ in density and is measured to be 3.7845E10 Pa for Young's modulus, 0.3077 Poisson's ratio, 3.28E10 Pa for bulk modulus, and 1.447E10 Pa for shear modulus. The remaining segments are made of Pentelic marble, a high-quantity calcium carbonate. As marble is not one of the available materials in ANSYS, the mechanical property of Pentelic marble is imported into the system. Pentelic marble is set to be 2.7 g/cm³ in density, with a coefficient of thermal expansion of 21 K-1 (AE. T. 2018). Concerning isotropic elasticity, the material of marble is measured to be 54 GPa for Young's modulus, 0.2 for Poisson's ratio, 3E10 Pa for bulk modulus, and 2.25E10 Pa for shear modulus (A. P. 2022). The material properties of Pentelic Mable, which are not available in ANSYS, are tabulated below in Table 1.

Table 1. Pentelic marble material properties.

Properties	Value	Unites
Density	2.7	g/cm³
Young's Modulus	54	GPa
Poisson's Ratio	0.2	–
Bulk Modulus	3E10	Pa
Shear Modulus	2.25E10	Pa

ANSYS automatically generated the mesh. Two manners of mesh were adopted. The first kind of mesh MESH1 is generated directly by using the default element size. The second kind of mesh MESH2 is more refined on significant components based on output from MESH1. For those less important parts in the structure, such as the platform and the roof, the mesh would just be kept as default. However, for columns and roof support, the mesh was reinforced for better analysis and verification purposes. For MESH1, there are nodes and elements in total, and MESH2 contains nodes and elements in total. The outputs from the two meshes are identical, which means the results obtained from ANSYS are reliable. The results will be discussed in detail in the next portion of this paper. Figure 2 shows the appearance of $MESH1$, and $MESH2$ is shown in Figure 3.

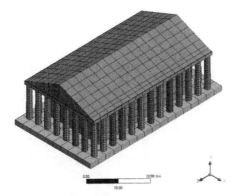 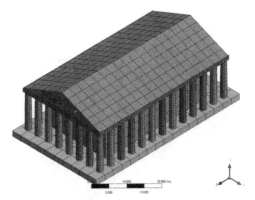

Figure 2. Default mesh.

Figure 3. Reinforced mesh on significant components.

The base of the Parthenon, made of limestone, was buried deep into the soil to ensure the stability of the upper structures. In the model of a structure like that of the Parthenon, the thickness of the base underground is not demonstrated. Therefore, as an essential boundary condition, the base is set with fixed support, simulating the ground foundation with stylobate in the original structure of the Parthenon. To be more specific, fixed support is set to the lower surface of the platform, which means any displacements and rotations are not permitted. This surface remains fixed for all analyses.

This paper has conducted five analyses: static structural analysis, modal analysis, harmonic response, response spectrum, and random vibration analysis. For essential boundary conditions, this surface would remain fixed for all research. For other components, the connection automatically generated by ANSYS would be adopted for stability. The natural boundary conditions, the external load in our case, would be added based on the analysis performed. For example, in modal analysis, no external load is applied since the natural frequency is what we are interested in. A specific spectrum is used to obtain the structure's random vibration and response spectrum.

For the first static structural analysis, the primary purpose is to analyze the deformation of the structure under its self-weight so that the self-weight can serve as a setup for all subsequent studies. This means the structure would be pre-stressed by the self-weight. The standard earth gravity would be inserted into the model to achieve this goal.

The modal analysis can be performed after the static analysis is done since the output from the modal analysis also serves as a setup for later analysis. First, the static structural analysis solution was connected to the modal setup for natural frequency analysis. In this situation, meshes and geometry are not required again because they have already been considered in the form. The bottom surface of the platform is still fixed on the ground. The maximum mode to find is regarded as six because fundamental modes are more important. The output from this analysis is six modes and the equivalent stress.

The following three analyses are all pre-stressed by their self-weight, and their output modes are superposed by frequency response and phase response. For harmonic analysis, a harmonic acceleration from the ground is inserted, and total deformation is the output.

Since the Parthenon is in a region with persistent seismic activity, it is significant to check this ancient structure's performance under earthquake excitation. SeismoArtif was used to generate this earthquake accelerogram and response spectra. The spectra were designed based on EuroCode 8, Part 3. The time series plot is shown in Figure 4, and the corresponding response spectra are shown in Figure 5.

The data obtained from the figures contains two columns. The first column is about the period, and the unit is in seconds. The second column is about acceleration, and its unit is g.

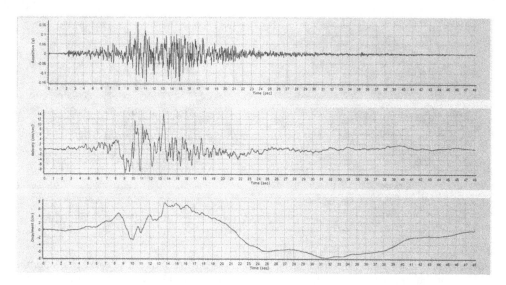

Figure 4. Earthquake accelerogram.

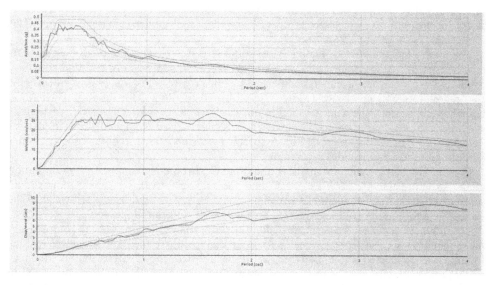

Figure 5. Response spectra.

A simple unit conversion should be performed before importing the data points into ANSYS. The results will be discussed in detail in the next section, and the obtained result will be verified from mesh-independent study reliability.

3 RESULTS

3.1 *Modal analysis*

The six fundamental modes are generated from their natural frequency for modal analysis. From Figures 6 to 11, six modes are shown. In this series, the default mesh is adopted.

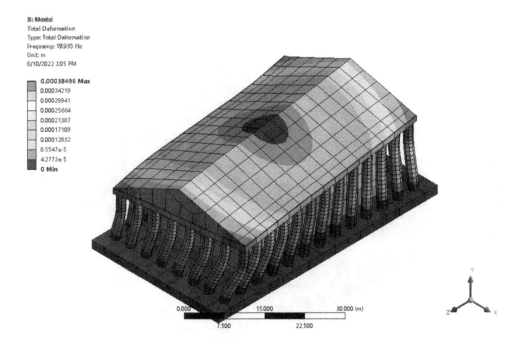

Figure 6. Mode 1 (A torsional mode).

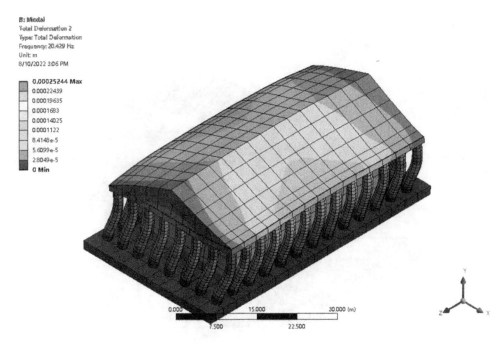

Figure 7. Mode 2 (A side-sway mode).

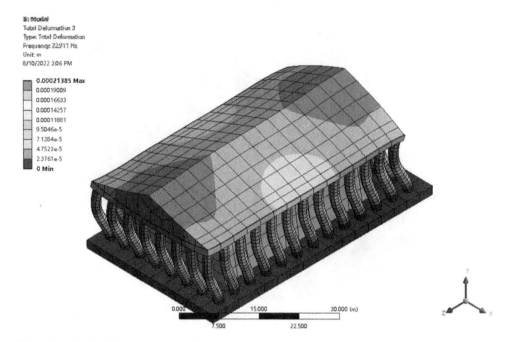

Figure 8. Mode 3 (A side-sway mode).

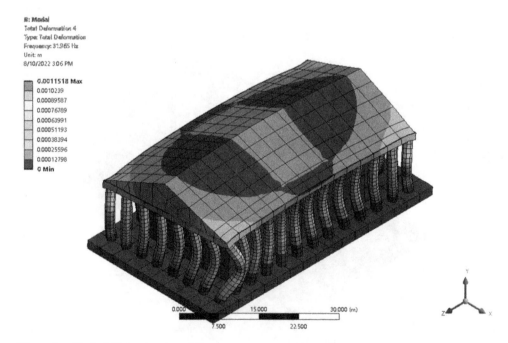

Figure 9. Mode 4 (A torsional mode).

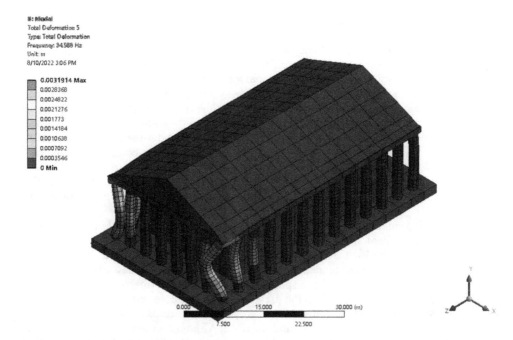

Figure 10.　Mode 5 (A buckling mode).

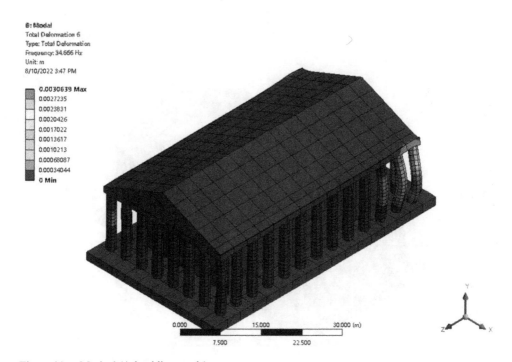

Figure 11.　Mode 6 (A buckling mode).

Mode 1 is a torsional mode: the structure is twisted. It is scarce for mode 1 to be a torsional mode. However, it is reasonable for the structure we are analyzing: Parthenon is a structure with low torsional stiffness. When twisted, distress in structural and non-structural components can happen due to the large deflection. In other words, twisting Parthenon requires the least energy. Therefore, the torsional mode can be mode 1. Both mode two and mode three are side-sway modes because side-sway movement occurs. The movement occurs along the longitudinal direction for mode 2, while the movement occurs along the transverse direction. For mode 4, the structure is bent along the transverse direction. Mode 1 to mode 4 are all vibrational modes: the structure vibrates under the natural frequency. For more five and mode six, these two modes are buckling modes: columns buckle symmetrically and anti-symmetrically, respectively. For all modes, we can detect that the maximum deformation always occurs on the corner columns or the connection between the corner columns and the plate. The corner columns could probably be the most vulnerable components.

The mesh-independent study verifies the six modes. MESH2 is adopted in this series of modes (i.e., local element size for columns and the plate is minimized to better approximate the solution.). The First 6 modes generated by using MESH2 are listed in Figure 12 to Figure 17. These six modes are identical to the abovementioned modes, which can verify the output. The magnitude of the displacement and the behavior of components are identical in the two modes. Similar to the previous result, the columns always suffer larger displacements than other components. Maximum deflection occurs on the corner columns and the connection between the column and the plate. Although in some modes, the largest displacement occurs at the joints, the main reason is the fragility of the columns. The columns are connected to the roof support plates, which will also shift when the columns are displaced.

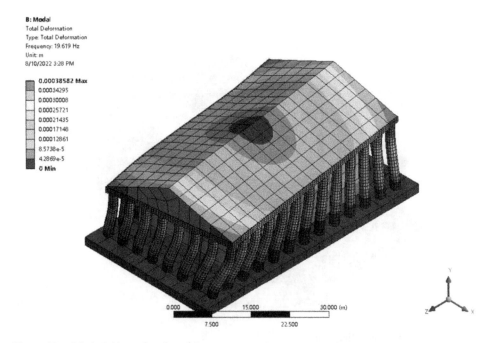

Figure 12. Mode 1 (A torsional mode).

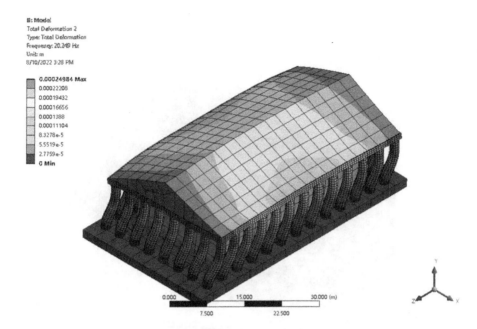

Figure 13. Mode 2 (A side-sway mode).

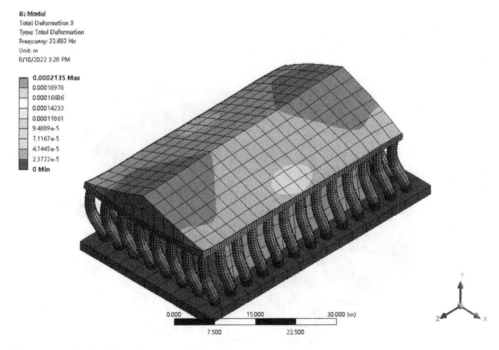

Figure 14. Mode 3 (A side-sway mode).

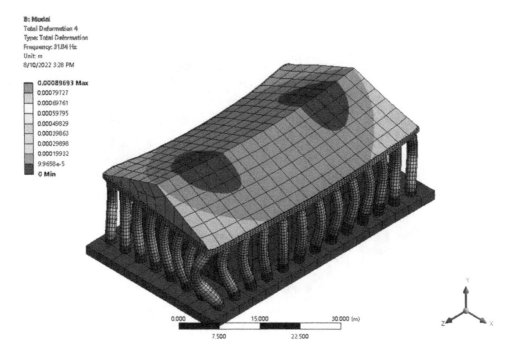

Figure 15. Mode 4 (A torsional mode).

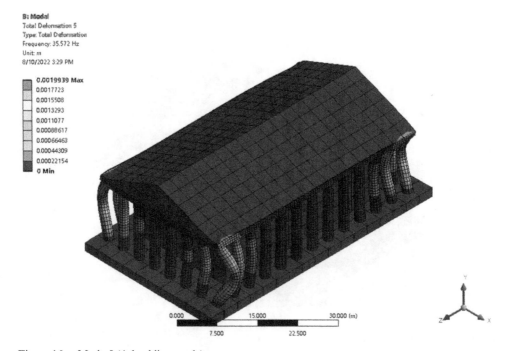

Figure 16. Mode 5 (A buckling mode).

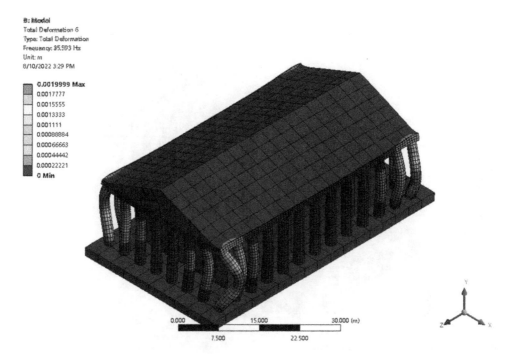

Figure 17.   Mode 6 (A buckling mode).

3.2   *Harmonic response*

For the harmonic response of the structure, the solution from modal analysis serves as a setup for it. The model to be analyzed in harmonic response is pre-stressed by its self-weight, and modal superposition is used to generate the harmonic response mode. The mode is generated by superposing two responses: frequency and phase. A simple harmonic load is applied on the bottom surface of the platform, and it is normal to the plate surface. This simulation of a harmonic load case from the ground can be achieved by applying this load. The mode of the structure studied is shown in Figure 18 below. The maximum deflection is 0.00013 meters. Unsurprisingly, it occurs in the middle of the corner columns. An independent mesh study is also performed for the harmonic analysis to verify the reliability of the output utilized in the default mesh in Figure 19. For the refined model, the magnitude of the maximum deflection is 0.00018 meters, which is very close to the previous output. The pattern of the deformations zones for the two modes follows the same trend. More specifically, from the front view, the deformation zones are formed by two tip-to-tip triangles: The deformation of columns closer to the edge is more significant, and the deformation of columns more proximate to the center is more minor. Other components, such as the plate and the roof, remain intact; much smaller deformations occur on them. In the modal analysis, columns are the most vulnerable components. The harmonic analysis illustrates this point again. Therefore, the conclusion that states the columns are weak is valid. For future maintenance activities, the columns should be paid more attention to.

3.3   *Response spectrum*

In response spectrum analysis, the steps are the same as the ones for the harmonic response. The only difference is that the spectra are random but not harmonic in the response spectrum analysis. The procedure for generating the spectra is elaborated on in the previous article. From Figure 20 to Figure 21, the total deformation is shown. The mesh adopted for this model is MESH1, the default mesh. Maximum deformation occurs in the middle of the corner columns, and the magnitude is

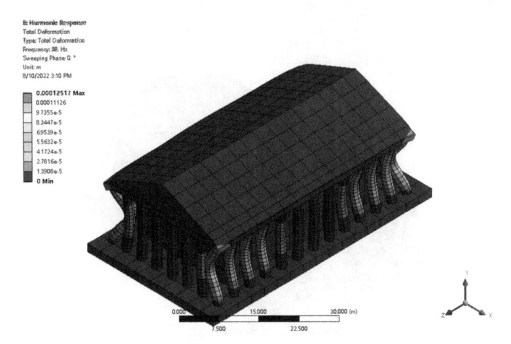

Figure 18. Harmonic response (MESH1).

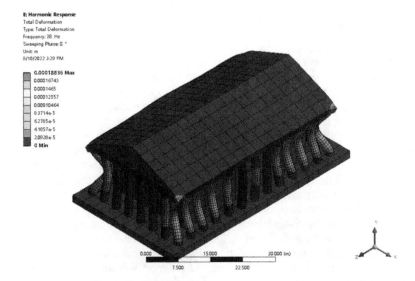

Figure 19. Harmonic response (MESH1).

2.7E-6 meters. The pattern of the deformation zones is like the one in harmonic analysis. The maximum stress also takes place in the middle of the corner columns. The magnitude is 14855 Pa. Since the property of this Pentelic marble column section is not available from either the open source or the manufacturer (i.e., the plastic property is not inserted into the ANSYS material database), we have no idea whether the column under this spectrum gets into its plastic region.

The current condition of the columns and the entire structure is unknown because of the lack of section properties. However, the mesh-independent study shows that this result is

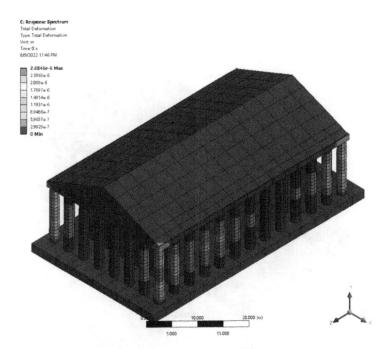

Figure 20. Total deformation (MESH1).

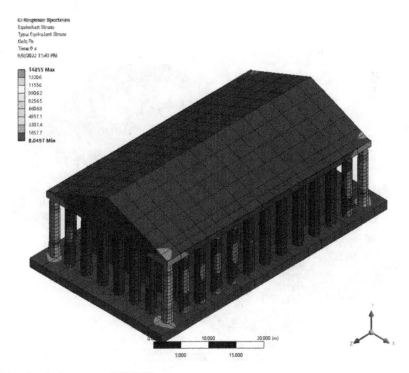

Figure 21. Equivalent stress (MESH1).

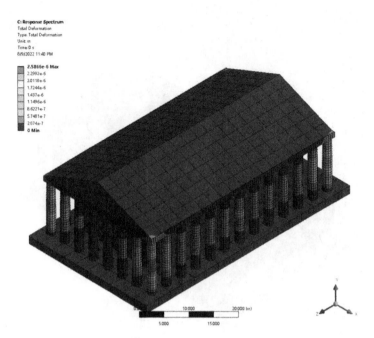

Figure 22. Total deformation (MESH2).

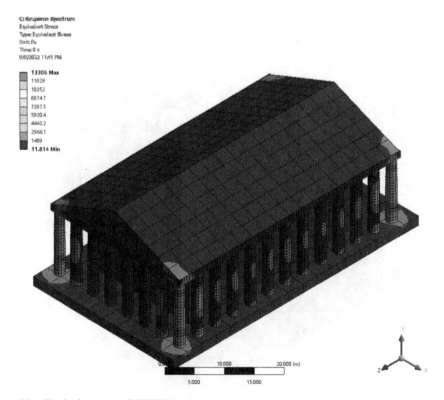

Figure 23. Equivalent stress (MESH2).

acceptable as the two models yield similar results. Figure 22 and Figure 23 illustrate the deformation and equivalent stress, respectively. The output is similar to the previous model utilizing the default mesh.

4 DISCUSSION ON RESTORATION

Based on the results of multiple analyses, the most vulnerable part of the structure is the marble column, which generally has the larger deformation and stress in the entire structure in most modes and under loads. In the future maintenance of the building, it is necessary to check the condition of the columns frequently. Moreover, among all columns, four corner columns are the component where maximum deflection and maximum stress would occur. The closer the column is to the corner, the greater the deformation and stress will be. The closer the column is to the middle, the less deformation and stress it will suffer. This is true for both columns on the longitudinal side and transverse side.

In terms of restoring the building, two possible approaches are proposed. The first approach is not to take any action, because any maintenance may bring harm to the building, and the second approach is to add a roof made of FRP to the Parthenon. Due to its chemical stability and low density, FRP will no longer cause damage to Parthenon, and FRP can be used to simulate marble roofs by painting. However, after a very preliminary static analysis of the ruins, the idea of this second proposal does not hold water. Based on the obtained output in the static structural analysis, with the addition of an FRP roof, the deflection due to self-weight will increase significantly. This is likely to cause secondary damage to the ancient building. Before the addition of this FRP roof, the vertical deformation of the ruin under its self-weight is 2.72E-6 meters. However, after the addition of the FRP roof, the vertical deformation of the roofed ruin is 7.7E-4 meters. Therefore, the roof dramatically adds weight and can make columns suffer. Figures 24 and 25 illustrate this situation.

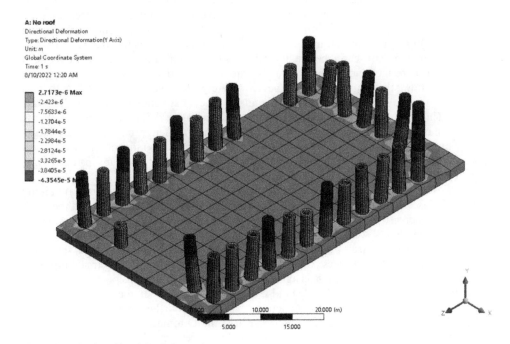

Figure 24. Ruin self-weight deformation.

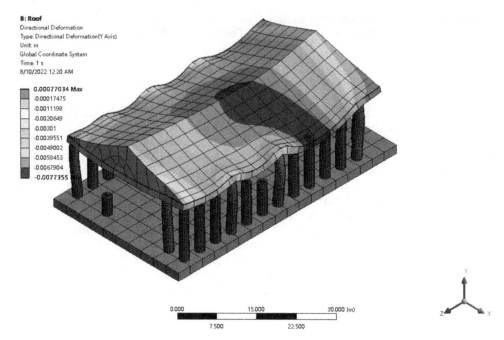

Figure 25. Roofed ruin self-weight deformation.

5 CONCLUSION

In this report, a similar structure to the Parthenon in the Acropolis of Athens was modeled and analyzed with ANSYS. Results from natural frequency, harmonic response, response spectrum, static structural, transient analysis, and explicit dynamics were obtained by using the finite element method analysis in the software. The objective of this research is to analyze the structure of the Parthenon before its destruction dynamically and with earthquake simulations. The results show the structure's stability to withstand seismic activity and substantiated how the Parthenon was never severely damaged by natural activities. However, results showed that the marble columns are the most vulnerable part under stress and loads. This part of the structure revealed the most extensive deformation, especially the corner columns. Nevertheless, the corner columns of the Parthenon have a slightly larger diameter in the actual design, which is consistent with the more significant stress these columns encounter. The Greek architects also created the columns out of drums instead of one straight cylinder to combat these stresses under seismic activity.

The finite element method tested results by using different mesh sizing methods, obtaining similar and reasonable solutions. A mesh independence study was conducted, and the mesh was refined to increase the number of nodes and elements to reduce the error from ANSYS. In addition, the trends were expected and validated by prior knowledge and sources. According to similar research on the seismic activity on the Parthenon columns, the paper states the more considerable stress on the corner columns and the increased stability of a larger column (Psycharis 2018); this is again consistent with our conclusion.

Although the Parthenon could withstand natural disasters and large earthquakes, it was still severely damaged in 1687 by human activity. Today, the Parthenon remains a ruin after the Venetians fired a cannon into the interior where the Ottomans had stored gunpowder (Kyriakos 2017) (Pollard & Pollard 2018). This explosion severely damaged the Parthenon, which has never been fully restored even today. Previous restoration attempts had failed as iron clamps, and inappropriate material damaged the marble that should have been preserved (Armstrong 2022).

Aside from the finite element analysis of the structure, we have also attempted to stimulate the explosion that destroyed the roof of the Parthenon and experimented with different loads and materials for a possible solution to the restoration of the roof. Current restoration projects have sought to use original pieces around the sight to recreate the structure. However, the architects have decided to preserve the Parthenon as a ruin as a reminder of the past (Glassman 2022). After static structural analysis in this study, it was also shown that adding a new roof, even with appropriate material, could still cause secondary damage to the structure.

The Acropolis of Athens is a symbol of ancient Greek civilization and remains one of the most important cultural monuments in the world. Efforts should continue to be made to preserve and restore these historic structures.

ACKNOWLEDGEMENT

Chelsey Tao: structure background, Material Properties
Xiaotao Shang: structure background, Material Properties
Haohuan Xu:
Construct Model in SolidWorks and AutoCAD;
Generate earthquake accelerogram and response spectra;
Conduct Static Structural Analysis, Modal Analysis, Harmonic Response Analysis, and Response Spectrum, in ANSYS workbench;
Propose roof restoration using FRP
Zhiqian Fang: History

REFERENCES

AE Television Networks. (2018, February 2). *Parthenon. History.com.* Retrieved August 9, 2022, from https://www.history.com/topics/ancient-greece/parthenon

Air Pollution, Droughts, and Rains are Washing Away Ancient Greek Monuments. *World Economic Forum.* (n.d.). Retrieved August 10, 2022, from https://www.weforum.org/agenda/2019/06/climate-change-is-taking-its-toll-on-greek-monuments-say-scientists/

Armstrong R. (n.d.). No. 3078: Restoring the Parthenon. No. 3078: *Restoring of the Parthenon.* Retrieved August 9, 2022, from https://www.uh.edu/engines/epi3078.htmL

Athens Acropolis Parthenon, Greece: Greeka. Greekacom. (n.d.). Retrieved August 9, 2022, from https://www.greeka.com/attica/athens/sightseeing/acropolis/

Chrysopoulos P. (2022, May 28). *How the Parthenon was Built to Withstand Anything.* GreekReporter.com. Retrieved August 9, 2022, from https://greekreporter.com/2022/05/28/pathenon-construction-engineering/

Glassman G. (n.d.). Nova | Secrets of the Parthenon | Restoring the Ruin. *PBS.* Retrieved August 9, 2022, from https://www.pbs.org/wgbh/nova/parthenon/rest-nf.html

How to Restore the Parthenon. *Greece Is.* (2022, May 25). Retrieved August 10, 2022, from https://www.greece-is.com/how-to-restore-the-parthenon/

iPedia. (2022, April 12). The Unique Architecture of the Parthenon Explained (Attic Order or Parthenon Order). YouTube. Retrieved August 9, 2022, from https://www.youtube.com/watch?v=3ESSysGgK1wabchannel=iPedia

Kyriakos. (2017, August 19). *"A Fortunate Shot": The Venetian Destruction of the Parthenon, 1687.* Artillery History. Retrieved August 9, 2022, from https://artilleryhistory.wordpress.com/2014/10/08/afortunateshotthevenetiandestructionoftheparthenon1687/

Natural Disasters. *Natural Disasters*: Greece. (n.d.). Retrieved August 10, 2022, from https://spark.liceodesio.edu.it/mod/book/view.php?id=1874chapterid=94

Natural Stone. *MakeItFrom.com.* (2020, May 30). Retrieved August 9, 2022, from https://www.makeitfrom.com/material-properties/Marble

Parthenon. *New World Encyclopedia*. (n.d.). Retrieved August 9, 2022, from https://www.newworldencyclopedia.org/entry/ParthenonDesignandconstruction

Pentelikon White Marble. *StoneContact*. (n.d.). Retrieved August 10, 2022, from https://www.stonecontact.com/pentelikon-white-marble/s2743

Pollard J. and Pollard S. (2018). *The Parthenon is blown up. History Today*. Retrieved August 9, 2022, from https://www.historytoday.com/archive/months-past/parthenonblown

Psycharis I.N., Fragiadakis M. and Stefanou,I. (2013). Seismic Reliability Assessment of Classical Columns Subjected to Near-fault Ground Motions. *Earthquake Engineering and Structural Dynamics*. https://doi.org/10.1002/eqe.2312

Seismosoft. (2022, July 1). *SeismoArtif – Artificial Earthquake Accelerograms*. https://seismosoft.com/products/seismoartif/

Woodford S. (2008). *The Parthenon*. Cambridge: Cambridge University Press.

Design and implementation of BIM + prefabricated building platform based on Unreal Engine 4

Bei Wu*, Chenjie Zou*, Binyan Ye, Xingyou Liu & Yanru Yang
Department of Economics and Management, Tianjin Tianjin University Renai College, Tianjin, China

ABSTRACT: BIM technology, prefabricated buildings, and game engines have all been combined at present. This study will find a feasible solution based on the exact and help. BIM technology, prefabricated buildings, and game engines will be constructed as a collaborative operation platform. Further improving the efficiency, quality, and safety of construction project management can greatly reduce redundant labor through the power of science and technology based on ensuring various needs, enhance the scientific and technological level of project management, and further promote the realization of smart city blueprints.

1 INTRODUCTION

1.1 Background

In recent years, with the rapid development of China's construction industry, the traditional residential construction model has had more and more defects, such as low production efficiency (Liu 2016), poor engineering quality, low construction technology, poor environmental benefits, and high building energy consumption. At the same time, with the large-scale construction of government-led low-income housing, governments at all levels actively promote prefabricated buildings. An aging population, fewer migrant workers in construction, and rising labor costs have contributed to the rapid growth of prefabricated buildings (Luo 2020). Although prefabricated buildings cannot in any situation replace conventional buildings, they have some characteristics, such as reduced construction time, higher safety during construction if compared to traditional buildings, and modularity, which make them competitive in specific markets and applications (Giovanni et al. 2018). To realize the deep integration of information, industrialization, and urbanization and build sustainable urban innovation ecology, the 13th Five-Year Plan has put forward new requirements and new goals for building a new smart city (Li 2019). BIM technology is increasingly functional in China's construction industry, and BIM integration technology is also developing and being explored rapidly.

1.2 Abroad research status

Platform development based on the game engine is a smart city construction idea. Through the game engine, an accurate virtual presentation of physical assets can be created, covering the subtle elements of buildings and any objectives of the city, and it can be updated continuously. Game engines provide an excellent platform for virtual environments and are

---

*Corresponding Authors: beiwu@tjrac.edu.cn and zoucj@foxmail.com

coupled with the models created through the use of BIM tools, and show great potential for presentation, visualization, education, and simulation (Ross et al. 2014). In Finland, ZOAN Studio used UE to create a virtual digital replica of the capital city of Helsinki, accommodating everything from 360° virtual real estate tools to city promotions at international exhibitions. In New Zealand, Buildmedia and the city council developed an accurate Wellington model using UE and now plan to integrate real-time data to create a true digital twin. BIM technology is still in the early stage of development and has great development potential for the future. Its combination of game engines will greatly improve the convenience of building cluster management and the accuracy of risk prediction (Figure 1).

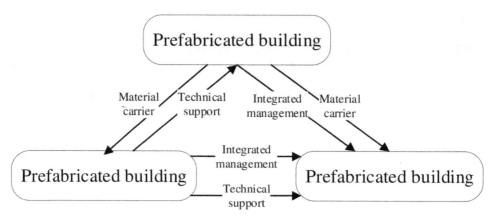

Figure 1. Implement process.

2 THE OVERALL DESIGN OF THE BIM + PREFABRICATED BUILDING PLATFORM

2.1 *The general framework*

The service objects of the BIM + prefabricated building platform are mainly project managers, data providers, background operation and maintenance managers, data reviewers, and task implementers. To achieve more information and visually integrated management of assembly projects, the platform adopts the development based on the Game engine Unreal Engine4 (hereinafter referred to as "UE4"), and various functions will be provided by the functional area system integrated with UE4.

The BIM + prefabricated building platform mainly provides BIM PC component information management, PC component production management, PC component quality testing, BIM visual management, and intelligent construction site (Figure 2).

2.2 *Design process*

The operation process of the BIM + prefabricated building platform includes data preparation, model making, terrain import, model import, production management, quality inspection, and intelligent site management.

2.3 *A brief introduction to the design of each functional module*

The encapsulation of the platform will directly affect the user experience of the platform, and the continuous optimization of UI designs is established to meet the user's comfortable and pleasant sensory experience. The components of sensory experience are

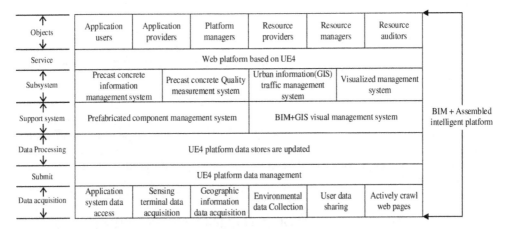

Figure 2. BIM + prefabricated building platform system composition diagram.

reflected by UI screen color, LOGO icon shape, text layout, overall frame, and other factors, and generally speaking, visual factors in UI design are presented. Figma is a browser-based UI design collaboration tool that keeps projects in the cloud at all times, allowing multiple users to comment on or modify their designs in real-time. The application user will enter the project information about this stage, and the database to store this data is essential. Third-party MySQL development deployment creates MySQL plug-in in UE4. Through Navicat design query function, connecting to MySQL, and writing query code can be used in UE4.

2.4 *Modeling*

The project was 3D modeled by Revit or Microstation, in which the precast concrete member (PC) models were incorporated into the relevant design parameters. At the present stage, most BIM projects have not reached the model accuracy of LOD500, so they can only carry out some simple electromechanical collision detection or analog roaming and input specific design parameters into the model component itself, which improves the model accuracy, facilitates the later system information integration and management, and enables the ability to query detailed data onto a click.

2.5 *Terrain data import*

The domestic 3D terrain data obtained by Supermap GIS is used in the UE4 project to match the world coordinates points and determine the exact location of the project. Not only can the powerful physics engine of UE4 be used for environment simulation, but it can also provide a real design change solution to the project.

2.6 *Model import*

Importing BIM models through Datasmith, a set of tool plug-ins that can import entire pre-built scenarios and complex accessory asset information created in various industry-standard design applications such as Revit, CATIA, SketchUp, IFC, 3ds Max into UE4. It is necessary to correspond each part of the model with the actual geographic coordinates to make the project information more real and accurate.

The PC component model is stored separately to obtain the PC component information base.

2.7 Production management

The BIM model is transformed into DWG format, and the NC code is produced by the professional NC programming software MASTERCAM. The manufacturer can download the corresponding NC code from the PC component library of the platform and input it into the NC machine tool for automatic production.

2.8 Quality test

In the UE4 platform, the function of "intelligent identification of prefabricated concrete components" was designed to take photos of the appearance of PC components, and the program found quality problems of PC components through appearance AI calculation and proposed solutions.

3 DESIGN AND REALIZATION OF INTELLIGENT IDENTIFICATION OF PREFABRICATED CONCRETE COMPONENTS

With the continuous improvement of China's industrial system and the advent of BIM technology, the design quality of precast concrete structures has been further improved. However, as a necessary condition of prefabricated concrete structure designed prefabricated concrete precasts components (hereinafter referred to as PC components), the quality of PC components is qualified for the prefabricated concrete structure of the building and plays a decisive role. At present, most of China's construction is still using the traditional construction method, assembly building processing, and transportation damage, leading to large investment costs, so the price is always higher than the traditional construction method.

3.1 Photo identification PC component technology analysis

3.1.1 The overall framework
Photo recording session; Checking the warehousing link; Comparison acquisition link. The three key extraction techniques can be summarized into two parts: data construction and algorithm research.

1) Data to construct

The purpose of data construction is to serve better the AI algorithm, which is used for subject detection, category prediction, and feature extraction of the pictures taken.

2) Algorithm research and development

Algorithm research and development is to make full use of the existing data to achieve the optimal compromise in accuracy and speed to identify each link of PC components, such as detection, category prediction, and retrieval feature extraction, to identify whether bump damage appears.

3.1.2 Construction of the data
Through the training data construction for model training (Figure 3), we can retrieve the PC component monitoring model and compare all the PC components in the existing PC components (Figure 4). But to clean up duplicate images and relieve storage pressure, we first need to use hash de-duplication (dHash algorithm) de-duplication.

3.1.3 Detecting database builds
From the overall framework, it can be seen that the most important step of photo identification PC component technology is subject detection, which is to take the PC component to be identified and to eliminate background interference in the future. To identify PC

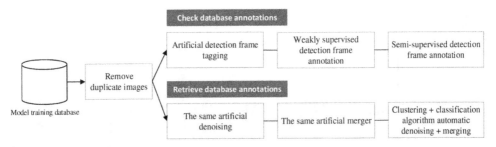

Figure 3. Training data construction (Visual module).

Image Hash Comparison		Time/s			Similarity		
		aHash	pHash	dHash	aHash	pHash	dHash
Image(a)	Image(a)	0.0005	0.0118	0.0001	100.00%	100.00%	100.00%
Image(a)	Brightness(b)	0.0008	0.0145	0.0002	92.19%	94.53%	93.75%
Image(a)	Zoom(c)	0.0007	0.0288	0.0002	98.44%	97.27%	98.44%
Image(a)	Contrast Enhancement(d)	0.0007	0.0149	0.0002	92.19%	90.27%	95.31%
Image(a)	Sharpen(e)	0.0016	0.0162	0.0003	93.75%	90.23%	90.62%
Image(a)	Fuzzy(f)	0.0011	0.0211	0.0004	93.75%	90.62%	92.19%
Image(a)	Color Enhancement(g)	0.0008	0.0159	0.0002	92.19%	97.27%	95.31%
Image(a)	Rotation(h)	0.0008	0.0154	0.0002	50.00%	56.25%	53.12%

Figure 4. Commonly used speed contrast algorithm.

components quickly and accurately, we use a more accurate object detection algorithm to determine PC components. Here we adopt the detection database as a semi-supervised label: based on a small amount of artificial tagging detection box + open-source database initialized the detection model, and then to the rest of the PC with automatic tagging model component database, and after model updating and automatic labeling, we use it again to update the testing model and add annotations (Figure 5).

After image de-duplication and subject detection, we use the same denoising algorithm based on automatic clustering and the same merging algorithm based on the confusion classification matrix. And using a clustering algorithm to automatically remove the noise in each PC component picture is a convenient and more accurate PC component.

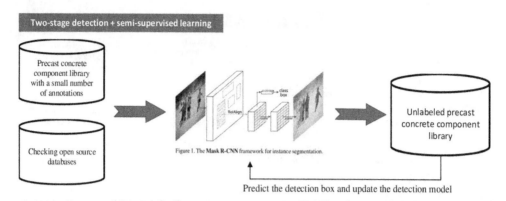

Figure 5. Schematic diagram of semi-supervised detection algorithm flow.

3.1.4 *Category forecast*
To judge the category of PC components in matting and facilitate the subsequent feature extraction and the same index to adopt the specified category model, we can use a massive online retrieval library to improve the accuracy of category prediction. Through detection + retrieval, it can finally greatly improve the accuracy of category prediction, convenient and quick comparison of PC components, and PC component bump problem.

3.1.5 *Object detection*
After designing the processing method for the photos taken, we will expand the detection of PC component entities. Considering that we need to pay special attention to the scale variation of PC components, we choose the retinanet as the detector.

3.1.6 *Feature extraction*
Comparison with the same paragraph. After completing the photo identification of PC components, we need to call the same type of PC components from the database for comparison (Figure 6), so that we can quickly find out the location of the collision of PC components in the process of transportation to facilitate the repair of workers. Due to the characteristics of PC components themselves, to distinguish PC components more accurately, we pay more attention to some significant areas, the characteristics of space attention and the characteristics of the channel, and focus on the combination of two kinds of attention (Figure 7). Through experimental comparison, we know that the model retrieval performance is improved by increasing the focus degree of feature space.

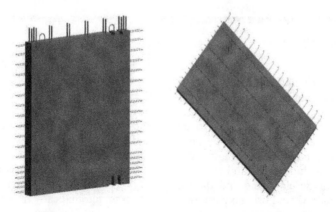

Figure 6. Different PC components.

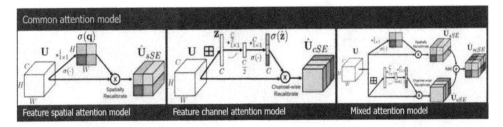

Figure 7. Attention model.

4 VISUAL DESIGN AND IMPLEMENTATION

This chapter is about the visual design and implementation of the BIM model and assembly component, which is convenient for personnel to view the information on the model and component. A complete prefabricated building BIM model with a design, production, and construction data chain is formed by combining BIM and RFID technology. This method can solve the problem of information island in the traditional prefabricated building design, production and construction management (Liu *et al.* 2020).

4.1 *BIM model visualization*

The establishment of the BIM model visualization platform can establish the 3D model through common modeling software, import it into UE4, and process the model with the material and texture in the engine (Ma & Fu 2020), so that the model can be displayed in the scene in 3d virtual mode, realize the visualization of BIM model, and meet the display and operation of the project, as shown in the figure.

4.2 *Visualization of prefabricated components*

The three-dimensional visualization of prefabricated components is a major focus of this project. There are nine common types of prefabricated components, including outer wall panels, balcony panels, laminated panels, air conditioning panels, inner wall panels, stairs, partition panels, precast columns, precast beams, etc. A single prefabricated component is very heavy or large, and very difficult to move. It must be prefabricated in the factory in advance and well preserved and maintained before it can be transported to the engineering assembly site in the later period. In the assembly-type prefabricated component visualization with the construction process interactive animation, the PC component is the core to configure a variety of resources. Through the BIM + assembly platform based on the UE4 game engine, information such as the size and material of components can be extracted on the platform. The manufacturer of prefabricated components can make drawings based on the model of the prefabricated components, and make components based on the extracted component information. In this way, the three processes of prefabricated component design, manufacturer's production, and site construction are combined, and BIM technology is used as the link so that the construction problems of prefabricated components can be effectively solved in the process of site construction (Wang *et al.* 2018).

4.3 *BIM-based prefabricated component production*

For standardized prefabricated components: Mechanical and electrical pipe, steel structure, etc., the manufacturer will use an NC machine tool for production and processing, and high cost is saved in the prefabricated construction based on the current BIM model, which can

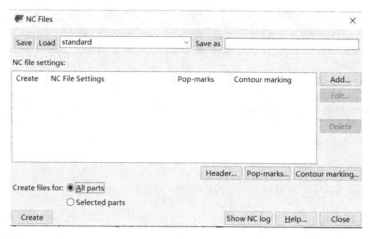

Figure 8. Tekla exports NC code.

export the corresponding NC code (Figure 8) so that we can save labor costs, and the refabricated factory can directly download the integration platform of prefabricated direct production of NC code to achieve design-production automation.

4.4 *Collaborative management of components based on BIM and RFID technology*

At present, the manufacturer of prefabricated components combines RFID technology with BIM technology to extract the material, size, and other information of components from BIM models and implant them into production components through RFID chips containing the date, size, and installation location, other information of components (Wang 2018). When the component leaves the factory, it is convenient to understand the transportation condition of the component by scanning the RFID chip on the vehicle and uploading the vehicle information on the platform (Hu *et al.* 2017). After the component arrives, personnel scan the RFID chip on the component to quickly obtain information on the component and determine the installation position of the component. If a collision occurs in the field installation, the component collision information can be input into the RFID chip to transmit information to the platform. Prefabricated component manufacturers can check the data on the platform and check the errors in the production and processing links. Prefabricated component designers through feedback information verify component design when there are no mistakes. RFID combined with BIM, concrete casting RFID chips implanted in identity, so that the artifacts from the production, quality inspection, delivery, assembly, and maintenance of the entire life cycle of information such as management, can realize visualization precise positioning, full cycle of real-time monitoring, trace the collaborative management (Zhang 2017), intelligent data analysis, the effective realization of raw material inventory management, Production planning management, real-time monitoring of prefabricated parts production, prefabricated parts quality inspection and prefabricated parts inventory management (Zou & Zheng 2019).

5 CONCLUSION

Through the research of the BIM + prefabricated building platform, this paper combines the PC information management system, PC quality inspection system, visual management system, and the Web platform based on UE4. The BIM + fabricated under the construction industry is implemented, and the rapid development of prefabricated meets with BIM technology. A component library is built with the help of a 3D model to deepen the design drawing. For materials, production data can be directly on the received equipment factory for the construction industry personnel in promoting management efficiency, saving cost, saving time limits, and laying a foundation. In the future, we expect to see this platform grow in the practical needs of production software and grow up to be fabricated as a systematic solution in the construction market. We also hope to have more to do with prefabricated enterprises. With the aid of this kind of openness, the data can be accessed by more systems, and we can build a rich standard library and make it your weapon.

ACKNOWLEDGMENTS

This work was financially supported by the Scientific Research Project of Tianjin University Renai College in 2020 (XX20007), and the Innovation and entrepreneurship training program for college students of Tianjin (202114038028).

REFERENCES

Giovanni Tumminia, Francesco Guarino, Sonia Longo (2018) *Renewable and Sustainable Energy Reviews*. pp. 272–283

Guojiang Liu (2016) Research on the Application of Special-shaped Column Frame Structure in the Design of the Civil Residence. *Development Orientation of Building Materials*. pp. 197–198.

Hao Liu, Jieru Hong, Mengxia Zhang, Jinyang Wang, Zhao Xu (2020) Research on Prefabricated Building Information Management Method Based on BIM and QR Code Technology. *Construction Technology*. pp. 110–118.

Hua Wang (2018) Application of BIM Technology in Prefabricated Buildings. Construction Engineering Technology and Design. pp.345.

Jiali Zou, Huanqi Zheng (2019) Application of Information Management System in the Production of Prefabricated Building Components. *Guangdong Civil Engineering and Architecture*. pp. 70–73.

Jian Luo (2020) Application of Prefabricated Building Technology in Engineering Cost Specialty. *Sichuan Cement*. pp 218–249.

Qiang Wang, Wei Wang, Wei Zhu (2018) Application Research of the Prefabricated Building Based on BIM Technology. *Journal of Hunan University of Arts and Sciences*. pp. 55–58.

Ross Bille, Shamus P. Smith, Kim Maund and Graham Brewer (2014) Exploring Building Information Modeling (BM) to Game Engine Conversion. *Air Working Paper Series*. pp. 1–24.

Shaochi Li (2019) A Study on the Countermeasures for Guangzhou to Build a New Smart City – Based on the Experience of Building a Smart City in London. *Smart City*. pp. 1–4.

Shaojiang Ma, Rui Fu (2020) Research on Visual Interactive Application Design of Building Structure Based on UE4 Blueprint Programming. *Shanxi Architecture*. pp. 197–198.

Weiwei Zhang (2017) Identification System of Expressway Prefabricated Parts Based on RFID-UNF Technology. *Telecom World*. pp. 245–246.

Yanhong Hu, Baoping Ou, Qiang Li (2017) Research on BIM Collaborative Work in Industrialization Project. *Construction Technology*. pp. 42–45.

Study on tensile mechanical properties of steel strand considering the damage

Shilong Gao, Yachao Hu, Xiaobin Zhang & Feng Liu*

Shandong Key Laboratory of Disaster Prevention and Mitigation in Civil Engineering, Shandong University of Science and Technology, Qingdao, Shandong, China

ABSTRACT: In order to study the tensile mechanical properties of steel strands, firstly, the static tensile test of steel wire and steel strand was carried out to obtain the Stress-Strain curve and failure patterns of the tests. The ABAQUS finite element analysis software was used to carry out the Numerical simulation of steel wire considering the damage. The Elastic-Plastic and damage parameters of steel wire were determined according to the repeated comparison between the simulation results and the test. The parameters obtained were used to simulate the steel strand. The simulation results are compared with the Stress-Strain curve and failure mode of the steel strand test to judge the parameters and the effectiveness of the test. The influence of different factors on the simulation of the tensile test of steel strands is analyzed. The simulation results show that the friction coefficient has little effect on the finite element simulation. After the steel strand breaks, the elastic energy is released, and a "birdcage" is formed during the rebound of each bundle of steel strand; the twist will affect the stress state of the steel strand and lead to the change of the overall mechanism of the steel strand.

1 INTRODUCTION

Prestressed steel strand is widely used in terminal buildings, cable-stayed bridges, and other long-span buildings because of their high tensile strength and simple construction operation. In recent years, many scholars have done extensive research on the static tensile test of prestressed steel strands. Hole Qing Kai *et al.* (Kong & Wan 2003) deduced the elastic modulus of steel strands, verified its accuracy by finite element simulation, and compared the softness of homogeneous round rods and steel strands. Chen Chong *et al.* (Chen & Yuan 2017) studied the effect of friction between steel strands on the cross-section stress distribution. Wu Zhijie *et al.* (Wu *et al.* 2018) obtained the contact area between the central steel wire and the outer steel wire of the steel strand and the phase of the outer steel wire by comparing the test with the finite element simulation. The mutual contact areas are in a complex stress state, while the other non-contact areas are still in a uniaxial tensile stress state. In Qian Haimin *et al.*'s work (Qian *et al.* 2019), the influence of twist angle on the overall mechanical properties of steel strands is analyzed. Jiang Jianwen *et al.* (2021) studied the influence of friction on the stress value and plastic development law of steel strands.

At present, most of the research on the static tensile test of steel strands is in the elasto-plastic stage, and there is no systematic theoretical research on the tensile failure stage of steel strands. In this paper, the Elastic-Plastic and damage parameters of steel wire are obtained by comparing the static tensile test with ABAQUS finite element analysis software.

*Corresponding Author: feng.liu@sdust.edu.cn

The parameters of steel wire finite element simulation are input into the finite element simulation of steel strand, and the stress-strain curve and failure mode of steel strands are obtained. It provides the basis of numerical simulation for the theoretical analysis of this kind of steel strand.

2 TENSILE TEST OF STEEL STRAND UNDER STATIC LOADING

In this paper, the specification is 1 × 7-1860-15.24-GB/T5224-2014 (GB/T 5224-2014), and selected prestressed steel strands are tested. The specifications and dimensions of the selected steel strands are shown in Table 1.

Table 1. Measured specifications of 1 × 7 steel strand.

Steel Strand Structure	Nominal Diameter D_a/mm	Measuring Diameter d/mm	Median Diameter (d_c)/mm	Side Diameter (d_w)/mm	Nominal Cross-sectional Area S/mm^2
1 × 7	15.20 (15.24)	15.1	5.4	5.1	140

Note: The values in brackets are those in the document (GB/T 5224-2014).

According to the test method of steel for prestressed concrete (GB/T21839-2019), the static tensile test of steel wire is carried out on the WEW-300D universal testing machine, and the loading rate is 0.5 mm/min. Because the displacement data collected by the computer is not accurate, the non-contact optical strain measurement system (DIC) is used to measure the displacement.

The mechanical properties of prestressed steel strands were tested on the WAW-600 universal testing machine, and the loading rate was 30 mm/min. DIC is also used to measure displacement.

According to the extensometer in the static tensile test of the steel strand, the elastic modulus is 201 GPa. The engineering stress-strain can be determined by Formula (1):

$$\sigma = \frac{F}{S} \quad \varepsilon = \frac{\Delta L_0}{L_0} \times 100\% \tag{1}$$

where σ is engineering stress; F is tensile force; S is the nominal sectional area; ε is the engineering strain; ΔL_0 is the elongation; L_0 is the original gauge distance.

The true stress, true strain, and plastic strain can be determined by Equations (2) and (3):

$$\sigma_t = \sigma(1+\varepsilon) \quad \varepsilon_t = \ln(1+\varepsilon) \tag{2}$$

$$\varepsilon_{pl} = |\varepsilon_t| - \frac{|\sigma_t|}{E} \tag{3}$$

where σ_t is the true stress; ε_t is the true strain; E is the elastic modulus; ε_{pl} is plastic strain.

Test values are shown in Table 2.

The engineering stress-strain relationship curve of steel wire and steel strand is shown in Figure 1.

It can be seen from Figure 1 that the elastic moduli are all 201 GPa. However, the tensile strength of the two is different, 2250 MPa and 2038 MPa, respectively, with a difference of

Table 2. Measured properties of 1 × 7 steel strand.

Nominal Tensile Strength /MPa	Maximum Strength /KN	Total Elongation/ %	Tensile Test (steel wire)					Tensile Test (steel strand)				
			Maximum Force/ KN	Elastic Modulus/ GPa	Yield Strength/ MPa	Tensile Strength/ MPa	Total Elongation/ %	Maximum Force/ KN	Elastic Modulus/ GPa	Yield Strength/ MPa	Tensile Strength/ MPa	Total Elongation/ %
1860	≥ 260	≥ 3.5	42.83	201	1800	2250	4.86	285.32	201	1804	2038	5.34

Note: The values in the table are those in literature (GB/T 5224-2014) and test.

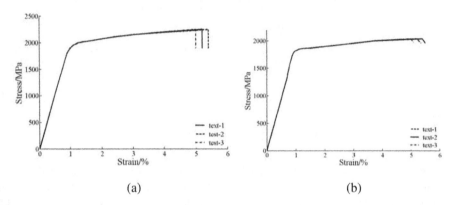

Figure 1. Engineering stress-strain relationship of steel wire and steel strand. (a) Single steel wire (b) 1 × 7 steel strand.

about 9%. At the same time, the elongation of the two is also different. The above tests are conducted with the same material, but the structural forms are different. The reason why the stress-strain relationship between the two is different is that the winding mode of the steel wire will lead to a change in the performance of the overall steel strand.

3 FINITE ELEMENT ANALYSIS

3.1 Finite element analysis of steel wire

3.1.1 Establishment of finite element model of steel wire

The finite element model of the steel wire is analyzed by using the solid element C3D8R, with 2128 elements in total. The finite element model is shown in Figure 2.

Figure 2. Finite element model of steel wire.

3.1.2 Definition of steel wire material parameters

The constitutive relationship of steel wire finite element analysis is determined through the test data. In order to eliminate the influence of structural effect, the PSO algorithm (Particle Swarm Optimization) in MATLAB is adopted through repeated comparison between the finite element simulation and the test results. PSO algorithm is an optimization algorithm for finding the optimal parameter solution. It only needs to determine the function form, specify the target value and limit the range of values. Then, the undetermined parameters in the function form can be determined according to the PSO algorithm, and finally, the constitutive relationship of materials can be determined.

The equivalent stress formula (Judge et al. 2017) is expressed as (4):

$$\sigma = \sigma_y + A\varepsilon_p{}^n \quad (4)$$

where σ is the equivalent stress; σ_y is the yield strength; ε_p is equivalent plastic strain; A and n are a parameter.

$$\sigma_y = 1800 \text{MPa}; \ A = 2125 \text{MPa}; \ n = 0.5927.$$

Figure 3 is the elastic-plastic-damage curve of the prestressed steel strand, in which section a-b is the elastic stage. Since the prestressed steel strand used in this paper is high-strength steel, the yield stage is relatively short. There is a short yield fluctuation stage at point b in the figure. After the strengthening stage of the steel strand at sections b-c, the bearing capacity of the steel strands will decrease after reaching point c. Therefore, point c is the key point of steel strand failure. According to the document (Gao et al. 2010), this point is called the starting criterion key point. At this time, D = 0, and D is the overall damage variable. When the test piece is continuously loaded until the steel strand is

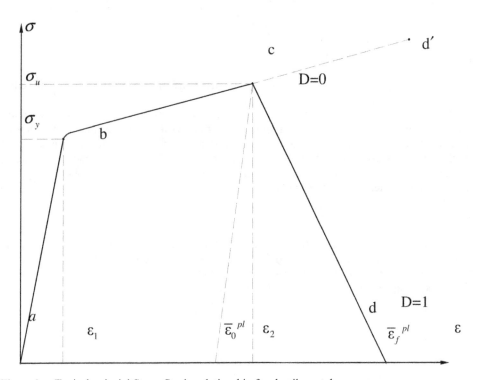

Figure 3. Typical uniaxial Stress-Strain relationship for ductile metal.

destroyed, it reaches point d. At this time, D = 1 means that the steel strand is destroyed and has no bearing capacity. And the stress sustained in the process of c-d can be calculated according to Formula (5),

$$\sigma = (1 - D)\bar{\sigma} \tag{5}$$

where $\bar{\sigma}$ represents the effective stress tensor in the current stress increment. The value range of D is 0-1.

In this simulation, the initial criterion to control whether the steel strand breaks is measured by the stress triaxial coefficient and the strain rate function.

When failure starts (Simulia 2012), Equations (6) and (7) shall be satisfied,

$$\omega_D = \int \frac{d\bar{\varepsilon}^{pl}}{\bar{\varepsilon}_D^{pl}(\eta, \dot{\bar{\varepsilon}}^{pl})} \tag{6}$$

$$\bar{\varepsilon}_D^{pl} = \bar{\varepsilon}_D^{pl}(\eta) \tag{7}$$

where ω_D is the state variable monotonically increasing with plastic deformation; $\dot{\bar{\varepsilon}}^{pl}$ is the equivalent plastic strain rate; Due to the lack of corresponding data, the strain rate effect is not considered in this paper; η is the triaxial coefficient of stress.

The stress triaxial coefficient can be obtained from Equations (8), (9), and (10),

$$\eta = \frac{p}{q} \tag{8}$$

$$p = \frac{1}{3}(\sigma_1 + \sigma_2 + \sigma_3) \tag{9}$$

$$q = \sqrt{\frac{(\sigma_1 - \sigma_2)^2 + (\sigma_2 - \sigma_3)^2 + (\sigma_3 - \sigma_1)^2}{2}} \tag{10}$$

where P is hydrostatic pressure; Q is Mises equivalent stress; $\sigma_1, \sigma_2, \sigma_3$ is the three principal stresses.

In the c-d segment, based on the above damage initiation criteria, there are two main damage evolution rules: energy criteria and displacement criteria. In this numerical analysis, the displacement criterion is used to measure the damage evolution law, and it is assumed that the damage variable is linearly related to the effective plastic displacement. Therefore, when the steel strand reaches the damage initiation criterion, the effective plastic displacement can be obtained from Formula (11),

$$\bar{\mu}^{pl} = l\bar{\varepsilon}^{pl} \tag{11}$$

where l represents the length of the feature direction unit; $\bar{\varepsilon}^{pl}$ represents equivalent plastic strain. When the prestressed steel strand is destroyed, the effective plastic displacement is expressed $\bar{\mu}^{pl}$. Specific parameters are shown in Table 3.

The Lode angle (Bai & Wierzbicki 2008) is determined by Equation (12),

$$\xi = \cos(3\bar{\theta}) = \left(\frac{r}{q}\right)^3 \tag{12}$$

where ξ is the stress Lode angle term of the finite element simulation output; is Cape lode; r is the third stress invariant; q is the Mises equivalent stress.

Table 3. Failure parameters of materials.

Steel Wire		Steel Strand			Material Failure Parameters				
L/m	d/m	L/m	d₀/m	d_c/m	μ	$\bar{\varepsilon}_0^{pl}$	$\bar{\varepsilon}_f^{pl}$	$\bar{\mu}_f^{pl}/m$	η
0.2	5.4	0.8	5.4	5.1	0.3	0.0486	0.0493	0.00055	0.333

The evolution of the Lode angle and stress triaxial coefficient of steel wire with time is shown in Figure 4.

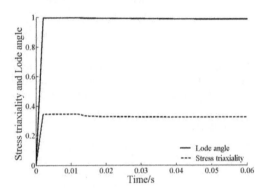

Figure 4. The time evolution of Stress triaxiality and Lode angle of steel wire.

Then $\bar{\theta} = 0.986$; $\eta = 0.333$.

The relationship between fracture strain and stress triaxial coefficient and Lode angle (Wang & Qu 2018) is confirmed by Formula (13).

$$\bar{\varepsilon}_f = \begin{cases} \left\{ \dfrac{A}{\sigma_t} \left\{ (1-\alpha)\eta + \dfrac{\alpha(1-b)}{\sqrt{3}(1+b)} \sin\left[\dfrac{\pi}{6}(1-\bar{\theta})\right] + \dfrac{(2+\alpha)}{3} \cos\left[\dfrac{\pi}{6}(1-\bar{\theta})\right] \right\} \right\}^{-\frac{1}{n}} \\ \quad 1 - \dfrac{6}{\pi}\arctan\left(\dfrac{\sqrt{3}}{2a+1}\right) \leq \bar{\theta} \leq 1 \\ \left\{ \dfrac{A}{\sigma_t} \left\{ (1-\alpha)\eta + \dfrac{1}{\sqrt{3}}\left(\alpha + \dfrac{b}{1+b}\right)\sin\left[\dfrac{\pi}{6}(1-\bar{\theta})\right] + \dfrac{1}{3}\left(\dfrac{2-b}{1+b}+\alpha\right)\cos\left[\dfrac{\pi}{6}(1-\bar{\theta})\right] \right\} \right\}^{-\frac{1}{n}} \\ \quad -1 \leq \bar{\theta} \leq 1 - \dfrac{6}{\pi}\arctan\left(\dfrac{\sqrt{3}}{2a+1}\right) \end{cases}$$

(13)

where $\bar{\varepsilon}_f$ is fracture strain; $A, b, n, \alpha, \sigma_t$ are material parameters; $\bar{\theta}$ is Cape lode; η is the triaxial degree of stress. The same PSO algorithm is used to get the optimal parameters, then $\bar{\varepsilon}_f = 0.486$; $A = 2125$ MPa; $b = 0$; $n = 0.5927$; $\alpha = 1$; $\sigma_t = 1381.496$; $\bar{\theta} = 0.986$; $\eta = 0.333$.

The relationship between fracture strain, Lode angle, and stress triaxial coefficient is shown in Figure 5.

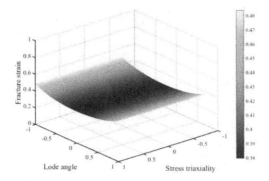

Figure 5. Relationship between fracture strain, lode angle, and stress triaxiality.

3.1.3 *Boundary conditions and loading methods of steel wire simulation*

Figure 6 is a schematic diagram of the static tensile calculation of steel wire. As shown in Figure 6, the loading method used for simulation is the same as that for the static tensile test of steel wire. In the simulation, A is the fixed end, and a displacement is applied at end B. 0-1 amplitude is defined for the displacement, and the value is consistent with the test displacement. The test piece with the length of L0 was fractured after the test, and the analysis step of the dynamic display was adopted.

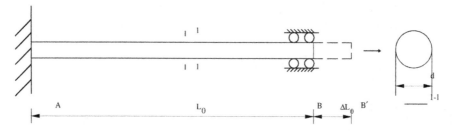

Figure 6. Schematic diagram of steel wire static tensile calculation.

3.1.4 *Verify the correctness of steel wire finite element*

It can be seen from Figure 7 that there is a deviation between the two curves, but the error is not more than 2%. It is judged that the finite element analysis model of the steel wire is

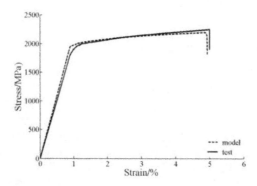

Figure 7. Comparison of Stress-Strain relationship between steel wire tensile test and finite element analysis.

correct, and the material parameters of the steel wire can be defined in the materials of the finite element simulation of the steel strand.

The comparison between the finite element simulation of steel wire tension and the failure mode of the test is shown in Figure 8.

It can be seen from Figure 8 that the failure mode of the finite element simulation is consistent with that of the steel wire tensile test.

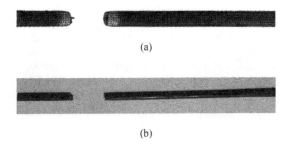

Figure 8. Comparison of failure modes between numerical simulation and test of steel wire tension. (a) Finite element simulation (b) Test.

3.2 Finite element analysis of steel strand

3.2.1 Establishment of finite element model of steel strand

The solid element C3D8R is used for the finite element simulation of the steel strands, with 122350 elements in total. The sectional view and side view of a typical finite element model are shown in Figure 9. According to the provisions of the literature (GB/T 5224-2014), the twist pitch of 1×7 steel strands is 12–16 times the nominal diameter. The twist pitch of this finite element simulation is 12 times the diameter. The influence of the twist pitch on the finite element simulation will be discussed below.

The steel strand is a spatial spiral structure, and there is a contact between steel wires. In the finite element simulation, it is defined as a general contact, calculated by the penalty function method, and its friction coefficient is 0.1 (Jiang *et al.* 1999). The influence of the friction coefficient on the finite element simulation will be discussed below.

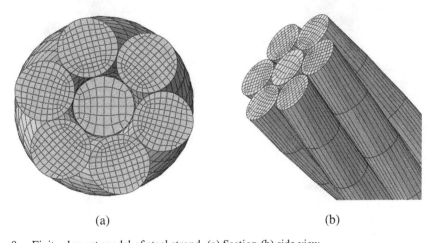

Figure 9. Finite element model of steel strand. (a) Section (b) side view.

3.2.2 Definition of material parameters of steel strand
When ABAQUS software is used for finite element analysis, the input material parameters are the same as steel wire.

3.2.3 Boundary conditions and loading methods of steel strand simulation
In the finite element simulation of steel strands, the two ends of steel strands are coupled, and the loading mode and boundary conditions are the same as those in the finite element simulation of steel wire.

3.2.4 Verify the correctness of steel strand finite element
It can be seen from Figure 10 that the curves of the two are relatively consistent in the elastic stage and the plastic stage, and there is an error in the damage stage, but it is not more than 2%. It is judged that the finite element analysis model of the steel strand is correct. After the fracture, the elastic energy is released, and each bundle of steel wires forms a "birdcage" during the rebound process. The comparison of the failure modes of the steel strand tensile test and its finite element simulation is shown in Figure 11. It can be

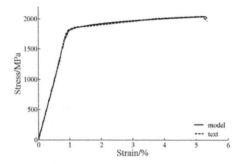

Figure 10. Comparison of Stress-Strain between static test and finite element simulation of steel strand.

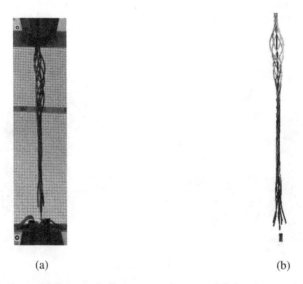

Figure 11. Comparison of failure modes between static test and finite element simulation of steel strand. (a) Tensile test of steel strand (b) finite element simulation of steel strand.

seen from Figure 11 that the failure modes of the finite element simulation and the test are relatively consistent.

4 FINITE ELEMENT ANALYSIS OF STEEL STRAND

4.1 Coefficient of friction

Since there is a contact between each steel wire of the steel strand, the influence of friction should be considered. There is oil inside the steel strand, and the friction coefficient should be less than 0.1, which is taken as 0.03, 0.05, 0.08, and 0.1 respectively. In many articles, the friction coefficient is taken as 0.115 (Judge et al. 2012). Therefore, in these five cases, the twist pitch is 12 times the nominal diameter, and the obtained stress-strain curve is shown in Figure 12. It can be seen from Figure 12 that under different friction coefficients, the obtained stress-strain curves are relatively consistent in the elastic stage and the plastic stage, and slightly different in the damage stage, indicating that the friction force has little effect on the tensile test of prestressed steel strands. The reason is that there are too few contact units between the wires of the prestressed steel strand, which is not enough to change the overall mechanism of the steel strand.

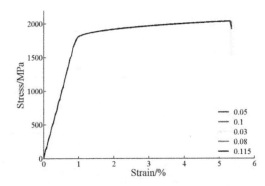

Figure 12. Comparison of Stress-Strain relationship in finite element simulation of steel strand under different friction coefficient.

4.2 Lay length

When considering the influence of the lay length on the finite element simulation of steel strand, the three cases where the lay length is 12, 14, and 16 times the nominal diameter are taken respectively, and the friction coefficient is 0.1. The model is shown in Figure 13.

The relationship between twist pitch and twist angle is shown in Formula (14) (Qian et al. 2019):

$$P = \frac{2\pi R_h}{\tan \alpha} \tag{14}$$

where P is the twist distance; R_h is the sum of the side filament R_w and the middle filament R_c; α is the twist angle.

Different twist angles corresponding to different twist pitches are obtained according to Formula (14), as shown in Table 4.

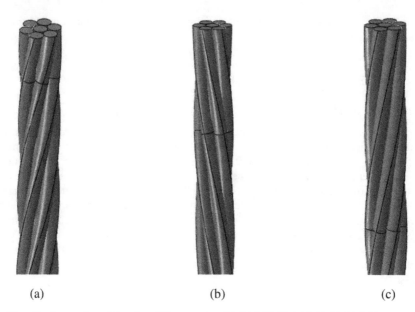

Figure 13. Steel strand model under different twist. (a) 12 fold (b) 14 fold (c) 16 fold.

Table 4. Twist angle corresponding to the different twist.

Nominal Diameter (D/mm)	Multiple	Lay Length (mm)	Twist Angle (°)
15.24	12	182.88	9.94
	14	213.36	8.54
	16	243.84	7.49

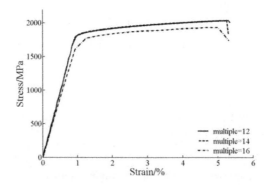

Figure 14. Comparison of Stress-Strain relationship in finite element simulation of steel strand under different twist.

The stress-strain curves of steel strands under different lay lengths are output, as shown in Figure 14. It can be seen from Figure 14 that when the lay lengths of steel strands are 12 and 16 times the nominal diameter respectively, the curves at the elastic stage and plastic stage are relatively consistent, and there are differences at the damage stage. As shown in

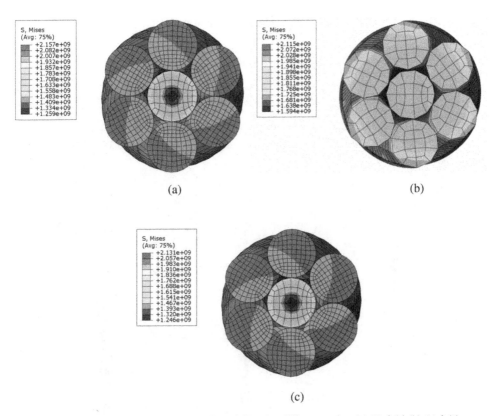

Figure 15. Stress program of steel strand model under different twist. (a) 12 fold (b) 14 fold (c) 16 fold.

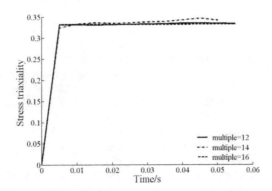

Figure 16. The time evolution of stress triaxiality of steel strand with a different twist.

Figure 15, the stress programs of the two are the same. The evolution diagram of the stress triaxial coefficient of the two with time is output, as shown in Figure 16. The curves are also basically consistent, but the load angles of the two are different, as shown in Table 5, resulting in the difference in the fracture strain of the two. When the twist pitch of the steel

Table 5. Lode angle, stress triaxiality, and fracture strain of steel strand with a different twist.

Nominal Diameter (D/mm)	Multiple	$\bar{\theta}$	η
15.24	12	0.986	0.333
	14	1	0.342
	16	1	0.333

Note: The data in the table are obtained according to the literature (GB/T 5224-2014) and Formula (12).

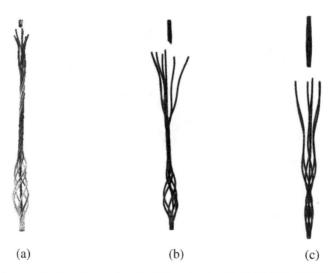

Figure 17. Failure mode of steel strand under different twist. (a) 12 fold (b) 14 fold (c) 16 fold.

strand is 14 times the nominal diameter, it can be seen from Figure 14 that the stress in the elastic stage, plastic stage, and damage stage is significantly reduced compared with that in the case of 12 or 16 times. It can also be seen from the stress cloud diagram in Figure 15 that this phenomenon is caused by the uneven stress distribution of the steel strand due to the increase of the twist pitch. The stress triaxial coefficient output in Figure 16 and the Lode angle in Table 5 are calculated according to Formula (13). When the twist distance is 14 times the nominal diameter, the fracture strain is significantly smaller than that in the case of 12 and 16 times. The failure modes of each model under different lay lengths are shown in Figure 17. It can be seen from Figure 17 that the failure modes and failure positions of each model are different. The reason is that the twist pitch will affect the stress state of the steel strand, resulting in a change in its overall mechanism.

5 CONCLUSION

The following works have been completed in this paper: first, the static tensile test of steel wire and prestressed steel strand; Second, the finite element simulation of steel wire and prestressed steel strand is carried out; Third, the influence of friction coefficient and lay length on finite element simulation of steel strand is considered:

(1) In the tensile test of steel strands, to get the test displacement more accurately, non-contact optical strain measurement is used to get accurate displacement.
(2) This paper defines that the material parameters of steel strand and steel wire are the same.
(3) Based on the existing experimental methods, the steel wire cannot obtain the equivalent plastic strain corresponding to the damage initiation of each stress state. Therefore, based on the unified theory of Wang Qu (2018), it is necessary to expand a small number of test results to various stress states to obtain the damaged surface.
(4) In this paper, the damage is considered, and the stress-strain curve obtained by finite element simulation is in good agreement with the test. After the steel strand breaks, the elastic energy is released, and each bundle of steel wires forms a "birdcage" during the rebound process, which is consistent with the failure mode obtained from the tensile test of the prestressed steel strand.
(5) In this paper, the influence of friction coefficient and lay length on finite element simulation of steel strand is considered. Because there are too few contact elements between the wires of the prestressed steel strand to change its overall mechanism, the friction coefficient has little effect on the finite element simulation, and the stress-strain curve obtained is consistent with the stress-strain curve of the tensile test of prestressed steel strand. The twist distance will affect the stress state of the steel strand, resulting in a change in its overall mechanism.

The disadvantage of this paper is that the displacement obtained from the test is not accurate enough, which results in a deviation between the test and the simulation.

ACKNOWLEDGMENTS

The financial support for this study was provided by the National Natural Science Foundation of China (12172198).

REFERENCES

Bai Y. and Wierzbicki T. A New Model of Metal Plasticity and Fracture with Pressure and Lode Dependence. *International Journal of Plasticity*, 2008, 24(6): 1071–1096.

Chen C. and Yuan X.F. Fine Analysis of Section Stress of Steel Strand. *Journal of Zhejiang University (Engineering Science)*, 2017, 51(5): 841–846.

Gao Y.F, Liang X.B, Dong L. et al. GB/T 228.1-2010, *Tensile Test of Metallic Materials Part I: Room Temperature Test Method*. Bei Jing: National Standards of the People's Republic of China, 2010.

GB/T 21839-2019. *Test Method of Steel for Prestressed Concrete* [S].

GB/T 5224-2014. *Steel Strand for Prestressed Concrete* [S].

Jiang J.W., Deng N.C., Guo Xi et al. Finite Element Simulation of Section Stress of Grade 160 Steel Strand. *China Sci*, 2021, 2(16): 193–204.

Jiang W.G., Yao M.S., Walton J.M. A Concise Finite Element Model for Simple Straight Wire Rope Strand. *International Journal of Mechanical Sciences*, 1999, 41(2): 143–161.

Judge R., Yang Z., Jones S.W. et al. Full 3D Finite Element Modeling of Spiral Strand Cables. *Construction and Building Materials*, 2012, 35: 452–459.

Judge R., Yang Z., Jones S.W., et al. Spiral Strand Cables Subjected to High-velocity Fragment Impact. *International Journal of Impact Engineering*, 2017, 107: 58–79.

Kong Q.K. and Wan P. Basic Mechanical Properties and Finite Element Method of the Stranded Wire. *Engineering Structure*, 2003, 23 (1): 20–22.

Qian H.M., Zong Z.H., Xie G.Y. et al. Static Elasto-Plastic Fine Simulation of Grade 1860 Steel Stand. *Journal of Southeast University (Natural Science Edition)*, 2019, 49(4): 624–630.

SIMULIA. *Abaqus Analysis User's Manual ver. 6.12* vols. 3 and 5. Providence, Rhode Island: Dassault Systèmes, 2012, 488–489.

Wang P. and Qu S. Analysis of Ductile Fracture by Extended Unified Strength Theory. *International Journal of Plasticity*, 2018, 104: 196–213.

Wu Z.J., Ding Z., Sun C.P. et al. Finite Element Analysis of Section Stress and Failure Mode of Steel Strand. *China Sci*, 2018, 13: 2623–2628.

Research on fine management of engineering projects based on BIM5D technology

Bei Wu*, Yuhe Zhao, Xiang Ou, Yun Bai & Ziyi Zhang
Department of Economics and Management, Tianjin Renai College, Tianjin, China

ABSTRACT: Refined management is a kind of concept and responsibility, but also the inevitable requirement of project management. It contains a logical division of social work, as well as the quality of service clarity, which is the inevitable requirement of modern management. Also, to achieve standardized management, personality management must go through the road. The current trend toward information technology in the construction industry is particularly on the rise, and BIM5D is a technology that is becoming increasingly important. Therefore, the rational application of this technology in this project has changed the management problems of traditional engineering construction in many ways, such as the joint management of construction progress, project budget, resource consumption, construction costs, construction agreements, and other related information, which has saved costs for the construction of the project and has truly implemented the concept of fine management into the project and solved practical problems for the construction engineering industry. The overall construction level of the project is improved in the process of combining innovative technology with high-quality management concepts.

1 INTRODUCTION

Currently, traditional construction management does not formulate the corresponding management system for various new technologies, nor can it supervise the whole construction process. There are some deficiencies in construction dynamic progress follow-up, resource allocation, quality supervision, and safety management. Slight negligence will lead to poor project quality, hidden dangers in construction safety, waste of resources, and so on.

Through the BIM5D construction platform, a digital information model related to all data in the construction process can be established, which can enable the ongoing construction projects to realize the fine management of construction projects and achieve the sharing of construction data to improve the quality, construction safety and save funds of construction projects, and improve the resolution ability and management efficiency of project construction site managers.

2 CORRELATION THEORY

2.1 BIM5D

By using BIM Technology to control and manage the overall construction process, the whole construction process of the project under construction can be simulated by integrating key

*Corresponding Author: beiwu@tjrac.edu.cn

information such as cost analysis, reasonable resource placement and allocation, and construction organization link layout through BIM digital model to timely provide accurate and effective core data such as image progress for labor distribution, production and other links in the construction process to improve the flexibility of construction and the coordination ability between various work links and help customers establish a digital construction management and control platform, so as to achieve the purpose of transparency and visualization of project implementation, saving time and economic cost and improving project management efficiency.

2.2 Fine management

Fine management of an engineering project is a systematic management method and system, including management theories and methods at different stages, careful design of drawings, improvement of construction organization scheme, drawing review before construction, cooperation and finalization of construction organization scheme by multiple units, and detailed disclosure of drawings and construction technology, which enables the construction personnel to clearly grasp the drawings and construction organization scheme to improve the management level of the whole project.

2.3 Reasons for adopting BIM technology

1. The degree of visualization is obvious, which not only realizes the visualization of the three-dimensional model of the structure but also realizes the visualization of the project construction process.
2. The simulation has a wide range of applications, which can not only accurately restore the architectural appearance, but also simulate the application scenarios in reality and optimize the construction simulation scheme.
3. Excellent coordination. Through the collision detection function of BIM Technology, the collision points between structures are found in advance, and the collision report is generated to provide the basis for scheme optimization.

2.4 Advantages of fine management in BIM5D

The three-dimensional collision inspection of BIM models of civil engineering and Electromechanical Specialty is supported, pipeline collision problems are timely found and modified, and the problems existing in drawing design are checked back to solve the disadvantage that it is difficult to find a collision in two-dimensional planarization, so as to achieve the goal of having a perfect three-dimensional visual spatial model (Ou & Wu 2020). Through various standardized collision inspection rules, it is ensured that the analysis results provide the optimization scheme before the project construction. The purpose of analyzing the collision results is to optimize the pipeline construction scheme in advance before the actual construction, save man hours and avoid unnecessary construction design changes and time waste. Visual construction disclosure is realized, secondary rework is avoided, communication costs are reduced, the construction period is shortened, and the construction level and practical application value of the project are improved.

3 RESEARCH STATUS AT HOME AND ABROAD

Since the 21st century, due to the technical needs of the industry at a certain stage and the gradual development of software technology, people have begun to pay attention to BIM Technology, followed by the introduction of corresponding technical standards and systems.

In 1982, Autodesk put forward the related concepts of building model informatization and simulated and analyzed the performance of products and projects in the real world to optimize the project scheme in advance, maximize the benefits in the process of simplifying complex projects, and gradually expand the innovative thinking into a competitive advantage. Therefore, BIM Technology continues to expand the coverage of professional knowledge in the gradual development and has become a widely used digital technology. Currently, most of the in-depth exploration and practical testing of smart construction sites by domestic experts and scholars are to explore how to promote theoretical knowledge to specific practice and lead the development trend of smart construction sites. It also analyzes the future development channel and application scope. Following the development perspective of information technologies such as cloud computing, Internet of things, mobile Internet, big data, smart city, and BIM and the emergence of the smart construction site, the construction site management has gradually moved towards informatization and intelligence, improved the project quality, accelerated the project progress, and provided a good visualization scheme for on-site construction safety management and on-site order stability.

4 PROJECT OVERVIEW

There are three buildings in a middle school in Beichen, Tianjin, with a total construction area of 104428.96 square meters. The ground is full-time primary and secondary schools and their ancillary facilities, and the underground is the garage, canteen, and spare room. The steel structure shall be reasonably selected for the project, the consumption of steel shall be reduced as much as possible on the premise of meeting the specifications, and the shear wall structure shall be selected.

5 PROJECT DYNAMIC MANAGEMENT STAGE

5.1 *Dynamic construction management*

BIM5D technology is used to coordinate and plan the overall scheme of the construction process, and the BIM model is taken as the prerequisite for project implementation to build a platform that is updated immediately and presents various contents, such as construction organization design. During the construction process, the progress, cost, and various resource data are associated with the model, the flow section operation is implemented, and the overall construction schedule and resource fund use plan can be checked (Chen 2020). The plan for each construction stage of the project is detailed, and the scheme is detailed and well-documented. The three-dimensional layout model of the construction site is loaded to avoid the temporary site layout and large mechanical equipment layout on the site. Completing the site layout model in advance can reasonably guide the operation of the construction site.

5.2 *3D rendering*

The application of 3D model rendering presents real buildings, meets people's real needs for three-dimensional effects, and also facilitates communication between designers and owners. After three-dimensional rendering (Figure 1), the model has a beautiful appearance and clear internal structure, which can be displayed and processed intuitively. For example, the optimized pipeline is easy to check and improves the visual effect.

5.3 *Progress control*

The progress management based on BIM5D technology can complete the formulation of the progress plan before construction. The construction progress management of each discipline

Figure 1. 3D rendering model.

and each construction stage can ensure the rationality of the plan, record the implementation during construction, ensure that the construction is in strict accordance with the plan, and strictly control the project progress (Gao & Pang 2020). The progress analysis is completed after construction. The digital information model established by the BIM platform is associated with schedule arrangement, personnel and material distribution, mechanical equipment for different purposes, and other resources to realize 4D construction simulation, which can analyze the completion rate and progress status of current schedule tasks, optimize the schedule and adjust the reasonable allocation of on-site resources to ensure the efficient completion of construction.

5.3.1 *Association list use*

BIM5D technology is to carry out the specific operation of construction, a single entity project is established in BIM5D of Guanglianda, and the model is imported into BIM5D of Guanglianda. The cost budget file in GBq format created in Guanglianda GCCP is imported into the data management in BIM5D. The quantities of each component are associated with list matching. Each component has quantities, which is conducive to seeing the changes in quantities more intuitively when checking the quantities in a specific period.

5.3.2 *Division of flow section*

Due to the problems that may occur in the on-site construction, such as a large number of building floors, the difficulty of large equipment working in the narrow area of the construction operation surface, the formwork construction, and the strong cycling of on-site pouring cycle, the plane segmented flow operation is particularly important. For the division of flow section, the factors such as project construction difficulty, details of total project amount, construction period requirements, and division and proportion conditions shall be taken as the consideration criteria, and the actual project problems shall be solved in combination with the on-site construction conditions.

In the project, to save cost and time, the flow section is used. For the construction of the foundation part and main structure part, the whole building complex is divided into four separate building construction sections to organize construction, and the flow construction method is used to construct in an orderly manner within the specified time. All components of the flow section are locked on each flow section, and the components of the flow section are associated with the time in the schedule in the progress control. The construction quantities of each flow section shall be basically the same. Compared with the traditional flow section division, it can first simulate the rhythm of each part, the construction period, and the sequence of flow construction in BIM5D, and query whether the flow section components constructed in a period are contradictory, so as to improve high resource utilization and construction efficiency.

5.3.3 *Progress correlation*

Taking the model as the basis, it is introduced into Guanglianda BIM5D for construction simulation, schedule correlation, and capital resource management. BIM5D technology is used to simulate the changes of funds and components from the foundation to the whole model, which is conducive to avoiding some technical errors in actual construction. In the model, disciplines such as water supply and drainage, civil engineering, HVAC, ventilation, and air conditioning are complicated. It is difficult to track the components in the progress preparation, and some disciplines will have collisions. In the progress association, the unknown collisions are simulated and optimized in advance. Guanglianda imports the prepared progress plan and associates it with the components and progress, and associates it with each part of the divided flow section. In the construction simulation of each flow section, it is clear that the components are continuously superimposed with the change of time. In BIM5D, if the planned time conflicts with the actual time, we will return to check the progress plan and modify it again or return to the flow section to see whether the components are fully associated, and there are red marks for lagging tasks. The corresponding view is opened to see the number of stranded tasks, and the schedule is modified to achieve accurate weekly control. The construction efficiency is improved, the duration and quantities of each component are accurately registered, and the quantities accurately overlap before and after.

5.4 *Virtual construction simulation*

Guanglianda BIM5D is used to carry out specific simulation operations of construction. After doing well in the early-stage progress correlation and list correlation, the construction simulation can carry out the accurate daily dynamic simulation and find the required information in the functions of component quantities (Wang *et al.* 2019). The bill of quantities includes the quantities of each stage of the project and the total amount of the project, as well as the project overview, preparation basis, divisional and subdivisional bill of quantities, and other project lists (You *et al.* 2020). The principles for handling the missing items and errors in the list shall include the precautions and methods when using the bill of quantities. After associating with the list, the list quantity used in each period is summarized into a curve in the virtual construction to observe whether the list quantity is wrong and strictly control it to avoid unnecessary waste of resources.

6 REFINED OPERATION AND MAINTENANCE MANAGEMENT STAGE

6.1 *Resource allocation*

Relying on BIM5D operation, material management can extract the supply and demand information of various materials. According to the extracted effective information, a reasonable plan is made, and the material stacking area is divided considering factors such as transportation cost and fire protection requirements to ensure the stability of on-site order. The difference between the expected consumption and the actual consumption is compared by checking the actual consumption of various materials. The material receiving details of each discipline are checked, the resource consumption is allocated reasonably, and the difference between the planned material consumption and the actual consumption is compared on-site to realize fine material management.

In the form of the bill of quantities, the quantities are calculated according to the design drawings and design standards, and the price is based on the quota standard and the grinding plate. Through the verification of BIM5D design and two-dimensional design, problems such as inconsistent dimensions and inconsistent quantities provided by the actual design in the design process can be found in time. Through discussion on changing drawings or model optimization, the components of the model and entity are unified, and the height is the same, which helps to reduce design changes.

6.2 *Quality assurance*

The five-dimensional information carrier encapsulated by the two dimensions of time and space in the BIM5D platform is used for construction simulation to ensure that the prepared schedule meets the national construction standards and that there is no conflict between various works. Through simulation, conflicts between various works and construction areas are avoided, and a simulation scheme is provided for project implementation. To a great extent, it can find and solve problems before construction and save time. In the process of construction simulation, if it is found that the schedule does not meet the requirements, it needs to be adjusted accordingly and meet the requirements (Han *et al.* 2018).

Considering that the project construction is affected by factors such as construction period and cost-effectiveness, the vertical intersection construction operation in the prepared project plan shall be organized as soon as possible for indoor plastering, floor, and other processes (Table 1). When the main structure is planned to complete the construction below three floors, the construction of indoor plastering, floor slab, and other processes on the first floor shall be started immediately. Before plastering, the dust, dirt, and oil stains on the surface of infilled walls, concrete walls, and other substrates shall be removed to create or expand the construction working surface for the main and key processes. Each layer shall be a separate construction operation unit, and the flow operation shall be carried out following the division of labor to ensure the project's progress and improve work efficiency. The process is reasonably arranged. The project adopts the principle of preparing for equipment mobilization and installation before the completion of the main process. This principle is fully reflected in early involvement in pipeline installation and equipment prefabrication and installation to reduce the construction progress. The orderly construction sequence shall ensure reasonable construction under the condition of having the construction operation surface.

Table 1. Schedule sequence.

Construction Schedule Sequence	
1	Foundation pile construction
2	Preparation of first-layer steel column and joint joints
3	Cushion pouring and pile protective layer construction
4	Rust point of one layer steel member and its coating treatment
5	Waterproof cushion and construction of a protective layer
6	Cast-in-place construction of supporting formwork for pile cap
7	Second floor steel column and joint connection preparation
8	Reinforcement of foundation underground column
9	Pouring of foundation underground column
10	Rust point and coating treatment of two-layer steel member
11	Construction of waterproof and protective layer of foundation basement column
12	Beam formwork and steel bar binding for the basement
13	Basement beam pouring
14	Three-layer steel column and joint connection preparation
15	Rust point and coating treatment of three-layer steel member
16	Foundation backfill

6.3 Fund management

The BIM model is associated with cost budget, contract formulation, cost control, and other contents, which can extract the dynamic physical quantities of the proposed plan and completed buildings in multiple ranges, and is conducive to the submission and application of progress payment and the review of the subcontracting distribution of quantities (Liu *et al.* 2020). By using BIM5D, the budget cost can be finely divided into entity model construction in each stage, and fine operation management and strict control measures such as cost calculation, re-examination, verification, and optimization in each period can be carried out.

The project has a large scale and a large number of quantities. Three-dimensional modeling is carried out through gtj, gqi, and other quantity calculation software to obtain the relevant list order of Tianjin to realize data sharing, avoid information and transmission distortion, make the project quantities closer to reality, improve the calculation accuracy and make the bidding quotation more reasonable. The settlement over budget caused by engineering change is reduced, labor productivity and economic benefits are improved, the smooth progress of production is ensured and the requirements of sustainable development are met. The smoothness of the capital and resource curve is analyzed (Figure 2), the capital demand is estimated, the rationality of the schedule is reviewed, the risk is controlled in advance, and adjusting the construction plan is assisted.

To realize the whole working condition, including the reasonable arrangement of material control, the quantity is quickly increased according to work, complicated calculations are avoided, and the project's progress is sped up. According to the distribution position of the key and difficult parts of the construction, the division of the construction period, the construction schedule and other conditions, the number of materials shall be extracted efficiently to ensure that each construction unit is orderly and the material distribution in each region is reasonable to the greatest extent, and the formulation of labor distribution plan and the preparation of reasonable material ratio plan is completed. It also provides theoretical support for the engineering department to complete the actual material demand plan and mobilization plan to the greatest extent to have a stable on-site order, so as to strengthen the management level of the whole project.

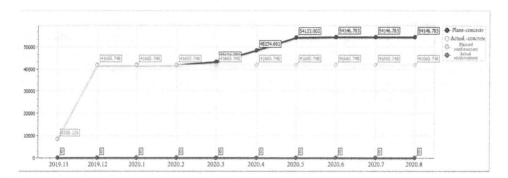

Figure 2. Fund resource curve management.

6.4 Security management

In the construction stage, there are many data of traditional quality and safety problems, which are difficult to collect, integrate, analyze and share, and are major problems in the construction. The quality and safety management based on BIM5D technology can use the mobile terminal to track problems in data association and collection, to achieve the real linkage between the map and the three-dimensional model, and upload the data to the cloud data repository to facilitate the project supervision department to find it at any time. And the data and solutions to quality problems are shared with relevant responsible personnel and participating units. BIM Technology can be used to track and obtain evidence of quality problems in real time to ensure that the rectification plan is determined within the specified time and that the overall control and timely rectification of the project status and quality positioning are carried out.

6.4.1 *Collision management*

The cost of safe and civilized construction measures includes many contents. The use of items such as safety protection articles and safety signs in the construction site is recorded in real time and uploaded to the BIM5D platform for statistics (Zhang 2020).

Pipeline collision is one of the common problems encountered in the construction process. If such a situation occurs on-site, most of them adopt on-site negotiation solutions to avoid unnecessary trouble caused by secondary rework. Due to the wide variety and complexity of pipelines, it is impossible to ensure whether the scheme is safe and reasonable, which will also increase a lot of time waste. To solve the above situation, the project shall carry out construction animation simulation before construction, visually check the pipeline problems in the whole project, find pipeline collision, mark the key points of the problems in BIM5D software, and share the results with the design unit in real time to facilitate the designers to find the problem after receiving feedback, and finally provide accurately and modify the optimized drawing.

6.4.2 *Labor management*

Detailed remarks are made on the causes of potential safety hazards, the causes of potential safety hazards are analyzed according to the actual situation and focused, and then safety training is arranged. The training times are determined according to the occurrence rate of potential safety hazards, the workers are specified to protect the places where potential safety hazards will occur according to the requirements, and the problem parts or areas in the form of pictures and text narration are recorded after completion, so as to facilitate the later problem tracking and return inspection. The safety simulation animation is used to remind the existing hidden dangers in an eye-catching position to prevent them from happening again.

On the BIM5D platform, with the help of the information processing advantages of intelligent construction systems and big data, we can fully improve the scientificity and effectiveness of labor personnel management. In the process of real-name registration, data exchange with the management platform of the real-name system can standardize the behavior of labor workers on the construction site and protect their own safety and legitimate rights and interests.

7 CONCLUSION

BIM5D is an emerging technology suitable for construction. Through BIM5D, the digital information project master control system with the objectives of "progress control," "quality inspection," "resource management" and "safety construction" can be realized to process data relatively perfectly, reduce costs and improve construction and production efficiency. Moreover, the cloud data sharing processing can be carried out through BIM5D, which greatly strengthens the mobility and organization coordination of construction management, and achieves Intelligent collaborative management and fine management. Its application in this project shows us the various advantages of this technology in construction management compared with traditional management methods. It also makes us realize that the application of this technology can improve construction efficiency in the project, and has built a good system architecture in management, operation, and maintenance.

ACKNOWLEDGMENTS

This paper was supported by Tianjin University Renai College Special projects of Natural Science (XX20007) "Research on the influence mechanism of collaborative governance of construction supply chain under BIM + IPD mode," and 2021 Tianjin University Students Innovation and entrepreneurship training program (202114038044) "Research on Simulation of fire emergency evacuation based on Pathfinder," and Ministry of Education Cooperative Education Project (202002113013).

REFERENCES

Chen Z. (2020) Analysis of the Application of BIM5D Technology in Large-scale Construction Project Management. *Bulk Cement*, 01: 38–40.
Gao D.T. and Pang Y.C. (2020) Research on Dynamic Management of BIM 5D in Project Construction Progress. *Urban Architecture*, 36: 90–91 + 125.
Han R.Y., Liu S.Z., Liang W.H. and Qiu X.q. (2018) Application and Prospect of BIM5D Technology in Project Cost. *Modern Property, Zhongxunjian*, 08: 71.
Liu C.X., Zhang M.Y., Zhou Hao, Zhang S.X. and Gai S.T. (2020) Project Management Application Based on BIM5D Platform. *Urban Housing*, 01: 222–223.
Ou H.L. and Wu E.M. (2020) Application of Smart Construction Site Based on BIM Technology in Highway Engineering Projects. *China Water Transportation, The Second Half of the Month*, 04: 48–49.
Wang Y.W., Zhu J.W., Yang D.F. and Yuan R.L. (2019) Dynamic Management and Resource Optimization of Construction Engineering Based on BIM5D. *Construction Technology*, S1: 249–253.
You T.L., Lv X.H., Zhang Y.B., Sun C.W., Zhao H.V. and Ran F. (2020) Integrated Construction Technology of BIM + Smart Site for Large Medical Buildings. *Construction Technology*, 06: 35–37.
Zhang Z.C. (2020) Analysis on Problems and Countermeasures of Construction Project Quality Management. *The Housing Industry*, 02: 176 + 178.

Civil Engineering and Energy-Environment – Gao & Duan (Eds)
© 2023 the Author(s), ISBN 978-1-032-56057-1

Research on waterproofing performance optimization of cabinet panels based on DOE experimental design

Mengbing Li*
Department of Intelligent Engineering, Guangzhou Huashang Vocational College, Guangzhou, China

Zhao Wang*
Department of Furniture and Art Design, Zhongnan Forestry University of Science and Technology, Changsha, China

ABSTRACT: The waterproof performance of the cabinet panels will directly affect the service life of the cabinet, so it is important to study the impact rate of different factors of the panel substrate and sealing process on the waterproof performance to improve and optimize the waterproof performance of the balcony cabinet panels. By adopting the DOE theory and the control factor test method, eight groups of experimental combination forms were analyzed. Based on combined experimental needs, 32 pieces of sample board with two different thicknesses were selected, then processed under two different edge sealing methods on top of four different substrates, and finally tested in indoor and outdoor environments to find the best combination of waterproof performance form. According to the experimental data, the edge sealing process is the most important waterproof performance influence factor; the best combination for waterproof performance is A brand ENF MDF or B brand ENF MDF with PUR sealing.

1 INTRODUCTION

DOE (i.e., Design of Experimental) is a mathematical and statistical method for arranging and analyzing experimental data [1]. Through the rational arrangement of experiments, ideal experimental results and scientific conclusions can be obtained with a smaller experimental scale and fewer tests, shorter test cycles, and lower costs. In order to optimize the waterproof performance of furniture panels [2], the DOE theory and control factor test method is used to examine the influence factors of substrate and sealing process of balcony cabinet pieces on waterproof performance and optimize the waterproof performance of furniture panels by timely finding the influencing factors with low mismeasurement rate [3].

2 DOE DATA ANALYSIS

The experiment includes three different factors: substrate material (ENF particle board, A brand ENF MDF, B brand ENF MDF, moisture resistant particle board), edge sealing process (EVA edge sealing, PUR edge sealing), and edge sealing thickness (thin edge, thick edge). According to the different level factors of each substrate (including four factors of the substrate, two factors of the sealing process, and two factors of sealing thickness), a total of

*Corresponding Authors: 526022484@qq.com and 809096389@qq.com

16 groups of tests are required to be conducted in the experiment in order to arrive at the impact rate of waterproof performance of each board. By using DOE data analysis, it was concluded that only eight sets of experiments were needed to draw conclusions, and the analytical data are shown in Table 1.

Table 1. Results of DOE data analysis.

	A	B	C
1	1	1	1
2	1	2	2
3	2	1	1
4	2	2	2
5	3	1	2
6	3	2	1
7	4	1	2
8	4	2	1

In Table 1, the horizontal headings A, B, and C are three different factors. A factor contains four vertical factors, B and C, each containing the corresponding two vertical factors. The details of the corresponding factors are shown in Table 2.

Table 2. Details of experimental combination factors.

Experiment Order	Substrates	Edge sealing process	Seam thickness
1	ENF particle board	EVA sealing	Thin edge
2	ENF particle board	FUR sealing	Thick edge
3	A brand ENF medium fiber board	EVA sealing	Thin edge
4	A brand ENF medium fiber board	FUR Sealing	Thick edge
5	B brand ENF medium fiber board	EVA sealing	Thick edge
6	B brand ENF medium fiber board	FUR Sealing	Thin edge
7	Moisture-resistant particle board	EVA sealing	Thick edge
8	Moisture-resistant particle board	FUR sealing	Thin edge

3 FURNITURE PANEL WATERPROOF PERFORMANCE EXPERIMENTAL TEST

Because the panels are required to be placed in indoor and outdoor environments respectively in the experiment, 16 sets of experimental data could be produced after combination with DOE data analysis. However, in order to avoid probabilistic events, such as board sealing problems or data anomalies, two or more pieces of the board should be selected in each group of the experiment; on the other hand, as much material as possible should be saved, so finally two pieces were selected per group in the experiment, that is, a total of 32 groups of tests. The specification of the sample boards was 250 mm x 250 mm x 18 mm, and A1, A2, A3, B1, B2, B3, C1, C2, C3, D1, D2, D3 measurement points were done in each plate. The sample boards were placed in two different environments: the indoor balcony and the outdoor balcony, as shown in Figure 1. In order to achieve the soaking treatment for the sample boards in the indoor balcony, four basins full of 90% of water were placed in the

Figure 1. Selection of sample plate.

indoor environment, into which the sample boards were placed, with stone pressure on top of them; otherwise, the sample boards would float. The sample boards should be completely immersed in water, and they should not overlap. Every three days, the water was replaced to prevent odor. During the experiment, the data from indoor and outdoor balcony environments were measured and recorded regularly. An experimental cycle of 44 days was completed for the indoor balcony environment, and the data was recorded once every two or three days; an experimental cycle of 17 days was completed for the outdoor balcony environment, and the data was recorded once every two or three days.

3.1. *Indoor environment*

The experiments were conducted in the order of the above-mentioned 8 groups, with 2 sample panels in each group. A total of 16 sample panels were placed in the indoor environment for testing. The experimental data were obtained by recording regular

Table 3. Experimental data table of indoor balcony environment.

(a) Experimental Data Sheet for Days 1 to 20.

Substrates	Edge sealing process	Seam thickness	Day 1	Day 3	Day 6	Day 8	Day 10	Day 13	Day 15	Day 17	Day 20
ENF particle board	EVA sealing	Thin edge	18.1400	18.3275	18.4592	18.8850	19.1258	19.3067	19.8417	20.3758	18.8025
ENF particle board	FUR sealing	Thick edge	18.2592	18.2450	18.2792	18.3033	18.35	18.3233	18.3667	18.4017	18.2658
A brand ENF medium fiber board	EVA sealing	Thin edge	18.6008	18.6667	18.7533	18.8333	19.1000	19.1092	19.6167	20.0067	18.8067
A brand ENF medium fiber board	FUR Sealing	Thick edge	18.4958	18.5317	18.5517	18.5617	18.6117	18.5900	18.6233	18.6650	18.6782
B brand ENF medium fiber board	EVA sealing	Thick edge	18.2392	18.31133	18.3583	18.4733	17.9133	18.6033	18.9592	18.4550	18.5050

(*continued*)

Table 3. Continued

(a) Experimental Data Sheet for Days 1 to 20.

Substrates	Edge sealing process	Seam thickness	Test day average								
			Day 1	Day 3	Day 6	Day 8	Day 10	Day 13	Day 15	Day 17	Day 20
B brand ENF medium fiber board	FUR Sealing	Thin edge	18.2350	18.2892	18.3417	18.3325	18.3767	18.3658	18.3917	18.4383	18.3999
Moisture-resistant particle board	EVA sealing	Thick edge	18.0067	18.1792	18.2717	27.1267	19.8925	19.8642	20.4158	20.6475	18.6433
Moisture-resistant particle board	FUR sealing	Thin edge	18.0158	18.0758	18.1467	18.1467	18.1892	18.2017	18.2342	18.2983	18.21170

(b) Experimental Data Sheet for Days 21 to 44.

Substrates	Edge sealing process	Seam thickness	Test day average							Day1-44 Total average
			Day 23	Day 25	Day 28	Day 31	Day 34	Day 37	Day 40	Day 44	
ENF particle board	EVA sealing	Thin edge	18.8542	18.8475	18.9742	18.9708	18.0408	18.9933	19.08	18.9225	18.66657
ENF particle board	FUR sealing	Thick edge	18.3358	18.3000	18.3408	18.2892	18.3225	18.3783	18.4975	18.3350	18.2823
A brand ENF medium fiber board	EVA sealing	Thin edge	18.8550	18.9085	18.9742	18.9625	18.9708	18.9917	19.0892	18.9608	18.8457
A brand ENF medium fiber board	FUR Sealing	Thick edge	18.7617	18.6983	18.71	18.685	18.6992	18.77	18.78	18.7533	18.67940
B brand ENF medium fiber board	EVA sealing	Thick edge	18.4533	18.5042	18.6025	18.5442	18.5667	18.5975	18.6367	18.5808	18.45078
B brand ENF medium fiber board	FUR Sealing	Thin edge	18.4392	18.4175	18.4683	18.405	18.4283	18.5000	18.5883	18.5033	18.385711
Moisture-resistant particle board	EVA sealing	Thick edge	18.6300	18.9742	19.1158	18.9375	18.9875	18.9375	18.9833	18.8942	18.58195
Moisture-resistant particle board	FUR sealing	Thin edge	18.2625	18.2067	18.2425	18.2067	18.2317	18.2700	18.3075	18.1517	18.16588

measurements and calculating the test day average for combinations of each group, as shown in Table 3.

3.2. *Outdoor environment*

The experiments were conducted in the order of the above-mentioned eight groups, with two

Table 4. Experimental data table of outdoor balcony environment.

Substrates	Edge sealing process	Seam thickness	Day 1	Day 3	Day 6	Day 8	Day 10	Day 13	Day 15	Day 17	Total average
ENF particle board	EVA sealing	Thin edge	18.14	18.3275	18.4592	18.8850	19.1258	19.3067	19.8417	20.3758	19.05771
ENF particle board	FUR sealing	Thick edge	18.2592	18.2450	18.2792	18.3033	18.35	18.3233	18.3667	18.4017	18.31605
A brand ENF medium fiber board	EVA sealing	Thin edge	18.6008	18.6667	18.7533	18.8333	19.1000	19.1092	19.6167	20.0067	19.08583
A brand ENF medium fiber board	FUR Sealing	Thick edge	18.4958	18.5317	18.5517	18.5617	18.6117	18.5900	18.6233	18.665	18.57886
B brand ENF medium fiber board	EVA sealing	Thick edge	18.2392	18.31133	18.3583	18.4733	17.9133	18.6033	18.9592	18.455	18.41411
B brand ENF medium fiber board	FUR Sealing	Thin edge	18.235	18.2892	18.3417	18.3325	18.3767	18.3658	18.3917	18.4383	18.4383
Moisture-resistant particle board	EVA sealing	Thick edge	18.0067	18.1792	18.2717	27.1267	19.8925	19.8642	20.4158	20.6475	20.6475
Moisture-resistant particle board	FUR sealing	Thin edge	18.0158	18.0758	18.1467	18.1467	18.1892	18.2017	18.2342	18.2983	18.2983

sample panels in each group. A total of 16 sample panels were placed in the outdoor environment for testing. The experimental data was obtained by recording regular measurements and calculating the test day average for combinations of each group, as shown in Table 4.

4 CONCLUSION

4.1 *Single-factor analysis*

The overall hair rise value of panel type is analyzed for every single factor, including the following three cases: (1) only the panel substrate is distinguished, without distinguishing the sealing process and sealing thickness; (2) only the sealing thickness is distinguished, without distinguishing the substrate and sealing process; (3) only the sealing process is distinguished,

Table 5. Experimental data in indoor balcony environment.

Classification		Average hair rise tolerance value		
		Overall hair rise value (single factor)	EVA sealing	PUR sealing
Plate base material	ENF particle board	0.4179	0.6925	0.1433
	A brand ENF medium fiber board	0.2587	0.3383	0.1791
	B brand ENF medium fiber board	0.3325	0.385	0.28
	Moisture-resistant particle board	0.46795	0.8242	0.1117
Seam thickness	Thick edge	0.3829	/	/
	Thin edge	0.355625	/	/
Edge sealing process	EVA sealing	0.56	/	/
	PUR sealing	0.178525	/	/

Table 6. Experimental data in outdoor balcony environment.

Classification		Average hair rise tolerance value		
		Overall hair rise value (single factor)	EVA sealing	PUR sealing
Plate base material	ENF particle board	1.18915	2.2358	0.1425
	A brand ENF medium fiber board	0.78755	1.4059	0.1692
	B brand ENF medium fiber board	0.20955	0.2158	0.2033
	Moisture-resistant particle board	1.46165	2.6408	0.2825
Seam thickness	Thick edge	1.031875	/	/
	Thin edge	0.792075	/	/
Edge sealing process	EVA sealing	1.624575	/	/
	PUR sealing	0.199375	/	/

without distinguishing the substrate and sealing thickness. According to the tests, the following data are obtained as shown in Tables 5 and 6.

It can be found from Tables 5 and 6 that when only the board substrate is considered, and the sealing process and sealing thickness are not, the overall rise value of A brand ENF medium fiber board and B brand ENF medium fiber board is lower than that of ENF particle board and moisture-proof particle board in both indoor and outdoor environment; there is little difference in the overall rise value of the sealing with a thick and thin edge; in the two sealing process, PUR sealing has significantly lower overall rise value than EVA. It can be concluded that among the three influencing factors, the edge sealing process has the greatest influence, the edge band has the least influence, and the type of board has little influence [4].

4.2. *8 Group combination data analysis*

The water resistance of the furniture panel and the board rise value are closely linked. Rise value tolerance is from the test data of the last day minus that of the first day, while the rise rate for the rise value difference is divided by the test data of the first day. According to the

Table 7. Indoor environmental fever value and fever rate.

Panel Type	Day 1 average	Day 44 average	Difference in development value	Development rate
ENF particle board thin edge EVA edge sealing	18.23	18.9225	0.6925	0.037986835
ENF chipboard thick edge PUR sealing	18.19166667	18.335	0.14333333	0.007879065
A brand ENF medium fiber board thin edge EVA sealing	18.6225	18.96083333	0.33833333	0.018167987
A brand ENF medium fiber board thick edge PUR sealing	18.57416667	18.75533333	0.18116666	0.00975369
B brand ENF medium fiber board thick edge EVA sealing	18.19583333	18.58083333	0.385	0.02115869
B brand ENF MDF thin edge PUR sealing	18.22333333	18.50333333	0.279999997	0.015364917
Damp-proof particle board with thick-edge EVA sealing	18.07	18.89416667	0.82416667	0.045609666
Damp-proof particle board thin edge PUR sealing	18.04	18.15166666	0.11166666	0.006189948

statistics, the indoor environment final rise value difference and rise rate data are shown in Table 7.

The lower the value of the rise, the better the waterproof performance of the board, and vice versa, the worse the waterproof performance. It can be derived from the experimental data that in the indoor environment, the top three board types with the overall value ranking from low to high are moisture-resistant particleboard with thin edge PUR sealing, ENF particleboard with thick edge PUR sealing, A brand ENF medium fiber board with thick edge PUR sealing [5].

The outdoor environment final rise value difference and rise rate data are shown in Table 8.

Table 8. Outdoor environmental fever value and fever rate.

Panel Type	Day 1 average	Day 44 average	Difference in development value	Development rate
ENF particle board thin edge EVA edge sealing	18.14	20.37583333	2.235833333	0.123254318
ENF chipboard thick edge PUR sealing	18.25916667	18.40166667	0.1425	0.007804299
A brand ENF medium fiber board thin edge EVA sealing	18.60083333	20.00666667	1.405833333	0.075579051
A brand ENF medium fiber board thick edge PUR sealing	18.49583333	18.665	0.169166667	0.009146204
B brand ENF medium fiber board thick edge EVA sealing	18.23916667	19.455	1.215833333	0.066660575
B brand ENF MDF thin edge PUR sealing	18.235	18.43833333	0.203333333	0.011150717
Damp-proof particle board with thick-edge EVA sealing	18.00666667	20.6475	2.640833333	0.146658645
Damp-proof particle board thin edge PUR sealing	18.01583333	18.29833333	0.2825	0.015680651

From the experimental data, it can be concluded that the top three board types with the overall value ranking from low to high in the outdoor environment are ENF particle board with thick edge PUR sealing, A brand ENF medium fiber board with thick edge PUR sealing, B brand ENF medium fiber board with thin edge PUR sealing.

Combining the data from indoor and outdoor environments, we can find that the value of the top three groups from low to high all use PUR sealing. It can be concluded that the sealing process can ensure the most stable waterproof performance, the board with the highest difference in value is the moisture-resistant particleboard with thick-edge EVA sealing, and the board with EVA sealing has the worst water resistance.

REFERENCES

[1] Zhang Zhonghai (2021) *Research on Optimization of Product Development Process of M Company Based on DOE Experimental Design*. D. Guangdong University of Technology.
[2] Yuan Lei, Zhang Daozhen (2009) Waterproof Conception Design of External Wall, Kitchen, Toilet and Balcony. *J. China Building Waterproofing*, 10: 16–19.
[3] Wang Shuyao (2004) Technique for Improving Water-resistance of Wood-based Panel (1)-New Water-repellents at Home and Abroad. *J. China Forest Products Industry*, 31: 53–54.
[4] Ding Yi, Ma Lianxiang, Fu Xiao (2017) The Research Progress of Edge Banding Technology of Panel Furniture. *J. Furniture*, 38: 17–19.
[5] Xu Jihong (2012) *Research on the Surface Waterproof Modification of Wood and Wood-based Panels*. D. Nanjing Forestry University.

Research on reinforcement technology of unstable rock slopes

Renjie Wu*
School of Civil Engineering, Chongqing University, Chongqing, China
Chongqing Chengtou Road and Bridge Administration Co. Ltd., Chongqing, China

Zheng Li & Tao Hu
Chongqing Chengtou Road and Bridge Administration Co. Ltd., Chongqing, China

Wengang Zhang
School of Civil Engineering, Chongqing University, Chongqing, China

Shilong Xiao, Dengsui Zhang, Chengwu Ming, Jianhua Huang, Zhangcan Kuang & Juan Pang
Chongqing Chengtou Road and Bridge Administration Co. Ltd., Chongqing, China

ABSTRACT: In recent years, with more human engineering activities on the destruction of nature resulting from the increase in infrastructure construction, collapse, landslide, debris flow, and other geological disasters are more serious, causing serious economic losses and a large number of casualties every year. Geological disasters have become a prominent problem affecting urban construction and people's living environment in China. This research analyzed the causes of unstable rock slopes, divided the failure types of rock slopes into several groups, and arrived at the corresponding reinforcement technologies. The research results have a certain guiding significance for the prevention and treatment of unstable rock slopes.

1 INTRODUCTION

China has a vast land area where the geological environment is complex. And the geological condition affecting the development of geological disasters is complex and diverse. Geological disasters have the characteristics of wide distribution, diversity, high frequency, and strong intensity. Collapses, landslides, debris flow, and other disasters have become China's most harmful geological disasters. Among them, the structure of rock slopes is extremely complex, and the prevention and reinforcement after its instability are also extremely difficult. At present, many domestic and foreign scholars have done a lot of research on unstable rock slopes and achieved fruitful results.

Based on six geological disaster prevention and control projects in Chongqing, in [1], a set of construction methods of anchoring technology were extracted. The research showed that this method could greatly save construction time and labor costs. According to the optimal distribution of reinforcement elements in critical areas of unstable rock slopes, Dehestani et al. [2] proposed a new geo-mechanical rating of reinforcement (GRR) method. According to the finite element method and the numerical simulation of each region's displacement, the displacement ratio matrix was calculated, and the distribution of reinforcement elements was

---

*Corresponding Author: reggie_v@sina.cn

obtained by calculating the GRR value. Bottelin et al. [3] used the ambient vibration method to monitor bolt support engineering and used a three-dimensional numerical simulation of rock pillar bolts to confirm their effectiveness. The results showed that the dynamic response of rock structure could be effectively monitored by a simple single-station passive seismic measurement. Li [4] analyzed the characteristics of four typical perilous rock masses in Yanting County, calculated the stability of perilous rock by stereographic projection method, evaluated the stability by calculating the falling trajectory and impact energy, and took targeted remediation measures for four perilous rock masses in combination with field investigation. Ma et al. [5] introduced the design calculation and monitoring of the wire rope anchor reinforcement method in special engineering of perilous rock treatment and analyzed the feasibility of wire rope anchor reinforcement combined with static blasting to remove perilous rock safely and stably. The monitoring results showed that the calculation method was effective. Zhang et al. [6] proposed a set of key technologies for the construction of cliff-type perilous rock groups, namely the cantilever scaffold design method, overhead cableway transportation design method, and hole-forming grouting construction technology for broken hole rock mass. This complete set of technology could make the cliff perilous rock mass get timely remediation, win time for post-disaster reconstruction, save costs, and effectively protect the fragile ecological environment in the earthquake-stricken area. Gong [7] proposed a new frame structure based on the comprehensive application of rectangular pile, bored pile, longitudinal beam, and transverse beam, and applied it to the reinforcement of a high and steep unstable slope cutting. The research results effectively solved the stability control problem of side slopes overburden. Based on the finite element numerical simulation method, Tan et al. [8] studied the length, incident angle, numbers, and spacing parameters of different bolts on the stress and deformation of unstable rock masses before and after rainfall and comprehensively evaluated the stability of unstable rock masses.

2 METHODS

2.1 *Influence factors of unstable rock slopes*

An unstable rock slope is mainly affected by internal and external factors [9]. The internal factors mainly include topographic and geomorphic factors, slope structure factors, geotechnical engineering geological conditions, etc. While the external factors mainly include earthquakes, rainfall, human activities, construction, etc. Under the influence of various external factors, the internal shear strength of rock and soil mass is decreased, and the stress balance of rock and soil mass is destroyed, so the stability is unbalanced.

2.1.1 *Internal factors*
2.1.1.1 *Topography*
The failure of rock slopes is directly related to topography. In the steep mountainous area, the topography is strong, which is unfavorable to slope stability. In the open and relatively flat basin area, the effect of topography is slow, and the influence on slope stability is relatively simple. The river section and the gentle slopes section in the mountain area are easy to collect groundwater and surface water, so they are easy to be scoured by water flow, which can easily lead to slope instability. Slopes with unfavorable shapes and scales often produce tensile stress and tensile cracks at the top of the slopes. Strong shear stress is produced, and a shear failure zone is formed at the toe of the slopes, which greatly reduces the stability of the slope.

2.1.1.2 *Geological structure*
The stability of rock slopes is easily affected by the geological structure. The geological structure determines the occurrence of rock strata, the nature and development degree of

joints and fissures, and the nature of fault fracture zones. Almost all rocks have crisscross gaps. If the joint gap is large and the weathering degree is not uniform enough, the rock mass structure will be fragmented. Joint development is not conducive to the infiltration of surface water, and it can lead to tensile stress and shear capacity weakened, increasing the probability of unstable rock slopes. Under the influence of geological structure, the development of joint fissures and broken rock mass in high slopes will seriously affect the stability of high slopes. The development of rock joints has a great influence on the slopes, and it is also the main controlling factor of unstable slopes.

2.1.1.3 *Lithologic structure*

Formation lithology and its combination are the material basis of slopes. Lithology determines rock strength and weathering resistance. If the rock is weak, then the degree of weathering is large, and the structure is seriously broken. When the height and steepness of a slope reach a certain threshold, slope instability is caused. The rock mass structure includes two factors: structural plane and structural body. The structural plane refers to various geological interfaces with a certain direction, shape, and scale of rock material discontinuity and differentiation surface. The structural body is composed of various structural planes with different occurrences, which combine the rock-cutting units. Surface properties and continuity of structural planes are the main factors affecting slope stability.

2.1.2 *External factors*

2.1.2.1 *Seismism*

Due to the horizontal seismic additional force generated by the earthquake, when the direction of the horizontal seismic additional force is unfavorable, the sliding force of the slopes increases, and the anti-sliding force of the sliding surface decreases, resulting in a decrease in slope stability. In addition, under the action of an earthquake, the increase of pore water pressure and the decrease of rock mass strength can easily cause rock slope instability.

2.1.2.2 *Hydrographic condition*

Atmospheric precipitation is the main external factor of slope instability. The effect of precipitation on the slopes is a dynamic process. Atmospheric precipitation is injected into the slopes to increase the water content and bulk density of the rock and soil. Thereby, it softens the rock mass and reduces the shear strength of the rock mass. Rainfall infiltrates into the bedrock surface or water-cut layer under the weathered rock and soil to reduce the anti-sliding stability of the contact surface. For most soft rocks, their density and strength are low, and slope instability with high strength generally occurs during the rainy season. If there is abundant groundwater inside the slopes and the lithology is weak, it often leads to large-scale deformation, such as slopes landslides. Whether there is groundwater and the degree of groundwater development are important factors affecting slope stability.

2.1.2.3 *Human factors*

Human factors, such as unreasonable design, blasting, excavation, or filling of the slopes, will affect the stability of the slopes. The rock slopes can be regarded as an isotropic homogeneous continuum, and the internal stress is in static equilibrium. The slopes excavation provides space conditions for slope instability. Namely, it causes the slopes to continuously unload along the free surface during the stress redistribution process, which makes the slopes structure relaxed and the physical and mechanical properties reduced. The infiltration of a large amount of production and living water can cause slope deformation or failure. The influence factors of slope engineering activities such as excavation, loading, and filling on slope stability mainly lie in slope height and slope ratio. The higher the slope height, the larger the slope ratio is, the worse the slope stability is, and the greater the probability of slope failure.

2.2 Failure types of unstable rock slopes

Rock slope deformation refers to the occurrence of slope rock mass local displacement or rupture with no significant slip or rolling and no overall instability of the slopes. Rock slopes failure refers to the large displacement of slopes rock mass at a certain speed, such as the overall sliding, rolling, and toppling. The deformation of rock slopes is the precursor of failure, and the failure of the slope is the result of further development of deformation. Types of deformation and failure of rock slopes can be divided into looseness, tensional fracture, peristalsis, spalling, collapse, and landslide [10].

2.2.1 Looseness

The surface layer of the slope's body appears to have cracks that are nearly parallel to the direction of the slope. The rock mass is cut by cracks, loosens, and moves toward free directions. This process and phenomenon are called looseness. Slope often has a variety of loose cracks. In engineering activities, the slope with loose cracks is often called the slope looseness zone. Slope looseness will reduce the strength of the slopes and make it easier for various factors to penetrate the slopes. The depth of the slope looseness zone is also controlled by the slope shape and the original stress state of the slope. The higher and steeper the slope is, the stronger the ground stress is; the more developed the slope's loose cracks are, and the greater the depth of the slope loose zone is.

2.2.2 Tensional fracture

A tensional fracture refers to the phenomenon of opening cracks in slope rock mass due to unloading rebound. It is the deformation in the process of slope stress adjustment. Generally speaking, the excavation of the cutting slope makes the original unloading cracks of rock further develop or form new unloading cracks. This crack is usually parallel to the slope's surface. At the top of the slopes or the top of the cut, a tensile zone is formed due to the tensile stress caused by unloading. The higher and steeper the slope is, the wider the tension band is.

2.2.3 Peristalsis

Peristalsis refers to the long-term slow deformation of slope rock mass under the action of gravity. This kind of deformation occurs in soft rock mass or soft and hard interbedded rock mass, often forming flexural deformation. When the artificial slope cuts the mountain, under weathering and water, some rock masses on the slope may rotate along the joints, resulting in toppling creep or traction large-scale collapse deformation. The further development of deformation can cause slope damage.

2.2.4 Spalling

The main reason for the spalling is the destruction of rock mass structure caused by various physical weathering, such as changes in temperature and humidity, which are important factors for the continuous weathering and fragmentation of surface rock mass. The fractured slope rock mass is stable. However, for the soft and hard rock slopes, the lower rock of the easily weathered slopes is often weathered and broken first, then spalling occurs, so the hard rock gradually highlights on the slopes. At this time, the upper protruding rock may collapse.

2.2.5 Collapse

The block separated by the steeply inclined tensile fracture surface in the slope rock mass suddenly falls off from the steeply inclined slopes, violently flips and jumps along the slopes, and finally piles up at the foot of the slopes. This phenomenon and process are called collapse. Rockfall refers to the phenomenon that individual rock blocks fall downward.

Collapses are sudden, violent, and destructive, often destroying buildings, damaging roads, and blocking waterways.

2.2.6 *Landslide*
Landslide refers to the phenomenon that the rock mass on the slopes slides downward along a certain weak structural plane or structural belt, which is one of the common deformation and failure forms of rock slopes. The specific failure modes in the slopes are mostly bedding sliding and double-sided wedge sliding.

2.3 *Reinforcement technology of unstable rock slopes*

If the safety factor of the slopes cannot meet the requirements, it directly affects the surrounding structures, engineering construction, and people's lives and property safety, and even induce serious accidents. Therefore, it is necessary to take appropriate reinforcement measures to improve slope stability and safety [11].

2.3.1 *Load reduction and obstacle removal*
In the process of prevention and control of unstable rock slopes, it is necessary to remove the loose rock mass in advance to reduce the risk of collapse. Load reduction and obstacle removal (shown in Figure 1 (a)) includes two ways: cutting head and cutting slopes. The cutting head is to reduce the total height of the slope for the purpose. The cutting slope is to cut off part of the unstable rock mass, so that to slow down the slope's gradient and reduce the sliding part of the landslide overweight, thereby improving slope stability. Both two types of load reduction and obstacle removal measures can reduce the sliding force of the slope.

2.3.2 *Anchoring reinforcement*
Anchoring reinforcement (shown in Figure 1 (b)) refers to the transmission of tension to a stable rock stratum through construction techniques such as bolts, anchor cables, and steel mesh. It is fixed through the node position of the frame to ensure the stability of the rock slopes to the greatest extent. The reinforcement method mainly includes the following aspects.

2.3.2.1 *Grouting reinforcement*
Grouting reinforcement technology injects the solidified slurry into the cracks or pores of the object by hydraulic or pneumatic pressure to change the physical and mechanical properties

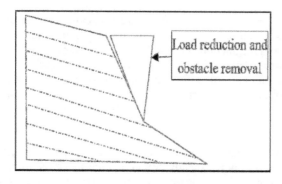 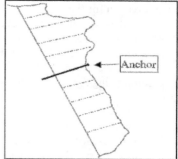

(a) Load reduction and obstacle removal   (b) Anchoring reinforcement

Figure 1. Reinforcement technology of unstable rock slopes.

of the grouting object. Grouting material and grouting technology are keys to grouting reinforcement technology. When the slope is broken, and the joint fissure is developed, the slope can be reinforced by pressure grouting. Under pressure, the grouting fluid penetrates the surrounding through the joint fissures cut around the borehole wall and cements the rock and soil mass of the broken slope to form a whole. In addition, the mortar column plays the role of bolt connection to the broken slope rock mass to improve the integrity and stability of the slope.

2.3.2.2 Anchor reinforcement
When the rock slope is broken, or the slope stratum is weak, a certain number of tension members are buried in the stratum to reinforce the slope to improve the strength and self-stabilizing ability of rock and soil. The anchor reinforcement mechanism is equivalent to the role of bolts. The anchor technology can greatly reduce the weight of the structure, save engineering materials, ensure the safety and stability of the project, and it presents significant social and economic benefits. It is widely used in engineering.

2.3.2.3 Soil nail reinforcement
For the soft rock slope, a sufficient number of soil nails can be inserted into the slope to reinforce the slope. Soil nails as the main force component, and their reinforcement mechanism is similar to the role of a group anchor. However, compared with anchor reinforcement, soil nail reinforcement has the characteristics of shortness and density, which is a shallow slope reinforcement technology. It has the advantages of fast construction speed, short construction period, and low cost.

2.3.2.4 Pre-stressed cable reinforcement
It refers to the use of high-strength steel strand pre-stressed anchor cable to apply a certain amount of pre-stress to the caving body to improve its stiffness. Through this process, the rock in the range of action of the pre-stressed anchor cable is correspondingly squeezed, the friction on the sliding surface or the rock fissure surface is increased, the self-bearing capacity is strengthened, and the partial deformation and displacement of the rock mass are effectively limited. Pre-stressed cable reinforcement is reliable. It does not produce disturbance and damage to the slope, and it can maintain the mechanical properties of the slope itself. The force can be evenly distributed on the slope of the reinforcement area, which has strong adaptability to the terrain and geological conditions.

2.3.3 Drainage

Drainage (shown in Figure 2 (a)) mainly includes surface drainage measures and slope drainage measures. According to the distribution location, surface drainage can be divided into two cases: inside the rock mass and outside the rock mass. Inside the rock mass, the structure and cracks of the rock mass are mainly used to build water diversion projects such as underground ditches or open ditches, so that the rainwater falling on the slope can be quickly discharged to prevent it from infiltrating into the slope and to reduce the infiltration of water into the slope. Outside the rock mass, the water interception ditch is mainly set up to intercept and divert the principle, so that the surface water does not flow into the unstable slope range. The drainage measures in the slope are determined according to the location and geological conditions of the slope. Drainage holes, drainage wells, large-diameter pipe wells, and horizontal drainage pipes can be selected. The role of drainage in the slope is to make the atmospheric rainfall and groundwater discharge from the slope as soon as possible, reduce the water content in the slope, reduce the water load of the slope, and avoid adverse effects on the slope stability.

2.3.4 Bracing, retaining wall, and slide-resistant pile

Bracing (shown in Figure 2 (b)) is the basic measure of rock slope reinforcement, which is a more reliable reinforcement technology. It solves the stability problem of perilous rock

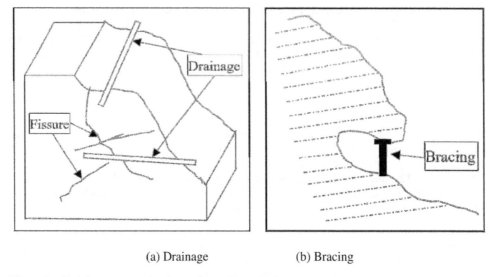

(a) Drainage (b) Bracing

Figure 2. Reinforcement technology of unstable rock slopes.

collapse from the outside of the slope. The support is usually arranged in the lower rock cavity of unstable rock and often forms composite reinforcement with the upper anchorage to strengthen the slope stability. The retaining wall (shown in Figure 3) is an engineering measure to block the sliding of an unstable rock mass. Its main function is to stabilize the landslide and prevent the damage caused by the collapse of the slope surface. In the process of prevention and control, the type and arrangement of the retaining wall should be comprehensively analyzed and considered according to the location, type, scale, and geological conditions of the slope. It is suitable for the treatment of small and medium-sized rock slopes formed by man-made cutting or river scouring. Slide-resistant pile (shown in Figure 3) is used to control unstable rock slopes. It can not only ensure that the pile is not cut, bent, or pushed down, but also ensure that the rock among piles does not slide away from the pile. When reinforcing the rock mass, the slide-resistant pile should be set in the middle and lower

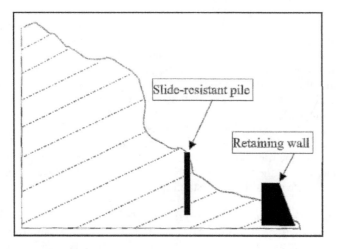

Figure 3. Retaining wall and slide-resistant pile.

part of the sliding mass. It needs to ensure that the pile has enough strength, depth, appropriate pile height, and pile spacing.

In addition to the above technologies, in the actual engineering operation, unstable rock slope reinforcement includes some auxiliary technical measures, such as on-site detection, controlled blasting, ecological protection network, etc.

3 CONCLUSION AND DISCUSSION

This study divided the influence factors of unstable rock slopes into internal and external factors. The internal factors include topography, geological structure, and lithologic structure. External factors include Seismism, hydrographic conditions, and human factors. On this basis, failure types of unstable rock slopes were divided into looseness, tensional fracture, peristalsis, spalling, collapse, landslide, and other types. In the end, corresponding reinforcement technologies were extracted, such as load reduction and obstacle removal, anchoring reinforcement, drainage, bracing, retaining wall and slide-resistant pile, etc.

The reinforcement technology needs to be diversified for unstable rock slopes because of their complex lithology, structure, hydrogeological conditions, and different failure modes. Many factors affect the stability of an unstable rock slope, but none is not independent, and each factor affects the stability of the slopes together. Therefore, in the actual engineering analysis process, it is necessary to carefully consider the limitations of each influence factor and to conduct a comprehensive analysis. At the same time, to obtain a more reliable, reasonable, and objective result, the unstable rock slope situation needs to be grasped in real time to formulate more effective, scientific, and reasonable prevention and control measures.

ACKNOWLEDGMENTS

This work was supported by the Natural Science Foundation of Chongqing (cstc2021jcyj-bshX0028). The authors thank reviewers and editors for their valuable comments and advice, which improved the quality of this paper.

REFERENCES

[1] Zheng X.Q. and Chen C.F. (1992) The Application of Anchorage Construction Technology to the Geological Hazard Control Projects. *Acta Geological Sichuan*, 4: 273–278.
[2] Dehestani H., Haddad A. and Balghour M.K. (2016) Reinforcement Optimization in Unstable Rock Slopes Using a Geomechanical Rating of Reinforcement. *Proceedings of the Romanian Academy, Series A*, 17(2): 160–168.
[3] Bottelin P., Baillet L., Larose E., Jongmans D., Hantz D., Brenguier O., Cadet H. and Helmstetter A. (2017) Monitoring Rock Reinforcement Works with Ambient Vibrations: La Bourne Case Study (Vercors, France). *Engineering Geology*, 226: 136–145.
[4] Li Z. (2019) The Analysis and Prevention of the Collapse Stability in Yanting County. *Journal of Geological Hazards and Environment Preservation*, 30(2): 27–34.
[5] Ma X.J., Zheng J. and WangD.K. (2019) Design of Wire Rope Anchored Structure for Dangerous Slopes Rock Treatment Engineering. *Guangdong Highway Communications*, 45(6): 63–66.
[6] Zhang L.M., Zhou Y., He M. and Wang S.Z. (2020) Key Technologies in Construction of Collapse Regulation Project for Cliff-Type Dangerous Rock Groups. *Geotechnical Engineering Technique*, 34(3): 167–173.
[7] Gong J.H. (2020) Discussion on Reinforcement Technology of High and Steep Unstable Cutting Slopes. *High Speed Railway Technology*, 11(3): 71–74.

[8] Tan Z.R., Wang M.H., Fu Q., Yuan F. and LiuY.R. (2020) Numerical Analysis of the Stability of the Dangerous Rock Strengthened by Bolt in Enshi Grand Canyon. *Journal of Water Resources and Architectural Engineering*, 18(1): 56–63+108.

[9] Xia K.Z., Liu X.M., Chen C.X., Song Y.F., Ou Z., Long Y. (2015) Analysis of Mechanism of Bedding Rock Slope Instability with Catastrophe Theory. *Rock and Soil Mechanics*, 36(2): 477–486.

[10] Lu H.F., Liu Q.S., Chen C.X., Wu Y.X. (2012) Disaster Mechanism of Hard and Soft Interbedding Slopes and its Preventive Measure. *Disaster Advance*s, 5(4): 1361–1366.

[11] Kaya Y. and Topal T. (2015) Evaluation of Rock Slope Stability for a Touristic Coastal Area Near Kusadasi, Aydin (Turkey). *Environmental Earth Sciences*, 74(5): 4187–4199. Amini M., Ardestani A. and Khosravi M.H. (2017) Stability Analysis of Slide-toe-toppling Failure. *Engineering Geology*, 228: 82–96.

Civil Engineering and Energy-Environment – Gao & Duan (Eds)
© 2023 the Author(s), ISBN 978-1-032-56057-1

Study on natural frequency of damage position of implicit glass curtain wall

Chongge Wang, Meng Zhang*, Yubiao Liu & Hui Li
Shandong University of Science and Technology, School of Civil Engineering and Architecture, Qingdao, Shandong, China

ABSTRACT: The safety of glass curtain walls has become a serious safety problem, especially when the glass plate falls off due to the failure of sealant. When it comes to the large glass curtain wall, the failure detection method of single glass structural adhesive is not efficient enough. Based on the finite element software, more than the symmetry of the glass curtain wall structure is set up, including an undamaged simulation analysis of a total of 37 conditions in the cases of inherent frequency variation, the damage position analysis of the same damage, and natural frequency changes of different glass, it is found that the natural frequencies of the symmetric structure damage location changes also have symmetry. The position of the two damaged glasses can be basically locked by the change of natural frequency. Through the change of natural frequency, the position of the two damaged glasses can be basically locked. Second, through the structural damage detection of a single glass, the detection time can be effectively reduced, and the efficiency of detection can be improved. It provides reference significance for glass damage detection.

1 INTRODUCTION

The application of glass curtain walls in the construction of our country began in the 1980s, more than 30 years ago, and its development is rapid in terms of both scale and speed. Glass curtain wall has a lightweight, short construction period and fashionable appearance, the glass curtain wall of skyscrapers in many city constructions has become a symbol of urban modernization. Currently, our country has established more than 200 million square meters of glass curtain wall, accounting for 85% of the world's total; our country has become the world's largest country of glass curtain wall production and use [1].

Compared with the rapid development of glass curtain walls, the curtain walls of existing buildings are still in a state of serious lag in the operation stage. Since there is no mandatory risk detection and maintenance requirement in the country, the relevant main units of curtain walls also lack the awareness of detection and maintenance in the operation stage, and the glass curtain walls built in the early stage have different degrees of hidden safety risk [2]. Due to the problems of non-standard design, backward construction technology, and inadequate construction supervision in the construction stage, it is difficult to guarantee the construction quality, so a large number of glass curtain walls have serious problems such as structural adhesive aging, reduced support capacity, poor stability, lack of reliability.

As an inherent characteristic, structural vibration performance is closely related to boundary conditions and physical characteristics. Liu *et al.* [3] proposed a method of using the pulse excitation method to obtain the natural frequency of curtain wall glass to identify

*Corresponding Author: tumuzm@163.com

DOI: 10.1201/9781003433644-13

the degree of glass curtain wall loosening and damage. Through experiments, it was found that glass loosening would cause the attenuation of natural frequency, which proved that curtain wall damage would cause the change of natural frequency.

The actual curtain wall structure and research specimens have certain differences, mainly in practical engineering. A single piece of glass curtain wall panel is connected to the main structure by steel and aluminum alloy keel; therefore, it is obtained by dynamic characteristics test, which is usually the natural frequency of curtain wall panels, aluminum alloy keel, fundamental frequency, and a single block of the steel skeleton as a whole unit panel frequency coupling [4].

Huang et al. [5] did the frequency of a single piece of glass experiment and concluded that the natural frequency of the single piece of glass would decrease as the silicone adhesive bonding length decreased. This change of natural frequency is used to detect the implicit damage situation of glass curtain wall, which provides the possibility through experimental analysis method; the bonding damage was studied, the influence of length by tapping instead of structural adhesive damage; different levels of bonding length damage condition were set up, modal parameters of the structure were obtained through modal test approach, and the damage condition of parameters was compared; finally, it is concluded that first-order natural frequency can be used as a hidden frame curtain wall glass bonding length of damage evaluation index. Tang Haochen [6] used finite element software to conduct finite element simulation on Huang Zhide's test result, which well verified Huang Zhide's experimental result, that is, the natural frequency of glass curtain wall will continuously decrease with the reduction of structural adhesive. The study of the natural frequency variation of glass curtain wall structure can effectively predict the damage location of structural adhesive.

2 MODEL INTRODUCTION AND ESTABLISHMENT

This article mainly uses the finite element software ABAQUS to simulate nine areas such as curtain wall mode changes and changes in the conditions for structural adhesive damage location. Local damage location can damage the natural frequency changes to determine the overall location. In order to simulate the possibility of damage as much as possible, nine pieces of glass with four sides of different damage positions were simulated, resulting in a total of 37 damage possibilities. The order ranges from 0 to 36, where 0 is the working condition without damage. For the sake of illustration, each piece of glass from the nine pieces is 1 to 9, and the 4 sides clockwise are A, B, C, and D. The position of damage is determined by the combination of numbers and letters. Finite element analysis is carried out for each working condition through a numerical simulation method. The external dimension of the aluminum alloy frame curtain wall is 3830 mm×3830 mm, the size of a single piece of glass is 1200 mm×1200 mm, the width of structural glue is 20 mm, and the thickness is 12 mm. The joints between the glass and the glass are filled with structural glue.

The connection between structural adhesive and glass, structural adhesive and aluminum alloy frame, and structural adhesive and aluminum alloy are bound. Division of meshing with C3D8R hexahedron units and glass curtain wall aluminum alloy frame is connected by bolts, and then through the structural adhesive bonding, the glass panel was on the frame, and through the rivet, the points of the two vertical boxes were fixed on the wall. In order to get a more realistic simulation, simulation conditions need to be as consistent as possible, like the actual working condition; therefore, in the finite element curtain wall analysis model, the gap between the glass is left, and the structural glue is added to the gap to simulate the real situation of the glass curtain wall. The connection between frames, the connection between glass and structural glue, and the connection between structural glue and frame are all binding constraints, and four fixed constraints are imposed on each mullion of the overall frame. The model is shown in Figure 1.

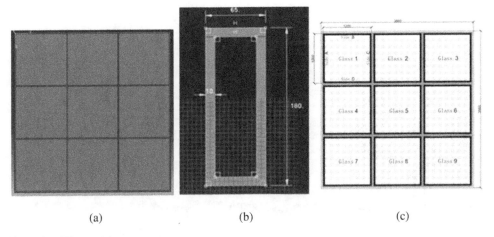

(a)   (b)   (c)

Figure 1. The model.

In order to be close to the real curtain wall state, the material properties of the glass curtain wall are from the actual project. The material properties of the structure used are shown in Table 1.

Table 1. Hidden frame curtain wall glass component material property table.

Material name	Young's modulus (MPa)	Density (kg/m^3)	Poisson's ratio
glass	72000	2700	0.2
aluminum alloy	70000	2730	0.33
silicone adhesive	0.8	1240	0.47

3 THE SIMULATION ANALYSIS OF THE MODEL

Different damage conditions were analyzed by finite element software, and the first-order natural frequency changes at different damage locations were obtained.

From the observation of 37 working conditions in Figure 2, it can be seen that when a structural glue of the structure is damaged, compared with the structure without damage, its natural frequency decreases significantly, which also verifies that when the curtain wall structure is damaged, its natural frequency will decrease significantly. However, compared with the change from no damage to damage, the change of natural frequencies of damage conditions at different locations is not as obvious as the change of natural frequencies from zero conditions to other conditions. Therefore, in order to study the natural frequency variation law of the same damage condition of different edges, we should not consider the natural frequency of the glass curtain wall in the undamaged state when analyzing.

From the 36 kinds of working conditions of the change of natural frequency shown in Figure 3, we can see that after the narrow ordinate, the inherent frequency curve of each edge damage is obvious, and it can be found by looking at some changing laws, for example, some point values show the identity and the symmetry curve segment in some places; for some reason, this phenomenon may be due to the symmetry of the structure. The position of

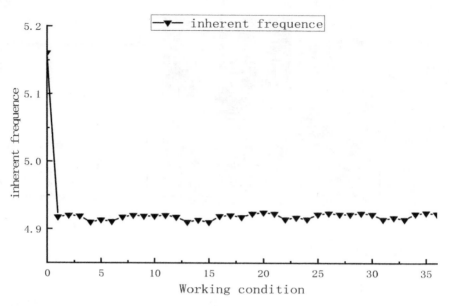

Figure 2. Variation of natural frequency in first-order 37 working conditions.

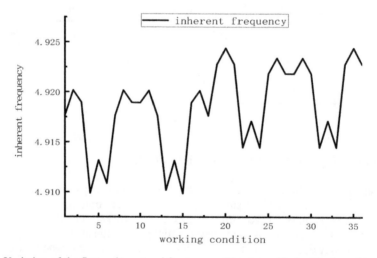

Figure 3. Variation of the first-order natural frequency without considering the 0 working condition.

the glass panel with a symmetrical edge can result in the homogeneity of the natural frequencies or symmetry of the curves.

In order to better study the symmetry of natural frequencies, the changes of natural frequencies in the absence of the same edge rubber strips of different glasses can be considered individually. Among them, the changes of natural frequencies of four edges A–D with location are shown in Figure 4.

Therefore, the first-order natural frequency was simulated and analyzed with the change of the damaged position of 9 pieces of glass. From its natural frequency variation diagram, it

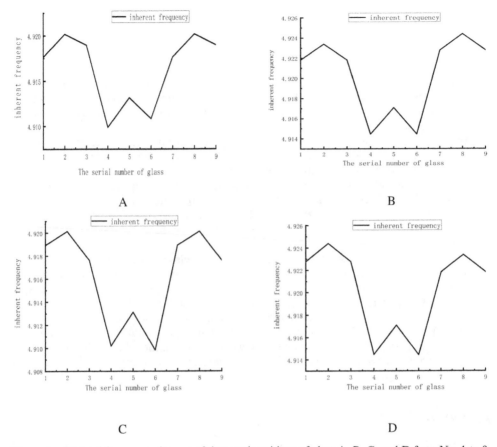

Figure 4. Natural frequency changes of damaged positions of glass A, B, C, and D from No. 1 to 9.

can be found that because the structure used is symmetric structure, its variation law shows symmetry. For A and C structural adhesive damage location, damage of structural adhesive for the vertical strip, 1 piece of glass and glass 7, 2 pieces of glass and glass 8, and 3 pieces of glass and glass 9 show the consistency; the natural frequency of observation 1, 2, 3, 7, 8, 9 positions can be found; and symmetry exists between 1 and 7, 2 and 8, 3 and 9 on the horizontal direction. For B and D structural adhesive damage location, damage structural adhesive for the transverse strip, 1 piece of glass and glass 3, 4 pieces of glass and glass 6, and 7 pieces of glass and glass 9 show the consistency; the natural frequency of observation 1, 3, 4, 6, 7, 9 positions can be found; and symmetry exists between 1 and 3, 4 and 6, 7 and 9 on vertical direction.

For the symmetric glass curtain wall, when we detect the damage to the whole-wall curtain wall, we can first detect the change in the overall natural frequency. By comparing the natural frequency change when there is no damage, we can find two symmetric positions of structural adhesive damage. Then, the final damage strip is determined by the specific detection of the symmetrical position glass. In the future, relevant tests and simulation work can be carried out in asymmetric structures or overall curtain walls without providing strong support for curtain wall damage detection.

4 CONCLUSION

Based on the results and discussions presented above, the conclusions are obtained as follows:

(1) From the perspective of the natural frequency change from no damage to damage process, the experimental results of Huang Zhide were verified. The damage to structural adhesive will cause the natural frequency change of the curtain wall, especially the first-order frequency change.
(2) According to the simulation results, the changes in the natural frequency of adhesive strip damage at positions A and C are the same in No. 1, 7, 2, 8, 3, and 9 glass, and the reason is that their positions are symmetric about the horizontal axis. The change of natural frequency of structural adhesive strip damage at positions B and D is the same on No. 1, 3, 4, 6, 7, and 9 glasses because No. 1, 3, 4, 6, 7, and 9 are symmetric about the vertical axis. For the glass curtain wall with a symmetric structure, the natural frequency change of the glass curtain wall also has symmetry after the structural adhesive strip is damaged.
(3) Usually, glass detection starts from a single glass, but glass, structural glue, and keel are considered as a whole, so we need to start from the overall structure to detect curtain wall damage. The damage detection efficiency of a single glass is low, and the cost is high. In this paper, the overall natural frequency variation of 9 glass curtain walls is simulated, although the natural frequency variation is not obvious to the damage of structural adhesive strips at different positions. Through the analysis, it can be found that a symmetrical structure can reduce the workload and improve the efficiency of glass curtain wall damage detection, which has a certain reference significance for glass curtain wall damage detection.

REFERENCES

[1] Q. Li and X. Zhu, Risk Identification and its Preventive Measures of Glass Curtain Wall, *Urban Probl.* 246(1)(2016)42–46 (In Chinese).
[2] Lei Bao, Cheng Huang, Wenbo Chen, Ziren Xiao, Review on Damage Detection Methods of Structural Adhesives for Existing Glass Curtain Walls [J]. *China Building Decoration and Decoration*, 2022(0 5):159–161.
[3] Xiaogen Liu, Yiwang Bao, Yile Song, et al. Evaluation of Safety Performance of Existing Glass Curtain Wall Based on Dynamic Method. *China Civil Engineering Journal*, 2009, 42(12): 11–15.
[4] Mingyu Wei, Yuanzhi Zhang, Shaole Yu, et al. Experimental Study on Boundary Relaxation of Double-layer Insulating Glass Curtain Wall with Semi-hidden Frame Structure Based on Vibration Test. *Building Structure*, 2021, 51(23): 54–60.
[5] Huang Z, Xie M, Song H, et al. Modal Analysis Related Safety-state Evaluation of Hidden Frame Supported Glass Curtain Wall. *Journal of Building Engineering*, 2018,20: 671–678.
[6] Haochen Tang *Research on Damage Identification Method of Hidden Frame Curtain Wall Glass Component [D]*. Shandong University of Architecture and Engineering, 2021.

Dynamic monitoring of citrus spatial distribution in Guilin based on GEE

Zhigang Qin, Haotian You*, Tingting Gan & Xu Tang
College of Geomatics and Geoinformation, Guilin University of Technology, Guilin, China

ABSTRACT: Citrus has become one of the most widely planted fruit trees in the south due to its high yield and good economic benefits. The citrus planting area is closely related to policy and economic factors, which leads to the continuous change of citrus planting areas in the process of historical development. However, due to the limited data acquisition and processing capabilities, there are few previous studies on monitoring the dynamic changes of citrus in large areas. With the development and popularization of cloud computing, it is possible to monitor the long-term dynamic changes of citrus in large areas based on cloud computing. Therefore, this paper takes Guilin City as the research area, based on the long time series Landsat-8 image as the basic data, uses the GEE cloud platform to process the long time series image data and extract the parameters, and uses the random forest, support vector machine, and decision tree algorithms to extract the spatial distribution of citrus. Through comparative study, the spatial resolution and classification algorithm of the optimal extraction results are selected to extract the spatial distribution of citrus in time series, to realize the dynamic monitoring of spatial distribution. The results show that the extraction result of 30 m spatial resolution is closer to the historical statistical area data and has higher extraction accuracy than that of 15 m spatial resolution. The results of the three classification algorithms show that the accuracy of random forest is the highest, the overall accuracy is 0.923, and the Kappa coefficient is 0.890. Citrus in Guilin is mainly distributed in the northeast, central, and southern parts of Guilin, and the planting area has been increasing year by year in the past five years. The research results can provide technical support for the large-scale operation and management of citrus in Guilin.

1 INTRODUCTION

China is a large country with various climate types and has various tropical climate conditions suitable for citrus growth, such as northern subtropical and central subtropical. Over the past decade, China has been the world's largest producer and marketer of citrus, accounting for 1/3 of the world's citrus production, more than 40 million tons. According to current statistics, Guilin is China's first domestic citrus production city [1]. With the rapid expansion of orchard areas, improper development methods have led to increasingly prominent environmental problems, such as the destruction of biological structures, which has aggravated the phenomenon of single biodiversity and imbalance of ecosystems such as soil erosion [2]. With the development of various remote sensing technologies, such as automatic recognition algorithms of remote sensing images, remote sensing technology has played a huge role and application potential in the field of vegetation feature recognition and extraction, which has changed the current situation of a time-consuming, long cycle and

---

*Corresponding Author: youht@glut.edu.cn

poor timeliness of manual investigation in traditional vegetation change monitoring research. Therefore, using remote sensing technology to monitor the growth dynamics of citrus orchards is conducive to the objective evaluation of the ecological impact of its area expansion and the diversification of citrus varieties, and the large-scale management of orchards, thereby increasing the diversity of the ecological environment.

However, large-scale remote sensing monitoring of vegetation requires high data volume, transmission speed, and computational efficiency. The complexity and workload of big data processing face enormous challenges, and the commonly used remote sensing data processing tools cannot complete the work in a short time. Google Earth Engine (GEE) provides an advanced cloud computing platform that perfectly solves the problems that need to be faced when processing and analyzing large-scale remote sensing data. It can obtain various remote sensing images and geographic data through online or offline programming, avoiding the tedious process of downloading data and preprocessing. Relying on the powerful background processor of the Google Cloud platform can also significantly improve computational efficiency [3]. The huge computing and processing power of GEE has played an important role in various fields, such as climate information, land surface dynamic monitoring [4], crop yield estimation [5], and forest coverage change [6]. Users only need to refer online without downloading the original data, and can directly access their databases for data analysis and visualization using Python or JavaScript programming language, which provides the possibility for large-scale remote sensing data mining and analysis [7]. For example, based on the GEE platform, Li et al. [8] solved the process of data download and preprocessing through online programming, and classified the forest types by combining the phenological differences of time series images and the spectral characteristics of ground objects. Wang et al. [9] combined Landsat-5 and Landsat-8 satellite data sets, used the GEE platform to estimate the vegetation coverage in Central Asia for 12 years, and combined remote sensing big data and geographic cloud computing to realize the dynamic monitoring of vegetation coverage in the region. The results show that GEE can provide technical support and quantitative data for the evaluation and analysis of ecological succession in a certain geographical range. Based on the GEE platform, He et al. [10] cited Sentinel-2 images to calculate vegetation index, texture, and terrain features, respectively, and completed the construction and optimization of original features. At the same time, four classifiers, such as naive Bayes (NB), support vector machine (SVM), Classification and Regression tree (CART), and random forest (RF), were used to extract the spatial distribution information of winter wheat and winter rapeseed. Based on Landsat and Sentinel-2 time series data, Xiao [11] used the GEE platform to carry out remote sensing monitoring of cultivated land change in Yunnan Province. The random forest classification method has high classification accuracy, and the average overall accuracy of the four cultivated land cover products is 0.974, and the average user accuracy is 0.940.

Therefore, this paper takes Guilin City in the northeast of Guangxi Zhuang Autonomous Region as the research area and uses the GEE platform to process the Landsat-8 images of different years and different resolutions in the study area, such as splicing, cutting, cloud removal, parameter extraction and so on. Three different classification methods of RF, SVM, and decision tree (DT) are used to extract the spatial distribution of citrus. Through comparative study, the optimal spatial resolution of extraction results and the optimal classification algorithm were selected to extract citrus resources in Guilin. The dynamic changes in spatial distribution were monitored to provide technical support for large-scale citrus management in Guilin.

2 MATERIALS AND METHODS

2.1 *Study area*

The study area was located in Guilin city, Guangxi Zhuang Autonomous Region, China (109°36'–111°29' E, 24°15'–26°23' N) (Figure 1), which is a subtropical monsoon climate

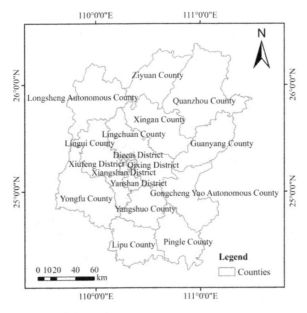

Figure 1. Location diagram of the study area.

zone. Guilin is the most suitable area for citrus production, and citrus is also a fruit variety listed in Guilin as a national dominant producing area. In 2019, the city's citrus planting area was 2.485 million mu, accounting for 66.3% of the total fruit planting area. Production reached 4.581 million tons, accounting for 67.5% of the city's total fruit production.

2.2 *Landsat-8 data*

The data used in this paper is a Landsat-8 image, including Operational Land Imager (OLI) and Thermal Infrared Sensor (TIRS). The specific band introduction and application are shown in Table 1.

Table 1. Landsat-8 satellite band and application introduction.

Bands name	Wavelength (μm)	Resolution/ m	Application
B1 (Coastal)	0.43–0.45	30	Coastal zone observation
B2 (Blue)	0.45–0.51	30	Water penetration and soil vegetation division
B3 (Green)	0.53–0.59	30	Distinguish vegetation
B4 (Red)	0.64–0.67	30	In the chlorophyll absorption zone
B5 (NIR)	0.85–0.88	30	Biomass estimation
B6 (SWIR -1)	1.57–1.65	30	Better Distinguish the Atmosphere, Clouds
B7 (SWIR -2)	2.11–2.29	30	Distinguish rocks, minerals, vegetation cover, etc.
B8 (Pan)	0.50–0.68	15	Panchromatic band
B9 (Cirrus)	1.36–1.38	30	Strong absorption characteristics containing water vapor, can be used for cloud detection
B10 (TIRS -1)	10.6–11.19	100	Target of induced thermal radiation
B11 (TIRS -2)	11.5–12.51	100	Target of induced thermal radiation

The Landsat-8 image data used in the study needs to be subjected to a series of operations such as cloud removal, splicing, cropping, and parameter extraction. The proposed parameters mainly include band reflectance, vegetation index, texture information, slope, and aspect data. All the above operations are completed within GEE.

2.3 Sample data

According to the historical images on the map of the sky, the samples are selected for the classification of the ground objects. The selected historical data is in the same year as the sample data, ensuring that the sample data and historical data are time synchronized. The number of ground object samples used in the study is shown in Table 2.

Table 2. Number of samples of various ground objects used in the research.

Period	Citrus	Water area	Construction land	Bare land	Other forests
2015	300	78	110	10	185
2016	300	84	108	12	203
2017	300	94	120	10	204
2018	300	83	111	10	186
2019	300	83	111	12	186
2020	300	84	101	10	208

2.4 Methodology

In this study, citrus spatial distribution extraction methods are RF, SVM, and DT three algorithms, and they are as follows:

(1) The RF algorithm is a new algorithm model composed of multiple decision trees. The prediction accuracy of the model is obtained by summarizing a large number of classification trees, which has the advantages of fast speed and good stability. The samples are input to be classified, and the output results are voted through the decision tree, which can better tolerate noise and outliers. Random forest uses decision tree clustering for classification prediction. Several samples are randomly selected from the original training sample set, and the classification results are generated by voting with the prediction results of the decision tree. In the classification phase, after the input of new data is classified, the integrated decision tree begins to estimate the distribution probability of its category and votes to determine the category of the data to be classified. Multiple decision trees are combined, and independent samples determine the establishment of each tree. The distribution of each tree in the forest is the same, and the classification error depends on the classification ability of each tree and the correlation between them.

(2) SVM is a machine learning method with limited samples. It originates from statistical theory and solves the problem of machine learning in an optimal way. It is suitable for solving small-sample, nonlinear, and high-dimensional pattern recognition problems. Its essence is to solve the convex quadratic programming problem based on the principle of structural risk minimization. The algorithm is fast and accurate and has good generalization ability under small sample constraints. Its basic model is a linear classifier with the largest interval defined in the feature space. The basic idea is to find the separation hyperplane with the largest interval in the feature space to obtain an efficient binary classification of data, but it usually requires a lot of cross-validation to find the best parameter-setting model.

(3) DT is a tree classifier based on the logic method, which is the most commonly used classical algorithm in data mining. It is usually used to classify and predict unknown

data and can be continuously applied to and greatly developed in different emerging application fields. It is a top-down tree structure in which each internal node represents a test on an attribute, each derived branch represents the output of a test result, and finally, each leaf node represents a classification result. The operation process is to use the prior knowledge of experts, adopt the top-down logical operation, and obtain the classification rules of ground objects through the statistical induction of big data.

2.5 Accuracy evaluation

The sample data in this paper is divided into training samples and verification samples in the ratio of 7:3. The confusion matrix is used to evaluate the accuracy of the classification results. The accuracy assessment indicators were the user's accuracy (UA), producer's accuracy (PA), overall accuracy (OA), and kappa coefficient. The calculation formulas are as follows:

$$UA_i = \frac{p_{ii}}{p_{i+}} \quad (1)$$

$$PA_i = \frac{p_{ii}}{p_{+i}} \quad (2)$$

$$OA = \frac{\sum_{i=1}^{k} p_{ii}}{p} \quad (3)$$

$$Kappa = \frac{p\sum_{i=1}^{k} p_{ii} - \sum_{i=1}^{k} p_{i+}p_{+i}}{p^2 - \sum_{i=1}^{k} p_{i+}p_{+i}} \quad (4)$$

where p is the total number of samples; k is the total number of categories; p_{ii} is the number of samples correctly classified; p_{+i} is the number of samples of category i; and p_{i+} is the number of samples predicted as category i.

3 RESULTS AND DISCUSSIONS

3.1 Extraction results of citrus spatial distribution with different spatial resolutions

The classification results for the 2018 and 2019 images based on two different spatial resolutions of 15 m and 30 m are shown in Figure 2. The comparison of the area extracted at

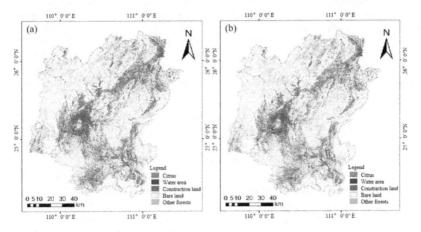

Figure 2. Extraction results of citrus spatial distribution with different spatial resolutions. (a) 15 m resolution in 2018; (b) 30 m resolution in 2018; (c) 15 m resolution in 2019; (d) 30 m resolution in 2019.

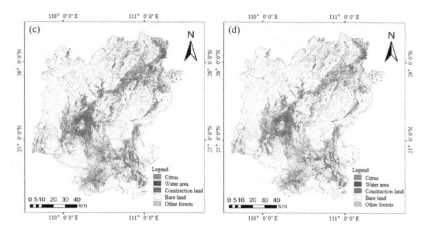

Figure 2. (Continued)

different resolutions in 2018 and 2019 with the historical statistical area is shown in Table 3. According to the analysis of Figure 2, the distribution of ground objects obtained from two different spatial resolutions, 15 m and 30 m, is roughly the same, and citrus is more concentrated in the study area.

By analyzing Table 3, the extraction areas of citrus at 15 m and 30 m spatial resolutions in 2018 were 3089 km^2 and 1519 km^2, respectively, and the statistical yearbook area was 1582 km^2. In 2019, the extraction area of citrus at 15 m and 30 m spatial resolution was 3125 km^2 and 1616 km^2, respectively, and the statistical yearbook area was 1611 km^2. Among them, comparing the classification results of 30 m resolution with historical images, it is easy to see that the citrus extraction area is basically the same as the planting area, and the area is closer to the historical statistical area, indicating that the classification effect of 30 m resolution is better than that of 15 m resolution. However, the results of the 15 m resolution have the problem of misclassifying other land use into citrus. The citrus area obtained has doubled, and the area of other types of features has decreased accordingly.

Table 3. Extraction results of citrus spatial distribution with different spatial resolutions.

Period	15 m resolution/km^2	30 m resolution/km^2	Historical statistics/km^2
2018	3089	1519	1582
2019	3125	1616	1611

Usually, compared with 30 m resolution, 15 m resolution has richer spatial information and texture information, and can show the details of ground objects more clearly, such as roads and buildings on the ground, but it is more affected by the noise of different ground objects. Because of the relatively low resolution, 30 m resolution remote sensing images can cover a large area of the ground, and each pixel represents a large area, so it is suitable to carry out some macro-feature monitoring in a wide range of areas. In addition, when using the surface vector tool to select samples, due to the low accuracy of visual interpretation and recognition, it may be selected to contain a large non-citrus area, resulting in high resolution. In this case, the non-citrus area contained in the surface sample will be identified as citrus. This kind of pixel-based classification method fails to effectively use information such as the structural level characteristics of the 15 m resolution image, which to some extent leads to the classification result of 15 m is not as good as that of 30 m. Therefore, in this study, 30 m is more suitable than 15 m when using different time series image sets to monitor the dynamic changes of citrus spatial distribution.

In summary, the results of citrus area extraction from Landsat-8 images with 30 m spatial resolution are ideal. By using 30 m spatial resolution, the long-term sequence citrus forest area in the study area can be quickly counted and a certain accuracy classification result can be obtained.

3.2 Extraction results of citrus spatial distribution by different classification algorithms

Based on the above ideal classification result of a 30-m spatial resolution image, the spatial distribution of citrus was extracted by RF, SVM, and DT, respectively. The accuracy comparison results of each classification algorithm in 2019 are shown in Table 4.

Table 4. Precision comparison of different image algorithms in 2019.

Classification algorithm	Overall accuracy	Kappa coefficient
RF	0.923	0.890
DT	0.846	0.787
SVM	0.462	0.222

The analysis of the results shown in Table 4 shows that the overall accuracy of the three methods of RF, DT, and SVM is 0.923, 0.846, and 0.462, respectively. Kappa coefficients were 0.890, 0.787, and 0.222, respectively. RF method and DT method are more accurate in citrus classification, and the SVM method has the lowest classification accuracy. Compared with SVM and DT classification algorithms, the RF classification algorithm can more accurately identify the distribution information of various types of ground objects, has higher classification accuracy and better applicability, and the extracted citrus area is closer to the actual area. Therefore, it is of great significance to select an appropriate classification algorithm to obtain high-precision and high-stability classification results. The extraction results of citrus spatial distribution in 2019 obtained by random forest classification algorithm are shown in Figure 3.

Overall, the RF method constructed based on the vegetation and its distribution characteristics in the study area can achieve better results in the extraction of citrus information in Guilin, and the overall accuracy and Kappa coefficient of the algorithm are relatively high. By using the random forest classification algorithm, the long-term citrus area in the study area can be quickly calculated, and a certain precision extraction result can be obtained.

3.3 Results of time series citrus spatial distribution monitoring

Based on the above analysis of the classification results of two different spatial resolutions and three different classification algorithms, the combination of 30 m spatial resolution and RF classification algorithm is the optimal parameter extraction model. In this study, the optimal parameter extraction model is used to extract the citrus planting area in the study area quickly, and the spatial distribution results of citrus from 2015 to 2020 are obtained, as shown in Figure 4.

It can be seen from Figure 4 that from 2015 to 2020, the citrus area showed an overall growth trend, from 1225 km^2 in 2015 to 1692 km^2 in 2020, with a total increase of 367 km^2 in 5 years. Among them, in 2015, citrus planting was more concentrated in Quanzhou and Xing'an counties in the northeast, and the extracted planting area was 1225 km^2. In 2016, the planting was concentrated in Yangshuo County and Lipu County in the south, and the

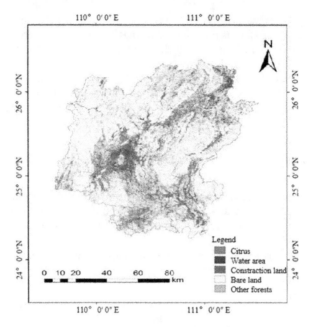

Figure 3. Extraction results of citrus spatial distribution in 2019.

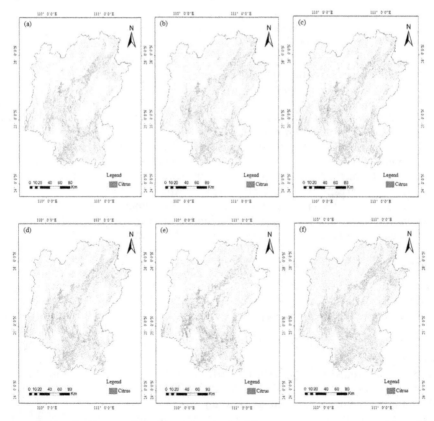

Figure 4. Spatial distribution of citrus in Guilin city in different years. (a) year 2015; (b) year 2016; (c) year 2017; (d) year 2018; (e) year 2019; (f) year 2020.

Table 5. Comparison of the citrus area in Guilin city from 2015 to 2020.

Period	Extracted citrus area/km²	Historical statistics/km²	Area difference/km²
2015	1225	1213	12
2016	1326	1307	19
2017	1455	1400	55
2018	1519	1582	63
2019	1616	1611	5
2020	1692	———	———

extracted area was 1326 km². In 2017, the planting was concentrated in Yangshuo County, Lipu County, and Lingui County in the southwest, with an extraction area of 1455 km². The areas with more planting in 2018 were Pingle County, Yangshuo County, and Lipu County, with an extraction area of 1519 km². The areas with more planting in 2019 were Lipu County, Yongfu County, and Yangshuo County, with an extraction area of 1616 km². The areas with more planting in 2020 are Quanzhou County, Lipu County, Yongfu County, and Pingle County, with an extraction area of 1692 km². The citrus planting area is almost all over 11 autonomous counties and six districts in Guilin City. The main planting areas are hilly and flat areas with good climatic conditions in the northeastern and central-southern regions. There are citrus forests in places with suitable planting conditions, such as roads, villages, and rivers. Among them, the areas with the widest coverage and relatively concentrated planting of citrus are Yongfu County, Lipu County, Quanzhou County, Lingui County, Yangshuo County, and Pingle County. It can be said that the citrus planted everywhere has become a unique landscape and development advantage of Guilin.

The citrus planting area extracted from 2015 to 2020 was compared with the historical area of the statistical yearbook, as shown in Table 5. By analyzing Table 5, the planting area of citrus in 2015 was 1213 km², which was 12 km² different from the experimental extraction area. In 2016, the planting area was 1306 km², which was 19 km² different from the extraction area. In 2017, the planting area was 1400 km², which was 55 km² different from the extraction area. In 2018, the planting area was 1582 km², which was 63 km² different from the extraction area. In 2019, the planting area was 1611 km², which was 5 km² different from the extracted area. The largest area difference is in 2018, not more than 100 km², and the smallest area difference is in 2019, only 5 km².

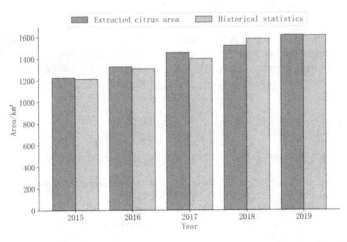

Figure 5. Histogram of citrus extraction area and historical data in Guilin city from 2015 to 2019.

From the results shown in Figure 5, it can be seen that the citrus planting area in Guilin increased year by year from 2015 to 2017, and the growth rate was roughly the same, with an average change of 100 km². In 2017, the citrus planting area reached 1400 km². In 2018, 1582 km² increased by nearly 200 km² compared with last year. The change in the citrus area was very obvious, then gradually slowed down and only increased by 30 km² in 2019. Overall, the citrus planting area showed an increasing trend from 2015 to 2020.

4 CONCLUSION

In this study, Guilin City is taken as the research area, and a series of processing such as splicing, cropping, cloud removal, and parameter extraction of Landsat-8 images of different years and different resolutions in the research area is carried out by using the GEE platform. Three different classification methods of RF, SVM, and DT are used to extract the spatial distribution of citrus. Through comparative study, the optimal spatial resolution of extraction results and the optimal classification algorithm were selected to extract citrus resources in Guilin, and the dynamic change monitoring of spatial distribution was realized. The main conclusions of this study are as follows.

(1) In the two spatial resolutions, the result of 30 m is the best. Taking the results of a classification in 2018 and 2019 as an example, the citrus planting area extracted at 15 m, and 30 m resolutions in 2018 were 3089 km² and 1519 km², respectively. The citrus planting area extracted by 15 m and 30 m resolution in 2019 was 3125 km² and 1616 km², respectively. The citrus area extracted by 30 m resolution in 2018 and 2019 was closer to the historical area of the statistical yearbook.
(2) Among the three classification algorithms, the random forest algorithm has the best results. Taking the classification results of 2019 as an example, the Kappa coefficients of random forest, decision tree, and support vector machine are 0.890, 0.787, and 0.222, respectively, and the overall accuracy is 0.923, 0.846, and 0.462, respectively. The accuracy of the classification results of the random forest algorithm is higher than that of the decision tree and the support vector machine.
(3) In the recent 5 years, the planting area of citrus in Guilin increased year by year. The expansion of citrus was rapid from 2015 to 2018, and although the citrus planting area in 2019 increased, the growth rate is far lower than in the previous four years.

ACKNOWLEDGMENTS

This study was supported by grants from the National Natural Science Foundation of China (41901370), Guangxi Science and Technology Base and Talent Project (GuikeAD19245032, GuikeAD19110064), Guangxi Natural Science Foundation (2020GXNSFBA297096), and the BaGuiScholars program of the provincial government of (Hongchang He).

REFERENCES

[1] Deng X. X. Development Trend of Citrus Industry and Adjustment of Citrus Variety Structure in Guilin. *Southern Horticulture*, 2020,31(06):1–4.
[2] Sun Y.M., Ye C., Wang X.X. et al. Gannan Navel Orange Orchard Soil Erosion Present Situation Investigation and Analysis. *Journal of Soil and Water Conservation Research.*, 2014, 21 (02): 67–71. The DOI: 10.13869 / j.carol carroll nki RSWC. 2014.02.013.
[3] Liu X., Hu X., Chen Y., et al. High-resolution Multitemporal Mapping of Global Urban Land Using Landsat Images Based on the Google Earth Engine platform. *Remote Sensing of Environment*, 2018, 209: 227–239.

[4] Huang H., Chen Y., Clinton N., et al. Mapping Major Land Cover Dynamics in Beijing using all Landsat Images in Google Earth Engine. *Remote Sensing of Environment*, 2017, 10: 166–176.
[5] Lobell D.B., Thau D., Seifert C.A., et al. A scalable satellite-based crop yield mapper. *Remote Sensing of Environment*, 2015, 164: 324–333.
[6] Chen B., Xiao X., Li X., et al. A Mangrove Forest Map of China in 2015: Analysis of Time Series Landsat 7/8 and Sentinel-1 A Imagery in Google Earth Engine Cloud Computing Platform. *IS-PRS Journal of Photogrammetry and Remote Sensing*, 2017, 131: 104–120.
[7] Gorelick N., Hancher M., Dixon M., et al. Google Earth Engine: Planetary-scale Geospatial Analysis for Everyone. *Remote Sensing of Environment*, 2017, 202: 18–27.
[8] Li R.N., Ou G.L, Dai Q.L., et al. Classification of Forest Types in Shangri-La based on GEE and Landsat Time Series Data. *Journal of Southwest Forestry University (Natural Science)*, 2020, 40(05):115–125.
[9] Wang H., Yang G.P., Tian Y.J., et al. Remote Sensing Monitoring of Vegetation Cover in Central Asia based on Multi-temporal Landsat images. *Arid Land Geography*, 2020, 43(04): 1023–1032.
[10] He Z.X., Zhang M., Wu B.F., et al. Remote Sensing Extraction of Summer Crops in Jiangsu Province based on Google Earth Engine. *Journal of Geo-Information Science*, 2019, 21(05): 126–140.
[11] Xiao W.J. *Remote Sensing Monitoring of Cultivated Land Change in Yunnan Province based on GEE in Recent Ten Years*. Yunnan: Yunnan Normal University, 2020.

Design and study of a steel truss arch bridge

Shui-Ping Fang
Jiangxi Communications Design And Research Institute Co., Ltd, Nanchang, Jiangxi, China

Jin-Liang Qiu
Jiangxi East Road Bridge Construction Group Co., Ltd, Fuzhou, Jiangxi, China

Fang Huang*
Naval University of Engineering, Wuhan, Hubei, China

Shuang Wang
Wuhan Longfang Engineering Technology Co., Ltd, Wuhan, Hubei, China

ABSTRACT: A triangular steel truss arch spanning the same distance has a lighter weight, smaller horizontal thrust, lower height, and a transparent, vivid overall structure. Therefore, it is a reasonable structure for segmental arch pedestrian bridges. Based on the design of a landscape pedestrian bridge in a sponge city, this study briefly explained the overall arrangement, structural form selection, structural design, and static analysis results of the triangular steel truss arch bridge, providing a reference for designing similar bridges and the basis for further investigation.

1 INTRODUCTION

The arch bridge is a bridge type widely used in China. Despite its large spanning capacity and beautiful appearance, it generates high horizontal thrust, increasing the amount of work for the substructure. A steel truss arch bridge is a structural system that combines a steel truss with an arch. A steel truss has a lightweight and excellent loading capacity. With the same span, a steel truss arch bridge not only effectively reduces the horizontal thrust at the foot of the arch but also presents the beautiful shape of the arch bridge and improves the transparency of the structure. Therefore, such a structure has a notable advantage in designing segmental arches.

2 BRIDGE ELECTROTYPES

To facilitate the people to cross the river and create a harmonious, beautiful cultural green corridor, a sponge city is planning to build a demonstrative landscape footbridge suitable for urban development and highlighting vitality and art. The bridge intersects the water system obliquely at 18.14°, and the plane is linear. The estuary where the bridge is located is approximately 30 m wide, with a once-in-a-century water level of 9.87 m. At the request of the owner, the bridge needs to cross the river and the plank roads on both sides. Each plank road has a clear width of 3 m.

---

*Corresponding Author: 150149184@qq.com

For a vibrant and artistic landscape bridge that spans 40 m, the deck arch is a suitable bridge type. For people to observe and get close to the water, the roads on both sides of the bridge should be close to its once-in-a-century water level. Additionally, the bridge should not be too steep so that pedestrians can walk comfortably. Hence, a suitable choice for a segmental arch bridge is the steel truss arch, which is transparent, vivid, and vibrant. Therefore, it was decided that the pedestrian landscape bridge would be a steel truss arch.

3 OVERALL PLAN

The calculated span of the steel truss arch bridge was set to 58 m, and the width of the bridge was set to 5 m based on the foot traffic intensity in the area. The length-to-width ratio along the arch axis is 11.6, and it is necessary to check the longitudinal and lateral stability of the bridge simultaneously. Because the bridge is for pedestrians, the specified fundamental frequency of natural vibration is not less than 3 Hz [1].

A triangle steel truss arch with a sag span of 58 m and a sag height of 4 m was adopted, whose arch axis was an arc with a radius of 108.55 m. The bridge deck used a combination of wooden and glass panels, allowing pedestrians to seem to walk on water. Such a design offers a novel, interesting view of the gurgling water under the bridge, producing a dynamic beauty for the landscape.

4 STRUCTURAL DESIGN

The triangle steel truss arch has been extensively used in landscape bridges at home and abroad. A high hollow rate at the superstructure enables it to reduce the action area of lateral wind loads effectively. Additionally, using the steel structure as the main force-bearing member has the advantage of being lightweight, thereby diminishing the horizontal thrust at its foot [2]. Furthermore, the concrete poured into the steel structure shores up the stiffness of the steel members.

4.1 *Superstructure*

The superstructure of the bridge is a single-span, unhinged arc-shaped steel truss arch. Its main structure formed an isosceles triangular section using three circular steel pipes, two on the upper layer and one on the lower layer. Vertical and horizontal I-beams were arranged between the upper pipes to create an orthogonal grid as the skeleton of the bridge deck. Triangularly arranged circular steel pipes were placed between the upper and lower pipes to form webs. The overall beam of the superstructure is 1.5 m high and 5 m wide.

The three steel pipes are all round, with a diameter of 500 mm. The wall thickness is 25 mm by standard and is increased to 40 mm within 7 m of the foot of the arch. C40 micro-expanded concrete was poured into the circular steel pipes to stabilize the structure. The webs are round steel pipes with a diameter of 203 mm and a wall thickness of 16 mm. The transverse beams and longitudinal beams of the skeleton of the bridge deck were made of I-beams. The transverse beams have top and bottom plates of 250 mm wide and 14 mm thick and webs of 250 mm high and 9 mm thick. The middle longitudinal beams have top and bottom plates of 200 mm wide and 12 mm thick and webs of 200 mm high and 8 mm thick. The side longitudinal beams have top and bottom plates of 300 mm wide and 15 mm thick and webs of 300 mm high and 10 mm thick.

4.2 *Substructure*

The bridge is located on a plain hilly terrain, where the soil layer is mainly composed of, from top to bottom, plain fill, fine sand, strongly weathered granite, and moderately weathered granite. The bearing platform is at the boundary between plain fill and 10 to 15 m thick fine sand. The moderately weathered granite can be used as the bearing layer of the pile foundation of buildings due to its high bearing capacity, stable geotechnical properties, and deep burial.

The bridge adopted bored cast-in-place piles (rock-socketed piles) to create a grouped pile foundation, with bearing platforms of 5 m thick. Under each platform are nine rock-socketed piles with a length of 33 m and a diameter of 1.8 m. The bearing layer is moderately weathered granite. The foundation mainly relies on the pile foundation to resist the horizontal force of the superstructure.

4.3 Structure of the bridge deck

The bridge deck is made of 60-mm-thick wooden and glass panels in different parts, connected with the deck skeleton through bolts. In bridge structures, wooden panels are more maturely used than glass panels [3].

The glass panels adopted three layers of 15-mm-thick tempered glass. There is a 1.78 mm thick film between every two layers to ensure that the bridge deck is strong enough to carry pedestrians even if two layers are damaged at the same time. Elastic rubber pads were arranged in the area where the glass panels contact the steel structure to guarantee the following ability of the deformation between the glass panels and the skeleton [4]. Parameters of the elastic rubber pads below and on the side of the glass panels were optimized to ensure sufficient clearance and deformation coordination ability of the glass structure under loads of people, temperature, wind, etc. The glass panels only bear local loads without participating in the overall stress of the bridge structure. Fixing parts were installed at the midpoints of the four sides of each piece of glass to constrain the vertical displacement of the glass structure in order to prevent the glass panels from breaking away from the stiffening beams due to aerodynamic lift in extreme wind conditions.

5 STRUCTURAL ANALYSIS

The load of the triangular steel truss arch bridge deck acts directly on the panels and is transmitted laterally to the longitudinal beams, through which it is then transmitted to the transverse beams. Finally, through the connection between the transverse beams and the upper circle steel pipes, the load is transmitted to the main truss and reaches the foundation. The whole process is in line with the assumption of the longitudinal and transverse beam force transmission system.

The finite element software Midas Civil was used to conduct spatial model calculations. Three-dimensional beam units were adopted to simulate the main members, which were connected using rigid arms. The pile-soil interaction was simulated using soil springs.

5.1 Calculation model

The model shown in Figure 1 was established using the spatial finite element Midas Civil, and the main beam was simulated using spatial beam units. Each unit consisted of two nodes, with six degrees of freedom (DOF) in each. There were 373 units on the main bridge. The spatial finite element model is shown in Figure 1:

5.2 Main load

The designed dead load included the dead weight of the structure (78.5 kN/m^3 for steel structure and 25 kN/m^3 for concrete) and a load of auxiliary facilities such as wooden and glass panels and railing. The influence of concrete shrinkage and creep was considered [5],

Figure 1. The finite element model.

and the uneven settlement difference of the foundation was set to 20 mm. The crowd load was valued as specified. The overall rise and fall of temperature was considered to be 20°, the nonlinear temperature rise was considered to be 20°C, and the nonlinear temperature fall was considered to be 6°C [6].

5.3 Internal force calculation

As a segmental arch, the triangular steel truss arch bridge has a large horizontal force at its foot, requiring a strong foundation. The main calculation members contained the main chord, web, transverse beam of the deck, longitudinal beam of the deck, and pile foundation. The transverse and longitudinal beams were calculated as bending members, and the rest were treated as compression members. The calculated internal force and analysis data of each control point are shown in Tables 1 and 2.

The foundation soil quality of the bridge is good, and the pile foundation is rock-socketed, with small uneven settlements. The superstructure is steel pipes filled with concrete, so the overall stiffness is not large. The bending moment of the member caused by the uneven settlement difference is not more than 2 KN.m, accounting for not more than 5.66% of the bending moment of the entire dead load. The live load effect is notable, with the bending moment on the upper part of the structure accounting for more than 46.5% of the bending moment of the dead load.

The table shows that the internal force effect of the pile foundation is notable under the main load, which is the control component of this project. The control operating conditions at the top of the pile foundation are: the horizontal force is 9,142 kN, the vertical force is 2,247 kN, and the bending moment is 8,161 kN.m.

5.4 Strength calculation

The superstructure is made of Q355 steel, whose strength was obtained by calculating the tensile, compressive, and shear stress of each member under the action of the basic combination. The stress calculation results are shown in Table 3.

The lower pile foundation is made of C35 underwater concrete, and the main reinforcement of the pile foundation uses 33 HRB400 steel pipes with a diameter of 28 mm. The section strength was calculated using the maximum bending moment and the minimum axial operating condition under the combined action of the standard value. At the top of the pile, the shear force is 952.4 kN, the axial force is 288.9 kN, and the bending moment is 2,968 kN.m. The pile foundation is a large eccentric compressed member, and the steel bar stress at the outermost edge of the tension zone is 108 Mpa, meeting the specified strength [7].

Table 1. Maximum values of the bending moment at the control point of each member of the superstructure under the main load (unit: kN.m).

Position	Operating condition of load	Dead weight of the structure	Phase-II load	Uneven settlement difference	Total dead load	Live load	Live load / Total dead load
Main chord	Upper edge pulled	155	69	2	226	105	46.5%
	Lower edge pulled	28	13	2	43	20	46.5%
Web	Upper edge pulled	3	2	0.3	5.3	2.6	49.1%
	Lower edge pulled	3	2	0.3	5.3	2.6	49.1%
Transverse beam of the bridge deck	Upper edge pulled	11	16	0.2	27.2	18	66.2%
	Lower edge pulled	3	2	0.2	5.2	6	115.4%
Longitudinal beam of the bridge deck	Upper edge pulled	8	7	0.2	15.2	9	59.2%
	Lower edge pulled	4	3	0.2	7.2	4	55.6%

Table 2. Control values of internal force at the top of the pile foundation under the main load.

Position	Operating condition of load	Dead weight of the structure	Phase-II load	Uneven settlement difference	Overall temperature rise	Nonlinear temperature rise	Live load
Top of the pile foundation	Horizontal force (kN)	2,955	1,460	0	1,189	1,340	2,198
	Vertical force (kN)	1,019	490	1	0	0	737
	Bending moment (kN.m)	-1,093	-510	38	3,411	7,083	-769

Table 3. Maximum values of the section stress at the control point of the superstructure under the action of the basic combination (unit: Mpa).

Stress \ Position	Main chord	Web	Transverse beam of the bridge deck	Longitudinal beam of the bridge deck	Allowable value
Tensile stress	190	129	171	94	270
Compressive stress	101	88	171	68	270
Shear stress	42	18	23	15	155

5.5 Fundamental frequency and buckling analysis

The vertical vibration reference frequency of the structure under dead load is shown in Table 4. The vertical vibration base frequency of the bridge structure under the dead load is 3.37 Hz [8], greater than 3 Hz, meeting the requirements for the frequency limit of pedestrian bridges.

Table 4. Vertical vibration reference frequency of structure under dead load.

Mode	Frequency	Period	Participation mass of vertical vibration mode (%)
1	3.369800	0.296754	58.20
2	3.624593	0.275893	0.00
3	4.159080	0.240438	0.00
4	5.275650	0.18955	0.00
5	6.551577	0.152635	23.22
6	7.134739	0.140159	0.00
7	9.347696	0.106978	0.00
8	9.374872	0.106668	0.00
9	11.574176	0.086399	0.00
10	12.559931	0.079618	5.91

The buckling stability of the bridge structure under dead load and crowd load is high, and the specific results are shown in Table 5.

Table 5. Buckling stability coefficient of the structure under dead load and crowd load.

Mode	1	2	3	4	5	6	7	8	9	10
Characteristic value	34.51	41.31	42.13	46.62	48.32	49.26	52.89	55.19	58.46	60.07

5.6 Stiffness calculation

The vertical deflection of the bridge structure under the action of crowd load is 15.5 mm, less than L/500, satisfying the specification (where L is the calculated span of an arch bridge).

5.7 Pile top displacement

According to the geotechnical investigation and specifications, the soil layer with an m value of 10,000 (kN/m4) was used to calculate the horizontal thrust stiffness of the foundation. The horizontal displacement of the pile foundation at the ground under the combined action of the upper load standard value has a maximum value of 3.5 mm, less than 6 mm, meeting the specifications.

6 CONCLUSION

Deck arch bridges are popular among pedestrian bridges for their landscape advantage of being spacious on the bridge and classical under the bridge. The steep axis of traditional concrete arch bridges makes it difficult to climb the slope. On the other hand, a segmental arch has a flatter axis that facilitates a comfortable crossing, but it requires a strong foundation due to the large horizontal thrust at its foot. A triangular steel truss arch spanning the same distance has a lighter weight, smaller horizontal thrust, lower height, and a transparent, vivid overall structure. Therefore, it is reasonable to use a triangular steel truss arch bridge in this project, which provides a valuable reference for bridge design in similar situations in the future and offers practical value.

REFERENCES

[1] Cheng W.H., Ma F., Shen Z.Z., et al. *CJJ 11-2011 Design Specifications for Urban Bridges (Version 2019)*. Beijing: China Construction Industry Press, 2019.
[2] Li G.H. *Stability and Vibration of Bridge Structures*. Beijing: China Railway Publishing House, 2002.
[3] Gui Y.K. *Bridge Construction Special Technical Manual*. Beijing: China Communications Press, 2004.
[4] Tian K.P., Zhang Z.X., Deng Y.X., et al. *JTG/T 3650-2020 Technical Specifications for Construction of Highway Bridges and Culverts*. Beijing: China Communications Press, 2020.
[5] Zhang X.G., Pei M.S., Zhao J.L., et al. *JTG D64-2015 Design Specifications for Highway Steel Structure Bridges*. Beijing: China Communications Press, 2015.
[6] Zhang X.G., Xu G.P., Zhao J.L., et al. *JTG D60-2015 General Specifications for Design of Highway Bridges and Culverts*. Beijing: China Communications Press, 2015.
[7] Yuan H., Zhao J.L., Gong W.M., et al. *JTG 3363-2019 Design Specifications for Subsoil and Foundations of Highway Bridges and Culverts*. Beijing: China Communications Press, 2020.
[8] Yuan H., Zhao J.L., Xu G.P., et al. *JTG 3362-2018 Design Specifications for Highway Reinforced Concrete and Prestressed Concrete Bridges and Culverts*. Beijing: China Communications Press, 2018.

Civil Engineering and Energy-Environment – Gao & Duan (Eds)
© 2023 the Author(s), ISBN 978-1-032-56057-1

Deformation analysis of inclined bar under vertical tensile

Enyang Zhu*, Shengjie Wang, Yan Li, Fang Fang, Bowen Li & Zhitong Pei
School of Civil Engineering, North China University of Technology, Beijing, China

ABSTRACT: Change of vertical included angle of the inclined bar under vertical tensile is usually ignored in deformation analysis. The relationship between the tensile force and two kinds of deformations is discussed to elaborate on the reasonability of this ignorance. Through an analysis of the total differential of the tensile force, contributions of length deformation increment and vertical included angle increment are respectively displayed. It turns out that the angle increment part is an infinitesimal of higher order when the vertical included angle is not very close to $\pi/2$. Consequently, the ignorance of the vertical included angle deformation is reasonable.

1 INTRODUCTION

Bar deformation is one of the fundamental issues in the Mechanics of Materials. If the tensile force coincides with the shaft, the relationship of tensile force to deformation is easy to calculate. However, if a tensile force acts on an inclined bar, as shown in Figure 1, both the direction and the length of the bar will change, then the relationship of force and deformation will no longer be simple as before (Higher Education Press 2015).

As shown in Figure 1: The cross-section of the inclined bar is A, the elastic modulus is E, the initial length of the bar is L_0, and the initial vertical included angle is α_0. When the vertical tensile force F acts on point B, the bar length changes into L, the vertical included angle becomes α, and the vertical tip displacement is δ. Suppose there are linear correlations between F and δ, the elastic strain energy $E_\varepsilon = (1/2) \cdot (F/\cos\alpha) \cdot [FL_0/(EA\cos\alpha)]$ is equal to the external force work $W = (1/2) \cdot F \cdot \delta$ (Sun et al. 2009). Approximately taking $\alpha \approx \alpha_0$, the relationship between F and δ can be expressed as:

$$F = EA\cos^2\alpha_0(\delta/L_0) \qquad (1)$$

In the above problem, both L and α change due to the vertical tensile force. However, only the length change is considered in the calculation, while the angle change is ignored. The length and angle change are small quantities, but only one is considered, which seems incomprehensible but is indeed reasonable. Contributions from the length change and the angle change are discussed in this paper, and the prerequisite of ignorance is given to elaborate on the reasonability of the above ignorance. It is of great significance for solving the engineering problems such as the lateral stability of cable-stayed bridge pylons (Xue et al. 2013) and tension rod-type steel cantilevered scaffold (Zhou et al. 2021).

---

*Corresponding Author: zhuenyang@ncut.edu.cn

DOI: 10.1201/9781003433644-16

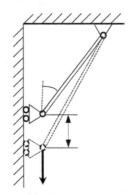

Figure 1. Inclined bar under the vertical tensile force F.

2 THE EXACT RELATIONSHIP BETWEEN VERTICAL TENSILE FORCE AND VERTICAL TIP DISPLACEMENT

According to the equilibrium Equation, the axial force of the bar is:

$$F \cos \alpha = EAL - L0L0 \tag{2}$$

Based on the geometrical relationship, the following relationships are obtained.

$$L \cdot \sin\alpha = L0 \cdot \sin\alpha 0 \tag{3}$$

$$L \cdot \cos\alpha = \delta + L0 \cdot \cos\alpha 0 \tag{4}$$

From Equations (3) and (4), L and $\cos\alpha$ can be described by δ as illustrated following.

$$L = \sqrt{L_0^2 \cdot \sin^2\alpha_0 + (\delta + L_0 \cdot \cos\alpha_0)^2} \tag{5}$$

$$\cos\alpha = \frac{\delta + L_0 \cdot \cos\alpha_0}{\sqrt{L_0^2 \cdot \sin^2\alpha_0 + (\delta + L_0 \cdot \cos\alpha_0)^2}} \tag{6}$$

Substituting Equations (5) and (6) into Equation (2), the vertical tensile force F can be expressed by the normalized displacement (δ/L_0):

$$F = EA\left(\frac{\delta}{L_0} + \cos\alpha_0\right) \left\{ 1 - \left[\left(\frac{\delta}{L_0} + \cos\alpha_0\right)^2 + \sin^2\alpha_0\right]^{-\frac{1}{2}} \right\} \tag{7}$$

Taking a rebar with a diameter of 12 mm as an example, the relationship between the normalized vertical tensile force $[F/(EA)]$ and the normalized displacement (δ/L_0) is shown in Figure 2. It can be seen that there is a positive relationship between the normalized vertical tensile force $[F/(EA)]$ and the normalized displacement (δ/L_0), and it is a nonlinear correlation. The gradient of the line is also changing with the increase of the normalized displacement (δ/L_0). The larger the initial angle α_0, the smaller the normalized vertical tensile force $[F/(EA)]$ is required to produce the same normalized displacement (δ/L_0).

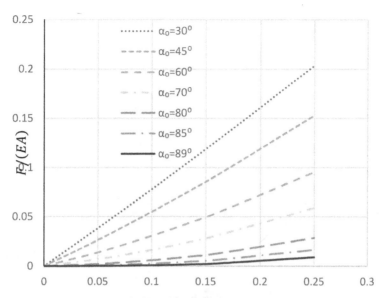

Figure 2. The relationship between $[F/(EA)]$ and (δ/L_0) at different initial angles.

Considering the total differential of Equation (7), being illustrated in Equation (8), it is obvious that the tangent modulus $K(\delta/L_0)$ is not a constant, which is related to the degree of deformation (δ/L_0) (Zhu 2017).

$$dF/d\left(\frac{\delta}{L_0}\right) = EA\left\{1 - \sin^2\alpha_0\left[\left(\frac{\delta}{L_0} + \cos\alpha_0\right)^2 + \sin^2\alpha_0\right]^{-\frac{3}{2}}\right\} = K\left(\frac{\delta}{L_0}\right) \quad (8)$$

In the initial process of tensile, when $(\delta/L_0) = 0$, Equation (8) degenerates into:

$$dF/d\left(\frac{\delta}{L_0}\right)\bigg|_{\frac{\delta}{L_0}=0} = EA\cos^2\alpha_0 = K(0) \quad (9)$$

Equation (9) is consistent with the Equation (1) expression, which neglects the vertical included angle change in the tensile.

In order to analyze the approximation of neglecting the angle change in the whole tensile process, a relative error of modulus ε_r is constructed.

$$\varepsilon_r = \frac{K(\delta/L_0) - K(0)}{K(\delta/L_0)} = \frac{1 - \sin^2\alpha_0\left[\left(\frac{\delta}{L_0} + \cos\alpha_0\right)^2 + \sin^2\alpha_0\right]^{-\frac{3}{2}} - \cos^2\alpha_0}{1 - \sin^2\alpha_0\left[\left(\frac{\delta}{L_0} + \cos\alpha_0\right)^2 + \sin^2\alpha_0\right]^{-\frac{3}{2}}} \quad (10)$$

As shown in Figure 3, the relative error in the whole tensile evolves with the deformation (δ/L_0) and the initial vertical angle α_0. It can be seen that the relative error increases with the development of deformation and the increase of angle α_0. Especially when $\alpha_0 = (\pi/2)$, the relative error $\varepsilon_r \to \infty$.

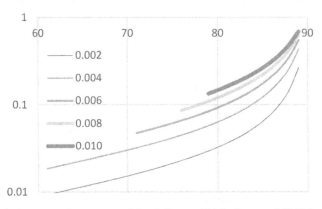

Figure 3. The relative error of tangent modulus influenced by both α_0 and (δ/L_0).

3 THE PREREQUISITE FOR IGNORING VERTICAL INCLUDED ANGLE CHANGE

So far, it is confirmed that the relationship between the vertical force F and the vertical deformation (δ/L_0) is nonlinear. The vertical force F is influenced by the length change dL and the angle change $d\alpha$, as illustrated by the total differential of Equation (2).

$$dF = \frac{EA}{L_0}[\cos\alpha\, dL - (L - L_0)\sin\alpha\, d\alpha] \quad (11)$$

The first item of Equation (11), named part A, is the contribution of length change. The second item of Equation (11), named part B, is the contribution of angle change. The ratio of these two items is:

$$\frac{part\ B}{part\ A} = \frac{-(L - L_0)\sin\alpha\, d\alpha}{\cos\alpha\, dL} \quad (12)$$

Considering Equation (3), the following incremental relationship is obtained.

$$d\alpha/dL = -\tan\alpha/L \quad (13)$$

Substituting Equation (13) into Equation (12), the ratio of part A and part B is:

$$\frac{part\ B}{part\ A} = \frac{(L - L_0)}{L}\tan^2\alpha \quad (14)$$

When $\alpha_0 \neq \pi/2$, $(L - L_0)/L$ is an infinitesimal and $\tan^2\alpha$ is a bounded quantity, so the value of $(part\ B/part\ A)$ is also an infinitesimal. The influence due to the vertical included angular change is much smaller than that due to the length change. Under this condition, the vertical included angular change of the bar can be ignored.

However, when $\alpha_0 = \pi/2$, $(L - L_0)/L$ is an infinitesimal but $\tan^2\alpha$ is an infinitely large quantity, the value of $(part\ B/part\ A)$ is no longer an infinitesimal. In the condition that $\alpha_0 = \pi/2$, when α is close to α_0, the limitation of $(part\ B/part\ A)$ is:

$$\lim_{\alpha\to\frac{\pi}{2}}\left(\frac{part\ B}{part\ A}\right) = \lim_{\alpha\to\frac{\pi}{2}}\left[\left(1 - \frac{\sin\alpha}{\sin\alpha_0}\right)\tan^2\alpha\right] = \frac{1}{2} \quad (15)$$

Considering Equation (15), neither part A nor part B can be neglected.

Generally, as the initial vertical included angle α_0 is not much close to $\pi/2$, the vertical included angle change can be ignored. After ignoring part B, Equation (11) degenerates into:

$$dF = \frac{EA}{L_0} \cos\alpha \, dL \tag{16}$$

Considering Equation (4) and its total differential, Equation (16) can be rewritten as:

$$dF = \frac{EA}{L_0} \cos^2\alpha \, d\delta \tag{17}$$

Integrating Equation (17), the vertical force F can be expressed as $F = EA\cos^2\alpha_0(\delta/L_0)$, the same as Equation (1).

4 CONCLUSION

Through the deep analysis of the whole deformation process of an inclined bar under vertical tensile, the following conclusion can be drawn:

When $\alpha_0 \neq \pi/2$, the vertical included angular deformation of the bar is too small, so it can be ignored. Moreover, when $\alpha_0 = \pi/2$, the bar length change and the vertical included angle change should be considered in the deformation analysis.

In *the Mechanics of Materials*, the Initial vertical included angle α_0 is generally less than $\pi/2$, so the vertical angular deformation can be omitted (Liu 2017), and the difference between the calculated and practical results is acceptable. This analysis also explains why force analysis does not consider the bar direction changes due to the external loading. The conclusion plays an important role in predicting the deformation of the inclined bar and analyzing the engineering problems such as truss arch bridges with oblique tension links and slant-legged rigid frame bridges. It also plays an irreplaceable role in calculating the stress and deformation of steel structures. (Guo et al. 2021)

REFERENCES

Guo S.S., Cui D.Y. and Ma S.K., (2021). Auxiliary Piers on Long-Span Specially Shaped Mixed Steel Structure Main Tower Cable-Stayed Bridge: Research on the Impact on the Dynamic Performance. *Materials Science and Engineering, Zhengzhou*, pp. 11.

Liu H.W. (2017). *Mechanics of Materials I*. Higher Education Press, Beijing.

Sun X.F., Fang X.S. and Guan L.T. (2009). *Mechanics of Materials*. Higher Education Press, Beijing.

University of Science and Technology Beijing, Northeastern University. (2015) *Engineering Mechanics*. Higher Education Press, Beijing.

Xue J., Li Z.L., Xing Y. and Ding H.Y. (2013). Influence of Rigid Rod Angle on Lateral Stability of Cable-Stayed Bridge Pylon. *Journal of Tianjin University (Science and Technology)*, 46(10):901–909.

Zhu E.Y. (2017). How are the Displacement at the end of a Bar and the Internal Force in the Bar Influenced by the Angle Between the Bar and the Horizontal Plane. *Mechanics in Engineering*, 39(1):88.

Zhou Y., Zhao R.Q., Zhang H.Q., Xing H.Y., Jin J.Q. (2021). Construction Technology of Tension Rod Type Steel Cantilevered Scaffold. *Building Structure*, 51(S2):1804–1807.

Application analysis of BIM technology in building safety design

Bei Wu*, Yunfan Peng*, Yanmin Li, Menghui Qiao, Zongli Hu & Xinglan Nie
Department of Construction Engineering, Tianjin Ren'ai College, Tianjing, China

ABSTRACT: With the modernization and information development of the construction engineering industry, promoting the application of BIM technology in construction projects has become the future development trend of the construction field. Implementing BIM technology to project safety design can realize the project design's intelligence, informatization, and safety. Based on BIM technology, this project conducts a comprehensive safety design analysis of a theater. In the design of building safety, we mainly carried out the analysis and design of building structure safety analysis, building seismic safety analysis, scaffolding, and formwork safety arrangement. We also explored the application and development of BIM technology in building projects' safety design to improve building design's safety and solve the problem of potential safety hazards in buildings.

1 INTRODUCTION

In recent years, with the development of digitalization and informatization in the construction engineering industry, BIM technology is increasingly widely used in the construction industry, and the safe construction of buildings has also become the focus of people's attention. This paper explores the application and development of BIM technology in building projects' safety design to improve the building design's safety and solve the problem of safety hazards in buildings.

In the construction process of steel structure, it is easy to cause safety and quality accidents due to the lack of steel structure design, which requires us to ensure the quality and safety of steel structure design and implementation. Glass curtain wall has been widely used in large public buildings in recent years. However, it is easy to produce large plane deformation, resulting in safety accidents, so the external curtain wall force analysis and safety design play an increasingly important role. So, we made scaffolding safety arrangements (Dong Fangfei 2014). A theater project structure volume is large, and the construction of the formwork and its support system for the erection of the work requirements is difficult. In order to ensure the safe implementation of the construction plan, the use of BIM technology for the formwork engineering safety design, the formwork construction for safety calculation.

2 PROJECT OVERVIEW

In this paper, the application analysis of BIM technology in building safety design is carried out, including the safety analysis of the building steel structure, the force analysis of the external curtain wall structure, the safety analysis of the main building structure, the analysis

---

*Corresponding Authors: 286456338@qq.com and 1007347998@qq.com

of building seismic safety, the safe arrangement of scaffolding and formwork, to provide new thinking and new roads for the application of BIM technology in building safety design under the premise of meeting national standards and the implementation of actual engineering projects. Through the exploration and application of safety design of building projects, problem-solving, summarizing experience, and finally realizing the full life cycle of BIM technology + safety, fully, accurately, and efficiently applied to the actual project, to achieve the sustainable development and intelligent development of construction engineering in the new era.

3 SAFETY ANALYSIS OF BUILDING STRUCTURE

3.1 Steel structure safety arrangement

The irregular roof of the Grand Theatre is made of steel structure. Its steel structure design is complex, the construction is difficult, and the engineering volume is relatively large (Zhu Mingquan 2007). By exporting the tekla model, exporting the 3D model to CAD, using the CAD model ID to output the coordinate position, you can determine the reference point at the site, use the location information to position the model to put the line, and then through the column installation, the cross-stringer installation, and the platform installation(see Figure 1), the steel structure model is produced (see Figure 2).

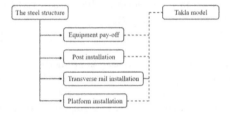

Figure 1. Etail drawing and on-site verification process.

Figure 2. Three-dimensional layout of steel structure.

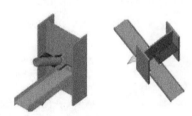

Figure 3. 3D diagram of steel structure node.

In order to achieve the safe design and construction of steel structures, we draw models of steel structures. Due to the large number of steel structure nodes and different shapes, node parameterization can solve the problem of difficult model drawing, and at the same time output details at the detailed points to guide construction (see Figure 3), thereby improving the safety of design and construction.

3.2 Force analysis of external curtain wall structure

3.2.1 Force analysis of external curtain wall

The outer curtain wall of the Grand Theater is a constructed curtain wall, the support system is a steel structure, and its geographical location is often typhoons in summer. Since the external environment of the outer curtain wall is usually the effect of the wind load, the effect of the wind load on the curtain wall must be considered in the design process(Yang Lifan 2017).

When using simulated wind loads for actual structural calculations, the following calculation equations are applied:

$$Wk = \xi \times \beta D \times \mu s \times \mu z \times Wo (KN/m^2)$$

in the formula:
Wk–Standard value of wind load acting on curtain wall(KN/m)
ξ–amplification factor
BD→→gust coefficient
μs→Body shape factor for wind load
μz–Height factor for wind load
Wo—basic wind pressure value
The maximum deflection of the glass span is:
$\mu = \eta \cdot W2 \cdot Wk \cdot a4/D$
in the formula:μ–The maximum deflection of the glass span is(mm)
W2–Maximum deflection coefficient at mid-span
a–Glass short side length(mm)
b–Glass long side length(mm)

In the calculation process, when the wind load is applied to the surface of the curtain wall in the form of a uniform load, the wind will cause a certain degree of deformation to the curtain wall structure, as shown in Figure 4 is the degree of structural deformation. Red is the place with a large degree of deformation, and the larger deformation will cause certain safety hazards to the building to design the outer curtain wall more safely and reasonably and reduce the deformation effect of the wind on the curtain wall. So, we build the outer curtain wall model, then mesh the external curtain wall geometry model, set the parameters, and so on to load and solve(Wang Jingli 2014). By presetting a uniform wind load of 0.1kN, it can be known that the maximum deformation caused to the curtain wall is 1.184 cm, and

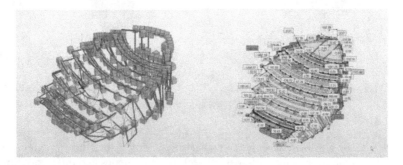

Figure 4. Exterior curtain wall structural deformation degree.

the minimum deformation is 0 cm, as shown in Figure 5 Structure Deformation Calculation Result Diagram, the calculation results are compared with the requirements of building codes, and the exterior curtain wall design is carried out under the premise of meeting the specifications, which greatly increases the safety of the curtain wall design and avoids safety hazards.

	MX(kNm)	MY(kNm)	MZ(kNm)	Deformation
Line type				
The proportion:(cm)	100.00	1500.00	1500.00	300.0
Max	142.11	983.59	85.47	355.2
Bar	590	586	272	76
Point	x = 0.0000	x = 1.0000	x = 0.0028	x = 0.5000
Working condition	3	3	3	3
Min	-111.34	-1984.38	-85.47	0.0
Bar	537	585	144	76
Point	x = 0.0000	x = 0.0000	x = 0.0028	x = 0.0000
Working condition	3	3	3	3

Figure 5. Calculation result of structural deformation of outer curtain wall.

3.3 *Force analysis of main structure*

3.3.1 *Structural force analysis*

Due to the complex overall structure of the Grand Theater and a large number of node connections, we use MIDAS GEN combined with Dynamo to analyze and detect the structure of the Grand Theater design. We directly use the Midas Link for Revit Structure interface program to import the Revit model data into Midas Gen and modify the model in it to update the Revit model file. Through concrete design, structural design analysis, calculation of the load (Figure 6), and structural damage value (Figure 7), according to Figure 7, it can be seen that the structure is light blue. Where the damage is large, the damage will cause structural cracks. According to Figure 8, to know the location of the dangerous node, red is the place with a larger degree, to strengthen the design of the dangerous truss node, thereby reducing the overall damage value of the structure, further improving the structural stability, and ensuring safety performance.

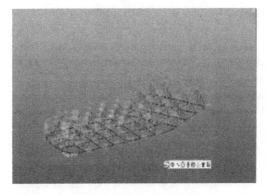
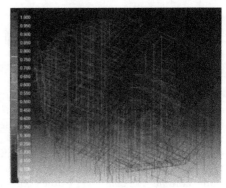

Figure 6. Calculated analysis load.   Figure 7. Calculated structural damage.

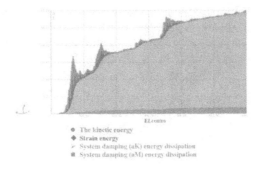

Figure 8. Elastic time history energy curve.

4 SEISMIC SAFETY ANALYSIS OF BUILDINGS

4.1 *Seismic type*

The structural seismic resistance of the Grand Theater calculates the fortification intensity of 6 degrees, and the structural fortification is 7 degrees. The venue category is Category IV. The seismic resistance of the frame is three, and the seismic resistance of the shear wall is the second degree, Designed by teleseismic. At the same time, we carry out the seismic design based on performance, and in order to improve the safety performance of the building, we conduct multi-model linear and nonlinear analysis of the main structure of the irregular over-limit complex high-rise building structure of a theater (Yan Weiming 2011). According to the two-stage design method stipulated in the Building Seismic Design Code (GB50011-2001), a two-stage seismic analysis is carried out on the main construction of the Grand Theater.

4.2 *Seismic analysis*

The seismic specification stipulates that at the beam and column nodes of the first, second and third stage frames, in addition to the top layer and the column axial pressure ratio less than 0.15, the design value of the column end combination bending moment should meet the following formula requirements.

$$\Sigma Mc = \eta c \Sigma Mb$$

9 degree and primary frame structure should still meet:

$$\Sigma Mc = 1.2 \Sigma Mbua$$

(1) Elastic analysis: Small earthquakes mainly through the elastic time course to calculate elastic deformation, as shown in Figure 8 for the energy curve of the elastic time range, it can be known that with the increase of seismic waves, the energy of its elastic time course also changes, the overall trend of increase, the purpose is to prevent the destruction of non-structural components under the earthquake, the important stress components of the structure, that is, the bearing capacity of the giant frame column at the mouth of the platform, the frame column, the cantilever frame column and the giant frame beam of the platform, using the non-yield review under the action of the middle earthquake and the elastic design under the middle earthquake. The elastic time-course calculation results show that the shear

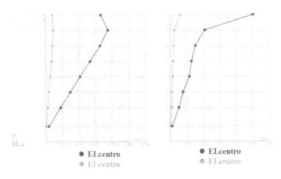

Figure 9. Elastic and elastoplastic interlaminar displacement curves.

bearing capacity of the giant frame column, the pick-up frame column, and the theater frame column meet the design requirements of the elastic bearing capacity. The results ensure that the structure can reach the goal of damage repairability at the second level (Wang Xiaohui 2020).

(2) Elastic-plastic analysis: Large earthquake, used to calculate the deformation of the building structure under the difficulty to meet the case of a large earthquake, through static elastoplastic analysis and dynamic elastoplastic time course analysis to calculate the elastoplastic interlayer displacement of the structure, as shown in Figure 8, we can see that with the increase of seismic waves, the displacement in the x and y directions is generally on the rise, and the collapse resistance and seismic performance of the structure of the grand theater can be evaluated, and the weak parts of the structure of the grand theater can be found. It is necessary to consider the design of important anti-lateral force components and nodes (the stage platform frame beam and column part. It is also important to increase the stiffness of the section steel and its ductility and improve the grip and wrapping force of concrete and section steel), the design of the weak part of the plane connection (the audience hall, the floor slab formed by the stage opens a large hole, and the width of the side beam of the hole is increased to increase its lateral stiffness) (Liang Shuping 2011).

The design of the building structure must be based on the seismic analysis of the building, the collapse resistance of the building under different magnitudes, and the safety design of the building according to the calculated data so as to ensure that the bearing capacity of the weak area of the structure and the stability, hardness, and stiffness of the building structure is within the safe range, thereby producing the resistance of the weakened earthquake and ensuring the safety and reliability of the building.

5 SCAFFOLDING SAFETY ARRANGEMENT

Due to the complex environment of the construction site, it has certain variability, and the architectural model of the Grand Theater belongs to the structure of the opposite sex, the scaffolding arrangement is complex, and the danger is high. By applying BIM technology, the traditional two-dimensional drawings use BIM scaffolding engineering design software to establish a scaffolding 3D model (see Figure 10), transmit safety information to the model, deepen the design, generate a 3D virtual model of the scaffolding through the model, you can clearly show the technical construction characteristics of the various components of the scaffolding, observe the possible safety hazards, so that the relevant personnel of the project can carry out the relevant safety management work in a targeted manner, focus on the management of key parts and the parts where there are or may have potential safety hazards, effectively avoid construction safety accidents, ensure that the subsequent stages of

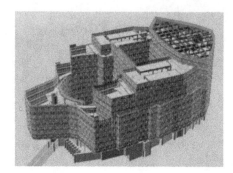

Figure 10. Scaffolding layout.

the project can be carried out smoothly, so that the safety design of the scaffolding is used to safety construction(Yin Yan 2021).

After the scaffolding arrangement is completed, it is safely reviewed:

①Calculation of connecting wall parts:

Anti-slip check:N1 = N wind+No=8.596kN ≥ Rc=8KN (does not meet specification requirements)

N wind=1.4 WkxAw

No In order to constrain the out-of-plane axial force of the scaffolding, take 3KN for single-row racks and 5KN for double-row racks

Stability check:N1/(ΦA) = 7.795 ×1000/(0.967 ×424)=19.012 N/mm2£0.85 f = 0.85 ×205 = 174.25 N/mm2 (meet specifications)

②Bearing capacity check

Required vertical rod axial force N ≤ Rd=40KN

Average pressure on the bottom of the pole P = N/A = 1 ×12.33/0.25 = 49.321KPa ≤ fg=mf xfak=140kpa (meet the specification requirements)

When a wooden board is placed under the pole, the effective area is 0.25 mm2 only when the area is greater than or equal to 200mmx200mm.

fg=Kcxfgk (standard value)

Kc is an adjustment coefficient, and the value will change when the geological conditions change.

In the initial analysis results, there was a situation that the anti-slip test was not passed, so after consulting the relevant specifications, the material specifications of the main beam and the size of the pressed steel bar were changed. Then, review and output the safety calculation book to pass the security audit; Once the safety review is passed, the output qualified calculation book and material table, as well as the output node detail and overall scaffolding model, can be used to guide the construction. Procurement personnel can also make reasonable planning for material purchase according to the analysis values, avoid the waste of materials, achieve the improvement of economic benefits, improve the turnover rate of materials, save resources and reduce costs.

6 FORMWORK SAFETY ARRANGEMENT

The formwork bracket is analyzed according to the engineering attributes, the support sequence of the support structure and the erection part are designed, and according to the relevant specifications of the formwork design, the horizontal rod strength, the stable bearing capacity of the pole, the support scaffolding overturning and the bearing capacity of the pole foundation are calculated, and then the formwork load design is carried out to meet the requirements of the "Building Construction Formwork Safety Technical Specification," and the load design of the beam template is carried out by a certain layer of beam formwork as an example, as shown in the following table (Xie Hui 2012).

Table 1. Beam formwork load design table.

Standard value of dead weight of formwork and bracket	Template(kN/m2)		0.3		
	Tseng(kN/m)		0.01		
	Lord Leng(kN/m)		0.038		
	Bracket(kN/m)		0.15		
	Standard value of dead weight of beam side formwork(kN/m2)		0.5		
Standard value of self-weight of freshly poured concrete (kN/m3)	24				
Standard value of self-weight of steel bar (kN/m3)	Beam	1.5			
	Plate	1.1			
Standard value of construction personnel and equipment load (kN/m2)	1				
Standard value of load generated when vibrating concrete (kN/m2)	2				
Standard value of wind loadωk (kN/m2)	Basic wind pressureω0 (kN/m2)	Return period		Once in 10 years	0.35	0.045
		City		Wenzhou city	
	Wind Load Height Variation Factorμz	Ground roughness		Class C	0.824
		The height of the top of the formwork support from the building ground(m)		26.4	
	Wind load form factorμs	Bracket	Formwork Support Condition	Open	0.155
			Direction of wind load	Acting laterally along the formwork support	
			Number of calculation element poles in the same plane as the wind loadn	10	
		Template			1.3	0.375

The main calculation contents of the formwork project are: 1, panel calculation: horizontal member bending test, $\sigma = M_{max}/W \leq [f]$, shear test $\tau = 3V_{max}/(2bh) \leq [\tau]$, deflection test $V = 5q`l4/(384EI) \leq [v]$ and strength calculation; 2. Secondary Len calculation: Subbine self-weight load: q1=γGQ; 3. Main frame (horizontal steel pipe) calculation: main frame self-weight load: q1=γGq; 4. Fastener anti-slip calculation; 5. The overall height-to-width ratio of the template bracket is calculated: the aspect ratio of the template bracket should be ≤ 5; 6. Pole calculation: length to detail ratio, wind load and stability calculation. Among them, the template calculation of the beam template is taken as an example:

Table 2. Template data sheet.

Template type	plywood	Template thicknesst(mm)	18
Design value of flexural strength of formwork[f](N/mm2)	15	Design value of shear strength of formwork[τ](N/mm2)	1.4
Template elastic modulus(N/mm2)	6000		

Calculated from a unit width of 1.0 m. The calculation diagram is as follows:
W = bh2/6 = 1000×182/6 = 54000mm3， I = bh3/12 = 1000×183/12 = 486000mm4
q = (γGΣqGk + γQΣqQk)=[1.35×[0.3 + (24 + 1.5)×0.6]×1.0 + 1.4×(1 + 2)×1.0]
=25.26kN/m
q static=γGΣqGk = 1.35×[0.3 + (24 + 1.5)×0.6]×1.0 = 21.06kN/m
q live=γQΣqQk = 1.4×(1 + 2)×1.0 = 4.2kN/m
q`=ΣqGk + ΣqQk = [0.3 + (24 + 1.5)×0.6]×1.0 + (1 + 2)×1.0 = 18.6kN/m
1.Bending check
Mmax=0.125q staticL2 + 0.125q liveL2=0.125×21.06×0.22 + 0.125×4.2×0.22= 0.126kN·m
σmax = Mmax/W = 0.126×106/54000 = 2.339 N/mm2 ≤ [f]=15 N/mm2
Meet the requirements!
2.Shear check
Qmax=0.5q staticL+0.5q liveL=0.5×21.06×0.2 + 0.5×4.2×0.2=2.526kN
τmax = 3Qmax/(2bh)=3×2.526×103/(2×1000×18)=0.211 N/mm2 ≤ [τ]=1.4 N/mm2
Meet the requirements!
3.Deflection check
νmax = 5q`l4/(384EI) = 5×18.6×2004/(384×6000×486000)=0.133 mm
νmax = 0.133 mm ≤ [ν]=min[L/250，5]=min[200/250，5]=0.8 mm
Meet the requirements!
4.Support reaction force
Design value:
R1 = R2 = 0.5q1L = 0.5×25.26×0.2=2.526kN
Standard value:
R`1 = R`2 = 0.5q`L = 0.5×18.6×0.2=2.526kN
Finally, the template design that meets the safety requirements is verified and verified, and the safe layout of the template is carried out, and the following figure is the three-dimensional layout of the template.

7 CONCLUSION

This research project aims to explore new building safety design ideas and methods and uses building safety design technologies such as building structure safety analysis, building seismic safety analysis, scaffolding, and formwork safety arrangement under the background of BIM technology to deeply integrate infrastructure construction with new information technology, study the intelligent and information-based design and construction methods of infrastructure construction, explore a new road of architectural design based on BIM technology and modern information big data, and finally achieve the support of visual analysis data. To improve the safety of building design, improve the residents' living comfort and security, and solve the problem of construction safety hazards in the current building. In the future, we will also conduct research on the implementation of construction methods, as well as the exploration and research of building safety operation and maintenance according to building safety design methods.

ACKNOWLEDGMENTS

This work was financially supported by the Teaching Reform Project of Tianjin Renai College in 2021 (2021-3-5).

REFERENCES

Fangfei D. Analysis on Key Points of Cantilever Beam Layout at Corner of Cantilever Scaffold in High rise Buildings. *Wireless Internet Technology*, 2014 (08). p. 113

Hui X. Cause Analysis and Prevention Measures for Collapse of Scaffold and Formwork System. *Steel Structure*, 2012,27 (03). pp. 68–70

Jingli W. and Ning L. Research on Wind Load Design of Glass Curtain Wall. *Sichuan Architecture*, 2014, 34 (02). pp.146–147

Lifan Y., Zeyu M. and Hongyan L. Dynamic Analysis of Curtain Wall Structures Under Wind and Earthquake [J]. *Anhui Architecture*, 2017, 24 (06). pp. 121–123.

Mingquan Z. Hoisting Technology of Steel Structure Roof of Huzhou Grand Theater. *Zhejiang Architecture*, 2007 (09). pp. 52–55.

Shuping L., Yong M., Jianmin J. and Congrong W. Seismic Design of Out of Gauge Complex Structure of Gansu Grand Theater. *Building Structure*, 2011, 41 (01). pp.45–49+62.

Weiming Y., Jin W., Xiangdong Z., Liang S., Weining W. Seismic Analysis and Design of a High-rise Shear Wall Residential Structure. *Building Structure*, 2011, 41 (01). pp. 59–62.

Xiaohui W., Yi S. and Yanlu Z. Structural Seismic Design of Dunhuang Grand Theater. *Building Structure*, 2020,50 (14). pp.73–80.

Yan Y. Application of BIM Technology in the Design and Construction of Formwork Scaffold. *Architectural Technology Development*, 2021,48 (14). pp. 87–88

Application of modern surveying technology in the digital mine

Xiaoping Shi*
School of Civil and Transportation Engineering, Shanghai Urban Construction Vocational College, Shanghai, China

ABSTRACT: Traditional mining methods have low efficiency and frequent mining accidents. The development of science and technology and the digital era have pointed out the future path for transforming the mining industry. The digital mine provides data support for the planning and design, exploration and construction, production and operation management of the mine, and the scrapping of the mine. It provides full coverage, real-time monitoring, and accurate early warning for the surface subsidence of the open pit slope, tailings pond, and goaf. It helps mining enterprises comprehensively improve safety supervision. The construction of a digital mine cannot be separated from the application of new surveying and mapping technology. Therefore, this paper first systematically analyzes the importance of digital mine construction, the advantages of new surveying and mapping technology in digital mine construction, and finally discusses the application of new surveying and mapping technology in digital mine construction to promote the long-term development of the green mine industry.

1 INTRODUCTION

Digital mine is an important part of the national strategic resource security guarantee system and an important database for evaluating the ecological environment of mine resources. Digital mine construction can improve the traditional extensive development mode of China's mining enterprises and achieve high-quality development of China's mining industry. Digital mine provides data support for mine planning and design, exploration and construction, production and operation management, and mine scrapping. At the same time, for the surface subsidence of open pit slope, tailing pond, and goaf, full coverage, real-time monitoring, and accurate early warning will be achieved to help mining enterprises comprehensively improve safety supervision. The informatization transformation of mines in developed countries has taken solid steps, and some have formulated long-term development plans. The development of surveying and mapping technology in China is relatively slow. Traditional surveying and mapping instruments can only obtain high-precision three-dimensional spatial data of a single point, which makes the overall digitalization and informatization level of China's mining industry insufficient. In recent years, with the development of modern surveying and mapping technologies such as GNSS surveying technology, UAV aerial survey technology, 3D laser scanning technology, inclining photogrammetry and geographic information system, digitization Information, automation, and intelligence construction.

Digital mine can be divided into the following seven main layers from bottom to top (Seng et al. 2005): basic data layer, model layer, simulation and optimization layer, design layer,

---

*Corresponding Author: shixiaoping1984@163.com

implementation and control layer, management layer, and decision support layer. The basic data and model layers are closely related to mine surveying and mapping technology. Therefore, this paper mainly studies how to collect the three-dimensional coordinate data of mine inherent information through modern surveying technology, such as surface topography, underground geology, underground engineering, etc., and organize them into a digital three-dimensional space according to the three-dimensional coordinates. Then embed all relevant information to form a more multi-dimensional digital model on this basis to build a digital, automated, information-based, and intelligent mine system. To realize digitalization and three-dimensional mine production and safety management.

2 ADVANTAGES OF NEW SURVEYING AND MAPPING TECHNOLOGY IN DIGITAL MINE CONSTRUCTION

Traditional surveying and mapping instruments, such as total station, can only obtain high-precision three-dimensional spatial data of a single point. Using these single-point data to reflect complex mines will inevitably lose a lot of real information. With the development of science and technology, computer, satellite navigation, and electronic technology have gradually matured and entered the surveying and mapping work, forming a new system of surveying and mapping instruments and technology. The survey technology, working mode, and service scope are constantly changing, such as GNSS technology, UAV aerial survey technology, 3D laser scanning technology, geographic information system, inertial measurement system, and other technologies. The UAV aerial survey technology, 3D laser scanning technology, and tilt camera are used to obtain 3D information about the mine quickly. The GIS system is used to realize the true correspondence between aerial images and geodetic coordinates, forming a 3D topographic and geological model. The mine survey tends to digitalize and network in the process of data collection, storage, and processing, which improves the efficiency and quality of surveying and mapping work, promotes and improves the construction of digital mines, and provides more timely, accurate, and rapid geospatial information for the construction of digital mines.

2.1 *GNSS survey technology and its application in digital mine construction*

GNSS surveying and mapping technology are mainly transmitted to ground receivers through satellite signals. The receiver can accurately grasp the measurement position and specific location information to achieve good measurement results. The method of simultaneous determination of three-dimensional coordinates by GNSS extends mapping and positioning technology from land and offshore to the entire ocean and outer space, from static to dynamic, from post-processing to real-time positioning and navigation. Global navigation satellite system (GNSS) is the infrastructure of national security and economy and an important symbol of great modern power and comprehensive national strength. With the continuous development of GNSS technology and the continuous improvement of the Beidou system, the measurement level has been continuously improved, and the measurement has become more comprehensive and reliable. Weather, terrain, and external conditions will not interfere with GNSS technology. It can complete the survey work efficiently and accurately and is not affected by external factors to produce measurement errors. It can effectively eliminate the measurement difficulties caused by terrain and environmental factors. GNSS positioning technology also plays a key role in the construction of digital mines. Using GNSS positioning technology, the coordinates of mine control points can be measured, providing control point coordinates for UAV aerial survey, 3D laser scanning, photogrammetry, and GIS system data processing and modeling.

2.2 Measurement technology of 3D laser scanner and its application in digital mine construction

It is called "real scene replication technology," another technological revolution in the surveying and mapping field after GPS technology. Using the laser beam high-speed scanning measurement method, it can quickly obtain the 3D coordinate data of each sampling point on the surface of the measured object in a non-contact way. It can quickly, large area, and high-resolution collect spatial point information and obtain solid points. The development of terrain surveys has promoted the development of a topographic survey with high-tech three-dimensional graphics.

The 3D laser scanners can be widely used in the following aspects:

(1) 3D modeling of buildings and structures, such as houses, pavilions, temples, towers, castles, churches, bridges, viaducts, overpasses, roads, offshore oil platforms, refinery pipelines, etc.
(2) Small-scale digital terrain or elevation models include golf courses, motorcycle steeplechase racetracks, and rock walls.
(3) 3D models of independent objects, such as airplanes, ships, automobiles, statues, etc.
(4) Three-dimensional models of natural landforms, such as caves. For example, with the continuous development of society, people's awareness of environmental protection is also higher and higher. With the implementation of a sustainable development strategy, constructing a digital mine is of great significance to protecting the ecological environment. With the increase of mining in China, the ecological environment has been seriously damaged. The mine information is measured through the 3D laser scanner, and the three-dimensional model of the mine is established to analyze the more seriously damaged areas. Some measures are taken to improve the mining ecosystem and avoid disasters.

Three-dimensional laser scanning has the following main applications in digital mine construction:

(1) 3D laser scanning technology can copy all the real information of the mine to the computer through point cloud data, which contains rich information and can be converted into digital information that can be browsed and analyzed by the computer to achieve accurate management of the digital mine.
(2) 3D laser scanning technology provides basic data for digital mine construction, builds a 3D model of the mining area to be mined or mined, and can build a digital model of the mine based on the 3D laser point cloud data obtained by 3D laser scanning technology. 3D laser scanning technology breaks through the limitations of traditional measurement and can collect spatial 3D information for targets in steep, complex, and high-risk areas by using non-contact measurements.
(3) The target's structural deformation, displacement, and change relationship can be accurately calculated by superimposing and analyzing the multiple scanning data model, which provides real and reliable basic data for guiding the safe mining of the mine (Shi 2021).

2.3 UAV aerial survey technology and its application in digital mine construction

The UAV aerial survey carried by the system refers to an advanced surveying and mapping technology that uses a multi-rotor, fixed-wing UAV platform, carries a single lens, multi-lens camera sensors, and small airborne radar for UAV measurement. It is a kind of aerial photogrammetry, mainly oriented to low altitude remote sensing, with low cost, fast and efficient, flexible, and flexible, and wide application. It is mainly used in topographic mapping, engineering construction, land resource survey, geological disaster emergency treatment, digital construction, etc.

Digital mine is the digital reproduction of the whole mine. Its core is to manage and integrate all kinds of mine information and mine information resources under unified time and space coordinates to ensure the standardization of the management process. Digital cameras, digital color aerial cameras, and other equipment shoot and measure the mine area, collect various data information about the mine from multiple angles and conduct comprehensive processing and analysis of the survey data through powerful information technology. They generate 2D and 3D visualization data such as DEM, 3D orthophoto map, 3D landscape model, and 3D surface model, which provides reliable data guarantee for the basic geographic information platform. Real 3D mine model is generated through advanced positioning, fusion, modeling, and other technologies. The application advantage of UAV surveying and mapping technology is that the equipment cost is low, and the surveying and mapping process is flexible. It can also effectively survey and map mine areas with complex terrain and harsh environment, so it has been widely used in the construction of digital mines (Jia & Wang 2021).

2.4 *Geographic Information System (GIS) and its application in digital mine construction*

Geographic Information System (GIS) belongs to the spatial information system. GIS technology is a technical system based on a geospatial database, supported by computer software and hardware, which adopts the geographic model analysis method. It applies the theory of system engineering and information science to collect, manage, operate, analyze, simulate, and express the data related to the geographical spatial distribution on the whole or part of the earth's surface. It provides various spatial geographic information for geographic research and decision-making services. GIS technology can collect, manage, analyze, and output a variety of geospatial information, which is spatial and dynamic. It aims at geographical research and decision-making, uses the geographical model method, has regional spatial analysis, multi-factor comprehensive analysis, and dynamic prediction capabilities, and generates high-level geographic information. It is supported by computer systems for spatial geographic data management, simulates conventional or specialized geographic analysis methods, and acts on spatial data. It generates useful information and completes tasks that are difficult for human beings to complete. Based on the powerful functions of the system, it can reasonably code various data such as survey positioning, graphics, impacts, and remote sensing attributes according to the unified geographic coordinates and carry out better positioning and qualitative and quantitative description. Spatial entities are described in digital form. It has powerful functions in data comprehensive analysis and simulation and can predict and simulate geographical spatial evolution.

In the construction of digital mines, it is often necessary to integrate spatial data of different sources and properties, generate 3D models, and perform visual expression, simulation, and analysis through 3D geoscience modeling with geological layer and geological body 3D visualization as the main research content. For example, the spatial data and images of mines are obtained through UAV aerial survey technology, 3D laser scanning technology, tilt photography, laser radar, and other technologies. However, the mining face is constantly updated, and the data is also constantly updated. The data in digitized 3D space and space are changing. The mine information is complex, massive, heterogeneous, uncertain, and dynamic, and multi-source, high-precision, Multi-temporal, and multi-scale, bringing difficulties to the unified management and data sharing of digital mines. Therefore, studying geographic information systems suitable for storing, managing, and analyzing mine information is necessary. Using the geographic information system to realize the true correspondence between aerial images and geodetic coordinates to form a three-dimensional terrain geological model is also necessary. A geographic information system can realize visual 3D modeling, making the design and construction of mine engineering clearer. At the same time, it can timely deal with adverse factors in mine engineering construction and prevent geological disasters. Through virtual reality technology, various mining production activities, such as virtual mining and virtual blasting, can be simulated with extremely realistic effects in the virtual environment of computers, providing a basis for judging the feasibility and safety of production activities.

2.5 *Lidar system and its application in digital mine construction*

The lidar system can obtain 3D ground geographic information and directly obtain low-cost, high-density, high-speed, and high-precision digital elevation or digital surface data. The obtained data can be widely used in resource exploration, urban planning, agricultural development, water conservancy engineering, land use, environmental monitoring, traffic communication, earthquake prevention, disaster reduction, national key points construction projects, etc. It provides extremely important raw materials for the national economy, social development, and scientific research and guarantees the multi-dimensional construction of digital mines.

3 CONCLUSION

This paper mainly studies the application and advantages of new survey technologies such as UAV aerial survey technology, 3D laser scanning technology, GNSS technology, and geographic information system in digital mine construction. The main conclusions can be summarized as follows: (1) With the continuous progress of science and technology, the continuous development of surveying and mapping science and technology, and the increasingly advanced measuring instruments and equipment. (2) Digital mine provides data support for mine planning and design, exploration and construction, production and operation management, and mine scrapping. At the same time, to achieve full coverage, real-time monitoring, and accurate early warning of surface subsidence of open pit slopes, tailings ponds, and goaf, help mining enterprises comprehensively improve the level of safety supervision and establish a systematic. Comprehensive digital mining is the development trend of future mine engineering, an important guarantee for the sustainable development of the mining industry and mine engineering, and a key indicator to measure whether a mine can develop healthily and continuously. (3) Modern surveying technology plays an important role in constructing digital mines and has obvious advantages. It uses UAV aerial surveying technology, 3D laser scanning technology, tilt photography, and other surveying technologies to obtain 3D information on mines. It also realizes the true correspondence between aerial images and geodetic coordinates through a geographic information system to form the 3D model of mines. In future work, I will strengthen the research of using more new surveying technologies to collect mine data, establish three-dimensional modeling of mines, and establish a more reasonable, systematic, and comprehensive digital, intelligent, and information-based digital mine system.

REFERENCES

An L.L., Chen J.P. and Yu M. (2012) Integration and R&D of 3D Digital Mine Information System. *Journal of Geology*. 36(3):180–184.

Du F.J. (2014) Talking About Mine Survey in Digital Mine Construction. *Research on Urban Construction Theory*. 17:741–742.

Jia C. and Wang J. (2021) Application of UAV Technology in Digital Mining. *Engineering and Technological Research*. 5:30–31.

Li N. (2018) Application Analysis of New Surveying and Mapping Technology in Mine Surveying. *Environmental Science*. 6:117.

Liu Y., Fang Y.M. and Ai C.L. (2012) Research on the Application of Skyline in Digital Mines. *Journal of Kunming University of Technology (Natural Science Edition)*. 37(1):5–10.

Meng F., Han K.F. and Huang Z.Z. (2006) *The Research of Building Digital Mine with LIDAR.Beijing Surveying and Mapping*. 4:11–14.

Peng J.S., Ye B., Li J. and Zhou G.M. (2018) Comprehensive Application of Three-dimensional Laser Technology in Mine Surveying. *Surveying and Mapping Notification*. Issue 11.

Seng D.W., Li Z.X. and Zhang S.T. (2005) Research on the Framework and Key Technologies of Digital Mine System. *Metal Mines*, 2:47–50.

Shi X.P. (2021) Application of New Surveying and Mapping Technology in the Smart City Construction. *ICUCEM2020*

Wang J., Li L. and Jiang Y. (2012) Discussion on Applying Tianbao 3D Laser Scanning Technology in Digital Mines. *Surveying and Mapping Notification*. 10:58–61.

Wu H.L. (2022) Application of GIS Technology and Digital Mapping Technology in Mine Surveying. *China Petroleum and Chemical Standards and Quality*. 42(6):173–174.

Wu L.X. and Zhu W.X. (2004) Zhang Ruixin. Digital Mine and the Future Development of the Mine in China. *Science and Technology Bulletin*. 7:29–31.

Ye J., Yuan C.Z. and Yu Q.B. (2014) Development and Realization of 3d Digital Mine Information System. *Surveying and Mapping Science*. 39(6):53–58.

Z G.b. (2019) Analyze the Application of Digital Surveying Technology in Mine Surveying. *Geological and Mineral Mapping* (2630–4732). 004:168–169.

Zheng B.B. and Zhang J.W. (2007) Modern Mine - the Concept and Basic Structure of Digital Mine. *Coal Technology*. 26 (7):1–2.

Zhou Y.P. and Hu J. (2012) Digital Mine Roaming System based on 3D Panorama Technology. *Metal Mine*. 5:116–120.

Research on robustness of space steel frames against progressive collapse based on component method

Zheng Tan*, Weihui Zhong & Yingzhao Qiu
School of Civil Engineering, Xi'an University of Architecture and Technology, Xi'an, China

ABSTRACT: In the security analysis of structural systems, how to quantitatively evaluate the robustness of the structure has always been the most research-leading frontier. This paper proposes a new model based on the existing structural progressive collapse robustness method to make a quantitative assessment of the progressive collapse performance of the space steel frame. And based on the principle of component method modeling, the simplified models of the spatial steel frames of welded flange-bolted joints and top and seat angles and double web angles joints were established, respectively. The finite element software LS-DYNA was used for modeling analysis. Through comparison, it can be found that the two plane layouts are the same structure, and different types of joints will significantly impact the structure's progressive collapse robustness.

1 INTRODUCTION

In the safety analysis of structural engineering systems, quantitative assessment of structural robustness has always been the most challenging frontier topic. Izzuddin (Izzuddin et al. 2008) believed that the energy absorption capacity, ductility, redundancy, and other indicators of the structure should not be used alone as indicators to evaluate the robustness of the structure. In comparison, the proposed static bearing capacity as an indicator comprehensively considers the above aspects. It is more suitable for the structure after the failure of the vertical load-bearing component. Khandelwal and EI-Tawil (2011) suggested using structural load coefficients to indicate the robustness of successive collapses of structures. Due to the limitations of analytical methods, most of the progressive collapse robustness studies on steel frames ignore the spatial effect (Tan et al. 2021, 2022), which plays a crucial role in studying the progressive collapse performance of the structure as a whole. How to quantitatively evaluate the collapse performance of spatial structures using simple and easy methods is still a problem worthy of further exploration in studying the progressive collapse robustness of structures. Different from the previous research ideas and research methods of progressive collapse robustness of structures, this paper uses the component method to establish the overall model of the structure and proposes a new easy-to-operate quantitative evaluation method for the robustness of the structure on how to quantitatively evaluate the robustness of the structure, to truly realize the quantitative evaluation of the overall resistance of the structure.

---

*Corresponding Author: tz1994@xauat.edu.cn

2 STRUCTURAL ROBUSTNESS EVALUATION METHOD BASED ON INSTANTANEOUS COLUMN REMOVAL METHOD AND PUSHDOWN

The combination of the instantaneous component removal method and the Pushdown method to systematically evaluate the robustness of the structure is defined as the LRE method, as shown in Figure 1. This LRE structural robustness analysis method assumes that the dynamic response within the initial damage span causes the progressive collapse of the structure. Instantaneous component removal method analysis is a nonlinear dynamic analysis method. The Pushdown method is a nonlinear static analysis method. And this paper will combine the two methods to evaluate the progressive collapse robustness of the structure.

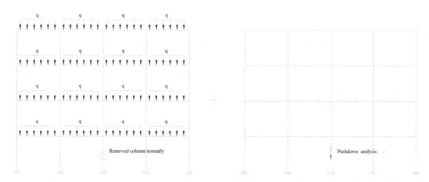

Figure 1. Schematic of a new structural robustness assessment method.

The first step of the LRE robustness analysis method is to dismantle the columns on the first floor in sequence according to the instantaneous dismantling method. Each time a column is removed, a nonlinear instantaneous dismantling method analysis is performed on the structure. After that, if the structure does not collapse progressively, continue to carry out the vertical Pushdown analysis of the structure after the removal of the column and divide the bearing capacity corresponding to the ultimate state deformation obtained by each pushdown analysis by the corresponding column before the removal of the column. The axial force is recorded as L_n. The second step is to remove the column corresponding to the smallest L_n in the first step, and the structure after the removal of the column is used as the beginning of the next analysis, and the same steps as the first step are performed. These steps were repeated until the column was removed, and the structural response of the residual dynamic nonlinear analysis showed that the structure had collapsed. Record the number of columns removed when the structure collapses consecutively as.

Through the above analysis, S_{RI1} and S_{RI2} are used as robustness measures for the progressive collapse of structures.

The first indicator is a global indicator, which represents the minimum number of bars that need to be removed if the bars cause progressive collapse:

$$S_{RI1} = \frac{n_r}{n_f} \quad (1)$$

where n_r is the minimum number of columns that need to be removed due to the progressive collapse of the structure and n_f is the number of all columns in the selected story.

The second indicator is a more effective quantitative evaluation:

$$S_{RI2} = \sum_{i=1}^{n_r} i * L_n^i \quad (2)$$

where L_n^i is the axial force magnification factor of the most critical component in each major analysis step.

The first step is to find the most critical component of the progressive collapse of the structure and remove the component from the structure in the next step of the analysis. The second step removes the columns adjacent to the primary pillar of the first step and then finds the most important components in the next step.

This robustness assessment method also has two significant advantages: the first is to convert the load-displacement curve of pushdown into a coefficient related to the resistance of the remaining system; the second is to reflect the potential for the progressive collapse of the remaining structures after the column is removed. This LRE robustness assessment method can accurately capture and reasonably assess different types of local structural failures.

3 PROGRESSIVE COLLAPSE ROBUSTNESS ANALYSIS OF SPACE STEEL FRAME MODELED BASED ON THE COMPONENT METHOD

Taking two space steel frames as an example, the component method simplifies the modeling method to establish two steel frames of different connection types. At the same time, the finite element software LS-DYNA is used to model and calculate to evaluate the progressive collapse robustness of the structure.

3.1 *Establishment of finite element analysis model of space steel frame*

The plane layout of the two steel frames studied is the same, but the types of the beam-column joints are different, namely the bolted welding joint (WUF), top and seat angles, and double web angles (TSDWA). Frames I and II have inter-column supports in spans A-B and B-E of 1-axis and 5-axis, and the inter-column supports use $200\times200\times8\times12$ steel sections. Both frames are 4 layers and 4×4 spans, with a floor height of 3 m and a plane size of 16 m x 16 m, as shown in Figure 2. Approximately take the transverse floor load as $5kN/m^2$, and the live load as $2.5kN/m^2$. The frame beams and columns are I-shaped sections, the section size of the column is $300\times300\times12\times16$ (mm), and the section size of the beam is $300\times200\times8\times12$ (mm). The beam and column steels are set to Q345B, yielding 400 MPa, and the ultimate tensile strength is 650 MPa; the bolts are all M20 bolts of grade 8.8. The details of the component modeling method of WUF and TSDWA can be found in the references (Tan et al. 2019, 2020). The finite element analysis model of a space steel frame is presented in Figure 3.

3.2 *Robustness analysis of bolted space steel frame*

First of all, taking Framework I as an example, using the theoretical analysis of the overall robustness of the proposed framework structure, the steps can be simplified to the following three stages to complete.

(1) The first stage

Due to the symmetry of the structural plane layout and the load distribution of Frame I, only one-quarter of the structural columns need to be analyzed. First, the internal force analysis is carried out for the complete Frame I under the combination of dead load and live load, and the axial force of the first layer column of the frame is recorded. The complete Frame I is analyzed by the instantaneous column removal method (the instantaneous column removal method is set to be completed within 0.07 s, simulating the structural response when the column is removed instantaneously, the same as below), and 1-A, 1-B, 1-C, and 2 are removed, respectively. Columns of 1-A, 2-B, 2-C, 3-A, 3-B, and 3-C columns, the displacement time history curves above the failed column corresponding to 9-column removal conditions were obtained. Based on the analysis results of

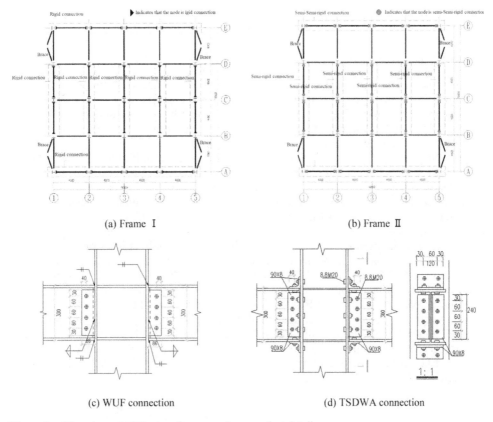

Figure 2. Plane layout of the two frames and connection details.

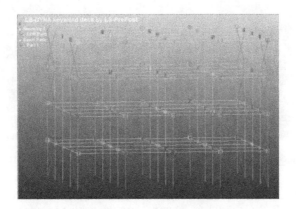

Figure 3. Finite element analysis model of a space steel frame.

the above instantaneous column removal method, pushdown analysis is performed for each column removal condition. It can be found that in the whole process, the value of column 3-BL_n is the smallest, and the value L_n^1 is 4.45, then column 3-B will be the first column to be removed and enter the next analysis.

(2) The second stage

The above analysis shows that column 3-B is the most critical vertical load-bearing member and has been removed as the primary component. It is only necessary to remove the three columns 2-B, 3-A, and 3-C adjacent to column 3-B. Columns 2-B, 3-A, and 3-C were subjected to instant unpacking and Pushdown analyses. The total dismantling analysis conditions in the second stage are as follows: dismantling the 3-B and 2-B columns simultaneously, dismantling the 3-B and 3-A columns simultaneously, and dismantling the 3-B and 3-C columns at the same time. The analysis obtained results after removing the 3-B column in the first stage. The axial forces of the 2-C, 2-B, and 3-A columns are re-read and recorded for the unified measurement of pushdown in this stage. The pushdown calculation result of the second stage shown in Figure 4 is processed with the recalculated axial force value to obtain the axial force amplification factor. By comparison, it can be found that the corresponding axial force amplification factor is the smallest under the conditions of removing the 3-B and 3-C columns. With a L_n^2 value of 2.4, column 3-C is used as the second member to be removed.

(3) The third stage

Based on dismantling 3-B and 3-C, the third stage of analysis is carried out, and the instantaneous column dismantling analysis and pushdown analysis are carried out on columns 2-B, 2-C, 3-A, and 3-D. The four working conditions that need to be considered in this stage are as follows: 3-B, 3-C, 2-B simultaneous demolition; 3-B, 3-C, 2-C simultaneous dismantling; 3-B, 3-C, 3-A simultaneous demolition; 3-B, 3-C, 3-D were dismantled at the same time. It was found that after the simultaneous demolition of 3-B, 3-C, and 3-A, the structure directly and partially progressively collapsed (beam angle greater than 6°) through the instantaneous demolition method. The calculation results of the instantaneous demolition method corresponding to 3-B, 3-C, and 3-A are shown in Figure 4. The overall robustness analysis of the structure ends at this stage.

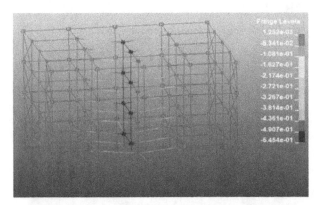

Figure 4. Instantaneous removal analysis of columns 3-B, 3-C, and 3-A of Frame I.

In the third stage, the structure collapses progressively under the condition of instantaneous removal of 3-B, 3-C, and 3-A columns, and the robust results of the Frame I can be obtained from Eq.s (1) and (2), and the result are shown as follows:

$$S_{RI1} = \frac{2}{25} = 0.08 \qquad (3)$$

$$S_{RI2} = 1 \times 4.4 + 2 \times 2.4 = 9.2 \qquad (4)$$

3.3 Robustness analysis of semi-rigid connected space steel frames

For the semi-rigid steel Frame II, progressive collapse robustness analysis is the same as framework I. The analysis process will not repeat repeated through the instantaneous column removal analysis of the steel Frame II (Figure 5). It can be observed that when the 3-C and 3-B columns are demolished simultaneously, the structure has a progressive collapse. The overall robustness analysis of framework II ends at this stage, as shown in Figure 5.

The robustness of Framework II can be calculated from Eq.s (1) and (2), and the result is shown as follows:

$$S_{RI1} = \frac{1}{25} = 0.04 \quad (5)$$

$$S_{RI2} = 1 \times 1.66 = 1.66 \quad (6)$$

Through the above analysis of Frame I and Frame II, the steel frame will collapse progressively when at least three columns are removed simultaneously for the Frame I. The structure will collapse progressively when at least two columns are removed simultaneously in Frame II. The overall robustness index of the Frame I is S_{RI2} = 9.2, and the overall robustness index of Frame II is S_{RI2} = 1.66. It can be considered that the resistance to the progressive collapse of Frame I is significantly higher than that of steel Frame II.

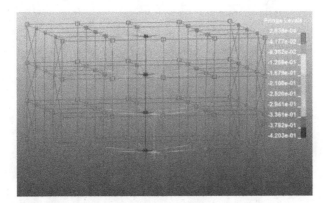

Figure 5. Instantaneous removal analysis of columns 3-B and 3-C of Frame II.

4 CONCLUSION

(1) Based on the existing research on structural robustness, a method for evaluating the robustness of the overall progressive collapse of the frame structure is further proposed, and the operation steps and principles of the evaluation method are discussed.
(2) LS-DYNA was used to model the space of the two structures based on the component method. In addition, the proposed robustness analysis method is used to quantitatively evaluate the overall progressive collapse robustness of the frame structure. Through comparison, it can be found that two structures with basically the same layout and different connection types will significantly affect the structure's overall resilience against progressive collapse.

ACKNOWLEDGMENTS

This work was supported by the National Natural Science Foundation of China [grant numbers 51678476, 51608433]. All opinions, findings, conclusions, and recommendations expressed in this paper are those of the authors and do not necessarily reflect the sponsors' views.

REFERENCES

Izzuddin B., Vlassis A., Elghazouli A. and Nethercot D. (2008). Progressive Collapse of Multistorey Buildings Due to Sudden Column Loss-part I: Simplified Assessment Framework. *Eng. Struct.* 30(5):1308–1318.

Khandelwal K. and El-Tawil S. (2011). Pushdown Resistance as a Measure of Robustness in Progressive Collapse Analysis. *Eng. Struct.* 33(9):2653–2661.

Tan Z., Zhong W.H., Tian L.M. et al. (2021). Quantitative Assessment of Resistant Contributions of Two-bay Beams with Unequal Spans, *Eng. Struct.* 242, 112445.

Tan Z., Zhong W.H., Meng B. et al. (2022). Effect of Various Boundary Constraints on the Collapse Behavior of Multi-story Composite Frames, *J. Build. Eng.* 52, 104412.

Tan Z., Zhong W.H. and Li C.F. (2020). On the Resistance to the Progressive Collapse of Steel Frame with Bolted Welding Joint Assembly Model. *J. Experi. Mechan.* 35(01):135–143.

Tan Z., Zhong W.H. and Li C.F. (2019). Research on Component Joint Models of the Semi-Rigid Joint Model with Top and Seat Angles and Double Web Angles Under Progressive Collapse. *J. Disast. Prevent. Mitigat. Eng.* 39(03):445–453.

Research on identification of key factors of construction quality based on AHP-DEMATEL method

Zhao Cheng* & Meng Li*
Evergrande School of Management, Wuhan University of Science and Technology, Wuhan, China

ABSTRACT: This paper conducts case analysis and identifies and summarizes the factors affecting the construction quality of the project through a combination of questionnaires and expert interviews based on the specific characteristics of the construction project. It also builds a hierarchical model of the factors affecting project quality, Human quality (B2), construction organization design (E3), quality awareness (B3), and technical solutions (E1) in the comprehensive impact weights calculated using the combination of the Analytic Hierarchy Process (AHP) and Decision Laboratory Method (DEMATEL). The comprehensive influence has a large weight, and corresponding optimization measures are put forward for the quality control of the project according to these key factors.

1 INTRODUCTION

Quality is the foundation of an enterprise, so project quality management is a necessary means to maintain and prolong the life of an enterprise, and it is also the key to winning the competition of an enterprise. (Zhang 2009) The quality management of construction projects in my country still faces many problems, such as insufficient management ability of managers, poor work quality of on-site construction workers, problems with incoming materials and equipment, and many uncertain environmental factors that indirectly affect the quality of construction projects. (Wang 2004)

Emuze and Mhlwa (2015) pointed out that by applying the PDCA quality control cycle theory and methods, building a reasonable implementation project quality management process is the core of building a good quality control system. (Emuze & Mhlwa 2015) Lukichev (2016) proposed the quality control method for related construction projects and explained that a major basis for the sustainable development of construction units is the construction of a comprehensive and reasonable quality management system for construction projects. (Lukichev 2016) Alic and Milena (2018) found that the overall project quality is largely related to the quality of construction personnel and put forward relevant suggestions and solutions. (Alic 2018)

Liu Fang (2010) proposed a management method for the key factors affecting the quality of the project during the construction phase. (Liu 2016) Weiwei Liu and Yujuan Ma (2011) emphatically expounded on the significance of quality control of construction projects and proposed effective control methods. (Liu & Ma 2011) Zhichun Qiao et al. (2015) showed that it is necessary to control the quality of personnel during the construction process and comprehensively control and prevent them. (Qiao et al. 2015) Lijuan Xi (2017) put forward the corresponding project quality management method for the reference of project managers. (Xi 2017) Yuan Zhou (2018) made a specific analysis and explanation of the key factors of

*Corresponding Authors: 2842825754@qq.com and 252026248@qq.com

quality management of construction projects, and found specific problems, analyzed and dealt with them in detail to do a good job in the construction of the construction unit. (Zhou 2018)

Chunfa Han (2020) found through research that the comprehensive quality level of management personnel, material quality management, quality management system, and the corresponding management supervision system are the key factors affecting the quality of water conservancy construction projects. (Han 2020), Zhengwei Shi (2020), and Bo Ming (2020) conducted research and analysis on quality control in the construction process and proposed effective improvement methods. (Shi 2020; Ming 2020) Yuanjing Li (2021) made a specific analysis and explanation of the key factors in the quality management of engineering construction projects through the causal analysis method. (Li 2021)

Most scholars have expounded on the key factors of quality management of construction projects and put forward relevant effective control and management methods. However, through the summary, it is found that many scholars use the causal analysis method, the PDCA cycle method, the SAD model method, and the expert investigation method to conduct research. Research is more limited.

2 RESEARCH METHODS

2.1 AHP method (Deng, Li & Zeng 2012)

(1) Constructing a judgment matrix

Through the questionnaire, the judgment matrix for pairwise comparison is obtained. The 1-9 scoring method used in this paper, that is, 1, 3, 5, 7, and 9, respectively, indicates that the two elements being compared are equally important, slightly important, more important, very important, very important, where 2, 4, 6, and 8 are between the two cases, and the reciprocal represents the opposite comparison.

(2) Calculate the weight

$$\omega_i = \frac{\prod_{j=1}^{n} a_{ij}}{\sum_{i=1}^{n} \left(\prod_{j=1}^{n} a_{ij}\right)^{\frac{1}{n}}} \quad i,j = 1,2,\cdots n \quad (1)$$

After normalizing the feature vector, the weight vector can be obtained $\omega_i = (w_1, w_2, \cdots, w_n)^T$.

(3) Consistency test

A consistency check is also required to ensure the accuracy of the requested data weights.

$$CI = \frac{\lambda_{max} - n}{n - 1} \quad (2)$$

$$\lambda_{max} = \sum \frac{(A\omega)_i}{n\omega_i} \quad (3)$$

Find the corresponding average stochastic consistency metric RI.

$$CR = \frac{CI}{RI} \quad (4)$$

When $CR \leq 0.1$, it means passing consistency.

2.2 DEMATEL method (Zhou & Zhang 2008)

(1) Constructing a direct impact matrix

The elements that affect the system are summarized according to the collected information starting from the research purpose. Then the degree of mutual influence between each element is quantified through expert interviews and other methods. 0, 1, 2, 3, and 4 indicate that the degree of influence is no, small, general, large, and very large, respectively, to obtain a direct influence matrix, representing elements' influence on elements.

(2) Calculate the normalized direct impact matrix

First, the sum of the elements of each row of the matrix is obtained, and the maximum value of each row is taken. Then each matrix element is divided by the maximum value, and the obtained matrix is the normalized direct influence matrix.

$$X = \lambda \times D \tag{5}$$

$$\lambda = \min \left(\frac{1}{\max_{1 \leq i \leq n} \sum_{j=1}^{n} |a_{ij}|}, \frac{1}{\max_{1 \leq j \leq n} \sum_{j=1}^{n} |a_{ij}|} \right) \tag{6}$$

(3) Determine the comprehensive impact matrix

The comprehensive impact matrix represents the degree of the combined influence of the element on the element or the degree of the combined influence of the element from the element.

$$T = \sum_{K=1}^{\infty} X^k = X(I - X)^{-1} \tag{7}$$

(4) Calculate the degree of influence, degree of influence, degree of centrality, and degree of the cause of each indicator

$$f = \sum_{j=1}^{n} t_{ij}, i = 1, 2, \cdots n \tag{8}$$

$$e = \sum_{i=1}^{n} t_{ij}, j = 1, 2, \cdots n \tag{9}$$

$$F = f + e \tag{10}$$

$$E = f - e \tag{11}$$

2.3 AHP-DEMATEL method

From the final calculation results of 2.1 and 2.2, the comprehensive influence degree of factors on the overall target can be calculated by Formula (12). The calculation formula is as follows:

$$z_i = \frac{F_i \cdot W_i}{\sum_{i=1}^{n} F_i \cdot W_i} \tag{12}$$

where F_i is the weight of each factor obtained by the AHP method, and W_i is the centrality of each factor obtained by the DEMATEL method.

3 CASE STUDY

3.1 General situation of the construction project

The project construction unit is H Company, and the design is a commercial project. The project construction period requirements are 12 months, and the quality requirements are qualified.

3.2 Index weight analysis based on AHP

3.2.1 Construction of construction quality index system

In order to make the results of the weight analysis of the influencing factors of quality control of the construction project more reasonable, scientific and effective, combined with the characteristics of the construction project itself and the research content of the relevant literature, the final evaluation index system is constructed with 4M1E, namely the five factors of people (A), materials (B), mechanical equipment (C), construction methods (D) and environment (E) are the first-level indicators, and the technical level (B1), human quality (B2), Quality Awareness (B3), Material Quality (C1), Material Storage (C2), Material Inspection (C3), Mechanical Logistics Support (D1), Maintenance and Maintenance of Mechanical Equipment (D2), On-site Inspection of Mechanical Equipment (D3), technical scheme (E1), technological process (E2), construction organization design (E3), engineering management environment (F1), engineering technology environment (F2) and engineering operation environment (F3) and other factors are secondary indicators, as shown in Figure 1.

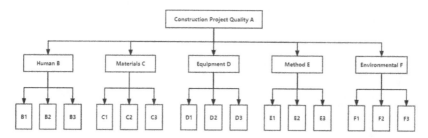

Figure 1. Hierarchical structure of factors influencing quality control of construction projects.

3.2.2 Determination of indicator weights

Invite senior experts in the construction project quality control field and management members such as leaders to form an evaluation expert group. Through a questionnaire survey, the expert group compares and scores the relative importance of the influencing factors. The above results can be obtained in Table 1 using the research method introduced in this paper.

CR = 0.069 < 0.10, calculated by Formula (4), and a comprehensive consistency test is carried out.

Table 1. The total sorted table calculated by AHP.

Evaluation objectives	First-tier indicators Name	First-tier indicators Weights (%)	Second-tier indicators Name	Second-tier indicators Weights (%)	Combination weights (%)	Sequence
Construction project quality	B	39.688	B1	12.262	2.867	7
			B2	53.714	22.112	1
			B3	32.024	12.71	3
	C	13.236	C1	60.796	9.263	4
			C2	27.21	2.146	8
			C3	11.994	1.827	12
	D	9.9	D1	60.796	6.019	6
			D2	27.21	2.694	11
			D3	11.994	1.187	14
	E	30.022	E1	27.21	8.169	5
			E2	11.994	3.601	9
			E3	60.796	18.252	2
	F	3.154	F1	60.796	3.133	10
			F2	27.21	1.402	13
			F3	11.994	0.618	15

3.3 Indicator weight analysis based on the DEMATEL method

3.3.1 Constructing the direct influence matrix

The direct influence matrix obtained by scoring by the relevant experts can be calculated by the above DEMATEL formula to obtain the structure shown in Table 2.

Table 2. Comprehensive influence relationship.

Influencing Factors	Influence	Sequence	Influenced	Sequence	Centrality	Sequence	Degree of Cause	Weights	Sequence
B1	1.131	3	0.093	14	1.224	7	1.037	0.070	7
B2	1.55	1	0.121	13	1.672	2	1.429	0.096	1
B3	1.232	2	0.093	14	1.326	6	1.139	0.076	6
C1	0.402	10	0.514	10	0.916	11	-0.112	0.052	11
C2	0.359	11	0.575	7	0.933	10	-0.216	0.053	10
C3	0.422	9	0.617	6	1.038	9	-0.195	0.059	9
D1	0.575	6	0.332	12	0.907	12	0.244	0.052	11
D2	0.197	13	0.547	9	0.743	13	-0.35	0.043	13
D3	0.16	15	0.554	8	0.714	15	-0.393	0.041	14
E1	0.66	4	1.013	1	1.673	1	-0.354	0.096	1
E2	0.174	14	0.981	3	1.155	8	-0.807	0.066	8
E3	0.458	8	0.889	5	1.347	5	-0.431	0.077	5
F1	0.641	5	1.011	2	1.652	3	-0.371	0.095	3
F2	0.48	7	0.962	4	1.442	4	-0.482	0.083	4
F3	0.293	12	0.432	11	0.724	14	-0.139	0.041	14

3.3.2 Draw influence correlation diagram

The correlation plot is drawn with the degree of the center as the horizontal axis and the degree of reason as the vertical axis. It can be seen from Figure 2 that B1, B2, and B3 are in

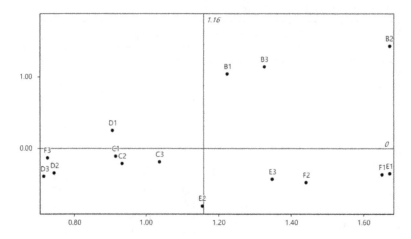

Figure 2. The causal structure diagram of influencing factors.

the first quadrant, where the elements are of high importance and are causal factors. D1 is in the second quadrant, where the element is of low importance and is a causal factor; C1, C2, C3, D2, D3, E2, and F3 are in the third quadrant, and the elements are of low importance and are outcome factors. E1, E3, F1, and F2 are in the fourth quadrant and are highly important outcome factors.

3.4 Indicator weight analysis based on the AHP-DEMATEL method

The comprehensive influence degree of each factor on the construction project quality can be calculated by Formula (12). It can be seen from Table 3 above that among the comprehensive influence weights calculated by the AHP-DEMATEL method, the comprehensive influence weights of B2, E3, B3, and E1 are relatively large., while F3, D3, and C3 are relatively small.

Table 3. Comprehensive influence weights of the AHP-DEMATEL method.

Influencing Factors	Centrality F	Weights W(%)	F*w	z	Sequence
B1	1.224	2.867	0.060	0.045	6
B2	1.672	22.112	0.370	0.279	1
B3	1.326	12.710	0.169	0.127	3
C1	0.916	9.263	0.085	0.064	5
C2	0.933	2.146	0.039	0.029	10
C3	1.038	1.827	0.019	0.014	13
D1	0.907	6.019	0.055	0.041	7
D2	0.743	2.694	0.020	0.015	12
D3	0.714	1.187	0.008	0.006	14
E1	1.673	8.169	0.137	0.103	4
E2	1.155	3.601	0.042	0.031	9
E3	1.347	18.252	0.246	0.186	2
F1	1.652	3.133	0.052	0.039	8
F2	1.442	1.402	0.020	0.015	11
F3	0.724	0.618	0.004	0.003	15

4 CONCLUSION

According to the data solved by the above method, the following analysis conclusions can be obtained: calculated by the AHP method, B2, E3, and B3 account for the largest weight; According to the calculation of the DEMATEL method, E1, B2 and F1 play a greater role in the system. The comprehensive use of these two methods can be obtained, and the comprehensive influence weight of B2, E3, B3, and E1 is large, which can be regarded as the most influential key factor in the quality control process of the construction project.

Combined with the results obtained from the above method analysis and the characteristics of the project, the following quality control optimization measures are proposed for the construction project to carry out better construction quality control. First, we should strengthen the training of comprehensive talents; second, we should strengthen the level of construction organization design and technical planning; third, we should strengthen the quality awareness of construction project personnel.

ACKNOWLEDGMENTS

This work was financially supported by the Key Project of Philosophy and Social Science Research of the Hubei Provincial Department of Education (19D011).

REFERENCES

Alic Milena. (2018) Integration of the ISO 9001 QMS with the Company's IT Business System. *Total Quality Management & Business Excellence*. pp. 1143–1160.
Bo Ming. (2020) Discussion on The Key Factors of Construction Quality Control of Housing Construction Projects. *Real Estate World*. pp. 57–59.
Chunfa Han. (2020) Analysis of Key Factors Affecting Construction Quality Control of Water Conservancy Projects. *Technological Innovation and Application*. pp. 186–187.
Dequn Zhou, Ling Zhang. (2008) Research on Hierarchical Division of Complex System Integrated Dematel-Ism. *Journal of Management Science*. pp. 20–26.
Emuze F.A., and Mhlwa C. (2015) Managing Quality on Construction Sites in South Africa: An Eastern Cape Study. *Journal of Construction Project Management & Innovation*. pp. 1224–1237.
Jian Wang, Erlie Liu, Gang Luo. (2004) Comprehensive Balance Optimization of Construction Period-cost-quality in Engineering Project Management. *Chinese Journal of Systems Engineering*. pp. 148–153.
Lijuan Xi. (2017) Research on Key Influencing Factors of Quality Management of Construction Projects. *Building Materials and Decoration*. pp. 135–136.
Liu Fang. (2010) Research on Key Factors of Quality Control in Engineering Construction Stage. *Modern Trade Industry*. pp. 375.
Sergey Lukichev. (2016) The Quality Management System as a Key Factor for the Sustainable Development of the Construction Companies. *Procedia Engineering*. pp. 17–21.
Weiwei Liu, Yujuan Ma. (2011) Quality Control in The Implementation Stage of Engineering Construction Projects. *Silicon Valley*. pp. 110.
Xue Deng, Jiaming Li, Haojian Zeng. (2012) Analysis and Application of AHP Weight Calculation Method. *Practice and Understanding of Mathematics*. pp. 93–100.
Yuan Zhou. (2018) Analysis of The Status Quo and Existing Problems of Quality Control of Engineering Projects in the Country. *Petrochemical Technology*. pp. 202.
Yuanjing Li. (2021) The Key Factors and Control Measures Affecting the Construction Quality of Prefabricated Buildings. *Fujian Building Materials*. pp. 108–110.
Zhengwei Shi. (2020) Analysis of The Key Points of Construction Quality Control of Housing Construction Projects. *Chinese Residential Facilities*. pp. 116–117.
Zhichun Qiao, Yingchun Sun, Jianzhao Zhao. (2015) Research on The Key Factors Affecting The Construction Quality of Construction Projects. *Coal Engineering*. pp. 144–147.
Zihai Zhang. (2009) Analysis of Project Quality Management. *Project Management Technology*. pp. 88–92.

A study on space-time evolution of landscape patterns of building lands in eco-friendly areas—Taking Dongting Lake as an example

Zhiyong Tang*
Wenzhou Urban Planning and Design Institute Company Ltd, Wenzhou, China

Jingtong Lv*
Jilin Urban and Rural Planning Research Institute, Jilin, China

Fuqiang Huang* & Suting Zhang*
Wenzhou Urban Planning and Design Institute Company Ltd, Wenzhou, China

ABSTRACT: With the acceleration of urbanization, the ecological environment of eco-friendly areas is deteriorating, and the contradiction between building land development and ecological protection is intensifying. The scientific identification of the space-time evolution of building lands is a prerequisite for optimizing the spatial development pattern of national lands. This study takes the Dongting Lake area as an example, clarifying the evolution process and spatial pattern characteristics of building land through spatial autocorrelation, cold hotspot analysis, and landscape pattern index based on land use data from 1990 to 2020. The results show that (1) the total area of building land in the Dongting Lake region increased by 996.81 km^2 from 1990 to 2020, with arable lands and forest lands being the main sources of expansion; (2) The spatial distribution of building lands varies significantly, generally presenting a contiguous distribution in low-value areas plus new high-value areas formed by expanding medium-high-value areas and medium-value areas. The global Moran's I index is increasing, and spatial aggregation is enhancing, with the high-high correlation areas, and hot spots mainly concentrated in the districts. Moreover, cities with better economic development, low-low correlation areas, and cold spots are distributed in the southeast and southwest mountainous areas; (3) The heterogeneity and fragmentation of the building land landscape have been alleviated, and its dominance has been gradually strengthened, focusing on urban construction and transportation construction and keeping the stability of rural settlements. Regarding spatial distribution, most regional patches are small and discrete, and the overall connectivity of the landscape is high. The research results can provide a reference for strengthening the control of building land in the Dongting Lake area and optimizing the spatial development pattern of the land.

1 INTRODUCTION

The study on driving forces of land use changes has been a core research area of Land Use/ Land Cover Change (LUCC) (Liu & Cao 2010). Since the reform and opening up of China, urbanization has increased significantly, with the urbanization rate of the resident

---

*Corresponding Authors: 156443740@qq.com, 2311896389@qq.com, 413256220@qq.com and 1692213995@qq.com

population exceeding 60% for the first time in 2020. Rapid urbanization has brought about many problems, such as reducing arable land, ecosystem degradation, and environmental pollution. As the most concentrated and intuitive reflection of urbanization, it is important for building lands to explore the process of its expansion and spatial distribution to curb the uncontrolled expansion of land and achieve sustainable urban development.

At present, scholars at home and abroad have made relevant studies on the spatial pattern of building lands. Still, they mainly focus on the quantitative measurement of the spatial distribution pattern of building lands (Ji & Chen 2018; Tan *et al.* 2007; Yang *et al.* 2019), the driving force of the change of the pattern of building land (Liu *et al.* 2012; Wu *et al.* 2010; Wu & Chen 2018; Zhang & Miao 2020), the expansion pattern of building lands (Lv 2012), and the landscape pattern index (Liu *et al.* 2017; Lv & Zhang *et al.* 2019; Tian *et al.* 2002). The application of multi-temporal time-series remote sensing image data and landscape indices has made studying the evolutionary process of landscape spatial patterns a hotspot of research in academia. Still, much research has been done mainly on the evolutionary patterns of wetland landscape patterns, farmland landscape patterns, and the landscape patterns of the whole region (Du *et al.* 2011; Fan *et al.* 2014; Fu *et al.* 2006; Li *et al.* 2008; Liu & Wang 2007; Zhong *et al.* 2014). Based on the above studies, it is found that relatively little research has been done on the spatial pattern evolution of the landscape building land in ecologically oriented areas.

The Dongting Lake area is an important production base for bulk agricultural products in China and an important part of the Yangtze River Economic Belt. At present, there are relatively abundant studies on ecological land in the lake area (Dai & Li 2021; Yin *et al.* 2017) and greater studies on spatial and temporal changes in the evolution of building land patterns (Li *et al.* 2021; 2020) and monitoring of water resources dynamics (Deng *et al.* 2021; Xiong *et al.* 2020), studies on while still lacking landscape patterns. Because of this, the present study takes the Dongting Lake region as an example, based on land use data from 1990 to 2020, clarifying the evolution process and spatial pattern characteristics of building lands through spatial autocorrelation, cold hotspot analysis, and landscape pattern index. It provides a reference for decision-making on the economical and intensive use of land, policy formulation, and the realization of regional sustainable development.

2 STUDY AREA AND DATA PROCESSING

2.1 *Study area*

The area of the Dongting Lake region (27°98′ - 30°23′N, 110°20′ - 114°14′E) is shown in Figure 1. It includes Yiyang City, Changde City, Yueyang City, Wangcheng District of Changsha City in Hunan Province, and Jingzhou City in Hubei Province, with a total of 33 counties (cities and districts). Of these, 10 are municipal districts (Ziyang District, Heshan District, Wuling District, Dingcheng District, Yueyanglou District, Junshan District, Yunxi District, Wangcheng District, Jingzhou District, and Shacheng District), 8 are county-level cities (including Yuanjiang City, Jin City, Miluo City, Linxiang City, Songzi City, Shishou City, Honghu City, and Jili City) and 9 are counties (Anhua County, Taojiang County, Nan County, Hanshou County, Taoyuan County, Linli County, Shimen County, Li County, Anxiang County). By the end of 2020, the resident population was about 20.304 million, and the GDP was 128.321 billion RMB. With the rapid growth of population and economy, the Dongting Lake area has shown ecological problems such as shrinking arable and forest land areas, decreasing biodiversity, and serious water pollution.

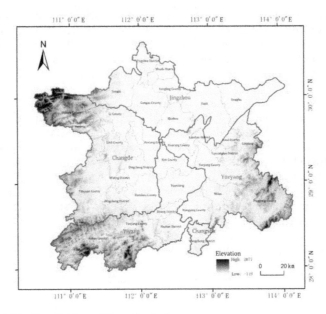

Figure 1. Administrative division of Dongting Lake area.

2.2 *Data source and processing*

Landsat TM and Landsat ETM remote sensing image data are applied to analyze data from 1990, 1995, 2000, 2005, and 2010, and Landsat 8 remote sensing image data are used to analyze data from the source in 2015 and 2020. The land use types in the Dongting Lake area are obtained through manual visual interpretation. Concerning the Classification of Current Land Use (GB/T 21010 - 2017), the land types in the study area are divided into eight categories: arable land, forest land, grassland, water area, urban land, rural settlement, other building land, and unused land (Figure 2). The accuracy of interpretation is 93.7% through random sampling verification of field survey points and random sampling verification of verification lines. Using DEM data provided by the National Geographic Information Center, image correction and slope analysis are performed to obtain elevation and slope elements. Considering the study area's scope and the data processing difficulty, the building land in the study area is divided into 3km×3km total of 4449 evaluation units using the fishnet creation function of ArcGIS 10.2.

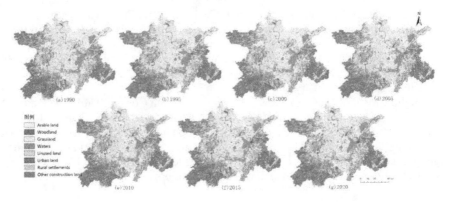

Figure 2. Distribution of land use types in the Dongting Lake area from 1990 to 2020.

3 RESEARCH METHODOLOGY

3.1 Land use dynamic attitude

The dynamic attitude of land use can reflect the drastic change in building land area, which is calculated by the following formula (Liu et al. 2018):

$$D_i = \left\{\sum_j^n \left(\frac{|\Delta U_{i,j}|}{U_a}\right)\right\} \times \frac{1}{t} \times 100\% \quad (1)$$

D_i is the dynamic attitude of built-up land, U_a is the total area of the study area, $|\Delta U_{i,j}|$ is the absolute value of the interconversion between built-up land and other types of land use from the start of monitoring to the end of monitoring, and t is the duration of the study.

3.2 Land use transfer matrix

The land use transfer matrix can reflect changes in the structural characteristics and functional types of building land and is calculated as follows (Pontius et al. 2003):

$$S_{ij} = \begin{bmatrix} S_{11} & \cdots & S_{1n} \\ \vdots & \ddots & \vdots \\ S_{n1} & \cdots & S_{nn} \end{bmatrix} \quad (2)$$

where S_{ij} is the area and n is the total number of land use types, i and j are the pre- and post-transfer land use types, respectively.

3.3 Kernel density estimation method

The kernel density estimation method forms continuous surface data based on known sample point data to explore the clustering of sample distribution in the region (Berke 2004). The study can reflect the spatial clustering characteristics of building lands more accurately through the kernel density analysis method, which is calculated by the following formula:

$$f(x) = \frac{1}{Dh}\sum_{i=1}^{D} k\left(\frac{x - x_i}{h}\right) \quad (3)$$

where f(x) is the kernel density estimate of the building land area; k(x-x$_i$/h) is the kernel function; D is the number of building land patches; (x-x$_i$) is the distance from x to sample point x$_i$; and h is the sample bandwidth. The study used the kernel density tool in ArcGIS10.2 to determine the bandwidth of 8km by using the area of building land patches as the statistical analysis field and the natural breakpoint method to classify the kernel density of building land into the low-value area, medium-low-value area, medium value area, medium-high value area, and high-value area, and to count the proportion of each class.

3.4 Spatial autocorrelation

Spatial autocorrelation is a method to test whether observations of sample data are significantly correlated with observations at their neighboring locations (Anselin 1995; Lu et al. 2019). The study uses global and local Moran's I indices to analyze the spatial autocorrelation of building land, with the global and local Moran's I indices calculated as follows:

$$\text{Global Moran's } I = \frac{\sum_{i=1}^{n} \sum_{j \neq 1}^{n} W_{ij}(X_i - \bar{X})(X_j - \bar{X})}{S^2 \sum_{i=1}^{n} \sum_{j=1}^{n} W_{ij}} \qquad (4)$$

$$\text{Local Moran's } I = \frac{n(X_i - \bar{X}) \sum_{j=1}^{n} W_{ij}(X_j - \bar{X})}{\sum_{i=1}^{n} (X_j - \bar{X})^2} \qquad (5)$$

where n is the number of evaluation units, X_i is the area of building land in evaluation unit i, and W_{ij} is the spatial weighting matrix.

3.5 Hot and cold analysis

The cold hotspot analysis method is used to identify statistically significant spatial clustering, which can further detect the apparent location and degree of the regional association of spatial clustering of indicator attributes based on global spatial autocorrelation (Getis & Ord 1992). The study explores the changes in the cold hotspot pattern of building land by calculating the Getis-Ord Gi* index for each evaluation unit with the following formula.

$$G_i^*(d) = \sum_{i=1}^{n} w_{ij}(d)x_i / \sum_{i=1}^{n} x_i \qquad (6)$$

where w_{ij} denotes the spatial weight between evaluation units i and j, and x_i is the building land area of evaluation unit i.

3.6 Landscape pattern index

The landscape index is a simple quantitative indicator that can reflect the landscape's structural composition and spatial configuration characteristics (Wu 2007), mainly implemented with the help of Fragstats 4.2 software. For comparison purposes, four landscape indices, number of patches (NP), edge density (ED), patch area standard deviation (PSSD), and connectivity (COHESION), are selected at both patch level and landscape level to reflect the basic characteristics of the regional landscape in terms of fragmentation, shape, and distribution, respectively. The landscape pattern indices and their ecological significance are shown in Table 1.

Table 1. Landscape pattern index and its ecological significance.

Landscape Index	Range of values	Ecological significance
Number of plaques NP/Number	$NP \geq 1$	Number of plaques, reflecting the degree of plaque fragmentation
Edge Density ED/ km^2	$ED \geq 0$	The extent to which the total landscape area is divided by patch edges, reflecting patch dominance and patch shape complexity
The standard deviation of plaque area PSSD/km^2	$PSSD \geq 0$	The gap between the size of each patch and the average size reflects the homogeneity of land cover types.
Degree of connectivity COHESION	$0 \leq COHESION \leq 100$	Natural connectivity of the relevant plaque types, reflecting the degree of plaque connectivity and aggregation

3.7 Moving window method

To reflect the regional differences in landscape indices in the Dongting Lake area during 1990–2020, the raster map of landscape indices is generated using the moving window method. The radius of 510m, 1500m, 2400m, 3600m, 4500m, and 5400m was used for screening in Fragstats 4.2 software to ensure sufficient spatial information while eliminating noise effects (Lv *et al.* 2019), and the final window size is set to 4500m × 4500m. The window is moved from the top left corner of the study area. The spatial expression of each landscape index is achieved by calculating the indices in each window that is moved from the top left corner of the study area. The spatial expression of each landscape index is achieved by calculating the index within each window and assigning it to the central raster.

4 ANALYSIS OF RESULTS

4.1 Change in building land area in the Dongting Lake area

The building land is a land type with more significant changes in the Dongting Lake area. As shown in Figure 3, the area of building lands increased from 1503.96km^2 to 2500.77km^2 from 1990 to 2020, with an area increase of 66.13% and an annual change rate of 2.21%. The proportion of urban building land increased from 23.51% to 26.33%, and the area increased by 86.20% (304.81 km2). The proportion of rural settlements decreased significantly from 73.68% to 46.85%, but the area still increased by 5.74% (63.63 km^2). The proportion of other building land increased significantly from 2.80% to 26.81%, and the area increased by 1490.67% (628.37 km2), with an annual change rate as high as 49.69%, much higher than the 2.87% for urban land and 0.19% for rural settlements. From the dynamic attitude of land use in each period, the dynamic attitude of other building land is the highest, followed by urban building land, and the dynamic attitude of rural settlements is the lowest. The overall dynamic attitude of building land and urban land is consistent, both rising in 2000–2010 and 2015–2020, with the maximum values appearing in 2005–2010, 0.05% and 0.09%, respectively, indicating that The overall dynamic attitude of building land is mainly influenced by urban land use.

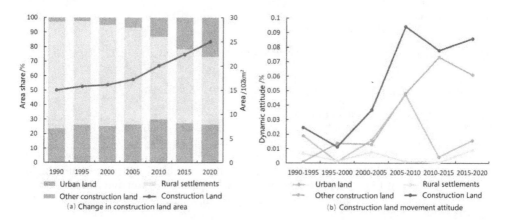

Figure 3. Changes in building land area in the Dongting Lake area, 1990–2020.

The conversion between building land and other land use types in the Dongting Lake area was frequent from 1990 to 2020. As shown in Figure 4, the characteristics of change in the area of various types of building land differ significantly. However, arable land and forest land are always the main sources of increase in building land, with a total of 649.65km² of arable land and 297.81km² of forest land converted into building land. Accounting for 65.16% and 29.87% of the net increase, urban building land expands rapidly through encroachment on arable land and forest land. From the changes in each period, rural settlements and building land have similar characteristics of change. In contrast, the magnitude of change in building land is mainly influenced by urban land and another building land. From 1990 to 2020, urban land and other building land grew significantly, accounting for 30.58% and 63.03% of the net increase in area, respectively, indicating that the Dongting Lake area is gradually dominated by urban construction and transportation construction and the demand for new land for rural settlements is relatively small, with urban development and construction stepping into a more active development period.

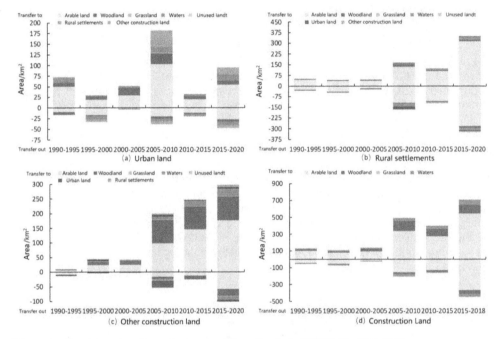

Figure 4. Land type transformation map of Dongting Lake REGION, 1990–2020.

4.2 *Spatial distribution of building land in the Dongting Lake area*

4.2.1 *Nuclear density of building land*

The results of the nuclear density analysis of building land in the Dongting Lake area from 1990 to 2020 are shown in Figure 5. The spatial distribution of different levels of building land changes significantly, with the low-value area mainly distributed in a row and the middle and high-value areas expanding and forming new high-value areas in Jiangling County, the north of Li County, the southwest of Wangcheng District and Miluo City. The originally scattered middle and low-value areas gradually spread and connected, indicating that the cities and counties in the Dongting Lake area are gradually connected.

The changes in the area of each grade of building land in the Dongting Lake area from 1990 to 2020 are shown in Table 2. The proportion of low-value areas decreases by 0.91% annually. However, it is still the largest grade in terms of area, accounting for more than 40%, mainly in Shimen County, Taoyuan County, Anhua County, and Pingjiang County. The high-value areas fit perfectly with county locations, with the smallest area expanding

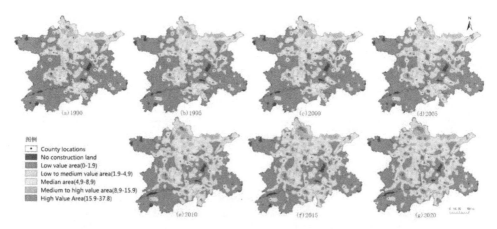

Figure 5. Analysis of the nuclear density of building land in the Dongting Lake area from 1990 to 2020.

significantly, increasing from 0.27% to 3.36%, with an average annual increase of 38.36%. The main increase areas are Jingzhou District, Shacheng District, Wuling District, Heshan District, Yueyanglou District, and southeast Wangcheng District. The proportion of medium-high, medium, and medium-low value areas is rising, with an average annual increase of 4.25%, 1.20%, and 0.24%, respectively.

Table 2. Proportion of nuclear density classes for building land in the Dongting Lake area, 1990–2020.

Grade Ratio/%	1990	1995	2000	2005	2010	2015	2020
Low-value area	55.49	55.01	53.97	51.86	46.25	42.88	40.35
Low to the medium-value area	26.77	25.78	26.28	26.75	29.00	29.06	28.69
Median Zone	13.28	14.15	14.44	15.17	16.13	17.28	18.06
Medium to the high-value area	4.19	4.47	4.74	5.48	7.26	8.56	9.55
High-Value Area	0.27	0.58	0.56	0.73	1.36	2.21	3.36

4.2.2 Spatial autocorrelation of building land

The results of the global spatial autocorrelation analysis of building land area in the Dongting Lake region from 1990 to 2020 are shown in Figure 6. z-scores ranged from 40 to 55. They all passed the significance test with 99.9% confidence, indicating that the spatial distribution of building land in the Dongting Lake region has obvious clustering characteristics. The global Moran's I index increased from 0.386 to 0.478, decreasing only in 2000, and the scatter plot axis parameter fluctuated from 14 to 9, rebounding only in 2005 and 2015, indicating the spatial aggregation of building land has increased. The differences between regions have gradually increased. They are more stable, while the points in the first quadrant (high-high agglomeration) gradually disperse and tend to converge to the fitted curve, indicating that the accumulation in the high-value building land area is becoming more and more obvious.

The global spatial autocorrelation can only judge the macroscopic characteristics of building land distribution. To further analyze the phenomenon of local spatial correlation, the local spatial autocorrelation of building land is depicted by the local Moran's I index. The results are shown in Figure 7. Most areas in the Dongting Lake area have no significant correlation from 1990 to 2020. The rest are mainly high correlation and low, low correlation.

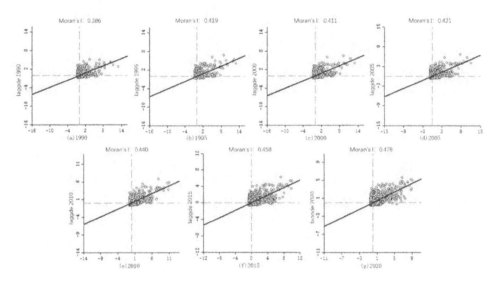

Figure 6. Moran's I scatterplot of building land in the Dongting Lake area from 1990 to 2020.

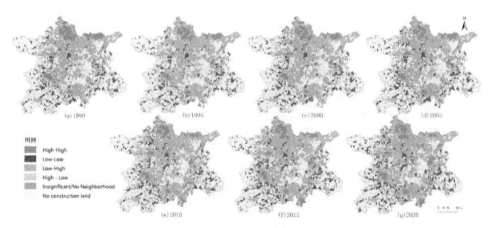

Figure 7. LISA clustering map of building land in the Dongting Lake area, 1990–2020.

The high-high correlation areas decreased from 359 to 296 in 1990–1995 and then continued to increase to 390 in 2020. In 1990, the high-high correlation areas were mainly distributed in the northern part of Jingzhou City and the Wuling District of Changde City. The northern high-high correlation areas shrank and broke afterward. The southern part of Li County, the northern part of Heshan District, and the Yueyanglou District gradually expanded into a piece. It formed a new high-high correlation area in the southeast of Wangcheng District. These areas have better economic development and greater demand for building land. The low-low association areas decreased from 516 to 504 in 1990–1995 and then continued to increase to 640 in 2020, mainly in the southwest and southeast, which are undulating and mostly natural forest land unsuitable for urban construction.

4.2.3 *Cold hotspot pattern of building land*

The results of spatial cold hot spot detection are shown in Figure 8. The number of cold hot spots on building land in the Dongting Lake area fluctuated slightly between 1990 and 2020, and the overall spatial distribution was stable. The number of hot spots, sub-hot spots, and sub-cold spots fluctuates and increases, from 703, 144, and 508 to 720, 173, and 712, respectively, while the number of cold spots fluctuates and decreases from 351 to 214. The hotspot areas are mainly located in the northern part of Jingzhou City, Wuling District, Heshan District, and Yueyanglou District, with Li County and Wangcheng District becoming new hotspot areas in 2000 and 2010, respectively. Except for the hotspot areas in the northern part of Jingzhou City, which gradually contracted, all other hotspot areas tend to spread to the surrounding areas, combined with the Statistical Yearbook. It can be seen that the economic development of these areas is better and has a certain spillover effect, which can drive the demand for building land in the surrounding areas. These areas have good economic development and have a certain spillover effect, which can drive up the demand for building land in the surrounding areas. The cold spot areas have gradually shrunk and been replaced by secondary cold spot areas, mainly in the mountainous areas of Taoyuan County, Anhua County, Taojiang County, Yueyang County, and Pingjiang County.

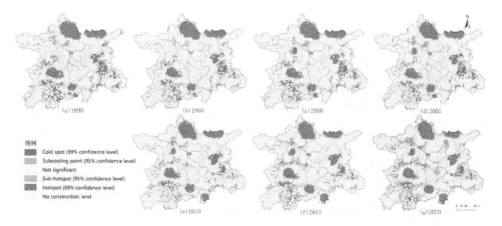

Figure 8. Cold hot spot distribution of building land in the Dongting Lake region, 1990–2020.

4.3 Evolution of landscape patterns of building land in the Dongting Lake area

4.3.1 Patchy horizontal landscape pattern

The trends of the landscape pattern index in the Dongting Lake area at the patch level from 1990 to 2020 are shown in Figure 9. Among the landscape types, rural settlements have absolute advantages in the number of patches and edge density. The dominant position is stable while maintaining a low level in the standard deviation of patch area and degree of connectivity, indicating that rural settlements have a high degree of fragmentation and shape complexity. Despite the decreasing proportion, small and uniform patch areas and discrete spatial distribution are still the dominant landscape in the regional building land. After 2010, in rural settlements, the degree of connectivity fluctuated and rises, indicating that the patches gradually changed from a state of scattered and disorderly spatial structure to concentrated and continuous construction. The standard deviation of area and connectivity of urban land is obvious. At the same time, the number of patches and edge density remains low, indicating that urban land tends to be concentrated in large patches, with the regular shape of patches and strong landscape connectivity, and the proportion is increasing. The number of patches and edge density always increased, and the growth rate increased after 2005, indicating that the fragmentation of other building land and the complexity of patch shape increased rapidly, the landscape dominance increased, fragmented patches gradually connected and merged, and the landscape connectivity increased. The standard deviation of patch area and connectivity of building land have similar changing characteristics with another building land. The number of patches decreased slightly after 2015, while the edge density increased significantly, indicating that the overall dominance of building land rises. The patch shape tends to be complex, gradually changing from fragmentation and dispersion to a concentrated and continuous whole. In general, the urbanization process in the Dongting Lake area has accelerated, and the rural settlements are relatively stable and tend to shift toward improving land use efficiency and intensification.

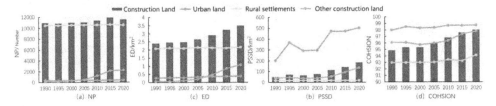

Figure 9. Changes in the level index of construction land patch types in the Dongting Lake area.

The trend of the landscape pattern index in the Dongting Lake area from 1990 to 2020 at the landscape level is shown in Figure 10. Edge density continues to rise, and connectivity rises slightly before declining. It indicates that human development activities have interrupted the otherwise continuous natural landscape, weakened connectivity and discrete spatial distribution, and changed landscape patterns from simple to complex. The number of patches and the standard deviation of area fluctuate between years, with the number of patches decreasing and then increasing, with a significant increase from 2010 to 2015, then decreasing after 2015 but remaining at a high level. After 2015, the effect of implementing ecological projects such as protective forests gradually became apparent, and the landscape pattern changed from heterogeneous and fragmented to homogeneous and holistic.

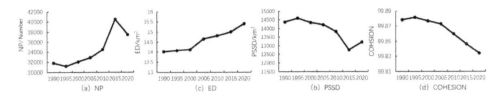

Figure 10. Changes in landscape level indices in the Dongting Lake area.

4.3.2 Landscape level landscape pattern

The trend of the landscape pattern index in the Dongting Lake area from 1990 to 2020 at the landscape level is shown in Figure 10. The edge density continues to rise, and the degree of connectivity increases slightly and then decreases, indicating that human development activities interrupt the originally continuous natural landscape, weakened connectivity, discrete spatial distribution, and a change of landscape pattern from simple to complex. The number of patches and the standard deviation of the area fluctuate between years, with the number of patches decreasing and then increasing. The growth rate was significant from 2010 to 2015 and decreased after 2015 but maintained a high level. Combined with the standard deviation of the patch area, the expansion of construction land leads to more and more fragmentation of other sites, the gap between the patch area and average area decreases, and the landscape fragmentation increases. After 2015, the implementation of environmental projects such as protective forests gradually shows the effect, and the landscape pattern is changing from heterogeneous and fragmentation to homogeneous and holistic.

4.3.3 *Spatial distribution of landscape pattern indices*

The spatial distribution of the landscape pattern index for building land in the Dongting Lake area in 2020 is shown in Figure 11. Most areas have a low number of patches, uniform patch size, low overall fragmentation of building land, and simple landscape shape. Yueyanglou District of Yueyang City and the southwestern edge of Wangcheng District of Changsha City have a high density and a small number of patches, with a large gap between individual patches and the average scale. It indicates that these areas have a low degree of fragmentation and a large contiguous distribution of building land, which is the dominant landscape type in the region. The number of patches and edge density in Jingzhou, Wuling District of Changde City, and Heshan District of Yiyang City is high, indicating that these areas have a concentrated distribution of patches, a complex landscape shape, and a high degree of fragmentation. The lower index of each landscape in the periphery and central part of the study area is due to the rugged topography and slope of the periphery of the lake area, which is not conducive to construction. In contrast, the central part is surrounded by Dongting Lake and has a well-developed water system, which limits land development for construction. The high overall connectivity of the patches indicates that the study area focuses on transport construction and improving the road network system, resulting in closer links between towns and increased landscape connectivity.

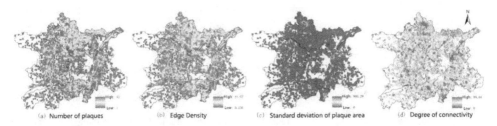

Figure 11. Spatial distribution of the landscape pattern index for building land in the Dongting Lake Region in 2020.

5 CONCLUSION AND DISCUSSION

5.1 *Conclusion*

Based on the land use data of 7 periods from 1990 to 2020, the study clarifies the distribution characteristics and evolution of building land in the Dongting Lake area with the help of spatial autocorrelation, cold and hot spot analysis method, and landscape pattern index:

(1) From 1990 to 2020, building land in the Dongting Lake area continued to increase, with the main sources being arable land and forest land. The overall dynamic attitude and transformation of building land are mainly influenced by urban land and another building land, and the demand for new land from rural settlements is small.
(2) The spatial distribution of the nuclear density of building land has changed significantly, and the degree of concentration has been increasing. High-value nuclear density areas, high-association areas, and hot spots are mainly distributed in the northern part of Jingzhou City, Yueyanglou District, Li County bordering Jin City, Wuling District and its surroundings, Ziyang District bordering Heshan District and the southeastern part of Wangcheng District. There are a few high-value areas in the southern part of Jingzhou

City, Linxiang County, and Shishou City, but no hot spots have been formed. Low-value nuclear density areas, low-association areas, and cold spots are mainly distributed in mountainous areas such as the southeast and southwest.
(3) The landscape pattern index shows that the landscape advantage of building land is gradually increasing, heterogeneity and fragmentation are alleviated, overall urban construction and transportation construction are dominant, and rural settlements are relatively stable and have a tendency to intensify. As for spatial distribution, the landscape pattern index of building land obtained from the moving window method has a lower degree of fragmentation, simple landscape shape, and good connectivity.

5.2 *Discussion*

The study results show that the building land area has increased significantly, and economic development is the leading factor promoting land development. The accelerated urbanization process and large-scale expansion of building land have encroached on the original arable land and forest land. Compared with developed areas, the ecosystem of Dongting Lake is more fragile, and the high frequency of land use transformation relationship is very likely to cause instability of regional development, which is not conducive to long-term sustainable development. Therefore, local governments need to coordinate the relationship between environmental protection and urban development, adhere to the implementation of the "total protection, not big development," and build a scientific and orderly pattern of spatial development and protection of the national land is the next research focus.

REFERENCES

Anselin L. (1995) Local Indicators of Spatial Association-LISA, *Geographical Analysis*,27(2): 93–115.
Baifa Zhang, Changhong Miao, (2020) Spatiotemporal Changes and Driving Forces of Land use in the Yellow River Basin, *Resources Science*,42(3):14.
Baoxiao Liu, Yaohuan Huang, Jingying Fu, (2012) Spatial Patterns of Built-up Areas Around Beijing, Acta Geographaga Sinica.
Cong Li, Xiangwen Li, Wu Zheng, *et al.*, (2008) Evolution of Wetland Landscape Pattern in Hengshui National Nature Reserve, *Resources Science*,30(10):1571–1578.
Dafang Wu, YanyanLiu, Yuxiang Dong, *et al.*, (2010) Analysis on the Spatial-temporal Change Characteristics of Building Land and its Driving Forces in Zhuhuai, *Economic Geography*,(2):7.
Getis A., and Ord J .K., (1992) The Analysis of Spatial Association by Use of Distance Statistics, *Geographical Analysis*, 24(3):189–206.
Guangjin Tian, Zengxiang Zhang, Guoping Zhang *et al.*, (2002) Landscape Dynamic Change Pattern of Haikou City by TM Imagery and GIS, Acta Ecologica Sinica.
Guanyi Yin, Liming Liu, Xilong Jiang, (2017) The Sustainable Arable Land use Pattern Under the Tradeoff of Agricultural Production, Economic Development, and Ecological Protection—an Analysis of Dongting Lake Basin, *Environmental Science and Pollution Research, Environmental Science and Pollution Researc,.* 24(32):25329–25345.
Huishi Du, HaSi. Mingyu Li, (2011) Evolvement of Urban Landscape Pattern in Yanji City in 1977㊀2008, *Scientia Geographica Sinica*,31(5):608–612.
Jianguo Wu, (2007) Landscape Ecology-Patterns, Processes, *Scales and Grades*,Higher Education Press. pp. 106–107.
Jinghua Liu, Weifeng Li, Weiqi Zhou, Lijian Han, Guoyu Qian, *et al.*, (2017) Spatial Patterns of Built-up Areas Around Beijing, *Acta Geographaga Sinica*,37(16):5324–5333.
Jingxia Lv, Weiguo Jiang, Wenjie Wang *et al.*, (2019) Wetland Landscape Evolution and its Relation to Human Disturbance in Xiong'an New Area based on the Moving Window Method, *Remote Sensing for Land and Resources*, 31(02):140–148.
Jiyuan Liu, Jia Ning, Wenhui Kuang *et al.*, (2018) Spatio-temporal Patterns and Characteristics of Land-use Change in China During 2010-2015, *Acta Geographica Sinica*,73(5):789–802.

Leting Lv, Jie Zhang *et al.*, (2019) Landscape Pattern Analysis and Prediction in the Dongjiang River Basin, *Acta Ecologica Sinica*,39(18):6850–6859.

Li Junhan, Zhou Kaichun, Dong Huimin, Xie Binggeng, (2020) Cultivated Land Change, Driving Forces and its Impact on Landscape Pattern Changes in the Dongting Lake basin, *International Journal of Environmental Research and Public Health*,17(21).

Lina Zhong, Wenwu Zhao, Yihe Lv *et al.*, (2014) Analysis of Landscape Pattern Evolution Characteristic in the Hilly and Gully Area of Loess Plateau: A Case Study in Yan'an City, *Acta Ecologica Sinica*,34(12):3368–3377.

Meichen Fu, Zhenqi Hu, Jingguo Wu, (2006) Analysis of Farmland Landscape Pattern Evolvement Rule on Zhongjie Friendship Farm, *Transactions of the CSAE*,22(3):63–67.

Minghong Tan, Huiyi Zhu, Lingshan Liu *et al.*, (2007) Spatial Patterns of Built-up Areas Around Beijing, *Acta Geographaga Sinica*,62(8):9.

Olaf Berke, (2004) Exploratory Disease Mapping: Kriging the Spatial Risk Function From Regional Count Data, *International Journal of Health Geographics*,3(1).

Pontius R. G., Shusas E., and McEachern M., (2003) Detecting Important Categorical land Changes While Accounting for Persistence. *Agriculture, Ecosystems and Environment*,101(2): 251–268.

Qiang Fan, Ting Du ,Jun Yang *et al.*, (2014) Landscape Pattern Changes for Nansihu Wetland From 1982 to 2012, *Resources Science*,36(4):865–873.

Qianming Li, Bohong Zheng, Yujun Xiong, (2021) Spatial-Temporal Expansion of the Dongting Lake Eco-economic Zone Urban Agglomeration Based on Nighttime Light Remote Sensing Data, *Economic Geography*,41(02):92–102.

SSM Yang, Qingxu Huang, Chunyang He *et al.*, (2019) Quantifying Spatial Pattern of Built-up Areas in China, *Journal of Geo-information Science*,(2):178–189.

Tao Liu, Guangzhong Cao, and Lupton, (2010) Progress in Urban Land Expansion and its Driving Forces. *Progress In Geography*,29(8):927–934.

Xianzhao Liu,Wei Wang, (2007) Changes of Land Use and Landscape Pattern in Yantai Coastland Areas, *Transactions of the CSAE*,23(10):79–85.

Xinhai Lu, Nan Ke, Bin Kuang *et al.*, (2019) Spatial-Temporal Features and Influencing Factors of Difference in Land Urbanization Level of Central China, *Economic Geography*,39(4):192.

Ying Xiong, Ming Wang, Haiping Yuan, Chunyan Du, Haipeng Wu, (2020) Landscape Ecological Risk Assessment and its Spatio-temporal Evolution in Dongting Lake area, *Ecology and Environmental*, 29(07):1292–1301.

Yunzhe Dai, Jiangfeng Li, (2021) Terrain Gradient Effect of Spatiotemporal Evolution of Ecological Land and Ecosystem Service Value in Dongting Lake area, *Research of Soil and Water Conservation*,25(03):197–204.

Zhaopeng Wu, Xuegang Chen, (2018) Analysis of Landscape Pattern Change and Driving Force in Urumqi City, *Ecological Science*, 37(1):9.

Zhenghua Deng, Liqi Dai, Bing Deng, Liping Deng *et al.*, (2021) Spatial-Temporal Evolution of Water Resources Carrying Capacity in Dongting Lake basin, *Economic Geography*,41(05):186–192.

Zhenjun Ji,Ying Chen, (2018) Evaluation of Urban Land Intensive Use and Analysis of Spatial Distribution Pattern in the Central Zone of Tianshui City, *Journal of Henan Agricultural University*,52(2):8.

Zhiqiang Lv , (2012) Analysis of Different Building Land Expansion Types and Their Driving Force, *Research of Soil and Water Conservation*,19(4):7.

/ Civil Engineering and Energy-Environment – Gao & Duan (Eds)
© 2023 the Author(s), ISBN 978-1-032-56057-1

Microwave heating removal and laboratory evaluation of pavement markings

Xiaoyong Zou & Wenxiu Wu*
Jinhua Highway and Transportation Administration Center, Jinhua, China

Yonglin Hu
Highway and Transportation Administration Center of Jindong District, Jinhua, China

Jing Liu & Lei Dong
Dongyang Highway and Transportation Administration Center, Dongyang, China

Biao Zhang
Jinhua Highway and Transportation Administration Center, Jinhua, China

Dapeng Li
Zhejiang Institute of Communications Co., Ltd, Hangzhou, China

ABSTRACT: This study proposes a novel method of removing pavement markings on asphalt pavements using microwave heating to solve the visual confusion and surface texture damage by designing an impedance-matching marking specimen (IMS). The corrosion, wear, and skid resistances of all five IMS groups were tested, and the results met the specified engineering requirements in laboratory tests. The marking removal efficiency of those five groups of IMS was 99.4%, 99.8%, 99.9%, 100%, and 100%, respectively, because the curing product showed strong thermoplasticity and fluidity. Results also indicated that the microwave removal of prepared markings would not destroy the texture of road surfaces and improve the anti-skid performance of these surfaces instead.

1 INTRODUCTION

Microwave heating is widely used in various industries due to its unique immediacy, high efficiency, selectivity, and safety (Li et al. 2021; Liu et al; 2021; 2022; 2022; 2021; Yang et al. 2019). The application of microwave heating in asphalt pavement can be traced back to the 1960s, mainly used for road deicing and snow removal (Liu et al. 2018), asphalt pavement heat-in-place regeneration and maintenance (Liu et al. 2022; 2021), and pavement inspection (Liu et al. 2022; 2019; 2022). Bosiso et al. (Cho et al. 2013) from Canada found that when 2.45 GHz microwave heating equipment was used in microwave heating of asphalt pavement. Its effective heating depth was 12 cm and would not cause surface layer coking. After enduring heavy traffic in winter, the asphalt pavement repaired by microwave heating still maintained good road performance. To save energy, reduce costs and reduce environmental pollution, Jeppson (Jeppson 1982) used microwave heating to treat old asphalt pavement in the patent published in 1982. The stone absorbs the microwave and transfers heat to asphalt. After the asphalt is softened by heat absorption, the original mixture becomes dispersed

---

*Corresponding Author: 277182929@qq.com

masses, which can be reprocessed. Thus, the high-efficiency recovery of asphalt mixture can be realized. Tang et al. (Liu et al. 2017) established the road based on the basic theory of microwave heating, a three-dimensional microwave heating model of microwave deicing, by changing the microwave frequency, electric field intensity, and heating height to carry on the simulation. The results show that increasing microwave frequency can significantly improve the deicing efficiency. 5.8 GHz microwave deicing efficiency is 2.45 GHz microwave deicing efficiency of three to five times.

Although the application of microwave heating technology in road engineering is becoming more and more mature, most are concentrated on asphalt pavement crack self-healing, plastic maintenance, and thermal regeneration of the scene, and have yet to have the use of microwave heating to clean up traffic line markings related research. This study used microwave heating to clear the thoughts of the original pavement marking.

2 PREPARATION AND TESTING FOR PAVEMENT MARKINGS

2.1 *Preparation of pavement markings*

As shown in Figure 1, the impedance-matching specimens (IMS) were designed for laboratory experiments that included corrosion resistance, wear resistance, anti-sliding resistance, microwave heating, and removal tests. The asphalt mixture used was AC-13, the asphalt used was SBS-modified asphalt, and the water-based marking used was waterborne epoxy marking (WEM). Among them, composite microwave absorbent (CMA) was mixed in a certain proportion of mixed carbonyl iron powder (CIP) and graphite powder (G.P.). Furthermore, the materials used for impedance-matching marking (IMM) contained a certain proportion of CMA, silane coupling agent, and antifoam agent.

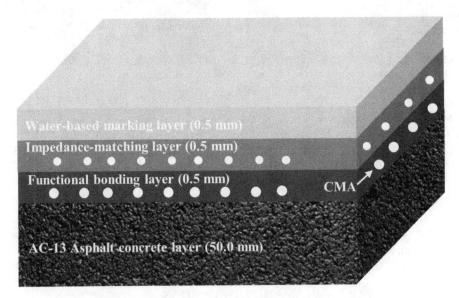

Figure 1. Schematic diagram of impedance-matching specimens.

Five groups of IMS specimens (IMS1~IMS5) were obtained by adjusting the dosages (5%, 10%, 15%, 20%, 25%) of the CMA in the IMS impedance matching layer, respectively.

2.2 Tests for pavement markings

This study tested the corrosion resistance, wear resistance, and anti-slip resistance of the markings according to the transport industry standard JTG E20-2011 (Pavement marking paint, People's Republic of China). The IMS1 were selected as the representatives of IMS for testing the corrosion and wear and the anti-sliding resistances of all the five groups of specimens (Liu et al. 2022; 2023; 2023). The tests were conducted as follows:

(1) Corrosion resistance

One group, IMS1, and the other were completely immersed in water and saturated Ca(OH)$_2$. After 24 h, the surface of the specimen was checked for any noticeable changes.

(2) Wear resistance at high temperature

The high-temperature wear resistances of the IMS were evaluated by observing the state of the marking surface after the test wheel was loaded for one hour.

(3) Anti-sliding resistance

The anti-sliding resistance was tested using the BM-III pendulum-type friction coefficient tester. The testing temperature was 14°C, and the corresponding temperature modification value was - 1.4 (Liu et al. 2022, Ren et al. 2021).

(4) Marking removal and evaluation

As shown in Figure 2, the FMS heated in the microwave oven for 3 min was removed and placed on the surface of a flat table. Then, the surface line was gently removed from the upper surface using heated forceps.

Figure 2. Schematic of microwave stripping of IMS.

Before and after microwave heating and removal, a digital camera was used to click photos of the five groups of IMS and five pavement core samples containing IMS5. Then MATLAB digital image processing technology was used to calculate the corresponding marking area using Equation 1 (Liu et al. 2022; Wang et al. 2022, 2022):

$$E = \left(1 - \frac{S_1}{S_2}\right) * 100\% \qquad (1)$$

where E is the removal efficiency of microwave heating, S_1 is the total area of the marking after removal, and S_2 is the total area of the marking before removal.

3 EXPERIMENTAL RESULTS AND DISCUSSIONS

(1) Corrosion resistance

As shown in Figure 3, results showed no discoloration, foaming, wrinkling, or shedding on the FMS surfaces, indicating that these surfaces had good water and alkali resistances.

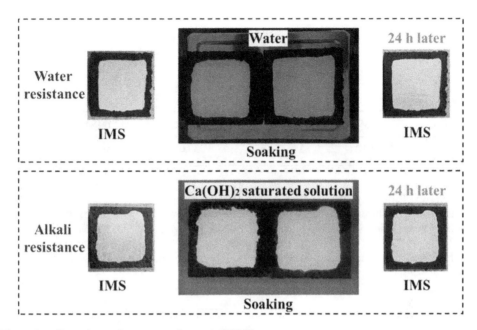

Figure 3.   Corrosion resistance test diagram of FMS.

(2) Wear resistance at high temperature

Figure 4 showed that the surfaces of IMS adhered more to black and brown asphalt in the rolling area; this was attributed to the adherence of the asphalt to the rubber wheel and remaining on the surface of the marking line at 60 °C. In addition, no abnormal phenomena such as spalling, fractures, and folds were observed on the line marking of the wheel rolling area or other areas around it, indicating that the specimens exhibited excellent wear resistance at high temperatures.

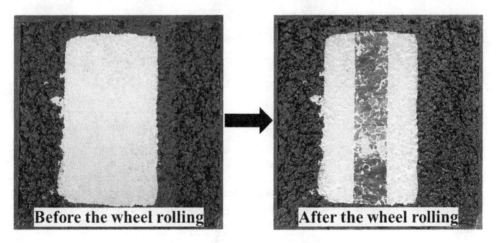

Figure 4.   Wear resistance test of FMS at high temperature.

(3) Corrosion resistance

Table 1 lists the testing results in BPN values. Results showed that all the BPN values of the IMS were between 55 and 58, meeting the specified requirements of BPN ≥ 45.

Table 1. Corrosion resistance testing results of IMS.

Specimen	IMS1	IMS2	IMS3	IMS4	IMS5
BPN	55.34	55.88	57.01	56.57	57.13

(4) Removal Efficiency

The removal efficiency of the five groups of IMS are shown in Figure 5. Results showed that the removal efficiencies of the 5 groups (IMS1, IMS2, IMS3, IMS4, and IMS5) were 99.4%, 99.8%, 99.9%, 100%, and 100%, respectively because the curing product showed strong thermoplasticity and fluidity, which could satisfy the practical engineering requirements.

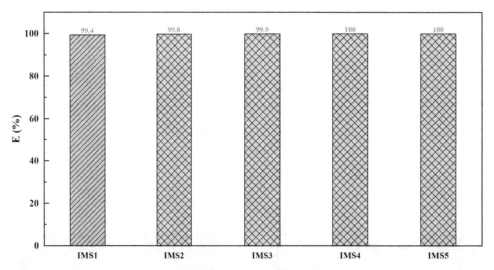

Figure 5. Removal efficiency of five groups of marking specimens using microwave heating.

4 CONCLUSION

The following conclusions can be obtained based on the study presented in this paper.

1) The IMS's corrosion, wear, and skid resistance met the required specifications. After marking removals using microwave heating, all the BPN values of these specimens were higher than before. After microwave cleaning, the pores on the asphalt mixture surface were visible, indicating that the microwave cleaning of the prepared markings would not destroy the texture of road surfaces and improve the anti-skid performance of these surfaces.
2) The removal efficiency of the 5 groups of IMS was 99.4%, 99.8%, 99.9%, 100%, and 100%, respectively, because the curing product showed strong thermoplasticity and fluidity, which could satisfy the practical engineering requirements.

ACKNOWLEDGMENTS

This study was sponsored by the Key Science and Technology Research Project of Jinhua, China, under Grant 2021-3-177.

REFERENCES

Cho Y., Kabassi K., Pyeon J.H., Choi K., Wang C., Norton T., Effectiveness Study of Methods for Removing Temporary Pavement Markings in Roadway Construction Zones, *J Constr Eng M* 139(3) (2013) 257–266.

Jeppson M.R., *Microwave Method and Apparatus for Reprocessing Pavements*, U.S., 1982.

Li S.W., Gu X.Y., Xu X.R., Xu D.W., Zhang T.J., Liu Z., Dong Q., Detection of Concealed Cracks From Ground Penetrating Radar Images Based on the Deep Learning Algorithm, *Constr Build Mater* 273 (2021).

Liu L., Yeoh J.K.W., Gu X., Dong Q., Chen Y., Wu W., Wang L., and Wang D., Automatic Pixel-level Detection of Vertical Cracks in Asphalt Pavement Based on GPR Investigation and Improved Mask R-CNN, *Automat Constr* 146 (2023) 104689.

Liu M.M., Han S., Pan J., Ren W.Y., Study on Cohesion Performance of Waterborne Epoxy Resin Emulsified Asphalt as Interlayer Materials, *Constr Build Mater* 177 (2018) 72–82.

Liu W., Miao P.H. and Wang S.Y., Increasing Microwave Heating Efficiency of Asphalt-Coated Aggregates Mixed with Modified Steel Slag Particles,. *J Mater Civil Eng* 29(10) (2017).

Liu Z., Chen Y.H., Gu X.Y., Yeoh J.K.W., and Zhang Q.P., Visibility Classification and Influencing-factors Analysis of Airport: A Deep Learning Approach, *Atmospheric Environment* 278 (2022).

Liu Z., Gu X., Chen J., Wang D., Chen Y., and Wang L., Automatic Recognition of Pavement Cracks From Combined GPR B-scan and C-scan Images Using Multiscale Feature Fusion Deep Neural Networks, *Automat Constr* 146 (2023) 104698.

Liu Z., Gu X., Chen Y., and Chen Y., System Architecture and Key Technologies for the Whole Life Cycle of Smart Road, *Journal of Physics: Conference Series, IOP Publishing*, 2021, p. 012105.

Liu Z., Gu X., Dong X., Cui B., and Hu D., Mechanism and Performance of Graphene Modified Asphalt: An Experimental Approach Combined with Molecular Dynamic Simulations, *Case Stud Constr Mat* (2022) e01749.

Liu Z., Gu X., Ren H., Wang X., and Dong Q., Three-dimensional Finite Element Analysis for Structural Parameters of Asphalt Pavement: *A Combined Laboratory and Field Accelerated Testing Approach*, Case Stud Constr Mat. (2022) e01221.

Liu Z., Gu X.Y. and Dong Q., *Multi-Scale 3D Display of the Internal Quality of the Pavement Based on BIM, 19th COTA International Conference of Transportation Professionals (CICTP) - Transportation in China 2025, Nanjing, Peoples R China*, 2019, pp. 4265–4273.

Liu Z., Gu X.Y., Dong Q., Tu S.S., and Li S.W., 3D Visualization of Airport Pavement Quality Based on BIM and WebGL Integration, J Transp Eng B-Pave 147(3) (2021).

Liu Z., Gu X.Y., Ren H., Zhou Z., Wang X., and Tang S., Analysis of the Dynamic Responses of Asphalt Pavement Based on Full-scale Accelerated Testing and Finite Element Simulation, Constr Build Mater 325 (2022).

Liu Z., Gu X.Y., Wu C.Y., Ren H., Zhou Z. and Tang S., Studies on the Validity of Strain Sensors for Pavement Monitoring: A Case Study for a Fiber Bragg Grating Sensor and Resistive Sensor, Constr Build Mater 321 (2022).

Liu Z., Gu X.Y., Wu W.X., Zou X.Y., Dong Q., and Wang L.T., GPR-based Detection of Internal Cracks in Asphalt Pavement: *A Combination Method of DeepAugment Data and Object Detection*, Measurement 197 (2022).

Liu Z., Gu X.Y., Yang H.L., Wang L.T., Chen Y.H., and Wang D.Y., Novel YOLOv3 Model With Structure and Hyperparameter Optimization for Detection of Pavement Concealed Cracks in GPR Images,. *IEEE T Intell Transp* (2022).

Liu Z., Wang S.Y., Gu X.Y., Li Z.G., Dong Q., and Cui B.Y., Application of a Novel EWMA-phi Chart on Quality Control in Asphalt Mixtures Production,. *Constr Build Mater* 323 (2022).

Liu Z., Wu W.X., Gu X.Y., Li S.W., Wang L.T., and Zhang T.J., Application of Combining YOLO Models and 3D GPR Images in Road Detection and Maintenance, *Remote Sens-Basel* 13(6) (2021).

Ren H., Gu X.Y. and Liu Z., Analysis of Mechanical Responses for Semi-Rigid Base Asphalt Pavement Based on MLS66 Accelerated Loading Test, *20th and 21st Joint COTA International Conference of*

Transportation Professionals - Advanced Transportation, Enhanced Connection, Xian, Peoples R China, 2021, pp. 732–742.

Wang D., Liu Z., Gu X., Wu W., Chen Y. and Wang L., Automatic Detection of Pothole Distress in Asphalt Pavement Using Improved Convolutional Neural Networks, *Remote Sens-Basel.* 14(16) (2022).

Wang L.T., Gu X.Y., Liu Z., Wu W.X., Wang D.Y., Automatic Detection of Asphalt Pavement Thickness: A Method Combining GPR Images and Improved Canny Algorithm, *Measurement* 196 (2022).

Yang G., Wang C., Fu H., Yan Z. and Yin W., Waterborne Epoxy Resin-Polyurethane-Emulsified Asphalt: Preparation and Properties, *J Mater Civil Eng* 31(11) (2019).

Research on prefabricated buildings cost management based on value chain theory

Ting Cao* & Tingting Liu
Shanghai Urban Construction Vocational College, Yangpu District, Shanghai, China

ABSTRACT: According to the characteristics and business process of prefabricated buildings and the manufacturing cost management model based on value chain theory, the index system affecting the cost of prefabricated buildings is constructed. Through the questionnaire survey of the prefabricated construction industry and principal component analysis using SPSS software, several key links that greatly influence the cost of prefabricated construction are obtained.

1 INTRODUCTION

In the rapid development of building industrialization, prefabricated buildings are widely praised for their fast construction speed, short construction period, and ability to synchronize with various professional construction on sites. However, the high cost still limits its development. Our country is in the stage of rapid development of prefabricated buildings. At this stage, exploring the cost management methods of prefabricated buildings will effectively promote its development. The cost management method based on the value chain theory can start from the various cost activities (Xu 2010), analyze the value of the cost of each link, can provide us with new prefabricated construction cost management ideas. Based on this, the value chain theory is applied to the cost management of prefabricated buildings to analyze and manage the cost value of each activity of the project.

2 COST IMPACT INDEX SYSTEM OF PREFABRICATED BUILDINGS

According to the value chain model of prefabricated buildings (Cao 2019), we construct the cost impact indicators of prefabricated buildings, as shown in Table 1.

Table 1. Cost impact index system of prefabricated construction.

Value Chain	Cost activity	Cost impact index	Index code
Auxiliary activities	Project infrastructure	Project management system	a1
		The strategic thinking, corporate culture, and working environment of the project	a2
		Project budget, accounting, information, and other management control systems	a3

(continued)

---

*Corresponding Author: caoting@succ.edu.cn

DOI: 10.1201/9781003433644-23

Table 1. Continued

Value Chain	Cost activity	Cost impact index	Index code
Basic activities	Human resource management	Project personnel selection and recruitment	a4
		Project staff salary	a5
		Evaluation of employee skills	a6
		Training and improvement of employee skills	a7
	Technology development	Construction organization design and technology development and improvement	a8
		Preparation of technical bids, construction of construction teams	a9
		Construction technical data	a10
	Purchase	Procurement of materials and equipment	a11
		Procurement and customization of prefabricated components	a12
		Bidding, a supply plan	a13
	Project contract	Project contracting	a14
	Internal logistics	Acceptance and inventory of materials and equipment	a15
		Reasonable allocation of resources	a16
	Project construction	Contract management in the construction process	a17
		Progress control during the construction process	a18
		Quality management in the construction process	a19
		Cost control in the construction process	a20
	Completion acceptance	Sorting out the project data after the completion	a21
		Analysis of commercial and technical data after the completion of the project	a22
		Data Archive	a23
	Warranty and service system construction	Warranty and service system construction	a24

3 PRINCIPAL COMPONENT ANALYSIS

According to the prefabricated construction cost impact index system (Cao 2019), a questionnaire was designed, a questionnaire survey was conducted in the prefabricated construction industry, and relatively objective and true survey results were obtained. The survey uses the Likert scale method to divide the prefabricated construction practitioners' views on the influencing factors of prefabricated construction costs into five categories, which are divided into two categories with positive attitudes, one with neutral attitudes, and two with negative attitudes. We use scores of 5, 4, 3, 2, and 1 to indicate that the impact is very large, the impact is relatively large, the impact is average, the impact is relatively small, and the impact is very small. Then, we use the SPSS statistical analysis tool to perform factor analysis on the questionnaire results to obtain the most important main components that affect the cost of prefabricated buildings. By strictly controlling these main factors, the cost of prefabricated buildings can be controlled from the value chain perspective.

The principal component analysis method is used to analyze the 98×24-order correlation matrix, and the explained total variance is shown in Table 2. It can be seen from the table that there are six factors with eigenvalues greater than 1, which are 10.114, 2.285, 1.959, 1.543, 1.321, and 1.119, respectively. The proportions of variance explained by these six factors are 42.141%, 9.521%, 8.162%, 6.429%, 5.503%, and 4.661%, respectively. The cumulative explained total variance is 76.418%.

Table 2. Explained total variance.

Ingredients	Initial eigenvalues Total	Extraction Sums of Squared Loadings Variance %	Cumulative %	Total	Variance%	Cumulative %	Total	Variance %	Cumulative %
1	10.114	42.141	42.141	10.114	42.141	42.141	4.855	20.230	20.230
2	2.285	9.521	51.663	2.285	9.521	51.663	3.560	14.832	35.063
3	1.959	8.162	59.825	1.959	8.162	59.825	3.488	14.533	49.596
4	1.543	6.429	66.254	1.543	6.429	66.254	3.358	13.992	63.588
5	1.321	5.503	71.757	1.321	5.503	71.757	1.542	6.426	70.013
6	1.119	4.661	76.418	1.119	4.661	76.418	1.537	6.405	76.418
7	.919	3.831	80.249						
8	.710	2.957	83.206						
9	.644	2.684	85.890						
10	.610	2.541	88.432						
11	.502	2.092	90.524						
12	.447	1.864	92.387						
13	.344	1.433	93.820						
14	.292	1.217	95.037						
15	.221	.921	95.958						
16	.194	.810	96.768						
17	.183	.762	97.530						
18	.150	.627	98.157						
19	.129	.537	98.693						
20	.090	.376	99.070						
21	.086	.357	99.427						
22	.071	.296	99.723						
23	.047	.194	99.917						
24	.020	.083	100.000						

Extraction method: a principal component analysis.

From the public factor gravel diagram (as shown in Figure 1), it can be seen that the eigenvalues of the first three public factors have changed significantly. Starting from the fourth eigenvalue, the changes tend to be stable, but the eigenvalues of the first six factors are greater than 1. It shows that the first six public factors significantly affect the information interpretation of the original variables. Therefore, six principal components are now extracted.

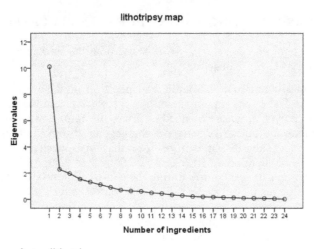

Figure 1. Common factor lithotripsy map.

In order to make the meaning of factors clear and facilitate the interpretation of factors, the maximum variance method is used to rotate the factor matrix to obtain the factor component matrix after rotation, as shown in Table 3.

Table 3. Rotation component matrix[a].

	Ingredients					
	1	2	3	4	5	6
VAR00001	.130	.076	.228	.014	**.883**	.021
VAR00002	.049	.011	.199	.118	.055	**.834**
VAR00003	.161	.377	.358	.577	.104	.201
VAR00004	.233	.132	−.158	.190	.495	.488
VAR00005	.321	.012	**.800**	.067	.128	.097
VAR00006	.370	.207	**.690**	−.117	−.145	.370
VAR00007	−.123	.335	**.692**	.140	.250	.022
VAR00008	.385	.597	−.111	.354	.355	.187
VAR00009	.241	.084	.174	.367	.036	.151
VAR00010	**.778**	.302	.196	.131	−.015	.131
VAR00011	**.725**	.054	-.051	.370	.239	.010
VAR00012	**.796**	.084	−.109	.586	.212	.020
VAR00013	.304	.308	.186	**.855**	−.030	.054
VAR00014	−.113	.290	.396	**.782**	−.199	.368
VAR00015	.360	.266	.665	.344	−.093	−.020
VAR00016	.291	.446	.453	.393	.038	−.337
VAR00017	.702	**.789**	−.035	.171	.253	.020
VAR00018	.331	**.804**	.122	.151	−.015	−.028
VAR00019	.108	**.807**	.384	.142	.071	.000
VAR00020	**.774**	.362	.321	.309	.165	−.123
VAR00021	.444	.435	.074	.085	.039	−.055
VAR00022	.285	.211	.362	.123	−.044	.189
VAR00023	.648	.148	.437	.190	.029	.166
VAR00024	.334	.139	.345	.152	.148	−.081

Extraction method: principal component analysis method.
Rotation method: Orthogonal rotation method with Kaiser standardization.
[a]The rotation converges after 20 iterations.

4 KEY FACTORS AFFECTING THE COST OF PREFABRICATED BUILDINGS

By analyzing the factor component matrix after rotation, the six key contents of the prefabricated building cost are summarized:

(1) Purchase of construction materials and components. From the explained total variance (shown in Table 2) and the common factor gravel plot (shown in Figure 1), it can be seen that the proportion of variance explained by principal component 1 is 42.141%, which is much larger than the other five principal components. From the rotating component matrix (shown in Table 3), it can be seen that a10 construction technical data, a11 materials, equipment procurement, a12 prefabricated component procurement and customization, and a20 cost control during the construction process. The load value of component 1 is larger than the other original variables, which are 0.778, 0.625, 0.796, and 0.774, respectively. The characteristics of these four factors can be summarized as construction materials and component procurement, the content that has the greatest impact on the cost of prefabricated construction.

(2) Project management during construction. In the same way, a17 (contract management in the construction process), a18 (schedule control in the construction process), and a19 (quality management in the construction process). The characteristics of these three factors are summarized as the project management during the construction process, as the second influencing the cost of prefabricated construction Items.
(3) Human resource management. a05 (the salary of project management personnel), a06 (the inspection and evaluation of employee skills), and a07 (the training and promotion of employee skills) are summarized as human resource management, which is another key content that affects the cost of prefabricated construction.
(4) Project bidding. a13(bidding, supply plan) and a14(project contracting), are summarized as project bidding. The project bidding link's cost control involves the operation of multiple departments, such as engineering, design, auditing, and marketing.
(5) Project management system. a01 (project management system), as an auxiliary function to support basic activities, good management of auxiliary functions can better support the project to carry out value-added activities.
(6) Strategic goals of the project. a02 (the strategic thinking, corporate culture, and working environment of the project) are summarized as the project's strategic goal, as the last key content that affects the cost of prefabricated construction.

5 PROPOSED TARGETED PREFABRICATED BUILDING COST MANAGEMENT

For the cost management of prefabricated buildings, combined with the all-around control idea of cost management, targeted cost control is carried out from the activities incurred, and the six key aspects that affect the cost of prefabricated buildings summarized in the previous section are respectively proposed. There are several strategies to control the cost of prefabricated buildings.

(1) Strengthen the cost control of materials and parts
From the perspective of cost occurrence, the procurement cost of prefabricated building components accounts for a high proportion of the project's total cost (Dai 2020). From the perspective of comprehensive cost management, increasing the control of the main proportion of the cost is also an effective way to reduce the total construction cost. Therefore, from the procurement perspective, the purpose of cost management of prefabricated buildings can be achieved through effective competition, market inquiry, and other ways to select the optimal procurement scheme.
(2) Deepen engineering project management
Enterprises should improve and implement the construction site management system to ensure safe and civilized construction and can effectively use information technology to strengthen the construction process management. With the promotion of global information construction, the construction industry's informatization is also developing daily, which provides more ways and methods for construction enterprises to carry out construction management. For example, BIM5D technology can effectively simulate the construction process in advance and avoid adverse factors that may affect the construction progress or quality of the real construction. It can also take the initiative to manage the project, prevent it in advance, and avoid the cost increase caused by the project rework. (Zhao 2020)
(3) Develop human resources management
The enterprise should develop a sound employee training mechanism and salary and reward system to ensure the material needs of the employees and let them have a long-term development plan and their own growth goals. In addition, because our country is still in the early prefabricated construction technology development, the enterprise needs relevant

professional and technical personnel to promote the project's construction. Therefore, the enterprise shall simultaneously introduce high-level professional talents and communication platforms for our employees and the outside world, promoting the staff's growth and technological innovation to seek the creative value of human resources.

(4) Strictly control bidding activities

The enterprise should adopt the bidding strategy in many aspects, give a reasonable bidding price in the bidding quotation link, and control the contract price of the project within the acceptable range. In addition, screening the subcontractors, strictly controlling the reputation and ability of the enterprises, allowing each subcontractor to compete in a fair, open environment, and selecting the most competitive subcontractor are the key measures to improve the economic benefits of the project.

(5) Reform the project management system

Following the principles of the value chain, reform the project management system, retain the instruction links that generate value, and streamline the communication procedures of work instructions. Therefore, the executors of the instructions can put more efficiency on value activities; in addition, in the management, when reforming the system, consider democratic management. Project leaders should listen to multiple voices and use digital information to manage the project. Finally, reforming the project management system, avoiding the phenomenon of "raising idlers" in the project, and relying on the value chain to determine the positions and responsibilities of employees will ensure the value of employee activities.

(6) Clarify the project's strategic objectives

The first step is to determine the mission objectives to complete a project. The cost, schedule, quality, and other project objectives are determined based on the overall strategic objectives of the project. Determining strategic objectives is the core of the project's development strategy. It is necessary to clarify the ultimate direction of the results completed by various value activities in the value chain model. Therefore, it is necessary to clarify the ultimate direction of its results to organize value activities according to the value chain model.

6 CONCLUSION

This paper proposes cost management based on a value chain to find an effective way for prefabricated construction enterprises to improve their benefits. The cost concept based on the value chain starts from the creation of value, its cost is to add value for the enterprise, and the non-value-added activities are streamlined to carry out cost control. This paper starts from the value chain composition of prefabricated construction cost and constructs the index system of prefabricated construction cost. Through principal component analysis, the dimensionality reduction of each cost index is analyzed, and effective strategies for cost management of prefabricated buildings are discussed.

REFERENCES

Jingbo Xu. Value Chain Analysis of Construction Enterprises. *Market Weekly (Theoretical Research)*, 2010, 9: 26–28.

Ting Cao. Value Chain Analysis of Prefabricated Buildings. *China Real Estate Industry*, 2019(12).

Yunfeng Dai. Cost Control and Cost Management of Prefabricated Buildings. *Green Environmental Protection Building Materials*. 2020, (09).

Yanli Zhao, Chunsheng Zhang, Yifan Liu. Research on the Cost Chain Composition and Optimization Direction of Prefabricated Buildings—Based on the Perspective of Real Estate Enterprises. *Construction Economy*. 2020, 41(11)

Shape and size effect on compressive strength of rammed earth

Tiegang Zhou, Dong Li*, Wei Tan & Hui Tao
School of Civil Engineering, Xi'an University of Architecture and Technology, Xi'an, China

ABSTRACT: This paper deals with the size and shape effects of compressive specimens that influence the mechanical properties of rammed earth. Three common ratios of rammed earth materials were adopted and mechanically rammed, and the compressive test was carried out after curing. The failure of rammed earth specimens was observed, and the failure mechanism was studied. The influence of different cement content, sizes, and shapes on the compressive strength of rammed earth specimens was compared and analyzed. The relationship between the axial compressive strength of prismatic specimens and the compressive strength of cube and cylinder specimens is fitted. Results show that the compressive strength of rammed earth has an obvious size effect. With the increase in size, the cube compressive strength increases first and then decreases without cement, and the cylinder compressive strength and prism axial compressive strength decrease gradually. After adding cement, the cube's compressive strength is the largest when the size is 150 × 150 × 150 mm. The compressive strength of the cylinder decreases first and then increases, and the axial compressive strength of the prism decreases gradually. The compressive strength of rammed earth has an obvious shape effect. Under the same ratio and test conditions, the cube compressive strength is 26 % ~ 101 % higher than the cylinder compressive strength, and the cylinder compressive strength is slightly higher than the prism axial compressive strength.

1 INTRODUCTION

As an important part of traditional architecture, the raw-soil structure has a widespread application worldwide. It attracts the attention of scholars in civil engineering due to its advantages of ecology, energy conservation, and environmental protection (Yihong 2015). To minimize the unsustainable use of natural resources and massive energy consumption in the manufacturing of building materials (such as cement and brick) and to protect the environment from critical natural hazards like global warming (due to the emission of CO_2 during the production phase). The green home technique (i.e., rammed earth construction) seems efficient (Binod & Manjip 2016; Zhao et al. 2011).

Rammed earth construction is an ancient technique using local soils that are compacted to form structural elements. This method has attracted renewed interest worldwide due to its social, economic, and environmental benefits. D. D. Tripura (Tripura & Singh 2016) conducted a detailed study on the bearing capacity of cement-stabilized rammed earth (CSRE) cylinders under axial compression. Tests were carried out on CSRE cylinders and columns to determine the effects of concentric axial loads and slenderness ratios. The specimen size and its slenderness can affect the compressive strength of CSRE elements (Venkatarama Reddy 2016). there is hardly any variation in the compressive strength of CSRE when height to thickness ratio of the specimen is within the range of 2–6 (Reddy et al. 2015).

Study the Size Effect of Unconfined Compressive Strength of Rammed Earthen Site's Soil Samples. (Wang et al. 2020) Two-dimensional discrete element models of the soil samples

---

*Corresponding Author: 1012235850@qq.com

are established to simulate the impact of different end-frictional conditions on the stress-strain processes of samples. The simulation results follow typical experiments, thus verifying the rationality of established discrete element models. Comparing the particle displacement directions and the respective proportions, the constraint caused by the loading plate on samples is proved to be one of the reasons for the size effect. Koutous, A (Koutous & Hilali 2019) explored the effects of grain shape and size on the mechanical behavior of compacted earthen materials. Rika, J (Rika et al. 2015) summarized the latest results of experimental research on mechanical, building physical and environmental properties of precast rammed earth.

The purpose of this paper is to figure out the failure mechanism of the rammed earth specimens, explore the influence of different conditions on the compressive strength of modern rammed earth, and clarify the compressive strength relationship of rammed earth under different conditions to provide a reference for the formulation of technical standards for rammed earth buildings and the application of engineering practice.

2 EXPERIMENTAL PROGRAM

2.1 Materials

The soil material is selected from the undisturbed soil layer in Gaoling District, Xi'an City, Shaanxi Province. The soil quality belongs to the common loess in northwest China. Sand material is selected from the natural medium sand in the suburbs of Xi'an, Shaanxi Province. The stone is the broken concrete stone of a stone factory in the suburb of Xi'an city, Shaanxi Province. Ordinary Portland cement (P.O 42.5) is used as the modified material. The main physical and mechanical indexes of soil are shown in Table 1.

Table 1. Characteristics of soil.

Natural moisture content ω/%	Maximum dry density ρ/(g/cm^3)	Liquid limit W_L(%)	Plastic limit W_p(%)	Plastic index I_p(%)	Particle size distribution(%)		
					>0.075mm	0.075~0.005mm	<0.005mm
4.38	1.9	26	16	14	10	75	15

2.2 Test design

The mass ratio of soil: sand: the stone was selected as 5: 2: 3 as the basic ratio of rammed earth. The specimens were divided into three types with a cement content of 0%, 5%, and 10% of the total mass of rammed earth mixture and made by mechanical ramming with steel molds. The specific test specimens are shown in Table 2.

The moisture content of the mixture is strictly controlled during the compaction process of the specimen. According to the Earthwork Testing Method Standard (GB / T50123-1999) (Qin 2010), the optimal moisture content of the rammed earth mixture is 10 % ± 1 %, which is reduced after adding cement—after the completion of the specimen, ramming sun protection, rain protection, and other measures, ventilation and drying for 2 months.

2.3 Test loading

The test was completed in the Structural and Seismic Laboratory of Xi'an University of Architecture and Technology. NYL-200D pressure testing machine was used for cube and cylinder specimens. The maximum experimental force was 2000kN and the accuracy could

Table 2. Test specimens.

Name of sample	Serial number	Size of the sample (mm)	The proportion of cement mass		
			0%	5%	10%
Cube	Cu150	150 × 150 × 150	JAa1~5	JBa1~5	JCa1~5
	Cu200	200 × 200 × 200	JAb1~5	JBb1~5	JCb1~5
	Cu250:	250 × 250 × 250	JAc1~5	JBc1~5	JCc1~5
Cylinder	Cy150	φ150 × 300	JAd1~5	JBd1~5	JCd1~5
	Cy200	φ200 × 400	JAe1~5	JBe1~5	JCe1~5
	Cy250	φ250 × 500	JAf1~5	JBf1~5	JCf1~5
Prism	Pr500	150 × 300 × 500	JA1~3	JB1~3	JC1~3
	Pr800	300 × 300× 800	KA1~3	KB1~3	KC1~3

reach 0.01kN. Prism axial compression test, using YAD-5000 (500T) microcomputer control electro-hydraulic servo pressure testing machine. Test loading is shown in Figure 1.

Figure 1. Test loading.

3 RESULTS AND DISCUSSIONS

3.1 Compression test results

The arithmetic means the value of each group's calculation results is taken as the representative value of the cube's compressive strength. In addition, considering the eccentric compression and micro-damage caused by pre-production, if one or more values are found to be more than 15% of the average value, it is considered to be discarded. In the end, there were 9 groups of data of 45 cubic specimens, of which 44 were involved in the statistics, accounting for 97.8% of the total. A total of 45 data were obtained from 9 groups of cylinder specimens, of which 43 were involved in the statistical results, accounting for 95.6% of the total. A total of 18 data were obtained from 6 groups of prismatic specimens, of which 18 were involved in the statistical results, accounting for 100% of the total. The compressive test results of effective specimens with different proportions, sizes, and shapes are shown in Table 3.

3.2 Analysis of size effect

According to the compressive test results, the compressive strength of specimens with various shapes also changes with the size change shown in Figure 2, indicating that the compressive strength of rammed earth specimens with different proportions has a side effect.

As for the cube specimen, with the increase in size, the compressive strength of the cube specimen increases first and then decreases without cement and reaches the maximum when

Table 3. Compression test results of specimens.

Name of sample	Size of sample(mm)	Cement content(%)	Compressive strength(MPa)	Standard deviation
Cube	150 × 150 × 150	0	2.15	0.08
	150 × 150 × 150	5	7.24	0.22
	150 × 150 × 150	10	10.07	0.35
Cube	200 × 200 × 200	0	2.61	0.14
	200 × 200 × 200	5	5.99	0.28
	200 × 200 × 200	10	8.16	0.71
Cube	250 × 250 × 250	0	2.12	0.11
	250 × 250 × 250	5	7.37	0.37
	250 × 250 × 250	10	8.07	0.39
Cylinder	150 × 300	0	1.70	0.15
	150 × 300	5	3.60	0.20
	150 × 300	10	5.33	0.39
Cylinder	200 × 400	0	1.37	0.06
	200 × 400	5	3.12	0.16
	200 × 400	10	4.59	0.27
Cylinder	250 × 500	0	1.11	0.08
	250 × 500	5	4.72	0.41
	250 × 500	10	6.43	0.41
Prism	150 × 300 × 500	0	1.42	0.30
	150 × 300 × 500	5	4.45	0.08
	150 × 300 × 500	10	5.29	0.50
Prism	300 × 300 × 800	0	1.01	0.46
	300 × 300 × 800	5	2.96	0.49
	300 × 300 × 800	10	4.15	0.28

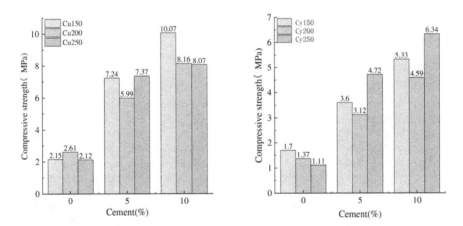

Figure 2. Strength comparison with different cement contents.

the size is 200 × 200 × 200mm, averaging 2.61MPa. After the addition of cement, the compressive strength of specimens decreases first and then increases. When the specimen size is 200 × 200 × 200mm, the compressive strength is the lowest, 5.99mpa and 8.16mpa, when the cement content is 5% and 10%, respectively. It shows that the addition of cement affects the size effect of the cube's compressive strength.

As for the cylinder specimen, with the increase in size, the compressive strength of the specimen decreases gradually without cement. With the addition of cement, the compressive strength of the specimen decreases first and then increases. When the cement content is 5% and 10%, the lowest values are 3.12MPa and 4.59MPa when the specimen size is $\varphi 200 \times 400$mm, respectively. It shows that the compressive strength of rammed earth cylinders with different proportions has a side effect, and the law is different before and after the cement is added.

The average axial compressive strain of Pr800 specimens is 53%–150% higher than that of Pr500 specimens and 0.85 times peak stress. When 5% cement was added, the axial compressive strain of the Pr500 specimen at peak stress decreased by 20% and that of the Pr800 specimen by 25%; When 10% cement was added, the axial compressive strain of the Pr500 specimen at peak stress decreased by 55% and Pr800 specimen by 47%. It indicates that adding cement reduces the axial deformation of rammed earth specimens and enhances their ability to resist deformation. With the increase in cement content, the enhancement effect becomes more obvious.

3.3 Analysis of shape effect

Due to the different shapes of rammed soil specimens, the compressive strength obtained is also different, indicating a shaping effect in the compressive strength of rammed earth. Under different proportions, the compressive strength of cubic rammed earth specimens is generally higher than that of cylinder specimens, which is between 26% and 101% higher. The compressive strength of the cylinder is slightly higher than the axial compressive strength of the prism. This result is friction between the specimen and the testing machine. This friction restages the transverse expansion deformation on the specimen. It produces horizontal pressure, affecting the cube specimen's whole range. The cylinder and the prism (because of the large slenderness comparison in this paper, the cylinder slenderness ratio is 2:1, Prism slenderness ratio of 10:3 and 8:3). The middle part of the region is not affected by it, which makes the specimen state of multi-axial compression, and ultimately improves the compressive strength of the specimen. Moreover, prisms establish a more uniform uniaxial compressive state at the middle end than cylinders, thus obtaining a lower and more ideal uniaxial compressive strength of rammed earth than cubes and cylinders.

The fitting relation between the axial compressive strength of rammed earth and cubic compressive strength under different sizes and proportions of the mechanical ramming method was obtained by linear regression. The final fitting formula and diagram are shown in Table 4 and Figure 3.

The fitting relationship between the axial compressive strength of rammed earth and the compressive strength of the cylinder is shown in Table 5 and Figure 4.

Table 4. Fitting the relation between prismatic and cube compressive strength.

Prism size	Cube size	Fitting formula	Graphic
Pr500	Cu150	$f_{cm} = 0.5 f_{cum} + 0.47$	Figure 3(a)
	Cu200	$f_{cm} = 0.71 f_{cum} - 0.27$	Figure 3(b)
	Cu250	$f_{cm} = 0.62 f_{cum} + 0.07$	Figure 3(c)
Pr800	Cu150	$f_{cm} = 0.39 f_{cum} - 0.15$	Figure 3(d)
	Cu200	$f_{cm} = 0.57 f_{cum} - 0.46$	Figure 3(e)
	Cu250	$f_{cm} = 0.47 f_{cum} - 0.04$	Figure 3(f)

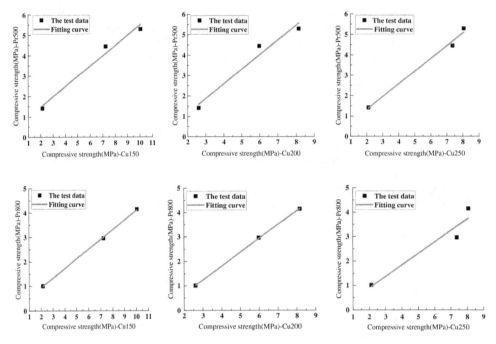

Figure 3. Fitting curve of compressive strength relationship between prism and cube.

Table 5. Fitting relation between prismatic and cylinder compressive strength.

Prism size (mm)	Cylinder size (mm)	Fitting formula	Graphic
Pr500	Cy150	$f_{cm} = -0.31 f_{cym}^2 + 3.21 f_{cym} - 3.16$	Figure 4(a)
	Cy200	$f_{cm} = -0.36 f_{cym}^2 + 3.35 f_{cym} - 2.49$	Figure 4(b)
	Cy250	$f_{cm} = -0.06 f_{cym}^2 + 1.2 f_{cym} + 0.17$	Figure 4(c)
Pr800	Cy150	$f_{cm} = -0.09 f_{cym}^2 + 1.52 f_{cym} - 1.31$	Figure 4(d)
	Cy200	$f_{cm} = -0.09 f_{cym}^2 + 1.54 f_{cym} - 0.92$	Figure 4(e)
	Cy250	$f_{cm} = 0.04 f_{cym}^2 + 0.32 f_{cym} + 0.61$	Figure 4(f)

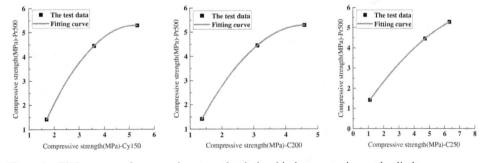

Figure 4. Fitting curve of compressive strength relationship between prism and cylinder.

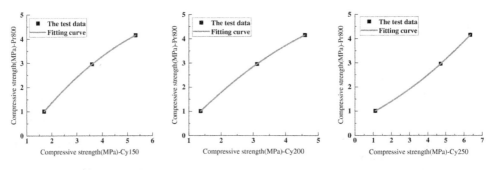

Figure 4. (Continued)

4 CONCLUSION

(1) The addition of cement impacts the size effect of cube compressive strength. With the increase in size, the compressive strength of cube specimens increases first and then decreases without cement under the same conditions. After adding cement, the compressive strength of the cube specimen decreases first and then increases.
(2) The compressive strength of rammed earth cylinders under different proportions has a size effect, and the size effect law before and after cement addition is different. With the change in size and cement content, the compressive strength of the rammed earth cylinder changes. When cement is not added to rammed earth, the compressive strength of the cylinder decreases with the increase in size. After adding cement, the compressive strength of the cylinder decreases first and then increases with the increase in size.
(3) The size effect of rammed earth prism compressive strength is slightly different from cube and cylinder. The average axial compressive strength of the Pr500 prism specimen is 27% $\sim$ 50% higher than that of the Pr800 specimen.
(4) Under the same experimental conditions, the compressive strength of the rammed earth cube is 26% $\sim$ 101% higher than that of the cylinder, and the compressive strength of the cylinder is slightly higher than that of the prism.
(5) The incorporation of cement is conducive to inhibiting the generation of dry shrinkage cracks in rammed soil specimens. With the increase in cement content, the cube's compressive strength increases gradually. The cube compressive strength increases by 130% $\sim$ 248% with 5 % cement and 213% $\sim$ 368% with 10% cement. The compressive strength of the cylinder was increased by 112% $\sim$ 325% by adding 5 % cement and by 214% $\sim$ 471% by adding 10% cement; the addition of 5% cement increased the axial compressive strength of the prism by 203 % on average, and the addition of 10% cement increased it by 292% on average.

ACKNOWLEDGMENTS

This work was supported by Shaanxi Key Industrial Innovation Chain Project in Agricultural Domain (Grant No.: 2020ZDLNY06-03).

REFERENCES

Binod K. and Manjip S. Comparative Compressive Strength of Stabilized and Un-stabilized Rammed Earth. *Materials and Structures*, 2016,49(9):3945–3955.

Koutous A. and Hilali E. Grain Shape Affects Compacted Earth's Mechanical Behavior. *Case Studies in Construction Materials*, 2019,11:e303.

Qin Z.L. To "Earthwork Testing Method Standard" (GB/T50123-1999) Solidifying Experiment Compression Module Formula Discussion. *Urban Geotechnical Investigation & Surveying*, 2010.

Reddy B., Suresh V. and Rao K. Specimen Slenderness Effect on Compressive Strength of Cement Stabilised Rammed Earth. *Specimen Slenderness Effect on Compressive Strength of Cement Stabilised Rammed Earth*, 2015.

Rika J., Havlik F., Richter J., *et al.* Advanced Prefabricated Rammed Earth Structures–Mechanical, Building Physical and Environmental Properties: *First International Conference on Rammed Earth Construction*, 2015[C].

Tripura D.D., Singh K.D. Behavior of Cement-stabilized Rammed Earth Circular Column Under Axial Loading. *Materials and Structures*, 2016,49(1–2):371–382.

Venkatarama Reddy B.V. Characteristic Compressive Strength of Cement-Stabilized Rammed Earth. *Journal of Materials in Civil Engineering*, 2016,29(2).

Wang N., Zhang J., Liao R., *et al.* Study on the Size Effect of Unconfined Compressive Strength of Rammed Earthen Site's Soil Samples. *Journal of Materials in Civil Engineering*, 2020,32(2):4019341–4019343.

Yihong W. and Jiqing Z. Review of Overseas Research on Raw-soil Structure. *China Civil Engineering Journal*, 2015,48(06):81–88.

Zhao D.J, Zhang Y., Lu J.L. Research on Construction of Rammed Earth Buildings. *Advanced Materials Research*, 2011,243–249:934–937.

Research on safety planning technology of water projects construction

Qian Fu*
River and Lake Protection, Construction and Operation Safety Center, Haihe River Water Conservancy Commission, MWR, Tianjin, China

Hui Tan
Center of Construction Management & Quality & Safety Supervision, Ministry of Water Resources, Beijing, China

Xue Leng
Tianjin International Science and Technology Consulting Co., Ltd, Tianjin, China

Meng Ting Huang
CHN Energy Dadu Rive Repair & Installation Co., Ltd, Sichuan, China

ABSTRACT: Safety planning technology for water project construction effectively improves the quality of safety work and reduces the proportion of industrial accidents in the construction field under the new situation. This study analyzes data on safety problems in 32 water projects under construction and finds that weak safety planning technology is the main reason for the problems. This paper proposes eight recommendations based on the industry policy standard level to fill the gaps to some extent.

1 INTRODUCTION

1.1 Concept

Safety planning technology for water project construction (in the future referred to as safety planning technology for the project) is a collection of systematic management processes. It has a specific logical relationship to eliminate and control a specific project's possible risks and achieve the project's production safety goal before implementation.

1.2 The safety planning technology specified in the regulations and standards are the methods of safety management and quality development

Article 11 of the Work Safety Law clarifies that production and operation units must implement the national standards or industry standards established by law to ensure safe production (Production Safety Law of the People's Republic of China 2021). National standards (Unified code for a technique for constructional safety (GB 50870 – 2013) (Xu et al. 2013) require that before the project starts, it is necessary to compile a construction safety technical plan (also known as "safety planning") in combination with the characteristics of the project. The planning content should cover the whole process of construction production. The national standard (Code for construction project management GBT

---
*Corresponding Author: fq400@sohu.com

50326-2017) 3.1.2 (Wu et al. 2017) requires organizations to follow the dynamic management principle of "Plan, Do, Check, Adjust" to determine the project management process. They establish a project management system, implement project system management, continuously improve management performance, enhance the level of satisfaction of relevant parties, and ensure the achievement of project management objectives. Among them, the "Plan, Do, Check, Adjust" (PDCA) cycle is one of the four pillars of quality management (Theory and method of quality management group 2013).

Therefore, safety planning is an activity that contains the concept of improving the quality of safety work. Safety planning technology is the methodology of safety planning. The above-mentioned national standards give principled requirements.

1.3 *Technical regulations, specific methods, and research on safety planning of water engineering projects are in a blank state*

The above study shows that safety planning technology is a systematic safety management and technical document that specifically arranges and guides project safety construction before project implementation. Its prevention-oriented and process-controlling properties indicate that it is a method to achieve high-quality development of safety management. However, the author could not find any article by searching "safety planning technology for water engineering construction project" as a keyword, and there is no result on the website CNKI. These indicate that the relevant regulations, specific methods, and research are in a blank state.

1.4 *New situation requires project safety planning technology to promote safety management and high-quality development*

From 2016–2021, the average proportion of production safety accidents in the field of water engineering construction reached 82.5% of industrial accidents, reducing the proportion as the top priority of safety work.

In July 2020, the State Council executive meeting identified 150 major water engineering projects. These projects have started construction one after another, involving flood prevention and disaster reduction, water resources optimization and allocation, irrigation and water supply, water ecology protection and restoration, intelligent water conservancy construction, and so on. Recently, these major water projects have started construction one after another. Due to the different categories of projects and large quantities, the safety risks of water project construction have increased (Xu 2021).

On May 25, 2022, the General Office of the State Council released Opinions of the General Office of the State Council on Further Revitalizing Stock Assets and Increasing Effective Investment (No. 19 [2022] of the General Office of the State Council), listing the water project as a key area to revitalize the stock of assets. The water project construction scale will further expand, increasing the probability of accidents. In addition, intelligent water construction, new technologies, and new methods of use also increased the safety risks of non-traditional production. Thus, the goal of reducing the proportion of accidents in the field of water engineering project construction has faced a double challenge.

Therefore, starting the research of safety planning technology with the connotation of high-quality development is of great practical significance to improve the quality of the current work of safety products in the field of water project construction to help high-quality development.

2 RESEARCH PURPOSE

Through the problems found in water project construction safety inspection using safety planning technology in large and medium-sized construction projects, this paper will analyze the causes. It will also put forward work recommendations to better coordinate development and safety and achieve high-quality development of water project construction safety work to provide a reference.

3 RESEARCH PROJECT SELECTION

The author analyzed 32 violations of production safety management of water projects under construction. The types of projects involve reservoir construction, reinforcement of dangerous reservoirs, river management, dams, water supply (water source replacement), pumping station (electric irrigation station upgrading and reconstruction) projects, etc. The projects are mostly large-scale, with high safety risks, difficult construction, strict technical requirements, and many cross-operations. They involve tunnel works, high side slopes, deep pits, underground concealed excavation works, tall formwork works, and other dangerous projects, so the study has typical significance.

4 PROBLEMS

4.1 *Legal project person has the largest proportion of problems in the safety planning technology*

The inspection found that the legal project person to implement the work is not following national standards in the safety planning technical requirements to carry out work. Among the 222 production safety management violations of the legal project person, 79 problems related to safety planning technology account for a maximum of 35.59%, which is the problem that needs to be focused on. Classification statistics are shown in Figure 1.

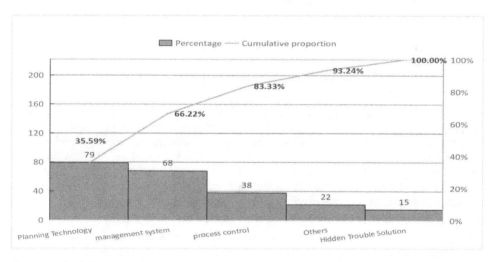

Figure 1. Statistical analysis chart of irregularities in safety production management of project legal persons found in inspections.

4.2 *Weak technical basis for safety planning of water project construction*

The 79 technical problems of safety planning found by the inspection were categorized and counted (Figure 2), among which the most problems were in the category of technical management, with 28 problems accounting for 35.44%; 20 problems of hazard identification and risk level evaluation, accounting for 25.32%; 18 problems of emergency management, accounting for 22.78%. There are ten problems of safety system establishment, accounting for 12.66%, and three problems of accident handling, accounting for 3.80%.

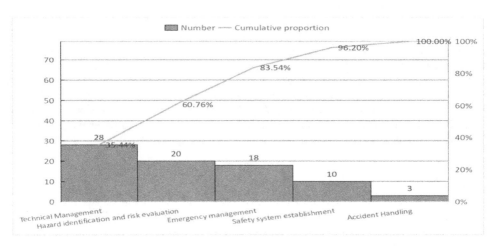

Figure 2. Statistical analysis chart of technical violations in safety planning of the legal project person found during the inspection.

Statistical analysis shows that there are problems in all aspects of safety planning technology, and the working basis is weak.

5 CAUSE ANALYSIS

5.1 *Project safety planning technology lacks industry policy provisions and standard specifications*

So far, the author could not find relevant content by using the keyword "Technical Standards and Specifications for Safety Planning of Water Project Construction." It indicates that the water project industry's relevant policy provisions and industry standards have not yet been based on national standards (Xu et al. 2013) (Wu et al. 2017) to implement safety planning technology.

The "Prevention-oriented" policy lacks standards in important aspects of the implementation and cannot meet the requirements of high-quality development.

5.2 *The lack of technical regulations for safety planning leads to an incomplete chain of high-quality development of project safety management*

To find a high-quality development path, the author integrates the "PDCA cycle principle" of quality management into the project safety production management and draws a flow chart of the safety production and high-quality management of water project construction (Figure 3). Thus, the lack of institutional guarantee for safety planning makes the chain of high-quality management incomplete, and difficult to implement the "prevention-oriented" safety policy. The weakness of safety planning technology makes the overall technical guarantee capability of the project vulnerable.

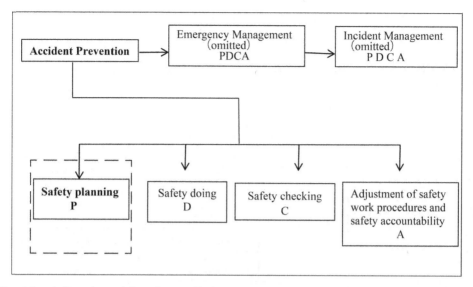

Figure 3. A flow chart of the safety production and high-quality management of water project construction.

6 RECOMMENDATION

In summary, strengthening the technical support for safety planning is one way to achieve project safety management from passive prevention of accidents to changing the taste from the source of governance, the whole process of management.

6.1 *Specify the project safety planning technology object*

Newly undertaken or being implemented in large water conservancy and hydropower engineering construction projects need to add a safety planning book in the construction organization design to implement the technical requirements of safety planning.

6.2 *Specify the working basis for project safety planning technology*

(1) national and industry regulations and standards on product safety and the standard regulations on production safety policies in the project site.
(2) higher production safety rules and regulations.
(3) enterprise production safety policy, objectives, rules, and regulations.
(4) project environment and characteristics, contracts, and other requirements of the owner.
(5) Hazard identification and risk assessment result in the design documents.

6.3 *Specify the technical working principles of project safety planning*

(1) systematic; (2) dynamic; (3) feasibility.

6.4 *Specify project safety planning technical workflow*

Mastering the basis of work → Putting forward the requirements of project safety process control →Developing project safety technical measures → Equipping with the necessary resources → Implementing executive planning → Improvement and enhancement

6.5 Specify the specific content of project safety planning technology

According to the industry standard (Code for construction project management (GBT 50326-2017)), combined with the characteristics of water project construction, the author draws the content map of the safety planning technology for water project construction, as shown in Figure 4.

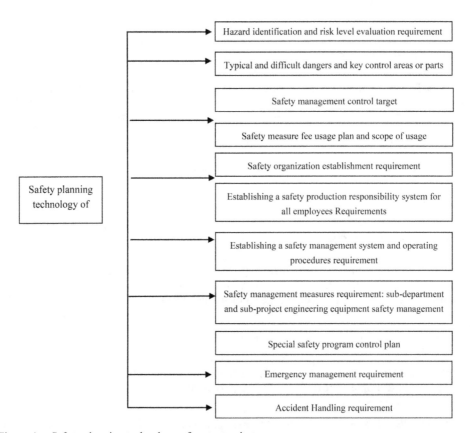

Figure 4. Safety planning technology of water project.

6.6 Specify project safety planning time requirements

Safety planning is an important part of engineering project planning. After the project contract is signed, before the project is implemented, the legal project person should immediately organize project planning, including safety planning, on how to perform the project. Phase planning can be carried out when necessary during the project performance.

6.7 Specify the staff and completion time of the safety plan

(1) The legal project person leads the project safety planning work. The project manager organizes the production, technology, safety, quality, and other departments to participate, and the design unit joins. Then the project director reviews it, and finally, the legal project person approves and implements it.

(2) project safety planning is included in the construction organization design-project planning book. After the planning is completed, it will be compiled into a book as required.
(3) The project safety plan should be completed within one month of establishing the project department.

6.8 *Specify the approval requirements for the safety planning document*

The approval of the Safety Planning Book includes internal and external review: the internal review of the project department takes the form of a project management staff meeting, review by the relevant departments of the company, and approval by the project leader in charge; after the internal review is passed, the legal project person organizes external review: review by the project director and then implementation after approval by the legal project person.

7 CONCLUSION

In this paper, the empirical study of 222 project legal person safety production violations of 32 water projects under construction found that the main reason for the violations was the weak safety planning technology. The study concludes that the formulation of safety planning (technology) and industry policy standards are conducive to improving the high-quality development chain of safe production and reducing production safety accidents in the current water project construction field. In addition, the research also puts forward specific suggestions on the work object, basis, principle, process, content, completion time limit, and approval requirements of safety planning technology. Research gaps are filled. In the future, the author will research difficulties and countermeasures of integrating the principle of the PDCA Cycle into safety planning technology to improve the application value of safety planning technology and develop higher-quality safety production of water projects.

REFERENCES

Production Safety Law of the People's Republic of China. (2021) China Legal Publishing House. Beijing. pp. 23.

Shu Fang Xu (2021) Research on the Analysis of Common Problems in Water Project Construction Safety Management. *Haihe River Water Conservancy*. 12 (Supplement), Tianjin. pp. 9.

Theory and Method of the Quality Management Group. (2013) China Quality and Standards Publishing & Media Co., Ltd, Beijing. pp.15.

Tao Wu, Wan Wu, Jun Li (2017) *Code for Construction Project Management*. China Architecture & Building Press., Beijing. pp.6–20.

Xue Jun Xu, Ai Guo Li, Qun Yi Wang (2013) *Unified Code for Technique for Constructional Safety*. China Planning Press. Beijing. pp.1–13.

Construction technology of bored pile in geotechnical engineering based on energy-saving concept

Chunbo Yin* & Yongge Hou
Tangshan Zhongdi Geological Engineering Co. Ltd., Tangshan, Hebei, China

Zehao Hou
Beijing Rongchuang Geotechnical Engineering Co. Ltd., Beijing, China

ABSTRACT: With the rise of China's construction industry and the increasing investment in engineering construction in karst areas, karst, as a typical adverse geological phenomenon, is a serious threat to the stability of geotechnical engineering construction. This paper proposes a study on the construction technology of bored piles in geotechnical engineering based on the concept of energy saving. In view of the special geological conditions of geotechnical engineering, the construction parameters of cast-in-place piles are determined. Based on the concept of energy saving, the composite pile composed of concrete pile core and cement soil ring is used to drill and form piles. The bearing capacity test of cast-in-place pile shows that under the load of 5000 kN, the settlement of composite pile with pile diameter of 1 m and 1.5 m is 13.6 mm and 12.4 mm, which proves that the pile-forming effect of this construction is good, and the construction quality is high. This research has important contribution value to ensure the smooth progress of pile foundation projects in karst areas.

1 INTRODUCTION

In recent years, China's civil engineering construction has stepped into a stage of rapid development. It has made some achievements in many fields, such as high-speed railways, subways, bridges, and building construction. Geotechnical engineering, which is involved in many infrastructure projects, greatly impacts engineering construction because of its unique construction environment. As the foundation of geotechnical engineering, foundation engineering can effectively guarantee the construction safety of geotechnical engineering. If there is a safety accident in foundation engineering, the geotechnical engineering will not be carried out smoothly. At present, pile foundation is widely used in the construction of large-scale geotechnical engineering in China. Due to the complexity and uncertainty of the geotechnical engineering construction site, if the pile foundation construction is not handled properly, there will be broken piles and ground subsidence, which not only seriously restricts the construction progress of geotechnical engineering but also threatens the safety of site construction. Therefore, how to successfully realize pile foundation engineering in geotechnical areas with complex stratum structures and frequent safety accidents, and ensure construction safety and quality, has become a key technical problem to be solved urgently in China's construction industry. In view of this topic, this paper refers to the related material and launches thorough research.

---

*Corresponding Author: yinchunbo79zhongdi@163.com

2 OVERVIEW OF GEOTECHNICAL ENGINEERING

The site area of a construction project is about $2 \times 10^6 \text{ m}^2$, which is located in the karst area. According to the regional survey report, the geological structure of the project site is relatively stable, with 5 different strata distributed, and there is no obvious activity of the nearby faults in the near future. The properties of rock and soil mass of each stratum are shown in Table 1.

Table 1. Geological characteristics of geotechnical engineering.

Ground layer	Soil type	Soil characteristics
Artificial filling layer	Silty clay	The soil is loose and wet, with poor bearing capacity
Alluvial-proluvial deposit	Sandy soil	Medium and unstable toughness of soil
Residual slope soil layer	Cohesive soil mixed with sand	Uneven soil texture and large porosity
Granite	Solid stone and strongly weathered sandstone	The integrity of the rock core is high, and the development degree of the joint fissure is low.
Marble	Solid stone and strongly weathered sandstone	Joints and fissures are well developed, and the rock is hard.

According to the survey results of the construction site, there are many kinds of rock and soil layers in the building site, and the thickness of each layer changes significantly, resulting in an uneven foundation. In order to control the stability of the geotechnical engineering site, it is necessary to take appropriate engineering measures to stabilize the foundation through bored pile construction (Qin *et al.* 2021).

3 CONSTRUCTION PROCESS OF THE BORED PILE BASED ON THE ENERGY-SAVING CONCEPT

3.1 *Determination of construction parameters of the cast-in-place pilot*

Due to the characteristics of geotechnical engineering, before formal construction, it is necessary to determine the relevant parameters of the pile to ensure the safety and reliability of the pile structure and maximize the mechanical properties of the cast-in-place pile (Cui *et al.* 2020). Firstly, according to the geological conditions of geotechnical engineering and the construction cost, a safe, reasonable, and economical pile type is selected. Then the feasible pile diameter and length are determined by comprehensively considering the construction experience, load size, and other factors (Wu *et al.* 2021). The number of completed piles is then determined by reference to the following equation:

$$N = \delta L[X] \qquad (1)$$

Where δ is the value of the non-uniform coefficient of multiple piles; L is the parameter of the vertical load acting on the pile foundation; $[X]$ is the parameter of the allowable force of a single pile. After the foundation conditions of the pile are obtained, the plane arrangement scheme of the pile can be determined. In the design of the pile layout scheme, it is necessary to set a reasonable pile spacing (Zhao 2020). Once the distance between the piles is too small, the bearing capacity of the pile foundation will be damaged by the soil compaction effect and the pile group effect. According to the stress condition of the pile foundation, the general layout includes single-row piles and multi-row piles. The layout of multi-row piles is divided into a row, column, and quincunx, as shown in Figure 1.

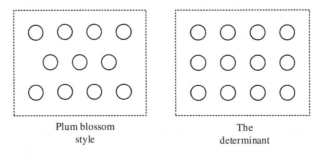

Figure 1. Layout of the multi-row piles.

Combined with the actual construction situation of geotechnical engineering, the appropriate pile foundation layout form is determined. Then the pile construction technology and the geological characteristics of rock and soil are comprehensively considered to determine the spacing between the pile foundations. On this basis, the following process is carried out.

3.2 *Drilling*

Drilling is the core process of geotechnical engineering cast-in-place pile construction (Shen 2021). Before drilling, it is necessary to use mud to stabilize the hole wall. The manufacturing parameters of soil need to be controlled according to the geological characteristics of geotechnical engineering, as shown in Table 2.

Table 2. Mud parameters.

Ground layer	Mud density/ (g/cm^3)	Mud viscosity/s
Artificial filling layer	1.10~1.15	20~24
Alluvial-proluvial deposit	1.18~1.24	28~32
Residual slope soil layer	1.18~1.24	28~32
Granite	1.20~1.30	30~35
Marble	1.20~1.30	30~35

Then, according to the geological exploration data of the construction site, the appropriate drill bit is selected, and the drilling speed and other indicators of the drilling rig are set. In the process of drilling with the drilling rig, the drill pipe shall be controlled in the vertical position, and the drilling shall be stabilized at a uniform drilling speed. Mud shall be replenished while drilling to avoid hole wall collapse. When the drilling rig drills into granite and marble strata, the drilling speed shall be slowed down. During the drilling construction, it is necessary to check the hole position and correct it in time if the deviation is too large (Li et al. 2020). When the drill bit reaches the design depth, the drilling stops. At this time, the construction personnel needs to check and record the position, depth, and other data of the hole to ensure its stability.

3.3 *Pile forming*

Based on the concept of energy saving, the composite pile body composed of a concrete pile core and cement soil ring is adopted in this construction (Liu et al. 2021). Under the condition that the bearing capacity of the pile foundation is the same, compared with the conventional concrete cast-in-place pile, this composite pile body can save more construction materials such as sand and cement, which can not only reduce the project cost but also reduce the impact of the composite pile construction technology on the surrounding environment. It is beneficial to protect the environment (Fan *et al.* 2021). The schematic diagram of the composite pile structure is as follows:

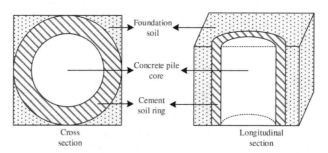

Figure 2. Schematic diagram of geotechnical engineering composite pile structure.

In the pile-forming process of the composite pile, first of all, the prefabricated components of the concrete pile core shall be fabricated in advance according to the construction parameters of the cast-in-place pile determined in the above section (Yu *et al.* 2022). Then the construction of the pressure grouting cement soil ring is carried out. The pressure grouting construction process of the composite pile cement soil ring is to grout the stirred cement soil slurry into a drill hole by using a conveying pipe, wherein the specific operation key points are as follows: the construction site and the interior of the drill hole are cleaned to ensure that no obstacle and sediment exist near the pile position. Then, according to the actual geological conditions of the geotechnical engineering construction site, the cement, water, and soil are mixed in a proper proportion and stirred by a stirrer to ensure that the quality of the cement-soil slurry meets the requirements of the geotechnical engineering composite pile (Sun & Yang 2020). The ground pump for conveying the cement slurry is arranged in place to ensure that the position of the ground pump is flat and is not allowed to move or tilt. When the ground pump conveys the cement-soil slurry, continuous grouting shall be ensured, and the cement-soil slurry in the hopper of the ground pump shall be stirred continuously to avoid the initial setting.

When grouting for a long distance at the bottom of the borehole, a skid can be set under the pump pipe. Keep the pump pipe in a horizontal state to avoid damage to the pump pipe. If the outside temperature is high on the day of construction, it is necessary to cool the pump pipe by sprinkling water and other methods so as to avoid the cement slurry blocking the pump tube due to lack of water. When the cement-soil slurry is poured to the top of the pile body, the cement-soil slurry needs to be slowly pulled out and vibrated by a vibrating rod to discharge bubbles in the cement-soil slurry so as to promote the structure of the cement-soil ring of the composite pile to be firmer. After the cement-soil slurry is deposited for a period of time, the concrete pile core is driven into the cement-soil pile body, which is not hardened, and then the composite pile is formed. In this process, attention should be paid to controlling the accuracy of the position of the concrete pile core. After the pile body is solidified and formed, the pile-forming construction process is completed. Because the cement-soil slurry can penetrate into the surrounding soil, the combination effect between the composite pile used in this construction and the soil is far superior to that of the conventional concrete cast-in-place pile, and it is more suitable for the foundation construction in geotechnical engineering.

4 TEST OF BEARING CAPACITY OF CAST-IN-PLACE PILE

For the construction of bored piles in geotechnical engineering, the most important thing is the bearing capacity of the pile body. Thus, after the completion of the construction, this paper makes a test pile to detect the bearing capacity of a single pile. At the same time, it makes a conventional concrete cast-in-place test pile as a comparison pile, through the static load test to determine whether the composite cast-in-place pile meets the needs of geotechnical engineering construction. The manufacturing information of the test pile for the bearing capacity test of the cast-in-place pile is shown in Table 3.

Table 3. Manufacturing information of bearing capacity test pile.

Test group	Pile no.	Construction process	Pile diameter/m
Test group 1	Test pile 1	Composite cast-in-place pile	1
	Comparison pile 1	Conventional concrete cast-in-place pile	1
Test group 2	Test pile 2	Composite cast-in-place pile	1.5
	Comparison pile 1	Conventional concrete cast-in-place pile	1.5

Then the static load test is carried out, and the changes in settlement of the two groups of test piles and comparison piles with the load are shown in Figure 3.

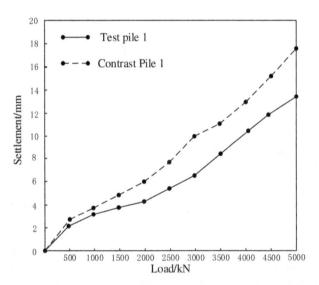

Figure 3. Static load test results of the first group of test piles and contrast piles.

It can be seen from Figure 4 that when the cast-in-place pile with a pile diameter of 1 m is under load, its settlement has greatly increased with the increase of load, of which the final settlement of Contrast pile 1 is 17.8 mm. The final settlement of Test pile 1 is 13.6 mm, which is 4.2 mm lower than that of Contrast pile 1. The slope of the settlement variation curve of Test pile 1 is smaller than that of Contrast pile 1, which indicates that the bearing capacity of test pile 1 is better than that of Contrast pile 1. When the load is below 2000 kN, the settlement of the cast-in-place pile with a diameter of 1.5 m does not change significantly. When the load exceeds 2000 kN, the settlement of the cast-in-place pile with a diameter of

1.5 m changes significantly. The final settlement of Contrast pile 2 is 15.2 mm, and the final settlement of Test pile 2 is 12.4 mm. It is 2.8 mm lower than that of Contrast pile 2, indicating that the bearing capacity of Test pile 2 is higher than that of Contrast pile 2. To sum up, the pile-forming effect of this geotechnical engineering bored pile construction based on the concept of energy saving is good, and the construction quality is high.

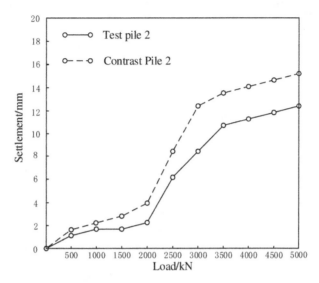

Figure 4. Static load test results of the second group of test piles and contrast piles.

5 CONCLUSION

In this paper, the construction technology of the geotechnical engineering pile foundation in karst areas is deeply studied with the concept of energy saving as the core, and the construction technology of a composite pile body composed of concrete pile core and cement-soil ring is proposed concerning the actual geological characteristics of karst areas. The composite pile has a better bearing capacity, saves energy, and protects the environment. Through the load test of the cast-in-place pile, it is proved that the construction technology of the cast-in-place pile proposed in this paper is feasible, which can effectively guarantee the quality and safety of the geotechnical engineering construction.

REFERENCES

Cui Bingchen, Lei Bin, Wang Tao, et al. (2020) Construction Technology of Long Spiral Follow-up Pipe and Rotary Drilling Cast-in-situ Piles in Deep and Weak Strata. *Construction Technology*, 49(19): 23–26.

Fan Zhibo, Xu Qigong, Guo Minlong, et al. (2021) Experimental Study on Seismic Performance of New Precast Concrete Composite Tubular Columns. *Building Structure*, 51(07): 46–51.

Li Zhuowen, Zhang Xiuchuan, Zhang Shuai, et al. (2020) Design and Construction Of Bored Piles in Dense Barrier Pile Area Based on Azimuth Full Casing Technology. *Construction Technology*, 49(23): 115–119.

Liu Jinbo, Liu Zhifu, Deng Yaguang, et al. (2021) Achievements of Geotechnical Engineering Construction Technology in my Country - Composite Pile. *Construction Technology*, 50(13): 69–75+112.

Qin Pengfei, Wang Weilin, Yuan Yuan. (2021) Research on Grouting Technology and its Application in Geotechnical engineering. *Geology and Exploration*, 57(03):631–639.

Shen Yi. (2021) Construction Technology of Chemical Slurry Powder Slurry Wall Protection for Underwater Rotary Drilling Bored Piles. *Construction Technology*, 50(07): 60–62+68.

Sun Xinshuo, Yang Yaping (2020) Research on the Construction Technology of Long Helical Bored Grouting Concrete Piles. *Building Structure*, 50(S1): 981–983.

Wu Bangshuo, Zhou Cheng, Xiong Jun, et al. (2021) Research on the Construction Technology of Supporting Cast-in-place Piles in the Foundation Pit of the Adjustment Reservoir. *Architecture Technology*, 52(12): 1431–1432.

Yu Jianlin, Xu Jiacheng, Zhou Jiajin, et al. (2022) Experimental Study on Friction Characteristics of Concrete-cement Interface of Concrete-core Cement-soil Composite Piles. *China Civil Engineering Journal*, 55(08): 93–104+117.

Zhao Bin (2020) Precise Measurement and Control Technology of Pile Top Elevation of Ultra-deep Pile Bored-in-situ Piles. *Construction Technology*, 49(S1): 1083–1085.

Earthquake hazard analysis and safety evaluation of East African Rift Valley

Yan Yu*
China Road & Bridge Corporation, Beijing, China
National Institute of Natural Hazards, Ministry of Emergency Management of the People's Republic of China, Beijing, China

Xin Zhang
China Road & Bridge Corporation, Beijing, China

ABSTRACT: In this paper, based on the seismic data, seismic, geological data, and field survey data within the area along the Nairobi Malaba Railway (no less than 150 km), the seismicity environment and seismotectonic environment are studied, the specific location and properties of the main active faults crossing the railway are given, and their seismic, geological impact on the Nairobi Malaba Railway Project is evaluated. In addition, based on the probabilistic seismic hazard analysis and calculation models at home and abroad, the paper carries out seismic hazard analysis and calculation of discrete points and important engineering sites along the Nairobi Malaba Railway. It also gives the zoning results of seismic peak acceleration with an exceedance probability of 10% in 50 years for general sites (medium hard) along the Nairobi Malaba Railway. The site seismic data, site response calculation results, and design ground motion parameters of important project sites are obtained through experiments.

1 INTRODUCTION

The total length of the East African Rift Valley is more than 6000 km, with typical continental rift characteristics, forming a series of narrow and deep canyons, lakes, and basins. The edges are parallel stepped fault groups, which are composed of the east branch of Ethiopia Kenya Rift Valley and the west branch of Tanganyika Rift Valley (Poggi et al. 2017). The east branch of Ethiopia Kenya Rift Valley is the main rift valley, with a total length of nearly 3000 km. The width of the rift valley here ranges from tens to 200 km, and the valley bottom is mostly flat. On both sides of the rift valley are towering lava platforms, huge volcanic cones, and steep cliffs. The height difference between the bottom of the valley and the top of the cliffs ranges from several hundred meters to 2000 m. The relevant research on the faults in the Kenya section of the East African Rift Valley shows that the main faults of the Rift Valley were first formed in the Neogene, and the Middle Pleistocene was also a stage of its main activity. They were still active in the Holocene, and their activity may have lasted until now. For example, a magnitude 7 earthquake occurred on January 6, 1928, on the NNE Laikipia-Marmanet fault that formed the Laikipia Cliff (the magnitude is also determined as 6.9 according to the data, and different data on the epicenter location also vary), which is the largest historical earthquake ever occurred in the eastern branch of the East African Rift Valley. Relevant research results show that the stress in the Kenyan section of the East African Rift Valley is mainly tensile stress, and its seismic activity is relatively

*Corresponding Author: yanyu@ninhm.ac.cn

active. The earthquakes are mainly small and medium earthquakes. The main faults of the rift zone are distributed at the rift boundary, and there are many branches and secondary faults in the rift. The seismic and geological disasters caused by these secondary faults greatly threaten major projects.

At present, the probabilistic seismic hazard analysis method is mainly used in the analysis of major engineering construction projects in the world, especially in developed countries such as Europe, the United States, and Japan. The basic ideas, such as the division of potential source areas, determination of activity parameters, probabilistic seismic hazard analysis, and calculation, are basically the same as those in China. There are two main differences: (1) The results of the design response spectrum given by the seismic safety evaluation are basically the same, with both the peak acceleration and characteristic period of the response spectrum. However, due to the different design response spectrum forms of specific projects in different countries, the design probability level and response spectrum forms are different. (2) The upper limit of earthquake magnitude and activity parameters in the division scheme of potential source areas are different. Considering the special significance of the Nairobi Malaba Railway, its seismic design is particularly important.

2 STUDY AREAS

There are two distinct domes in the Great Rift Valley and its surrounding terrain, one is the Ethiopian dome (2500-3000 m) in the north, and the other is the Kenyan dome (1000 m) in the south. The area is basically located on the Kenyan fornix. From the digital topographic map, the terrain in the region is generally high in the west and low in the east, high in the middle, and low on both sides (Ayele 2017). Most areas are between 1,000 and 2,000 m above sea level, with the highest altitude greater than 5,000 m. The highest peak in Africa, Mount Kilimanjaro (5895 m), the second highest peak of Mount Kenya (5199 m), and the third highest peak of Kenya, Mount Elgon (4321 m), are located in this area. Some areas in the rift valley are less than 1000 m above sea level. The eastern edge is a plain area with an elevation of less than 1000 m (Figure 1).

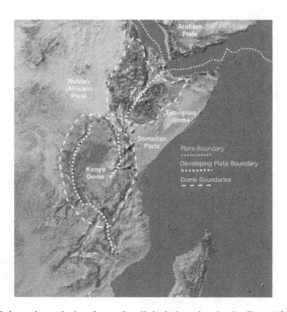

Figure 1. Plate and dome boundaries shown by digital elevation in the East African Rift Valley.

The regional strata can be roughly divided into three parts. The first part is the crystalline basement, belonging to the Precambrian, a set of deep metamorphic rock series widely distributed. The second part is the Neogene developed with the formation of the East African Rift Valley. Regional faults are relatively developed, and most of them belong to the faults related to the eastern branch of the East African Rift System. The northern section of the rift fault is mainly NN-trending, the middle section is NNW, and the southern section is NN-trending, with an overall S-shaped distribution. Rift faults can be roughly divided into primary faults and secondary faults. Other faults are mainly the Nandi fault, Siria fault, and faults on both sides of Kisumu. The volcanic and fault activities in the rift segment in the region can be roughly divided into four stages. (1) From the Late Miocene to the Early Cene, the central eruption of strong alkaline lava and the development of major rift faults; (2) The fractured volcanic eruption of trachytes and the development of some secondary faults; (3) In the late Middle Pleistocene, the second stage was mainly faulted, forming a grid-like fault system in a nearly north-south direction; (4) The trachyte eruption with pyroclastic deposition continued until the Holocene.

3 EARTHQUAKE HAZARD ANALYSIS

3.1 Analysis method

The probabilistic seismic hazard analysis method specified in the national standard "Evaluation of Seismic Safety of Engineering Sites" (GB 17741-2005) is adopted, and its main feature is that the spatial and temporal inhomogeneity of seismic activity is considered (Lemenkova 2022). The basic ideas and calculation methods are summarized as follows:

(1) First, determine the seismic statistical unit (seismic zone or seismic area) as the basic unit for considering the temporal non-uniformity of seismic activity and determining the level of seismic activity in the next century and the relative spatial distribution probability of seismic risk. Seismic activity within the seismic statistical area is inhomogeneous in both space and time.

The time course of earthquakes in the seismic statistical area conforms to the piecewise Poisson process. Let the upper limit of the magnitude of the seismic zone be m_{uz} and the lower limit of the magnitude of the earthquake shall be m_0, the average annual occurrence rate of earthquakes between m_0 and m_{uz} in t year, which v_0 is determined by the future trend of seismic activity, then the probability of n earthquakes occurring in the statistical area within t years is:

$$P(n) = \frac{(v_0 t)^n}{n!} e^{-v_0 t} \qquad (1)$$

At the same time, the seismicity in the seismic statistical area follows the modified magnitude-frequency relationship, and the corresponding magnitude probability density function is:

$$f(m) = \frac{\beta \exp\left[-\beta \left(m - m_0\right)\right]}{1 - \exp\left[-\beta \left(m_{uz} - m_0\right)\right]} \qquad (2)$$

Among them, $\beta = b \ln 10$, where b is the slope of the magnitude-frequency relationship. In practical work, the magnitude m is divided into N m bins, and mj represents the magnitude bins whose magnitude range is ($m_j \pm \frac{1}{2}\Delta m$). Then the probability of occurrence of mj-level earthquakes in the earthquake statistical area is:

$$P(m_j) = \frac{2}{\beta} \cdot f(m_j) \cdot Sh(\tfrac{1}{2} \beta \Delta m) \qquad (3)$$

(2) Divide the potential source area within the earthquake statistical area and use the spatial distribution function of the potential source area f_{i,m_j} to reflect the spatial inhomogeneity of earthquakes of each magnitude in each potential source area. The seismicity within the potential source area is consistent. It is assumed that there is a total of N_s potential hypocenter areas in the seismic zone $\{S_1, S_2, S_{Ns}\}$.

(3) According to the piecewise Poisson distribution model and the full probability formula, the annual exceedance probability of the earthquake occurring in the earthquake statistical area affecting the ground motion parameter value A of the site exceeding the given value a is:

$$P_k(A \geq a) = 1 - \exp\left\{-\frac{2v_0}{\beta} \cdot \sum_{j=1}^{N_m} \sum_{i=1}^{N_s} \iiint P(A \geq a|E) \cdot f(\theta) \cdot \frac{f_{i,mj}}{A(S_i)} \cdot f(m_j) \cdot Sh\left(\frac{1}{2}\beta\Delta m\right) dxdy\,d\theta\right\} \quad (4)$$

$A(S_i)$ is the area of the ith potential source area $P(A \geq a|E)$ within the seismic statistical area, and is the site-point earthquake when a specific seismic event (epicenter (x,y), magnitude $m_j \pm \frac{1}{2}\Delta m$, and rupture direction are determined) occurs in the ith potential source area within the seismic statistical area. The probability of $f(\theta)$ moving beyond a is the probability density function of the rupture direction.

(4) Assuming that there are N_z seismic statistical areas that have an influence on the site, then the influence of all seismic statistical areas can be combined to get:

$$P(A \geq a) = 1 - \prod_{k=1}^{N_z}(1 - P_k(A \geq a)) \quad (5)$$

3.2 Determination of activity parameters

The Nairobi Malaba Railway is located inside the African plate. According to the global earthquake epicenter distribution map from 1973 to 2012, a total of 2007 earthquakes were selected inside the plate, and the cumulative frequency of magnitude 4.5 - 7 was used as a sample. The b-value curve was fitted (Figure 2), and the b-value inside the African plate is 1.033. To be conservative, we take b = 1 as the basis for determining the occurrence rate of earthquakes in the potential source area.

Since there may be serious shortages of earthquakes of magnitude 4 to 5 in the project area, in order to avoid underestimating the seismic risk of the site, we use the actual annual average occurrence rate of earthquakes of magnitude 5 and above to calculate the annual average occurrence of earthquakes of magnitude 4 and above in the potential source area.

It is worth considering that due to the backward economic and cultural development in the African region, many countries have suffered years of wars, poor living conditions, and other reasons. Therefore, the history of earthquake records in this region is almost blank. The earthquake monitoring capacity in the region is very limited and even lacks the possibility to detect severe earthquakes above 4.5 (Mohajer et al. 1992). In addition, we know that earthquake activity has a certain periodicity, which is related to the different periods of seismic stress accumulation and release. At different stages of the seismic activity cycle, the difference in the annual average occurrence rate of earthquakes is also very huge (Balagizi et al. 2018). The historical seismic data are recorded for a short period, and it is impossible to

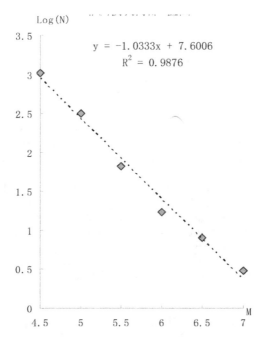

Figure 2. The curve of the magnitude frequency relationship within the African plate.

assess the periodicity of seismic activity in this area and the active stage of the current seismic cycle.

3.3 Analysis results

According to the national standard GB 17741-2005 "Evaluation of Seismic Safety of Engineering Sites", the corresponding relationship between the peak ground motion acceleration of general sites (Class II building sites) and the peak ground motion acceleration of bedrock (Formula 6 and Formula 7) can be obtained. Peak ground motion acceleration of each spatial control point under the condition of Class II building site). a_{hs} is the peak ground motion acceleration of the general site, a_r is the peak ground motion acceleration of the bedrock, and k_s is the conversion coefficient.

$$a_{hs} = k_s\, a_r \tag{6}$$

$$k_s \begin{cases} 1.25 & a \leq 62.5 \\ 1.25 - (a - 62.5)/1250 & 62.5 < a \leq 375 \\ 1 & a > 375 \end{cases} \tag{7}$$

Based on the changes in the calculation results at the spatial control points a_{hs}, according to the classification principle of the ground motion peak acceleration, the areas on both sides of the railway project are classified into the ground motion acceleration peak 20 km (Table 1).

The peak ground motion acceleration with an exceedance probability of 10% in 50 years under the condition of the general site (Class II building site) within 20 km on both sides of the railway project is calculated by using Equations (6) and (7). On this basis, based on the principle of classification and zoning of seismic peak acceleration, the final seismic peak

Table 1. Ground motion peak acceleration (gal) grading specified values.

Peak acceleration gear	50	100	150	200	300	400
Calculate peak acceleration	[40~90]	[90~140]	[140~190]	[190~280]	[280~380]	[380~750]

acceleration zoning map with a 50-year exceedance probability of 10% for general sites (Class II construction sites) within 20 km on both sides of the whole railway line is prepared. The characteristic period of the seismic acceleration response spectrum of each zone is determined according to the normalized seismic acceleration response spectrum with a damping ratio of 5%.

There are mainly seven important project sites for the Nairobi Malaba Railway, including the Suswa Bridge, DK54 Bridge, Ngong 3 # Bridge, Ngong 2 # Bridge, Ngong 1 # Bridge, DK40 Bridge, and NGONG Tunnel. Because seven important projects are linear structures, three calculation control points are selected for each project, which are two endpoints and intermediate points of the project. The maximum risk analysis results of the three control points are taken as the risk analysis results of each project site. The horizontal peak accelerations of bedrock in the proposed seven project sites are listed in Table 2.

Table 2. Horizontal peak acceleration of bedrock at seven important engineering sites.

Proposed project	50-year transcendence probability			100-year transcendence probability		
	63%	10%	2%	63%	10%	2%
Suswat Bridge	61.1	189.4	359.2	90.2	252.0	452.5
DK54 Bridge	75.8	228.8	425.5	110.8	302.0	530.7
Ngong 3# Extra Large Bridge	76.0	229.5	426.1	111.1	302.7	531.4
Ngong 2# Extra Large Bridge	75.8	229.2	425.8	110.9	302.4	531.1
Ngong 1# Extra Large Bridge	75.5	228.2	424.6	110.4	301.3	530.0
DK40 Bridge	74.9	227.3	423.5	109.7	300.3	528.8
Ngong Tunnel	74.7	226.3	422.4	109.3	299.2	527.6

For the East African rift belt with strong seismic activity, the project team divided the potential source area of the East African East Rift Belt (Sources 2, 3, 13~18) and the East African West Rift according to the spatial images of seismic activity and the East African rift fault belt. In the potential source area of the valley belt (Sources 19~22), the upper limit of the magnitude of the earthquake is 7.5. For the middle non-shear fault zone of the Mesozoic rift system with sparse seismic activity, according to its tectonic location, the seismic activity, and volcanic activity in the surrounding area, a potential source area (Source 1) of the Central African shear fault zone is divided. The upper limit of magnitude is 7.0. For the boundary rift system of the African plate, the potential source area of the Red Sea (Source 10) and the potential source area of the Gulf of Aden (Source 11) are divided according to the characteristics of seismic activity, and the upper limit of the magnitude is 7.5.

4 CONCLUSIONS

A total of 649 earthquakes of magnitude 1.0 or above occurred within the project site area of CK0-CK120 Section of Nairobi Malaba Railway from 1902 to 2015, including 34 destructive earthquakes of magnitude 4.7 or above and 615 earthquakes of magnitude 4.7 or below. Among the destructive earthquakes, there were 18 earthquakes of magnitude 4.7~4.9, 14 earthquakes of magnitude 5.0~5.9, and one with a magnitude of 6.0~6.9. There was one earthquake of magnitude 7.0 or above, and the largest earthquake was the earthquake of magnitude 7.0 on January 6, 1928. The statistical results of focal depth of modern small earthquakes show that most earthquakes are shallow earthquakes. During the 114 years from 1902 to 2015, 44 earthquakes of magnitude 1.0 and above occurred in the near-field area, and no destructive earthquake of magnitude 4.7 and above occurred. The highest modern earthquake magnitude in the near-field area was the earthquake of magnitude 4.4 on March 26, 1977. On the whole, earthquakes in the near-field area are distributed sporadically and are relatively dense in the southwest. In the southern region, it presents a north-south stripe with obvious clustering characteristics and clustering characteristics. In other parts of the region, the distribution of modern small earthquakes is relatively scattered, and the seismic activity level is relatively low.

ACKNOWLEDGMENTS

This work was financially supported by the Major scientific research project of CCCC in 2017 (2017-ZJKJ-08), "Research on key technologies of railway design and construction across the Great Rift Valley in East Africa."

REFERENCES

Ayele A. (2017). Probabilistic Seismic Hazard Analysis (PSHA) for Ethiopia and the Neighboring Region. *Journal of African Earth Sciences*, 134, 257–264.

Balagizi C.M., Kies A., Kasereka M.M., Tedesco D., Yalire M.M., and McCausland, W.A. (2018). Natural Hazards in Goma and the Surrounding Villages, East African Rift System. Natural Hazards, 93(1), 31–66.

Lemenkova P. (2022). Seismicity in the Afar Depression and Great Rift Valley, Ethiopia. *Environmental Research, Engineering and Management*, 78(1), 83–96.

Mohajer A., Eyles N., and Rogojina C. (1992). Neotectonic Faulting in Metropolitan Toronto: Implications for Earthquake Hazard Assessment in the Lake Ontario Region. *Geology*, 20(11), 1003–1006.

Poggi V., Durrheim R., Tuluka G.M., Weatherill G., Gee R., Pagani M. and Delvaux D. (2017). Assessing Seismic Hazard of the East African Rift: a Pilot Study from GEM and AfricaArray. *Bulletin of Earthquake Engineering*, 15(11), 4499–4529.

Modelling one-dimensional compression on structured soils considering time effects

Enyang Zhu*, Yukun Chen, Xiyang Li, Chongqing Xu & Zhenghao Zhang
School of Civil Engineering, North China University of Technology, Beijing, China

ABSTRACT: In order to simulate the coupling effects of soil structure and time of natural soft clays in one-dimensional compression tests, an elastic visco-plastic unified hardening model of one-dimensional compression for structured soils was established by introducing an internal time variable into the structured unified hardening model. Comparison between the test data and the model simulations of one-dimensional CRS tests of Batiscan clay, Wenzhou clay, and Berthierville clay show that the model is qualified to simulate the one-dimensional compression behaviors of natural soft clay under different strain rates.

1 INTRODUCTION

The soil structure and time effects of natural soft clays are two important factors that need to be considered in geotechnical engineering, which affect the compressive deformation of soils and their stability. Therefore, the establishment of a mathematical model that can describe the coupled effects of soil structure and time effects of natural soils will be of great help to solving basic scientific problems such as long-term deformation prediction and long-term performance evaluation of soils in engineering.

So far, scholars have established different constitutive models for the time-dependent properties of naturally structured soft clays. For example, Hinchberger and Qu (2009) extended the original elastic visco-plastic model for reconstituted soils into an elastic visco-plastic model for undisturbed structured soils by introducing structural state-related viscous parameters. Based on the equivalent time concept proposed by Yin and Graham (1989;1994) and considering the compression characteristics of naturally structured soils, Zeng *et al.* (2012) developed a modified EVP model considering the effects of soil structure. Karim *et al.* (2013) developed an elastic visco-plastic model for structured soils by describing the effect of time on the damage degree of soil structures through the relative distance between the overconsolidation boundary surface and the static yield surface. Ke *et al.* (2016) introduced the concept of constant visco-plastic strain rate lines based on Bjerrum (1967)'s timelines and established a one-dimensional elastic visco-plastic model for structural soft clays by considering the influence of soil structure.

The unified hardening framework (Yao 2015) based on the critical state theory has gradually matured. The model proposed in this paper is built on the basis of the UH model for structured soils proposed by Zhu and Yao (2015) and considered the effect of time effect through time variable $\bar{t}$. The reasonability of the proposed model is verified by the one-dimensional constant rate of strain (CRS) test simulations of three naturally structured soils.

---

*Corresponding Author: zhuenyang@ncut.edu.cn

2 MODEL DESCRIPTION

According to the instantaneous and delayed compression theory, the strain increment $d\varepsilon_{ij}$ is divided into three parts: the instantaneous elastic volumetric strain increment $d\varepsilon_{ij}^e$, the instantaneous plastic volumetric strain increment $d\varepsilon_{ij}^{sp}$, and the visco-plastic strain increment $d\varepsilon_{ij}^{tp}$.

$$d\varepsilon_{ij} = d\varepsilon_{ij}^e + d\varepsilon_{ij}^{sp} + d\varepsilon_{ij}^{tp} \tag{1}$$

In Equation (1), strain increment due to time effect is represented by $d\varepsilon_{ij}^{tp}$.

According to the generalized Hooke's law, the elastic strain increments are expressed as:

$$d\varepsilon_v^e = \frac{dp}{K} = \frac{\kappa}{1+e_0}\frac{dp}{p} \tag{2}$$

$$d\varepsilon_d^e = \frac{dq}{3G} = \frac{2\kappa(1+\nu)}{(1-2\nu)(1+e_0)}\frac{dq}{9p} \tag{3}$$

In Equations (2) and (3): $d\varepsilon_v^e$ and $d\varepsilon_d^e$ are elastic volumetric strain increment and elastic shear strain increment, respectively; dp and dq are mean principal stress increment and generalized shear stress increment, respectively; e_0, κ and ν are initial void ratio, slope of rebound line of reconstituted soil, and Poisson's ratio, respectively; K and G are the bulk modulus and the shear modulus, respectively.

The magnitude and direction of the plastic volumetric strain increment $d\varepsilon_v^p$ and plastic shear strain increment $d\varepsilon_d^p$ are determined by the yield functions and hardening law. In the $q \sim p$ stress space, the current yield function f and the reference yield function $\bar{f}$ of the elastic visco-plastic UH model for structured soils can be expressed as:

$$\begin{cases} f = p\left(1 + \dfrac{\eta^2}{M^2}\right) - p_x = 0 \\ \bar{f} = \bar{p}\left(\dfrac{1+\bar{\eta}^2}{M^2}\right) - \overline{p_x} = 0 \end{cases} \tag{4}$$

In Equation (4): M is the critical state stress ratio; $\eta = q/p$ and $\bar{\eta} = \bar{q}/\bar{p}$ are the stress ratio of the current yield surface and the reference yield surface, respectively; p_x and $\overline{p_x}$ are the intercepts of the current yield surface and the reference yield surface on the p-axis, respectively.

$$p_x = p_{x0}\exp\left(\frac{H}{c_p} - \bar{i}\right) \tag{5}$$

$$\overline{p_x} = \overline{p_{x0}}\exp\left(\frac{\int d\varepsilon_v^p}{c_p} + \frac{\int d(\Delta e)}{\lambda - \kappa}\right) \tag{6}$$

In Equations (5) and (6): p_{x0} and $\overline{p_{x0}}$ are the initial values of p_x and $\overline{p_x}$, respectively; $c_p = (\lambda - \kappa)/(1+e_0)$; λ, κ and e_0 are the slope of the normal consolidation line of the reconstituted soil, the slope of the reconstituted soil rebound line, and the initial void ratio in the $e \sim \ln p$ plane, respectively; H is the hardening parameter expressed as:

$$H = \int R^{\frac{\Delta e}{\Delta e_0}(\eta - M_f)} \frac{M_f^4 - \eta^4}{M^4 - \eta^4}\left(d\varepsilon_v^{sp} + d\varepsilon_v^{tp}\right) \tag{7}$$

M_f is the potential stress ratio strength, which is expressed as:

$$M_f = 6\left[\sqrt{\frac{\chi}{R}\left(1+\frac{\chi}{R}\right)} - \frac{\chi}{R}\right] \qquad (8)$$

In Equation (8), $\chi = M^2/[12(3-M)]$; R is an internal variable expressing the overconsolidation, defined as:

$$R = p_x/\overline{p_x} \qquad (9)$$

Δe is the soil structured potential, whose initial value is Δe_0. The evolution of Δe is expressed as:

$$d(\Delta e) = -\zeta \cdot \Delta e \cdot |d\varepsilon_v^p| \qquad (10)$$

$\bar{t}$ is the nominal time, which is expressed as:

$$\bar{t} = \frac{C_{\alpha e}}{\lambda - \kappa} \int R^{\frac{\Delta e}{\Delta e_0}(\eta - M_f)} \frac{M_f^4}{M^4} R_t^\alpha dt \qquad (11)$$

$C_{\alpha e}$ is the coefficient of secondary consolidation; $\alpha = (\lambda - \kappa)/C_{\alpha e}$; $R_t \in (0,1)$ is a modify variable of the inter variable R, which is applied to calculate the viscous strain of structured soil. The internal variable R_t is formulated as follow:

$$R_t = \frac{R}{R+1} \cdot \frac{\Delta e}{N+\Delta e} + \frac{1}{2}(1+R-|1-R|)\frac{N}{N+\Delta e} \qquad (12)$$

In Equation (12): N is the intercept of the normal compression line on the e-axis in the $e \sim \ln p$ plane.

The presented model applies the associated flow rule, thus the relationship of plastic volumetric strain increment $d\varepsilon_v^p$ and the plastic shear strain increment $d\varepsilon_d^p$ can be described as:

$$\frac{d\varepsilon_v^p}{d\varepsilon_d^p} = \frac{M^2 - \eta^2}{2\eta} = \frac{d\varepsilon_v^{sp} + d\varepsilon_v^{tp}}{d\varepsilon_d^{sp} + d\varepsilon_d^{tp}} \qquad (13)$$

3 MODEL VERIFICATION

To verify the reasonability of the proposed model, the test results of three structured soils are compared with the model predictions in this section. They are Batiscan clay (Leroueil et al. 1985), Wenzhou clay (Dan 2009), and Berthierville clay (Leroueil et al. 1988). All the basic parameters used in the model are listed in Table 1, where the parameters $C_{\alpha e}$, λ, κ, ν, N and M can be determined from isotropic compression tests and triaxial shear tests of

Table 1. Model parameters in predictions.

Structured soils	λ	κ	ν	N	M	Δe_0	ζ	$C_{\alpha e}$
Wenzhou clay	0.384	0.042	0.3	3.52	1.23	0.15	8.0	0.023
Batiscan clay	0.41	0.037	0.3	3.45	0.98	0.58	5.0	0.026
Berthierville clay	0.3647	0.025	0.08	3.16	1.20	0.16	15.0	0.021

reconstituted soils. The parameters e_0 and ζ can be determined from isotropic compression tests of structured soils.

Wenzhou clay samples were taken from a silt layer at a depth of 11 m below the surface in Wenzhou, China, with a soil thickness of about 20~30 m and has strong structural properties.

Batiscan clay is located on the north bank of the St. Lawrence River, about 110 km west of Quebec City, Canada. The samples were taken from a depth of 7.25-7.46 m from the surface, which has a natural moisture content of 80%, a plasticity index of 21, a liquidity index of 2.7, and significant structural properties.

Berthierville clay is located on the north bank of the St. Lawrence River between Montreal and Quebec City, Canada. The samples were taken from a gray powdery clay layer at a depth of 3.23 - 3.48 m from the surface, with a thickness of 3.2 m. Figure 3 shows the results of the one-dimensional CRS tests and model predictions for the Berthierville clay. Figures 1 - 3 show model predictions for Wenzhou clay, Batiscan clay, and Berthierville clay compared with the corresponding one-dimensional CRS tests. According to the comparison between the test data and model simulations, the proposed model is qualified to simulate not only the evolution patterns but also the related characteristics of the above 3 structured soils under different volume strain loading rates.

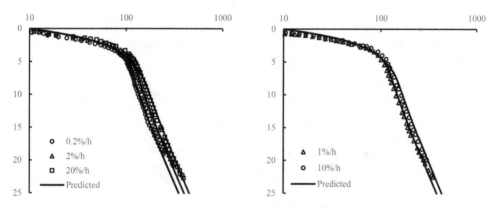

Figure 1. Prediction and test data of natural Wenzhou clay in one-dimensional CRS test.

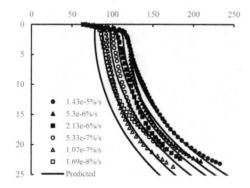

Figure 2. Prediction and test data of natural Batiscan clay in one-dimensional CRS test.

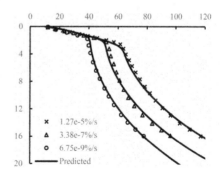

Figure 3. Prediction and test data of natural Berthierville clay in one-dimensional CRS test.

4 CONCLUSION

This paper establishes an elastic visco-plastic UH model of one-dimensional compression for structured soils based on the structured UH model. A modified internal variable R_t is formulated to calculate the viscous strain. By comparing the simulation results and the experimental data of the one-dimensional CRS tests of three structured soils, it is shown that the proposed model is qualified to stimulate the compression behaviors of structured soil in different strain rates.

REFERENCES

Bjerrum L. (1967) Engineering Geology of Norwegian Normally-consolidated Marine Clays as Related to Settlements of Buildings. *Geotechnique*, 17(02): 83–118.
Dan H.B. (2009) *Time Dependent Behavior of Natural Soft Clays*. Zhejiang University.
Hinchberger S.D. and Qu G. (2009) Viscoplastic Constitutive Approach for Rate-sensitive Structured Clays. *Canadian Geotechnical Journal*, 46(06): 609–626.
Karim M.R., Oka F., Krabbenhoft K., *et al.* (2013) Simulation of Long-term Consolidation Behavior of Soft Sensitive Clay Using an Elasto-viscoplastic Constitutive Model. *International Journal for Numerical and Analytical Methods in Geomechanics*, 37(16): 2801–2824.
Ke W.H., Chen J., Sheng Q., *et al.* (2016) One-dimensional Elastic Visco-plastic Modelling of Time-dependent Behavior of Structured Soft Clays. *Rock and Soil Mechanics*, 37(09): 2561–2568.
Leroueil S., Kabbai M., Tavenas F., *et al.* (1985) Stress–strain–strain Rate Relation for the Compressibility of Sensitive Natural Clays. *Géotechnique*, 35(02): 159–180.
Leroueil S., Kabbai M. and Tavenas F. (1988) Study of the Validity of a $\sigma'_v - \varepsilon_v - \dot{\varepsilon}_v$ Model in in situ Conditions. *Soils and Foundations*, 28(03): 13–25.
Yao Y.P. (2015) Advanced UH Models for Soils. *Chinese Journal of Geotechnical Engineering*, 37(02): 193–217.
Yin J.H. and Graham J. (1989) Viscous-elastic-plastic Modeling of One-dimensional Time-dependent Behaviour of Clays. *Canadian Geotechnical Journal*, 26 (01): 199–209.
Yin J.H. and Graham J. (1994) Equivalent Times and One-dimensional Elastic Visco-plastic Modelling of Time-dependent Stress-strain Behavior of Clays. *Canadian Geotechnical Journal*, 31(01): 42–52.
Zeng L.L., Liu S.Y., Hong Z.S. (2012) Modified EVP Model Considering Effect of Soil Structure. *Journal of Southeast University*, 42(02): 346–351.
Zhu E.Y., Yao Y.P. (2015) A UH Constitutive Model for Structured Soils. *Rock and Mechanics*, 36(11): 3101–3110+3228.

Research on the application of green building design based on BIM technology

Bei Wu*, Yihan Cheng*, Ya Dang, Yunfan Peng, Wen Zhao & Zhijun Ouyang
Tianjin Renai College, Tianjin, China

ABSTRACT: This paper expounds on the design and research of BIM technology in green buildings. Taking a theater as an example, the public construction project is analyzed and transformed from four aspects: health and comfort, livable environment, resource-saving, improvement, and innovation. With the assistance of BIM technology, the disadvantages of insufficient information and inconspicuous visualization effects under 2D design have been changed. At the same time, the designer's ideas are in line with reality and comfort, making the architectural design more reasonable, energy-saving and comfortable. It is hoped that with the popularization of BIM technology, promoting the further development of green buildings can also save design and construction costs. There are also some shortcomings in this study. When transforming the indoor and outdoor environment, the performance and function of building materials are considered, but the price of building materials is not considered enough, which increases the cost of transformation. Under the analysis of ventilation and sunshine, the influence of surrounding buildings on the building is not considered, so the analysis value does not completely match the actual value.

1 INTRODUCTION

With the construction of digital China, the key application of BIM technology in the construction engineering industry is gradually popularized. While living safely, green buildings have also become one of the criteria for judging whether a building is feasible.

Combined with the performance of the building itself and the influence of the surrounding environment, the green building comprehensively evaluates the five categories of indicators of safety and durability, health and comfort, resource conservation, living convenience, and environmental livability throughout the life cycle of the building.

2 RESEARCH BACKGROUND IN GREEN BUILDINGS BASED ON BIM TECHNOLOGY

2.1 *BIM concept*

The full name of BIM is Building Information Modeling, which combines various building elements to establish their model information. It links the entire life cycle of the building and the practical application of the project. BIM technology can visualize the building model in the early stage, can find problems to solve at any time, and quickly decide whether to modify the plan. In the whole life cycle of buildings, BIM technology is often used for project

---

*Corresponding Authors: 286456338@qq.com and 2640152830@qq.com

evaluation, budgeting, and model visualization to improve the efficiency of the early stage of design to create a better and more accurate design.

2.2 *The green building concept*

Green building is a high-quality building that saves resources, protects the environment, reduces pollution, provides people with healthy, suitable, and efficient use space, and maximizes the harmonious coexistence between man and nature during the entire life cycle (Xing 2021).

The basic connotations of green buildings can be summarized as follows:

(1) They can reduce the pollution of buildings to the environment, that is, save resources;
(2) They can provide a safe, healthy, and livable living circle;
(3) They can adapt to the natural environment and realize the concept of harmonious coexistence and sustainable development of people, buildings, and the environment.

2.3 *Common building problems*

In Chinese urban buildings, there are many old-fashioned communities. Due to the certain years of use and the relatively long design years, many requirements for green buildings have not been considered. The layout does not consider the ventilation design, resulting in poor ventilation in many community areas. On the contrary, roads, parking lots, and surrounding squares lack greening, have long sunshine times, and changeable temperature difference between day and night; hence, the hardened pavement in the community is not permeable. Bricks and other highly permeable materials can increase the permeability of hardened ground materials, resulting in flooded roads in rainy weather.

2.4 *The connection between BIM and green building*

BIM is based on all the information of the construction project and the multi-party data information involved in the construction. It uses the visualization and simulation technology of BIM to combine with green building software to realize the mutual cooperation and unified management of all participating green building work. At present, the green building software adjusts and dynamically simulates the extracted BIM model information according to green building standards. The obtained green building analysis report provides guidance and data comparison for green building design work.

3 PROJECT OVERVIEW

3.1 *Case introduction*

The study is based on the Grand Theater, with a total area of more than 20,000 square meters and a building area of about 36,000 square meters. Since the theater is a public building with a large volume and high overall energy consumption, the study calculates the lighting, sound environment, wind environment, sunshine, thermal environment, indoor comfort, energy saving, etc., to determine whether the building meets the requirements of green buildings. The building structure is optimized and transformed, and the scheme that meets the green building standards is obtained through experimental calculation.

3.2 *Regional natural condition analysis*

The area is moderately cold and hot, rich in heat, has a prominent monsoon, four distinct seasons, and moderate annual temperatures. It has sunlight, abundant rainfall, and humid air is synchronous with seasonal changes in rain and heat and has a diverse configuration of climatic resources and many meteorological hazards. It belongs to the subtropical monsoon climate (Wang 2017).

4 APPLICATION ANALYSIS OF BIM IN GREEN BUILDING DESIGN

4.1 Health and comfort

4.1.1 Analysis of indoor acoustic environment
The indoor acoustic environment is simulated, and the sound insulation performance is obtained from the construction method of the indoor wall, the surface density, the source of the sound insulation, the octave center frequency, the frequency division sound insulation, the adverse deviation, the weighted sound insulation, and the spectral correction. The sound insulation limit is compared to judge whether the wall meets the requirements. After the judgment is not satisfied, the theater itself will be renovated, and a large number of trees and shrubs will be planted around to absorb noise and reduce the impact of external sound sources on the building.

4.1.2 Lighting analysis
The lighting design gives full play to the natural conditions of the building itself. Natural light is the best light source for human use. Making full use of natural lighting can also effectively achieve the effect of green energy saving, making the building design closer to green energy saving (Dong et al. 2020). Figure 1 shows that the lighting coefficient of the building decreases gradually from the exterior to the interior of the building in the west. The research object is a theater. The interior concert hall and opera house have a low lighting coefficient. In order to meet the lighting requirements, the lighting coefficient is increased by changing the material of the curtain wall, as shown in Figure 2. After the improvement of the curtain wall material, the daylighting coefficient has increased intuitively. The daylighting coefficient of the west side has increased from about 4.0 to 56.4. At the same time, the interior lighting coefficient has increased from the original 0.5 to a maximum of 7, so the lighting effect is also significant.

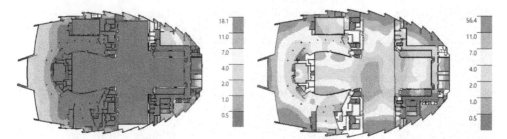

Figure 1. Lighting analysis lightmap.

Figure 2. Lighting analysis lightmap.

4.1.3 Outdoor wind environment design
Through the simulation analysis of the outdoor wind environment of the theater, the wind speed, wind speed amplification factor, wind pressure, etc., can be obtained to carry out the reasonable transformation of building ventilation according to the data, which can save the consumption of building materials, and achieve the maximum ventilation effect under the requirement of ergonomics.

Therefore, two methods were adopted for the renovation of the theater. ① A window sill with a height of 800 and a window height of 1500 was placed behind the scaly curtain wall of a theater. Because the scaly curtain wall of a theater is mostly for lounges, restaurants, and air intakes, air vents and placing windows here can not only facilitate air circulation but also will not affect the stage performances in the theater. ② By planting wind-guiding trees in summer, the wind can be guided upwards and enter the room through the modified curtain wall windows; planting wind-proof trees in winter can effectively block the entry of wind and maintain the indoor temperature (Wu 2020).

The calculated results after the design and renovation are shown in Table 1. It is concluded that the outdoor wind environment meets the requirements of the "Green Building Evaluation Standard" (GB/T 50378-2019) and "Building Ventilation Effect Test and Evaluation Standard" (JGJ/T 309-2013).

Table 1. Judgment table for the completion of the transformation.

Evaluation item	Standard requirement	Project calculation results	Judgment of reaching the standard	Score
Wind speed Wind speed amplification factor	If the wind speed is less than 5 m/s at the height of 1.5 m from the ground in the pedestrian area around the building, the wind speed in the outdoor rest area and children's entertainment area is less than 2 m/s, and the outdoor wind speed amplification factor is less than 2, 3 points are awarded.	There is no area with a wind speed greater than 5 m/s in the pedestrian area, and no area with a wind speed greater than 2 m/s in the outdoor rest area and children's entertainment area There is no area with a wind speed amplification factor greater than or equal to 2 in the pedestrian area	Up to standard	3 points
Wind pressure value on the windward/leeward side of the building	Except for the first row of buildings facing the wind, the wind pressure difference between the windward side and the leeward side of the building does not exceed 5 Pa, 2 points	There is no building with a surface wind pressure difference greater than 5 Pa between the windward side and the leeward side of the building in this project.	Up to standard	3 points

4.1.4 *Sunshine analysis*

According to the sunshine analysis time chart of the theater, it can be seen that the occlusion of a certain theater by the surrounding buildings changes with time. At different times, the occlusion area of the building will first increase and then decrease with the transfer of sunlight. When the sun goes down, the occluder provides the least occlusion for a theater. In order to avoid the theater being blocked by surrounding buildings and to ensure that a certain theater has sufficient sunlight, a certain theater is selected as the building boundary. From the shadow of the winter solstice, it can be seen that the building blocks a large area of the theater during that particular time. A variety of trees can be used in sunny areas to form a shading effect, provide a resting place, and meet people's living needs.

4.1.5 *Architectural orientation analysis transformation*

Take the location of the Grand Theater as an example. If there is no shelter, as shown in Figure 3, the indoor sunshine range in winter is mostly within 60° west longitude, and the sunshine time in the direction of the winter solstice exceeds 4 hours. The maximum altitude angle is 47°, within 30° of east (west) north, and there is no sunlight during the winter

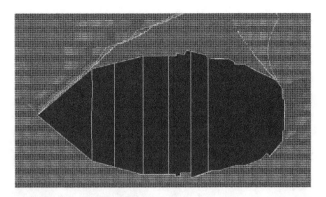

Figure 3. Plane iso-sun line.

solstice. The sunshine range in summer is within 20° to the west of the south, the sunshine time is short, and the covering sunshine area is small. Compared with winter, the indoor sunshine time in summer is generally between 2 and 6 hours, and the sunshine area is only 5% to 7% of that in winter (Xi et al. 2019).

The annual total radiation in the area is 4.4 GJ/m^{2}y, and the monthly average temperature is 24.6°C in June, 28.0°C in July, 28.0°C in August, and 24.9°C in September. The direct solar radiation intensity is generally weaker in the morning than in the afternoon. In contrast, the solar radiation heat in the west is slightly higher than that in the east in winter or summer. The highest outdoor temperature in summer usually occurs between 1:00 pm and 5:00 pm. At this time, the sun is at the level of the west for half a day. It can be seen that the building orientation is 20°-80° west-south. At its highest, the building can absorb better sunlight and make better use of the photovoltaic curtain wall. In winter, rooms in all directions are exposed to UV rays. Considering the number of UV rays received, the building orientation range is preferably between 30°E and 90°W.

In severe cold regions, in order to avoid cold in the building in winter, all the main rooms should be arranged to avoid facing the main wind direction to avoid excessive heat loss. The main wind direction in winter in this area is the north-westerly wind, which is on the leeward side in the area from 45° east of north to 90° west of south, an ideal orientation for the building to keep out the cold in winter.

To sum up, the building orientation analysis is mainly determined by the lighting performance, thermal environment, and ventilation performance of the building. Through the comprehensive analysis of the three, a good orientation of the building can be obtained. The building orientation of the theater is 45° southwest. The orientation to 80° is more reasonable.

4.1.6 *Analysis of outdoor acoustic environment*

The outdoor sound environment is simulated and analyzed by the software, and the outdoor noise decibel distribution map is obtained. In Figure 4, the area close to the road is purple, the range is between 60 decibels and 70 decibels, and most of the red is between 55 decibels and 60 decibels. Among them, the same minority is light red, and the area is between 50 decibels and 55 decibels. The environmental noise comprehensive score table is compared with the "Green Building Evaluation Standard" GB50378 - 2019. The maximum value of noise in the daytime is 65 decibels, which is greater than the noise limit of 60 decibels, and the maximum noise at night is 51 decibels, which also exceeds the noise limit by 50 decibels. Therefore, the ambient noise in this theater venue was initially substandard, as shown in Table 2.

Analysis of outdoor sound sources shows that different colors in Figure 4 represent different decibel ranges. Road sound sources, such as the intersection of Fudong Road and

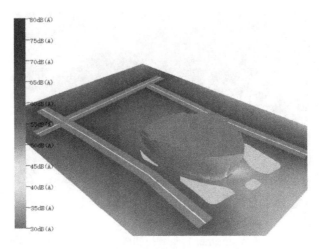

Figure 4. Aerial view of site noise distribution (daytime).

Table 2. Acoustic functional area compliance statistics table.

Outdoor layout	Type	Contains buildings	Noise maximum Daytime	Noise maximum At night	Noise Limit Daytime	Noise Limit At night	Compliance
A theater	Category 2	A theater	68	51	60	50	Not to tandard

Shifu Road around the building, have a greater impact on the building. In addition, the large theater produces a lot of noise, which has a greater impact on the adjacent rooms. A large number of trees and shrubs are planted around the roadside of the Grand Theater to absorb noise and reduce the impact of external sound sources on the building.

For the building itself, through the transformation of the wall, the thick wall adopts a composite wall combining sound insulation and sound-absorbing materials, and the thin-plate composite wall is used for the limited thickness of the wall. After the transformation, the simulation analysis of the outdoor acoustic environment was continued, and the conclusion was drawn that the maximum noise in the daytime was 56 decibels, the night-time noise was 48 decibels, the class 2 noise limit was 60 decibels, and the night-time noise was 50 decibels. The final score was 5 points. If the standard is met, the project will finally be judged to meet the "Green Building Evaluation Standard."

Table 3. Comprehensive evaluation table of the outdoor acoustic environment.

Outdoor layout	Type	Contains buildings	Noise maximum Daytime	Noise maximum At night	Noise Limit Daytime	Noise Limit At night	Compliance
A theater	Category 2	A theater	56	48	60	50	Not to standard

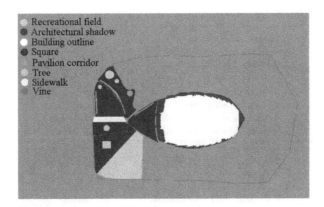

Figure 5. Outdoor layout.

4.1.7 *Thermal environment analysis of the residential area*
In Figure 5, different colors represent different categories, including squares paved with permeable bricks, pavilions, corridors, and arbors. Through thermal environment simulation, by comparing the average windward area in summer and the shading coverage limit of the activity site in the residential area, we judge whether the theater complies with the "Code for Thermal Environment Design of Urban Residential Areas" and draw a preliminary conclusion that the temperature reached by the building without greening is as high as 43°C. The building itself has a few adjacent high-rise buildings. The surface area of cement-hardened pavement is light and is directly exposed to sunlight, so the temperature caused by it is not suitable. After renovation, green plants are added around the building, and the roof is greened to increase the greening rate and enrich the landscape. The curtain wall is set as a BIPV photovoltaic curtain wall that converts light energy into electric energy while absorbing heat, which is more energy-saving and environmentally friendly and achieves the purpose of green construction. Furthermore, adding water features, green space, and permeable bricks in the activity venue around the building, combined with the layout, can reduce the intensity of the heat island while maintaining a reasonable and beautiful layout.

4.1.8 *Indoor and outdoor garden materials and renovation*
To increase the local green area of the project, by analyzing the surrounding environment of a theater, the local climate, and comprehensive regional characteristics, banyan trees are selected to increase the green area, thereby increasing the greening rate and satisfying the standard as much as possible.

In addition, there are relatively few urban green spaces and water bodies, and the ground is mostly impervious. However, the impervious ground will bring a lot of pressure on the local rainwater pipes, which will cause inconvenience to the municipal engineers. At the same time, the impervious surface easily damages the surface water circulation, and the groundwater replenishment is blocked, which will seriously lead to partial subsidence of urban areas. Therefore, by modifying the ground material to save energy, the effect of rainwater recycling is achieved. The cement mortar floor is changed to a permeable brick floor.

4.2 *Save resources*

4.2.1 *Energy saving improvement in the scheme design stage*
In Swell energy-saving software, a single model can be established through three stages: model processing stage, engineering structure setting stage, and calculation stage. Then in

Table 4. After the energy-saving design.

Serial number	Check items	In conclusion
1	Window-to-wall ratio	Inappropriate
2	Visible light transmittance	Satisfy
3	Sunroof type	No roof translucent part
4	Roof construction	Satisfy
5	Exterior wall structure	Satisfy
6	Cantilevered floor structure	Satisfy
7	External window thermal work	Satisfy
8	Effective ventilation area	Satisfy
9	Non-hollow window area ratio	Satisfy
10	Air tightness of exterior windows	Satisfy
11	Curtain wall air tightness	Satisfy
Conclusion		Satisfy

the ventilation software, the PL line is used to draw the general drawing model, and building parameters, building red lines, floor frames, etc., are set. A general graph model is established, and finally, a complete model can be obtained through the ontology entry.

4.2.2 *Energy saving improvement in the construction drawing design stage*

The energy-saving report that uses the default engineering structure will show unsatisfactory items. Through the energy-saving analysis, we observe the thermal characteristics of the building and whether the envelope structure meets the green standards. Through the analysis, it can be obtained that the window wall of the building is relatively low, and the thermal characteristics of the external window are also relatively low. The thermal design index of the envelope structure in the energy-saving design of this project does not meet the basic requirements of the thermal performance trade-off judgment of the envelope structure of the public building energy-saving design standard GB50189 - 2015. The design, as shown in Table 4, meets the requirement for the energy-saving design and achieves building energy-saving.

4.2.3 *Energy consumption analysis*

In public buildings, controlling the heating and cooling demand time is also a major way to save energy loss. According to the building envelope and internal equipment settings, the peak load bar graph and the load sub-item bar graph of the hourly load throughout the year are analyzed. The peak load shows that the annual heat load is mainly distributed from January to March and December, and the cooling load is mainly distributed from March to November. There is no heat recovery. It is concluded that the main cooling and heating time is mainly set from June to September, and the heating time is mainly controlled from November to March of the next year to reduce energy loss and make the building greener and energy-saving.

5 CONCLUSION

To sum up, the green building simulation analysis of the theater is carried out in different aspects, mainly including indoor acoustic environment analysis, lighting analysis, indoor thermal comfort analysis, building orientation analysis, sunlight analysis, outdoor wind environment analysis, outdoor acoustic environment analysis, and residential thermal environment analysis. Using the analysis data to compare with the green building evaluation standards, a preliminary conclusion is finally drawn whether the theater meets the standards.

For items that do not meet the standards, the theater itself should be renovated. The final result was that the theater did not meet the standards, and an improvement plan and corresponding data were obtained. For the building orientation, according to the analysis data of the building's lighting performance, thermal environment, and ventilation performance, it is concluded that the orientation of 45° to 80° in the west-southwest is more reasonable; for the exterior design of the theater, it can be used in summer. We can plant wind-guiding trees to guide the wind from outside to inside to achieve maximum ventilation. Planting windproof trees in winter can effectively block the entry of wind and maintain indoor temperature. For the interior, through the transformation of the wall, the thick wall adopts a composite wall combining sound insulation and sound-absorbing materials. The thickness of the wall is limited, and a thin-plate composite wall is used to meet the sound shell requirements of the room, and the sound insulation performance is 59, which meets the average requirements. In terms of resources, the main cooling and heating time are rationally arranged. The cooling time is set mainly from June to September, and the heating time is controlled from November to March of the next year to reduce energy loss and make the building more efficient, greener, and energy-saving.

ACKNOWLEDGMENTS

This work was financially supported by the Teaching Reform Project of Tianjin Renai College in 2021 (2021-3-5).

REFERENCES

Dong Meihua, Wang Zhen, Fu Xu, Li Wenru, Li Qian, Zhang Youheng & Wang Qing-yong. (2020). Analysis of Multi-storey Building Energy Saving Design Based on Green BIM Concept. (eds.) The 7th International Conference on BIM Technology – Proceedings on the Innovation and Development of Intelligent Construction and Building Industrialization (pp. 252–257). *Journal of Information Technology in Civil Engineering Engineering and Architecture*).

Wang X.M. (2017). *Landscape Ecological Disturbance Effects of Land Use Change in the Yangtze River Delta* (Master's Thesis, Nanjing Agricultural University).

Wu Xiaolong (2020). *Research on Low-carbon Reconstruction Strategy of existing Rural Residential Buildings in Luonan Area* (Master's Thesis, Xi'an University of Architecture and Technology).

Xi Fei, Ruan Xuejun & Zhang Chengfeng. (2019). Research on the Influence of the Layout of Rural Residential Buildings in Jiangnan on the Thermal Insulation Performance. *Art and Design (Theory)* (06), 78–80.

Xing Yudong. (2021). *Research on Spatio-temporal Evolution Characteristics and Influencing Factors of Green Building Development* (Master's Thesis, Shandong Jianzhu University).

Experimental study on slag improvement in a power shield tunnel in Xi'an

Jie Liu* & Xuanrong Zheng*
School of Architecture and Civil Engineering, Xi'an University of Science and Technology, Xi'an, Shaanxi, China

Jiahui Qi*
Yunji Intelligent Engineering Co, Shenzhen, Guangdong, China

ABSTRACT: When a shield machine traverses different strata, in most geological cases, it is necessary to improve the slag soil in the soil or soil bin in front of the shield machine's cutter deck boring to ensure smooth construction. In this paper, an experimental study on the improvement of slag soil in the shield interval of a water-rich sand layer of a power shield tunnel in Xi'an was carried out by means of indoor experiments and field practice on fine and medium coarse sands, respectively. The study results show that the sandy soil can be effectively reduced in permeability by using a sodium-based bentonite slurry with a soil-to-water ratio of 1:8. The optimum volume addition ratios of fine, medium, and coarse sands are 8%, 10%, and 16%. Field practice shows that: after the improvement and optimization of the slurry, the flow plasticity is significantly improved, the total thrust value of the shield is reduced, the tunneling speed is significantly accelerated, and can provide a reference for certain projects in Xi'an with the same geology.

1 INTRODUCTION

Unlike ordinary metro shield tunnels, most power shield tunnels use small diameter shield machines with a diameter of 4 m to reduce construction costs while reasonably using space and meeting design and usage requirements. When working in water-rich sand layers, most of them need to be modified for bad soils to speed up the boring speed and reduce safety accidents. Wei (2007) investigated the interaction between various amendments and residual soils by using an indoor experimental method. Liu et al. (2020) evaluated the permeability coefficient of the slag on-site by infiltration experiments based on the shield of Kunming Metro Line 4, evaluated the fluidity of the actual slag out of the site by slump experiments, and also analyzed the influence of the flow plastic state of the slag on the total thrust, torque, specific thrust, specific torque, and tunneling speed of the shield. By means of indoor experiments and numerical simulations, Li (2020) studied the influence of different types of improvers on the permeability of sandy soil in earth pressure shield tunneling in Xi'an. The results of orthogonal experiments showed that different mud injection ratios had the greatest influence on the permeability coefficient of the improved sandy soil (Li 2020). Through a series of experimental studies, this paper takes a new power tunnel in Xi'an as an example to

---

*Corresponding Authors: 20204228087@stu.xust.edu.cn; 254519207@qq.com and 2375927606@qq.com

arrive at the most suitable bentonite slurry mix ratio for this project improvement and to provide a reference for similar projects in Xi'an.

2 PROJECT OVERVIEW

A new power cable tunnel of about 21.69 km in Xi'an adopts an earth-pressure balanced shield machine with an outer diameter of 4 m, an inner diameter of 3.5 m, a ring width of 1.2 m, and a thickness of 0.25 m. As can be seen from the strata traversed by the shield interval of this project, the strata traversed mainly are powder clay layers, water-rich coarse sand layers, and water-rich medium sand layers. The water source in the submerged aquifer is mainly rainfall infiltration and river infiltration recharge, and the sand stratum here is extremely rich in water content. The risk of accidents is high in this sandy layer, so the object of this sludge improvement experiment is selected to be water-rich fine to medium coarse sandy soil and powdered clay.

3 EXPERIMENTAL PROGRAMME AND CONTENT

Sand samples of unimproved residual soil were taken on-site. The samples are completely dried and processed for the sand particle sieving experiment, as shown in Figure 1. Adequate amounts of fine, medium, and coarse sand were prepared according to the sand grading curves in the survey report. The grain gradations of the three sand samples are shown in Table 1.

Figure 1. Particle sieving experiment.

3.1 *Experimental scheme*

According to the different grain gradations of the traversing sand layer, respectively configured with varying gradations of grains of fine sand, medium sand, and coarse sand layer, the three sand samples carried out slump test and permeability test (Yang *et al.* 2022).

Table 1. Sand and soil particle gradation.

Name	≥ 20.0 mm (%)	20.0~2.0 mm (%)	2.0~0.5 mm (%)	0.5~0.25 mm (%)	0.25~0.075 mm (%)	<0.075 mm (%)
Fine sand	0	5.3	12.7	30.4	36.5	15.1
Medium sand	3.9	8.4	21.7	27.6	21.4	17
Coarse sand	6.8	17.1	26.3	18.2	12.4	19.2

The viscosity and specific gravity of the bentonite slurry are measured to obtain the type of bentonite suitable for the formation and the concentration of the slurry at which the bentonite expands best. The slump and permeability coefficients of the different sands in their initial state were determined separately. Then, the slump and permeability coefficients of the three types of sands were determined by mixing them with different concentrations of bentonite slurry to find the optimum values.

3.2 *Bentonite slurry optimization experiment*

Calcium-based bentonite and sodium-based bentonite were selected and formulated into different concentrations of bentonite slurry, which were stirred and expanded for 24 hours. Then, the viscosity and specific gravity of the slurry at each concentration were measured to obtain the optimum calcium-based and sodium-based bentonite concentrations. The experimental data are shown in Table 2, and the data curves are shown in Figure 2.

Table 2. Specific gravity and viscosity of calcium-based and sodium-based bentonite slurries at different concentrations.

Bentonite Data Mud mix proportion	Calcium base Specific gravity (g/cm^3)	Viscosity (s)	Sodium base Specific gravity (g/cm^3)	Viscosity (s)
1:2	1.19	68.66	1.19	78.66
1:3	1.17	22.18	1.18	52.18
1:4	1.14	19.28	1.15	39.28
1:6	1.08	17.13	1.13	26.75
1:8	1.07	16.99	1.11	17.55
1:10	1.03	16.42	1.10	16.33
1:12	1.02	15.36	1.07	15.87

As seen in Figure 2, the specific gravity and viscosity of the bentonite slurry decrease as the slurry ratio increases. For calcium-based bentonite slurries below 1:3, the change in viscosity value is more significant, and for slurries greater than 1:3, the change in viscosity value with slurry concentration is less. When the sodium-based bentonite slurry is below 1:8, the change in concentration has a greater effect on the viscosity value. When the slurry ratio is greater than 1:8, the viscosity changes less with concentration, and the basic viscosity value does not change significantly. When the slurry ratio is below 1:4, the difference between the specific gravity values of calcium-based bentonite and sodium-based bentonite of the same concentration is small. The difference between the specific gravity of calcium bentonite and

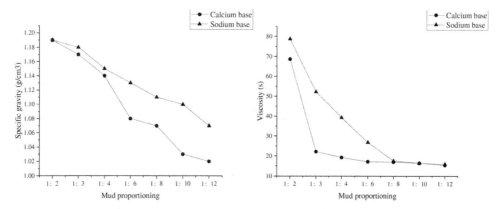

Figure 2. Variation of specific gravity and viscosity values for different concentrations and types of bentonite slurry.

sodium bentonite increases as the slurry concentration decreases, indicating that the difference between sodium and calcium bentonite in the concentration of small, improved sandy soils is greater. Therefore, the ratio of calcium-based bentonite slurry should be chosen to 1:3, and the ratio of sodium-based bentonite slurry should be chosen to 1:8.

According to the bentonite slurry optimization results, this experiment uses 1:8 sodium-based bentonite slurry to improve the three water-rich conditions of the sand samples, in turn, mixed with a mass fraction of 2%, 4%, 6%, 8%, 10%, 12%, 14% of the sodium-based bentonite slurry, the slurry to improve the three kinds of sand were slump test and permeability test.

3.3 Slump test

The sand improvement slump test is similar to the powdered clay improvement test. According to the conclusion of existing studies, the slump of water-rich sandy soil is between 100 and 150 mm. The slump test results are shown in Table 3, and the slump variation curve in the improvement chamber is shown in Figure 3.

Table 3. Sand slump for different bentonite slurry injections.

Bentonite injection mass ratio (%)									
Soil sample		0	2	4	6	8	10	12	14
Fine sand	Slump (mm)	4	12	26	71	83	123	184	231
Medium sand		3	8	22	66	78	106	137	211
Coarse sand		0	11	15	28	39	72	93	116

As can be seen from Figure 3, the sandy soil had basically no slump and poor flow plasticity of the soil for the three different particle gradations before improvement. When the bentonite slurry addition and soil sample mass ratio at 10%, the slump values of fine sand and medium sand reached 123 mm and 106 mm, respectively, both within the best slump requirements; when the bentonite slurry addition and soil sample mass ratio reached 14%, the slump values of improved fine sand and medium sand were much larger than the best slump requirements, at this time, the slump of coarse sand met the best flow plasticity of the

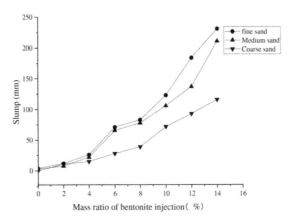

Figure 3. Variation of slump within the water-rich sandy soil improvement chamber.3.

residual soil. Therefore, in shield construction, fine sand, medium, and coarse sand strata can be improved by using a soil-to-water mass ratio of 1:8 and adding 10%, 10%, and 14% of the mass of the residue to the sodium-based bentonite slurry, respectively.

3.4 Infiltration experiments

The infiltration experiment was carried out to determine the permeability coefficients of the three remodeled grains of sand before and after improvement. The infiltration experiment apparatus was based on the infiltration experiment apparatus of Zhong Xiaochun and Zhongtian Chen, and a homemade variable head infiltration experiment apparatus was made. The apparatus mainly consists of a permeation cylinder, air compressor, rubber hose, pressure gauge, etc. The permeation coefficient experimental apparatus is shown in Figure 4. Table 4 shows the permeation experimental data results, and the permeation experimental change curve is shown in Figure 5.

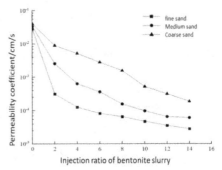

Figure 4. Water-rich sandy soil improved permeability tester.

Figure 5. Variation in permeability coefficients of water-rich sandy soil amendments.

As can be seen from Table 4 and Figure 5, the permeability coefficients of all three remodeled grains of sand were large before improvement. When the bentonite slurry was added, the permeability coefficient was significantly reduced, and the best effect was

Table 4. Permeation experiment data sheet.

Soil samples		Mud injection ratio (%) 0	2	4	6	8	10	12	14
Fine sand	Permeability coefficient (cm/s)	2.89×10^{-2}	3.16×10^{-4}	1.28×10^{-4}	8.27×10^{-5}	6.63×10^{-5}	4.77×10^{-5}	3.59×10^{-5}	2.86×10^{-5}
Medium sand		3.47×10^{-2}	2.58×10^{-3}	6.34×10^{-4}	3.79×10^{-4}	1.59×10^{-4}	1.36×10^{-4}	6.62×10^{-5}	6.13×10^{-5}
Coarse sand		4.05×10^{-2}	9.04×10^{-3}	5.19×10^{-3}	2.84×10^{-3}	1.59×10^{-3}	5.23×10^{-4}	3.24×10^{-4}	1.91×10^{-4}

achieved for fine sands, followed by medium sands. The worst effect was achieved for coarse sands. At a slurry injection ratio of 6%, the permeability coefficient of fine sand was reduced to the order of 10-5 cm/s; at a slurry injection ratio of 12%, the permeability coefficient of fine sand was reduced to the order of 10-5 cm/s. Therefore, the optimal mud injection ratio for fine sand permeability improvement in shield tunneling should be around 8%, and the optimal mud injection ratio for medium sand permeability improvement should be around 10%. Therefore, the optimal mud injection ratios for fine, medium, and coarse sand permeability improvement in shield tunneling should be around 8%, 10%, and greater than 14%, or the bentonite mud matching ratio should be increased.

4 FIELD APPLICATION AND ANALYSIS OF TUNNELING PARAMETERS

According to the above indoor experimental results, the shield machine residue improvement parameters are set in Table 5.

Table 5. Shield machine residue improvement parameter settings.

Tunneling stratum	Improver	Proportion of bentonite slurry (%)	Mud flow (L/min)	Mud injection pressure (bar)
Fine sand	Bentonite	11	48	2~4
Medium sand	Bentonite	11	60	2~4
Coarse sand	Bentonite	11	84	2~4

Data tracking and statistics were carried out on the shield boring parameters to obtain slag improvement parameters for the total shield thrust and cutter torque before and after optimization. Boring parameters of rings 10-110 were selected for one section of the project, where rings 10-60 and 60-110 are the improved and optimized parameters before and after, respectively, as shown in Figures 6 and 7.

From Figures 6 and 7, it can be seen that the total thrust force and cutter torque before improvement and optimization are greater than after improvement and optimization, indicating that the slag soil improvement and optimization have significantly enhanced the fluidic properties of the slag soil and reduced the total thrust force value of the shield. According to the construction conditions on site, the optimized slag soil can significantly reduce the total thrust force and cutter torque of the shield, reduce cutter wear and increase the digging speed, which further proves that the above slag soil improvement experimental results have important guidance and reference significance for the shield digging under this geological condition.

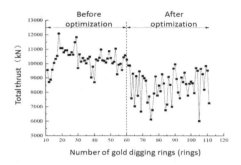 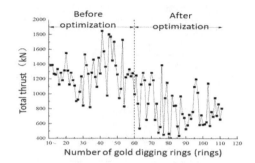

Figure 6. Change in total shield thrust before and after modification.

Figure 7. Change in shield blade torque before and after modification.

5 CONCLUSION

In this paper, indoor slurry improvement tests were carried out on three different particle gradations of water-rich sandy soils. Slump and permeability tests were used to evaluate the improvement effect and derive the slurry improvement parameters applicable to the construction. The main conclusions are as follows: for fine, medium, and coarse formations with different grain gradations, the injection ratio of sodium-based bentonite slurry is also different. In fine, medium, and coarse sand formations, the optimum injection ratios of sodium-based bentonite slurry are 8%, 10%, and 16%. Moreover, the improved mud can be seen in the shield to significantly reduce the wear on the blades. The shield boring efficiency can be improved to provide a reference for similar geological projects in Xi'an.

REFERENCES

Li W.H., *Study on the Effect of Improver on Sandy Soil Permeability in Earth Pressure Balanced Shield.* Beijing: China University of Geosciences (Beijing), 2020.

Liu F., Yang X.L., Ran J.L., et al., Experimental Study on the Improvement of Residual Soil in Water-rich Gravelly Sand Strata Based on Shield Boring Effect. *Tunnel Construction (in English and Chinese)*, 2020,40 (10):1426–1432.

Wei K.L., Micromechanical Analysis of Foam and Bentonite Improved Soil in Earth Pressure Balanced Shield Construction. *Modern Tunneling Technology*, 2007 (01): 73–77.

Yang G.L., Xu M.H., Liu H., et al., Experimental Study on the Improvement of Hengshield Mud Sludge Soil for Shield Excavation in Water-rich Stone Strata. *Journal of Huazhong University of Science and Technology (Natural Science Edition)*:1–8 [2022-10-20]. DOI: 10.13245/j.hust.238892

Experimental study on the effect of particle grade on the compressive strength of rammed earth

Tiegang Zhou, Mengyi Li*, Wei Tan & Kan Hu
School of Civil Engineering, Xi'an University of Architecture and Technology, Xi'an, China

ABSTRACT: This study looked into how particle size affected the compressive strength of rammed earth materials in the Guanzhong area of Shaanxi Province. A reasonable grading design for rammed earth materials in the Guanzhong area was carried out using Houben and Guillaud's suggested particle size distribution curves. Thirteen ratios were established for the test, and uniaxial compressive strength tests were carried out on cubic specimens made from the ratios. In the case of only three materials, namely soil, synthetic sand, and stone, the test results demonstrated that the F ratio (soil: synthetic sand: stone = 0.5:0.25:0.25) was the better ratio. Additionally, the soil-sand-stone content's impact on the compressive strength was examined, as well as the equation for the upper and lower limits of the grading curve that applies to the rammed soil materials in the Guanzhong area.

1 INTRODUCTION

A rammed earth building is a building that is constructed by ramming the earth between the forms with a ramming tool (Li et al. 2016). It is widely used as living space because it is a convenient material, has good heat preservation performance, and is economical and practical. At present, nearly 100 million people in rural areas of China still live in rammed earth buildings due to various reasons such as climatic environment and economic conditions (Wang & Lv 2001). The heating and cooling of current buildings consume about 10% of the world's energy (Beckett et al. 2018). Rammed earth building is one of the important ways to realize building energy saving. However, traditional rammed earth materials have low strength and often undergo brittle damage under load. Therefore, traditional rammed earth materials need to be improved to enhance their compressive strength to meet the requirements of modern rammed earth buildings for safety and stability.

The effect of particle gradation on the mechanical properties of rammed earth materials is often overlooked, but particle gradation plays an important role in the design of geotechnical construction materials because it controls the ability of soil particles to aggregate into denser structures in real-time when compressed under a given force (Cuccurullo et al. 2021). Based on experiments that the particle gradation curve satisfies the parabolic line when the coarse and fine grains are well-matched, the mixture can achieve the maximum density with the fewest voids. Fuller and Thompson (1907) proposed an ideal gradation, or the maximum density curve, and proposed the expression of the gradation equation. Xu (2022) showed that specimens with less dense particle gradations had greater horizontal strains at different loading stages, reflecting their greater resistance to fracture deformation. Hubert (2020) used artificial intelligence to rank the parameters that affect the compressive strength of rammed earth in order of magnitude: cement content, moisture content, clay content, sand content,

---

*Corresponding Author: 582472166@qq.com

and gravel content. Ciancio (2013) examined the validity of applying grading curves for soil selection by testing ten batches of soil and suggested continued experimental examination. In conclusion, there is little systematic research on the impact of individual raw materials in rammed soil materials, as well as limited studies on the influence of particle grading on the compressive strength of rammed soils, most of which focus on just a few ratios.

2 MATERIALS AND METHODS

2.1 Earth characterization

2.1.1 Basic materials

The soil material used in this test is loess from the Xi'an area. The soil particle analysis test and the joint determination test of liquid and plastic limits of soil were carried out according to the standard "Geotechnical Test Methods" (2019), and the particle distribution curve and physical and mechanical indexes and chemical composition of the soil material used in this test were obtained in Figure 1 and Table 1.

Table 1. Main properties of the base soil.

Atterberg limits (%)		Particle size distribution (%)		Mineralogical composition (%)	
Liquid limit W_L	26	> 0.075 mm	6	SiO_2	68.4
Plastic limit W_P	16	0.075~0.005 mm	62.75	Al_2O_3	11
Plasticity index I_P	14	<0.005 mm	31.25	Fe_2O_3	9.2
Natural moisture content W	3.09			MgO	5.4

The sand used in the test was the local natural medium sand in Xi'an, which met the basic requirements for natural sand in the national standard "Sand for Construction" (2011), and the specific indexes are shown in Table 2.

Table 2. Main properties of the base sand.

Fineness modulus	Apparent density (kg/m^3)	Loose Bulk Density (kg/m^3)	Void ratio (%)	Mud content (%)	Mud lump content (%)	Organic matter content
2.48	≥ 2400	≥ 1420	≤ 43	≤ 2.5	≤ 1.0	Qualified

The coarse aggregate used in this test is selected according to the needs of the test, which is 05 stone (particle size 0 ~ 10 mm), 12 stone (particle size 5 ~ 20 mm), and 13 stone (particle size 10 ~ 30 mm). The particle size distribution curves of the sand and stone were obtained by referring to the "Highway Engineering Aggregate Test Procedure" (2005) for the particle sieving test, as shown in Figure 1.

2.1.2 Reconstituting the natural soil to make it suitable for rammed earth construction

According to Hall (2004), the composition of rammed earth materials is similar to that of concrete, with cohesive soils serving as the binder and granular soils serving as the inert aggregate (silt and clay). According to Keable (1996), optimal rammed earth construction

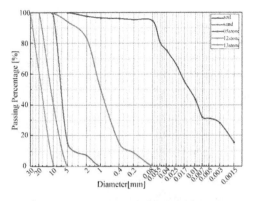 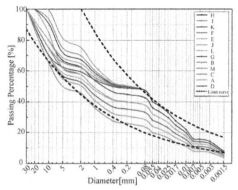

Figure 1. Particle size distribution curve of the test material.

Figure 2. Gradation curve for the test.

soils should have a high sand concentration, a low gravel content, some silt, and just enough clay to serve as a binder and promote soil compaction.

According to prior research, denser rammed earth demonstrates increased strength and stiffness (Bruno et al. 2016). Houben and Guillaud (1995) developed various criteria based on Fuller's grading rule to evaluate the feasibility of soils for rammed earth constructions by looking at the limitations of the particle size distribution (as shown by the dashed line in Figure 2). According to engineering reality and the physical characteristics of the loess soil in the Guanzhong area, 13 ratios were designed in this study. Their gradation curves are shown in Figure 2, and ratios are shown in Table 3. These ratios were fitted with the particle size distribution proposed by Houben and Guillaud.

Table 3. Test scheme and calculation of compressive strength of rammed earth cubes.

Specimen grouping	Constituents soil: synthetic sand: stone (%)	Specimen number	Average initial cracking load (kN)	Average damage load (kN)	Average compressive strength (MPa)	Standard deviation
A	50:50:0	A01-A05	46.85	84.21	2.11	0.24
B	50:40:10 (12 stones)	B01-B05	47.69	97.24	2.43	0.17
C	40:35:15 (12stones)	C01-C05	49.68	111.66	2.60	0.2
D	50:30:15 (12 stones)	D01-D05	59.70	105.42	2.64	0.14
E	50:30:20	E01-E05	45.49	106.84	2.67	0.23
F	50:25:25	F01-F05	67.21	112.53	2.81	0.17
G	50:20:30	G01-G05	39.90	105.38	2.63	0.18
H	45:35:20	H01-H05	40.16	98.37	2.46	0.21
I	40:35:25	I01-I05	40.68	97.32	2.43	0.20
J	40:30:30	J01-J05	40.27	94.14	2.35	0.18
K	35:35:30	K01-K05	36.42	89.29	2.23	0.18
L	30:40:30	L01-L05	34.52	86.14	2.15	0.1
M	25:40:35	M01-M05	33.90	77.30	1.93	0.21

Note: Table synthetic sand that sand and 05 stone according to 6:4 mix when the mixture.

2.2 Compression test

In order to study the compressive strength of rammed soil cubes with different rammed soil gradations, 200 mm × 200 mm × 200 mm (Su 2019) as the size of the cube specimen, the moisture content was strictly controlled between 8% and 10% when the specimens were rammed. When ramming, each specimen was filled in 3 times. The specimens were maintained in a cool place for two months after fabrication for subsequent test loading. The specific test protocol is shown in Table 3.

3 TEST OUTCOMES AND ANALYSIS

3.1 Damage pattern and damage mechanism

The test phenomena of the rammed earth cube specimens were found to be roughly divided into three stages during the loading process, namely the elastic stress stage, the crack development stage, and the ultimate damage stage, as shown in Figure 3. In the elastic stress stage, small dry shrinkage cracks can be found in a few of the specimens themselves. The applied load reaches 30% to 50% of the peak load during the crack development. With increasing load, the crack at the top begins to extend continuously downward while the specimen exhibits a slight longitudinal deformation, which is locally accompanied by falling soil fragments. The coarse aggregate of crushed stone in the cube and the soil produces a bond slip. The most severe stage of damage occurs when many fractures pierce through the cube elevation, reaching a maximum of 3 mm. A local bulge also forms in the lateral direction, and this is accompanied by the loss of aggregate. The internal force of the soil was then redistributed as a result of a specific movement and reorganization of coarse aggregates of crushed stone. The load applied to the specimen ceased developing after a sluggish growth and attained the ultimate load.

The damage pattern of the rammed earth cube under compression can be roughly divided into three kinds, according to the summary of the damage pattern of 13 groups of specimens with different ratios. The first kind is the typical conical damage, in which the cracks initially only develop to the middle of the facade with an increase in the load before expanding to the bottom two ends, forming two similar semicircles. The second type of damage is longitudinal penetration damage. Initially, a small crack appears in the middle of the top of the facade; however, as the load increases, a longitudinal main crack appears in the areas of the facade close to the two sides. Finally, a nearly parallel penetration crack appears in the specimen's four corners, severing it into strips. The third kind is when the applied load reaches the initial cracking load, it is seen that oblique cracks and longitudinal penetration cracks appear at the top of the two sides of the facade. As the applied load increases, the longitudinal cracks

Figure 3. Three stages of the specimen loading process. (a) Elastic force stage (b) Crack development stage (c) Ultimate damage stage.

extend through to the bottom, forming a local cone, and the oblique cracks penetrate to the middle of the facade. Figure 4 illustrates the coexistence of the damage types of damage. After the specimen is loaded, the damaged interface is observed. It is discovered that there is slippage at the bonding surface of the gravel skeleton and soil. A few coarse aggregates have fractured, and the specimen as a whole exhibits obvious brittle damage characteristics. The damage surfaces of the three damage forms are primarily shown on the bonding interface between coarse aggregate and soil.

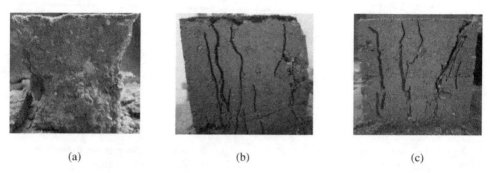

(a)　　　　　　　　　　　　　　(b)　　　　　　　　　　　　　　(c)

Figure 4. Cube damage form under pressure. (a) Conical damage (b) Longitudinal penetration damage (c) Composite damage.

3.2 *Analysis of cubic compressive strength index*

Referring to the standard "Masonry Basic Mechanical Properties Test Methods" (2011), the compressive strength of rammed earth cubes is calculated according to the following formula:

$$f_{cu} = \frac{N_u}{A}$$

The average compressive strength of the rammed soil cube with 13 different soil-sand-gravel ratios in Table 3 was analyzed and plotted in Figure 5. As the overall coarseness of the mixture gradually increased from small to large, the average compressive strength of the rammed soil cube experienced a process of increasing from 2.11 MPa to 2.81 MPa and then decreasing to 1.93 MPa, with an obvious peak compressive strength. This indicates that the overall particle size of the mixture was small or large cube would not achieve the ideal strength effect. When the mixture is small (A, B ratio), the skeleton effect of coarse aggregate in the rammed cube is not obvious. The strength of the cube specimen is mainly controlled by the strength of the soil, and the strength of the soil itself is very low, so the compressive strength of the cube specimen is relatively low. When the mixture is large (K, L, M ratio), the content of coarse aggregate is relatively high, and the cube specimen can form a certain amount of aggregate. The gap of coarse aggregate is mainly filled by soil and sand, and the clay particles in the soil are the only particles that play the role of adhesion in the mixture. The reduction of soil will lead to the poor integrity and stability of the skeleton, thus leading to the role the skeleton cannot play in the early stage of loading the cube cracks. Soon, the cube will collapse and cannot bear the larger load.

The rammed soil mixture in the transitional grain size ratio (C, D, E, F, G, H, I, J ratio) has relatively good gradation. The content of soil, sand, and gravel in the cube specimen is suitable, and the gaps formed between coarse aggregates are filled with dense soil and sand agglomerates. Because the distribution density of coarse aggregates is moderate, the internal friction resistance is larger due to mutual crowding and occlusion during ramming. It can fully adhere to the clay particles in the soil material to form a stable with a certain stiffness of the space skeleton. The skeleton can bear a considerable part of the load so that the strength of the rammed earth cube in a certain degree.

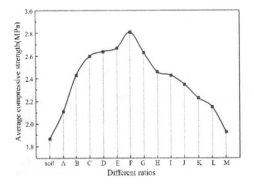

Figure 5. Average compressive strength of cubes with different ratios.

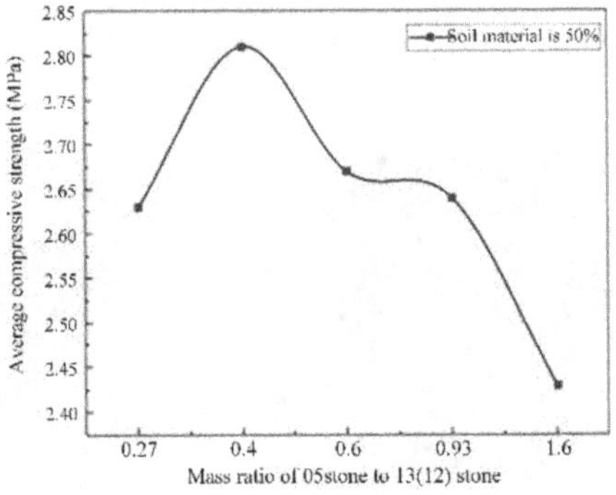

Figure 6. Average compressive strength of cubes with different mass ratios of gravels.

Analysis of Figure 6 reveals that the compressive strength of the cube is the largest when the mass ratio of 05 stone to 13 (12) stone is 0.4, reaching 2.81 MPa. As the 05 stone content increases, the large voids between the 13 (12) stones are gradually filled by 05 stones continuously during ramming, making the skeleton of the cube more dense and rigid. When the maximum strength peak is reached, the large voids of the skeleton are filled with 05 stones to complete. As the content of 05 stones continues to increase, the excess 05 stones cannot fill the skeleton. Then the particle interference effect occurs, resulting in a large number of 05 stones in a discrete distribution.

Figure 7 analysis reveals that when the gravel content is 30%, the aggregate content in the mixture is adequate. The gravel can form a certain spatial skeleton when ramming by squeezing and nibbling each other. However, as the soil content increases, the clay content in the soil also increases, while the sand content decreases, and the sand itself only fills the void without the binding effect. Therefore, when controlling the soil content at no more than 50%, the bonding effect of the soil on the skeleton is stronger with an increase in soil content, which increases the cubic specimen's overall stiffness and compressive strength. Similar

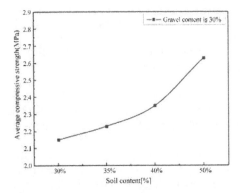
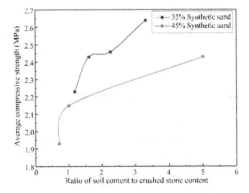

Figure 7. Average value of cubic compressive strength under different soil content.

Figure 8. Average value of cubic compressive strength under different soil to stone ratio.

conclusions can be drawn from Figure 8, where a constant amount of synthetic sand results in a cube's compressive strength increasing with an increase in the ratio of soil-to-stone content within a certain range and a cube's mechanical properties performing better at a 35% synthetic sand content.

By comparing the compressive strength indexes for the 13 rammed earth mixes created by the experiment in the study mentioned above, it can be seen that all 12 mixes' compressive strengths are greater than 2 MPa, with the exception of the M mix's strength of 1.93 MPa and the plain soil's strength of 1.87 MPa (Burroughs 2008). This study proposes using the 10 mixes with the letters B–L because of the security and affordability of rammed earth buildings in engineering applications. As illustrated in Figure 9, the upper and lower gradation limit formulae are provided with a fitted gradation curve range for the rammed earth materials in the Guanzhong area. The upper and lower limits of the grading curve of rammed earth materials in the Guanzhong area proposed in this study have high reliability. They are of reference value for engineering ratio design because the value of n in the equation of grading limit derived in this chapter is closer to the range of n proposed by Professor Hugo Houben of the International Center for Biotechnical Construction (n = 0.20~0.25).

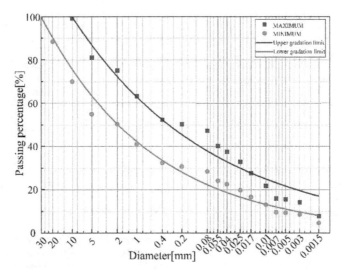

Figure 9. Range of rammed soil gradation design curve.

4 CONCLUSION

This paper adopts a combination of material test research and theoretical analysis to study the gradation optimization mechanism and basic mechanical properties of rammed earth materials in combination with the research needs of the group. In order to improve the mechanical properties of rammed earth materials, the range of grading curves and the more ideal improved ratios for rammed earth materials in the Guanzhong area are formed, which provides some theoretical support for the subsequent research. The main conclusions from the research of this paper are as follows:

1. The rammed earth cube specimen undergoes three stages in the loading process; namely, elastic stress stage, crack development stage, and ultimate damage stage; the damage forms of the specimen are conical damage, longitudinal penetration damage, and composite damage.
2. When the mixture switched from small to large particle size ratios, the rammed earth cube's average compressive strength increased from 2.11 MPa to 2.81 MPa and then decreased to 1.93 MPa. The compressive strength of the cube corresponding to the F ratio (soil: synthetic

sand: stone = 0.5:0.25:0.25) was at its highest when only three materials were available, reaching 2.81 MPa, which is 50.27% higher than that of the unimproved "plain soil."

3. In this study, 11 ratios numbered B~L are suggested as the reference range for the design of the rammed soil ratio. The equations of upper and lower limits of the grading curve basically applicable to rammed soil in the Guanzhong area are fitted, in which the upper limit equation of the grading is $p_x = 100 \times \left(\frac{d_x}{10}\right)^{0.201}$ (%); the lower limit equation of the grading is $p_x = 100 \times \left(\frac{d_x}{30}\right)^{0.253}$ (%).

ACKNOWLEDGMENTS

This work was supported by Shaanxi Key Industrial Innovation Chain Project in Agricultural Domain (Grant No.: 2020ZDLNY06-03).

REFERENCES

Anysz H., Brzozowski L., Kretowicz W et al. Feature Importance of Stabilised Rammed Earth Components Affecting the Compressive Strength Calculated with Explainable Artificial Intelligence Tools. *Materials*, 2020, 13(10): 20.

Beckett C.T.S., Cardell-Oliver R., Ciancio D. et al. Measured and Simulated Thermal Behavior in Rammed Earth Houses in a Hot-arid Climate. Part A: Structural behavior. *J Build Eng*, 2018, 15(243–51).

Bruno A.W., Gallipoli D., Perlot C. et al. Effect of Very High Compaction Pressures on the Physical and Mechanical Properties of Earthen Materials; Proceedings of the 3rd European Conference on Unsaturated Soils (E-UNSAT), Paris, FRANCE, F Sep 12–14, 2016. *E D P Sciences*: CEDEX A, 2016.

Burroughs S. Soil Property Criteria For Rammed Earth Stabilization. *J Mater Civ Eng*, 2008, 20(3): 264–73.

Ciancio D., Jaquin P. and Walker P. Advances on the Assessment of Soil Suitability for Rammed Earth. *Constr Build Mater*, 2013, 42(40–7).

Cuccurullo A., Gallipoli D., Bruno A.W et al. A Comparative Study of the Effects of Particle Grading and Compaction Effort on the Strength and Stiffness of earth Building Materials at Different Humidity Levels. *Constr Build Mater*, 2021, 306(10.

Fuller W.B. and Thompson S E. The Laws of Proportioning, Concrete. *Transactions of the American Society of Civil Engineers* 1907.

General Institute of Water Resources and Hydropower Planning and Design, Ministry of Water Resources, Nanjing Institute of Water Resources Science. Geotechnical Test Methods Standard. *Ministry of Housing and Urban-Rural Development of the People's Republic of China; State Administration of Market Supervision and Administration*. 2019: 717.

Hall M. and Djerbib Y. Rammed Earth Sample Production: Context, Recommendations, and Consistency. *Constr Build Mater*, 2004, 18(4): 281–6.

Institute of Highway Science, Ministry of Communications. Highway Engineering Aggregate Test Procedure. *Industry standard-transportation*. 2005: 147P.; A4.

Julian, International K J H. Earth Construction: A Comprehensive Guide: H. Houben and H. Guillaud, Intermediate Technology Publications, London, 1994, 362 pp., £25.00 paperback. 1995.

Keable J. and Keable R. Prelims – Rammed Earth Structures. 1996, 10.3362/9781780440668(i-xi.

Li C.H., Zhou M.Q., Chen W.K., et al. In-plane Shear Performance Tests of Reinforced Rammed Earth Wall Sheets %J *Journal of Central South University (Natural Science Sand for construction*. 2011.

Sichuan Research Institute of Building Science, Shanxi Four Construction Group Co., Hunan University *et al.* Standard for Basic Mechanical Properties of Masonry Test Methods. *National standard of the People's Republic of China*. 2011: 55p: A4.

Su Kui-Wen. Experimental Study on the Factors Influencing the Compressive Performance of Rammed Earth Materials. *Xi'an University of Architecture and Technology*, 2019.

Wang Jun, Lv Dongjun. Towards the Future of Vernacular Architecture %J *Journal of Xi'an University of Architecture and Technology (Natural Science Edition)*. 2001, 02): 147–9.

Xu X.F., Zhu T.B., Li Y.W et al. Effect of Particle Grading on Fracture Behavior and Thermal Shock Resistance of MgO-C Refractories. *J Eur Ceram Soc*, 2022, 42(2): 672–81.

Temperature sensitivity analysis of long-span arch bridge cable hoisting construction

Jiashou Dao*
Construction Headquarters of Liming Bridge on Lancang River in Xishuangbanna, Yunnan Province, China

Qinghua Yang
Liangshan Prefecture Highway Construction Service Center, Sichuan, China

Yonglaing Yu & Hongfei Zhuang
Construction Headquarters of Liming Bridge on Lancang River in Xishuangbanna, Yunnan Province, China

ABSTRACT: In the process of cable hoisting construction of the long-span arch bridge, the cable and mechanical properties of the arch rib caused by temperature change are important problems at the construction site. One side of the cable is connected to the tower, and the other side is connected to the arch rib. The change in the cable force will affect and cause the change in the arch rib alignment, internal force, and stress. This study explores the influence of temperature change on the cable force of cable and the line shape, internal force, and stress of the arch rib during the cable hoisting construction of a long-span steel box-tied arch bridge. In this paper, the finite element model of the whole bridge in the construction stage is established by Midas/Civil, and the influence of temperature on the cable force of the cable and the mechanical properties of the arch rib is analyzed. The calculation results show that the cable force decreases with the increase of the overall structure temperature, and the linear variation of the arch rib increases. The change in temperature will also have a certain impact on the subsequent construction stage of buckle relaxation. The calculation results can provide some reference for the construction of the same type of arch bridge.

1 INTRODUCTION

In the construction process of a long-span steel box-tied arch bridge, it is easy to be restricted by the geographical environment, construction site, and other factors. A cable hoisting system is often used for hoisting construction of the main arch rib and main beam. Although the current oblique pulling and hanging construction is a mature and economic construction method, the internal force and linear state of the bridge are completely controlled by the buckling force. In view of different engineering construction processes, it is often faced with the influence of construction environment temperature, which affects the stress state of key components of the structure. Therefore, it is necessary to clarify the stress state of key components in the design process according to the actual project. Moreover, it is necessary to carry out the sensitivity analysis of temperature parameters to ensure that the stress state of the structure in the construction process is consistent with the design state, which is of great practical significance. On the basis of the Hejiang Yangtze River Highway Bridge, Fu (2020) studied the

---

*Corresponding Author: 1647984756@qq.com

calculation method of the cable hoisting system, the bearing capacity, and stability of the fastening system of class 500 concrete-filled steel tube arch bridge and clarified the key technology of hoisting this type of structure. Qin *et al.* (2020) took the Hongshui River Bridge in Matan as the research object. They (Qin *et al.* 2020) analyzed the bending moment of the arch foot caused by the cable fastening force and the self-weight of the arch ring, the change law of cable fastening force with the arch ring alignment during construction, the deviation between the actual alignment and the target alignment, and the influence law of each arch foot sealing opportunity on the structural alignment and cable fastening force. Wang (2012) determined the reasonable lifting sequence of the arch rib of a concrete-filled steel tube arch bridge, the reasonable initial tension value of the cable, and the pre-lifting amount of the arch rib based on the forward iteration method of the finite element theory. Mei (2015) studied the deflection caused by the structure of the tower under unbalanced horizontal force. The researcher (Mei 2015) also showed that the installation elevation of the arch rib in the construction control should consider the influence of the tower deflection. Deng (2009) deduced the calculation formula for the influence of the tower deviation on the elevation of the arch rib section by using the geometric analysis method. Combined with the cable crane system of the new Longmen Bridge, the influence of the deviation of the tower and the main tower on the elevation of the arch rib section is analyzed. He *et al.* (1999) proposed a reliable cable force adjustment method based on optimization theory, taking the length of the buckled cable pulled through the cable saddle point as the design variable and the vertical displacement of the elevation control point as the control variable. The optimization result can determine the cable force of the buckled cable when each elevation control point reaches its vertical control displacement. The extension of each buckled cable can be determined from the optimized design variable value to achieve the "double control" of the cable force and extension. Chen *et al.* (2003) took a concrete-filled steel tube arch bridge in Hubei Province as an example to track the construction process and calculate the locking cable force. The results are in good agreement with the monitoring results.

In this paper, the influence of temperature on cable relaxation construction is mainly carried out from three aspects. First, the influence of system temperature change on the cable force before the cable relaxation process is analyzed. Secondly, the influence of system temperature change on the main arch alignment and the main arch stress state before cable relaxation construction is analyzed, and the influence of temperature on the structural stress state is clarified.

2 PROJECT OVERVIEW

2.1 *Cable structure working condition*

The cable system is a double tower three-span structure. The span arrangement is 186 + 485 + 190 m. The main components of the cable hoisting system are towers, anchorages, tramcars, saddles, cables, and motor equipment. The overall layout of the cable pulling and fastening construction is shown in Figure 1. The main cable is supported on the saddles of

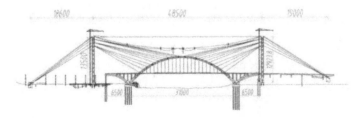

Figure 1. Overall layout of inclined tension hanging construction (unit: cm).

the towers on both sides. The angle between the horizontal line of the anchor span on the north bank and the horizontal line of the anchor span on the south bank is 36.4° and 31.8°, respectively. In order to explore the influence of various temperature conditions on the cable force before cable relaxation and combined with the changes in the main arch rib alignment and axial force, the mechanical properties of the arch foot of the main arch concrete section and the flying swallow section, the influence of the system temperature difference on the cable relaxation construction process is clarified.

2.2 Temperature condition

The average temperature of this bridge site has been 21.7°C for many years, with a maximum value of 41°C and a minimum value of 2.7°C. The climatic conditions in the region are generally unfavorable to the construction, and the temperature is the main factor affecting the cable relaxation of the bridge. Therefore, this bridge focuses on the influence of system temperature change on cable force.

The cable and steel box arch rib of the bridge will produce large temperature changes under sufficient sunlight, which will change the cable force. Therefore, to avoid errors, the temperature value of the finite element model cannot be directly designed as the construction temperature value of the cable. Therefore, given the influence of system temperature change on the cable relaxation process, the lock relaxation construction process is taken as the research object. The design reference temperature value is selected as the reference condition. Three groups of comparison models are selected: The temperature difference of the system with −10°C (working condition 1), 10°C (working condition 2), and 20°C (working condition 3) is applied to analyze the variation law of three different working conditions compared with the reference condition.

3 CALCULATION AND ANALYSIS

In this paper, the finite element analysis software Midas/Civil is used to establish the finite element model of the whole bridge, as shown in Figure 2.

Figure 2. Schematic diagram of finite element model of the full bridge rod system.

3.1 Effect of temperature on cable force before cable relaxation

Due to the different distances between the middle span and the location of the tower on the north and south bank, the angle between the buckle cable and the arch rib on the north and the south banks is different. Therefore, this section studies the actual cable force of the oblique buckle cable under different temperature load conditions on the north and south bank. Then, it compares the cable force with the design reference temperature condition to explore the influence of temperature on the relaxation construction of the buckle cable. After MIDAS/civil calculation and analysis, the calculation results of the cable forces of the north bank and the south bank before the cable is relaxed under various temperature conditions are shown in Figures 3–6.

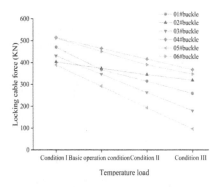
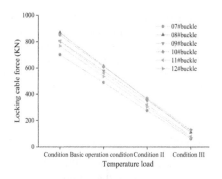

Figure 3. Cable force change of 01# ~ 06# Cable of the North Bank.

Figure 4. Variation law of cable force of 07# ~ 12# Cable of the North Bank.

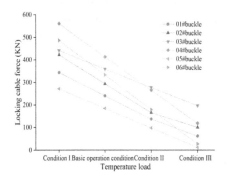
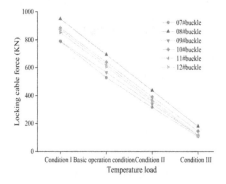

Figure 5. Cable force change of 01'# ~ 06'# cable of the South Bank.

Figure 6. Variation law of cable force of 07'# ~ 12'# cable of the South Bank.

According to the change rule diagram of the cable force of the north and south banks under different temperature load conditions, the cable force value of the north and south bank under the pre-process of the cable relaxation after the arch rib decreases with the increase of the system temperature. Among them, the maximum cable force amplitude of each buckle on the north bank is the No.7 buckle. The cable force value of the No.7 buckle under the three system temperatures is 640.01 kN lower than that of the design reference condition, and the amplitude is 91.20%. The cable force of each buckle on the south bank decreases with the increase in temperature, and the cable force of the No. 05 buckle is the largest. The cable forces under the temperature load of the three working conditions are reduced by 95.83% compared with the design reference condition. The cable with the largest variation is the No.08 cable, and the cable force value is reduced by 769.34 kN compared with the first condition at the third condition, and the amplitude is 81.06%.

3.2 *Effect of temperature on arch rib alignment*

In the previous paper, the temperature condition of the system is calculated. Because the design reference temperature of the bridge is 20°C, the temperature calculation value of the system is used as the theoretical control value to calculate the elevation of each steel arch rib section under each working condition and compared with the theoretical value under the design reference temperature to obtain the displacement variation of each section. The specific displacement change calculation results are shown in Figures 7–14.

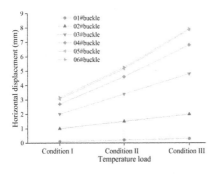
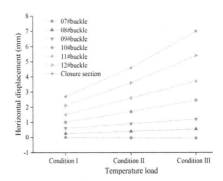

Figure 7. Horizontal displacement variation 01# ~ 06# cable of the North Bank.

Figure 8. Horizontal displacement variation of 07# ~ 12# cable of the North Bank.

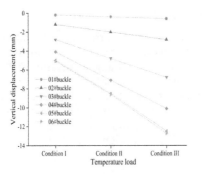
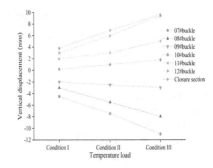

Figure 9. Vertical displacement variation of 01# ~ 06# cable of the North Bank.

Figure 10. Vertical displacement variation of 07# ~ 12# cable of the North Bank.

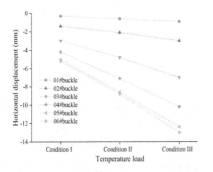
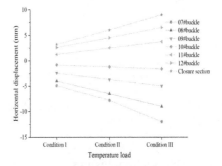

Figure 11. Horizontal displacement variation of 01'# ~ 06'# cable of the South Bank.

Figure 12. Horizontal displacement variation of 07'# ~ 12'# cable of the South Bank.

It can be seen from Figures 7–14 that under the premise of not changing the design and construction process, only the cables are relaxed at different system temperatures. After the cables are relaxed in each working condition, the arch rib alignment of the north and south banks changes greatly with the design reference line of the process. The horizontal and vertical displacement changes of each section are greatly changed, but the degree of change is not the same.

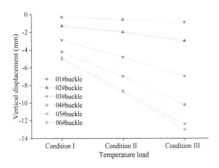
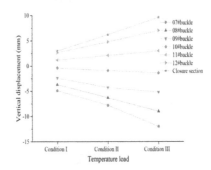

Figure 13. Vertical displacement variation of 01'# ~ 06'# cable of the South Bank.

Figure 14. Vertical displacement variation of 07'# ~ 12'# cable of the South Bank.

3.3 Influence of temperature on the axial force of arch rib

The calculation results in the previous section show that only considering the difference between the system temperature and the reference temperature greatly influences the cable force before the cable relaxation and then affects the arch rib alignment after the cable relaxation. Therefore, it is necessary to further study the influence of the temperature change on the cable force before the cable relaxation, resulting in the influence of the axial force of the main arch rib after the cable relaxation. The axial force values of the arch rib in each section of the main arch after the cable relaxation under four different system temperature conditions are calculated. The calculation results are shown in Figures 15 and 16.

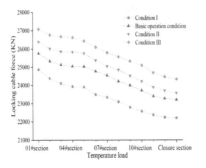
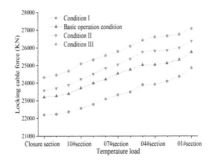

Figure 15. Variation law of axial force of steel arch rib on the north bank.

Figure 16. Variation law of axial force of steel arch rib on the south bank.

It can be seen from Figures 15 and 16 that under various temperature conditions, the axial force of arch ribs in each section of the main arch gradually decreases from stage 01# to the closure section. The axial force of arch ribs in each section changes smoothly, and the axial force of arch ribs in the north and south banks is roughly symmetrical. With the increase of the system temperature before the cable relaxation, the axial force of the arch ribs in each section of the arch ribs in the north and south banks increases after the cable relaxation. It can be seen that the temperature change of the system before the cable relaxation greatly influences the axial force of the arch rib of each section of the main arch. The error between the axial force of the arch rib of each section and the theoretical value of the design state increases with the increase of temperature difference.

266

3.4 Effect of temperature on mechanical properties of key components

This part calculates the change rule of the relaxation buckle and the mechanical properties of the arch under different system temperature conditions. The thrust calculation results of the arch abutment on the South and North banks under different temperature load conditions are shown in Figures 17 and 18.

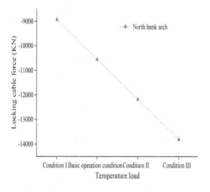 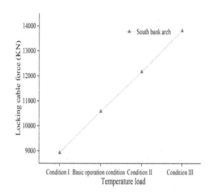

Figure 17. Variation law of horizontal thrust of the north bank arch abutment

Figure 18. Variation law of horizontal thrust of south bank arch abutment.

From Figures 17 and 18, it can be seen that the horizontal thrust value of the arch abutment on the north and south bank increases with the system temperature increase before the cable relaxation process. The thrust of the arch abutment on the north bank increases by 3261.65N, and the increase is about 23.62%. The horizontal thrust of the south bank arch increased by 3238.51 kN, with an increase of about 23.44%. Therefore, the system temperature changes significantly impact the horizontal thrust of the arch.

4 CONCLUSIONS

1. Before the cable relaxation, the cable force decreases with the increase of the overall structure temperature, and the variation of arch rib alignment also increases, which has a large error with the arch rib alignment in the design reference state.
2. In actual construction, the loose buckle should be avoided under the condition of large temperature changes, and the loose buckle should be as close as possible to the design reference temperature. Suppose the temperature rise is inevitable during construction. In that case, it is necessary to control the arch rib alignment in advance and monitor the arch seat displacement in real-time to ensure the safety of the structure.

REFERENCES

Dayan Qin, Zheng Jilian, Du Hailong, Han Yu, Zheng Jian, Kui Leijun. (2020). Optimization Calculation Method and Application of cable Force of Cable-stayed Buckle with One-Time Tension. *J. China Railway Science*. 41 (06), 52–60.

Gaiwei Mei. (2015). The Influence of the Deviation of the Tower on the Installation of the Arch Rib Section During the Cable Hoisting of an Arch Bridge. *J. Chongqing Architecture*. 14 (07), 34–37.

Jiangming Deng. (2009). Geometric Analysis of the Influence of Cable Hoisting Tower Deviation on Arch Rib Elevation. *Journal of Chongqing Jiaotong University*. 28 (03), 505–507.

Jincheng Fu. (2020). Research on the Key Technology of the Construction of 500 m Concrete Filled Steel Tubular Arch Bridge. D. Chongqing Jiaotong University.

Liang Chen, Liu Chunsheng, Wu Huijun. (2003). Construction and Cable Force Analysis of Concrete-Filled Steel Tubular Arch Bridge. *Journal of Wuhan University of Technology (traffic science and Engineering Edition)*. (06), 837–840.

Xiongjun He, Shen Chengwu, Chen Qiaosheng, Zhang Hang. (1999). Adjustment of Cable Force of Steel Pipe Cable Lifting Buckle for Main Arch of Concrete-Filled Steel Tube Arch Bridge. *Journal of Wuhan Jiaotong University of science and technology*. (05), 575–578.

Yuanfeng Wang. (2012). Study on Reasonable Construction Sequence of Cable-Stayed Buckles of Concrete-Filled Steel Tubular Srch Bridge. *J. Chongqing Architecture*. 14 (07), 34–37.

Green building analysis and energy-saving and low-carbon transformation of existing buildings based on green building standards

Bei Wu*, Fujie Liu* & Lingkun Jing
Tianjin Renai College, Tianjing, China

ABSTRACT: In recent years, green building has been one of the mainstream topics in the construction industry. Green, low-carbon, and energy-saving have become indispensable elements of modern architecture. Local governments have successively issued relevant policies to support the construction of ultra-low energy consumption green buildings. Building energy conservation has been vigorously promoted and is included in the 14th Five-Year Plan of many localities. Based on green building evaluation standards and green building related technologies, this paper selects a university library in Hebei province to conduct green building simulation analysis from the perspective of green, low carbon, and energy saving, including lighting, ventilation, sound environment, housing heat, and other related analysis. After that, according to the local environment, measures taken according to local conditions, reasonable innovation, and green building design requirements, implement the green and low-carbon concept, and carry out green construction and transformation. It provides a certain reference for the subsequent green simulation transformation of other similar campus buildings.

1 INTRODUCTION

With the country's economic growth, the related environmental problems have become increasingly serious. Since the country put forward the goal of carbon peak and carbon neutrality, various places have also launched carbon emission and green building related policies. As a large carbon emitter in the construction industry, low-carbon reform is imminent.

At present, old buildings with early designs consume the most energy and waste the most, so the low-carbon green transformation of buildings is very necessary. Although the transformation range of the current old buildings is large, most of them are still based on the improvement or repair on the surface, which lacks a more accurate system transformation program process and can rarely achieve a standardized transformation of energy consumption and carbon emission.

Among the three stages of building life cycle design, construction, operation, and maintenance, the most energy consumption and carbon emission are in building operation and maintenance. For this reason, this paper carries out a simulation analysis of indoor and outdoor buildings through green building analysis software. It then combines the actual situation and refers to the green Building Evaluation Standard and other relevant specifications to carry out partial low-carbon green transformation for the project buildings to realize the transformation of low energy consumption and low emissions.

---

*Corresponding Authors: 286456338@qq.com and 2295803440@qq.com

2 PROJECT OVERVIEW

This paper selects a library in Hebei Province, with a building area of 71208 m². The building height is 34.4 m; The main body adopts a reinforced concrete frame structure. The grade of architectural project design specification is the first-class library. With the breathing glass curtain wall of the facade, the internal rooms include a reading hall, day hall, dense bookshelves, offices, research rooms, and so on.

The project is located in Handan, Hebei province, the junction of Shanxi, Hebei, Shandong, and Henan provinces. The area has a warm temperate semi-humid and semi-arid continental monsoon climate. Handan is hot and dry in June and July, humid and sultry in August, dry and cold in winter, and windy and sandy in spring. The annual average temperature is 13.5°C, and the annual sunshine duration is 2557 hours. The diurnal and monthly variations of wind speed are single-peak forms.

3 GREEN BUILDING SIMULATION ANALYSIS

The project builds the internal and external simulation analysis, including lighting, ventilation, residential thermal environment, and sound environment. It also examines the building's internal and external problems on the basis of *Green Building Evaluation Standard (GB/T 50378-2019)* (China Architecture and Architecture Press 2019) and other relevant standards for the green building improvement project and the energy consumption of the green building.

3.1 Lighting

3.1.1 Building daylighting analysis

According to Architectural Lighting Design Standard (China Architecture and Architecture Press 2013), the lighting analysis of the library is carried out to make it meet the visual function requirements under the specified outdoor natural light design illumination. In this project, the lighting coefficient is calculated by simulation method to analyze each functional room (Figure 1).

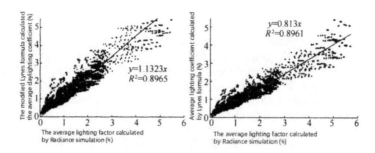

Figure 1. Relationship between simulated value and theoretical calculation.

In a completely overcast sky, the light reflection times were calculated 3 times, and the average daylighting coefficient in the building was calculated to be higher than the corresponding standard value, with the highest value of 6.97%. The annual dynamic lighting analysis was conducted on the interior space of the building, and the lighting data were obtained. The total lighting area was 29747.56 m², and the weighted average multi-area hours were 7.6 h/d (Figure 2).

Based on the project's architectural lighting education standard, after investigation and analysis of the architectural lighting diagram, we found that due to the large curtain wall of the library, sunshade measures were not taken (Baoqi *et al.* 2019). The second to the fourth

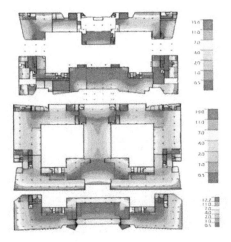

Figure 2. Building daylighting diagram.

floors of the building are the southern border reading area and some of the east-west existence of direct solar radiation into the interior.

3.1.2 *Glare analysis*

The uncomfortable glare of windows is an important index to evaluate the quality of daylight. Lighting simulation is carried out according to relevant standards such as the Building Daylighting Design Standard (GB50033-2013). Through glare analysis and calculation of the main function rooms of this project, under the condition of an overcast sky and 3300 Lux of outdoor illumination, all rooms are below the DGI limit of 25, and the maximum is only 19.5. All the analysis meets the requirements. Too much direct light and bright surface reflection are avoided so as to avoid the occurrence of glare phenomenon, thus ensuring that the staff in the library will not feel the visual discomfort caused by glare.

3.2 *Building ventilation*

3.2.1 *Building openable area*

According to the Green Building Evaluation Standard (GB/T50378-2014) (China Architecture and Architecture Press 2014), the ventilation analysis of the open outer window of the building is 45.3%, achieving an excellent ventilation effect. However, the proportion of the open area of the glass curtain wall is 4.7%, only meeting the qualified requirements. Ventilation can well adjust the indoor temperature and humidity environment and maintain the cleanliness of indoor air; especially in the transition season, outdoor air temperature and humidity can meet the requirements of the human body for comfort. Because there is a large peripheral building curtain wall, the outside of the window can be opened. Still, the average ratio is too small, so the effect of indoor natural ventilation is poor, and good wind resource utilization is unlikely to achieve. For a closed environment, only changing the parameters of the indoor air conditioning system after a long time can reduce indoor environment quality and rise of all kinds of harmful substances, making the person feels unwell. If the fresh air system is added, the energy burden will be further increased (Minfang 2019), which has a certain impact on the energy consumption of buildings.

3.2.2 *Indoor hot and humid environment*

Thermal and humid environment is the most important content of the building environment, which is mainly reflected in the thermal and humid characteristics of the air environment and its influence on the comfort degree of human beings in the building.

The relationship between PPD and PMV is shown as follows (Figure 3).

$$PPD = 100 - 95 \cdot \exp(-0{,}033\,53 \cdot PMV^4 - 0{,}217\,9 \cdot PMV^2)$$

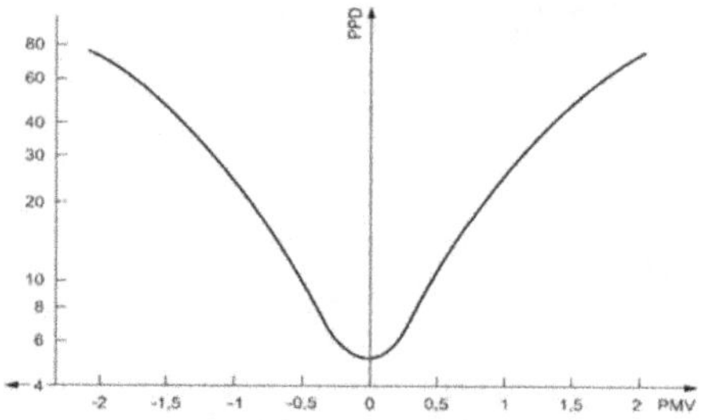

Figure 3. Relationship between PPD and PMV.

Through analysis and calculation, 75.75% of the area of PMV and PPD of the main function rooms of the project reached the overall evaluation level II, and the indoor thermal and humidity environment reached the green building standard, which ensured that the staff would not feel uncomfortable in the building for a long time.

3.2.3 *Outdoor wind environment*

A reasonable outdoor wind environment is conducive to the natural ventilation of the building, reduces the operation time of air conditioning equipment, and saves resources.

The results show that the wind speed amplification coefficient is < 2, with no over-limit area. The wind pressure difference between the windward side and the leeward side of the building is no more than 5 Pa (Xiaoli *et al.* 2010), which meets the requirements of the green building standard. The working conditions in winter are all up to the standard, and the design of the building ventilation environment is reasonable (Figures 4 and 5).

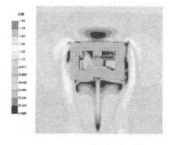

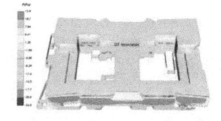

Figure 5. Cloud chart of wind pressure on the windward side of the building.

Figure 4. Cloud diagram of wind speed magnification factor at 1.5 m height.

3.3 *Residential thermal environment*

The urban residential thermal environment is an important part of the urban natural environment. The perfect urban residential thermal environment design can reduce the urban heat island problem, improve the residential heating environmental protection, and reduce the building energy consumption optimization.

According to the surroundings of the library and the campus, the drawings were converted to give the actual site green, shading, and other environmental information. The shading coverage rate, heat island intensity, and wet bulb black bulb temperature around the building were calculated. Under the condition that the site area is 69691.8 m², the project environmental cover coverage reaches 30%, and the coverage limit reaches 25%. According to the actual site, combined with the previous year's temperature, radiation warming, long-wave radiation cooling, evaporation heat transfer cooling, and other data that affect the intensity of the heat island. The calculated mean heat island intensity is 1.56°C. Combined with the local temperature, solar radiation, relative humidity, and other factors that affect the wet-bulb black bulb temperature, the maximum wet-bulb black bulb temperature of the building is 31.88°C, which meets the requirement that the hourly wet-bulb black bulb temperature of the residential area should not exceed 33°C (Figure 6). It also meets the green building and sponge city construction standards.

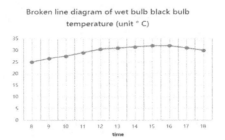

Figure 6. Broken line diagram of wet bulb black bulb temperature.

According to analysis, the heat island intensity of a construction park higher than 1.5°C does not meet the standard of average heat island intensity of campus buildings in summer. In order to solve the heat island effect under the high temperature in summer, we should reduce the indoor temperature and make the indoor air circulation. The use of air conditioning electric fans is often increased, resulting in increased energy consumption.

3.4 Building sound insulation

3.4.1 Outdoor noise

The sound environment outside the building is one of the important indicators affecting the living conditions inside the building. The building is the school library, located in the middle of the campus, and has stricter requirements for the outdoor sound environment. Through software simulation calculation, the site noise distribution during the day and night is predicted, as shown in Figure 7 and Table 1 below.

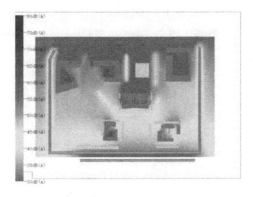

Figure 7. Distribution of sound pressure level at the height of 1.5 m (daytime).

Table 1. Comprehensive score of environmental noise unit: dB (A).

	Maximum noise	Class 2 noise limit	Class 3 noise limits
Daytime	49	60	65
At night	42	50	55

To sum up, through software simulation and statistical analysis of the results, it is found that the maximum noise in the library is 65 dB during the day and 55 dB at night due to the influence of the surrounding environment. In this regard, noise reduction technology is adopted to install the impedance compound muffler on the ventilation pipe and install the muffler louvers in the position of the air outlet. In addition, a green anti-noise forest was planted outside the campus to reduce the impact of roads, and the building was finally judged to meet the requirements of green building noise control.

3.4.2 Sound insulation of building components

There are two kinds of noise in building construction. One is the air sound, and the other is the crash sound. The noises are mainly caused by sound waves reflecting off building materials. Calculation of different sound insulation materials in two cases of air sound and impact sound is carried out by formula: In the reading room, postgraduate entrance examination area, research room, and other areas with high sound insulation requirements, the single-value evaluation value and spectrum correction value of air sound insulation performance of an external wall or partition wall are about 54 dB. The reading room, book area, office, and other important sound control areas on the upper roof floor brought by the impact of the sound pressure level are controlled at 56 dB. According to the evaluation requirements of Code for Sound Insulation Design of Civil Buildings GB50118-2010 (China Architecture and Architecture Press, 2010), the requirements for the evaluation of air sound insulation performance of green buildings are met.

4 ARCHITECTURAL TRANSFORMATION

Through green building simulation analysis and evaluation in terms of safety and comfort, health and comfort, resource-saving and environmental livable in combination with *Green Building Evaluation Standard GB/T 50378-2019*, the library of this project gets a score of 68 points by comparing various evaluation indexes and weight calculation. The reasonable part of the building design reaches the green building standard, but the lighting and ventilation part does not meet the use requirements and can be further improved in terms of energy saving.

Transformation concept: In line with the concept of taking measures in accordance with local conditions and giving priority to energy conservation, combined with the library's own conditions and reasons, the library integrates advanced domestic energy-saving technology and runs it to combine its building with practical application and create an energy-saving and healthy green library (Mustaffa & Mat Isa 2021) (existing problems and transformation direction in Table 2 below).

Table 2. Existing problems and transformation direction.

Existing problems	Transformation direction
Lighting problem + ventilation problem	Curtain wall systems: changing curtain wall and window styles
Heat island problem	Roof reconstruction: add green vegetation

4.1 Roof reconstruction

In view of the heat island problem, combined with the actual situation, the sixth-floor roof of the library was transformed to create a roof garden and more green plants in other places. After the transformation, the landscape of the project is mainly planted with drought-resistant coarse plants, and compound greening, including turf and shrubs, is adopted. The sixth and seventh floors are planted with onychia, hydrangea, small shrubs, etc., increasing the green area of the roof with a green rate of over 42% and providing multi-level thermal insulation measures for the roof (Papoyan et al. 2021).

4.2 Curtain wall reconstruction

Based on the analysis and investigation, it is understood that the main problem of lighting and ventilation brought by the building is the curtain wall. The original curtain wall system of the building adopts the combination curtain wall of dry hanging ceramic board and partial glass curtain wall. For this transformation, the fixed curtain wall on the north and south sides adopts a double-layer breathing curtain wall with movable louvers to shade the sun.

In terms of lighting, adjustable aluminum alloy louver curtain or electric rolling curtain is arranged in the double layer hot channel so that the shading angle can be controlled manually or electrically (see Figures 8 and 9 for details) to effectively adjust the sun exposure (Alkali et al. 2021). In terms of ventilation, through the control of the inlet and outlet of the curtain wall, the purpose of conveying fresh air from the ventilation layer to the building interior is achieved so as to optimize the ventilation quality of the building. In addition, by opening the inlet and exhaust vents and relying on the chimney effect to take away the heat energy in the sandwich under the radiation of sunlight, the working temperature of the inner glass surface can be greatly reduced to save the air conditioning power. After closing the inlet and exhaust vents, the air in the interlayer rises at room temperature under the sunlight, thus forming a kind of small greenhouse, which can effectively increase the working temperature of the inner glass, thereby reducing the building's heating resources.

   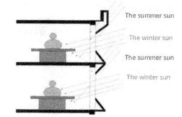

Figure 8. Chimney stack effect.   Figure 9. Shading effect.

5 CONCLUSION

This paper takes library transformation as an example to achieve the goal of building energy conservation and emission reduction through transformation and renewal. To sum up, the project renovation takes measures according to local conditions. It simulates the running state of the building from the aspects of green construction analysis, lighting, ventilation, and sound environment. The project refers to the *Green Building Evaluation Standard* and other relevant specifications and requirements to carry out the targeted passive renovation. In terms of heating and cooling energy consumption, since the building adopts sub-district heating of radiator and air conditioner, there has not been a detailed calculation of corresponding equipment. In terms of architectural structure, the project adopts the measures of replacing the double-layer breathing curtain wall and roof garden to enhance lighting, ventilation, energy saving, and carbon reduction. This can be used as a reference for the reconstruction and optimization of related similar buildings.

ACKNOWLEDGMENTS

This work was financially supported by the Scientific Research Project of Tianjin University Renai College in 2020 (XX20007) and the Innovation and entrepreneurship training program for college students of Tianjin (202114038001).

REFERENCES

Alkali M.A., Jie L., Dalibi S.G., Danja I.I., Nasir M.H., Inuwa L., Abdullahi M.U.and Kabiru A. (2021) Optimizing Building Orientation for Reduced Cooling Load in Northeast Nigeria's Residential Architecture. *Proceedings of the 5th International Conference on Environmental and Energy Engineering*, Yangzhou, 220–226.

GB 50118-2010, *Code for sound insulation design of civil buildings*. (2010) China Architecture and Architecture Press, Beijing.

GB 50378-2014, *Green building evaluation standard*. (2014) China Architecture and Architecture Press, Beijing.

GB 50378-2019, *Green building evaluation standard*. (2019) China Architecture and Architecture Press, Beijing.

GB50033-2013, *Building lighting design standard*. (2013) China Architecture and Architecture Press, Beijing.

Minfang Z. (2019) *Design of book information Center of new campus of Henan University of Science and Technology*. Engineering construction and design, Beijing, 12:15–20.

Mustaffa N.K., Mat Isa C.M. and Ibrahim C.K.I.C. (2021) *Top-down bottom-up strategic green building development framework: Case studies in Malaysia*. Building and Environment, England, 203.

Papoyan A., Changhong Z. and Xueying H. (2021) Problem Analysis of Residential Buildings in Armenia In View of Green Architecture Concept. *IOP Conference Series: Earth and Environmental Science*, England, 1:814.

Sengfei S., Baoqi S., Jinlei Z. and Yongchao C. (2019) Study on Lighting Environment Simulation and Analysis of a University Teaching Building. *Symposium on Construction and Efficient Operation of heating Engineering*. Tianjin Post Newspaper and Periodicals Distribution Bureau, Tianjin, 622–630.

Xiaoli B., Yangyang X. and Shunyao Z. (2010) Discussion on Green Renovation Design of Old Industrial Buildings – Taking the Assembly Workshop of Lanzhou Wood Factory as an Example. *Building energy efficiency*, Dongbei, 01:115–121.

Research on zoning design method of high embankment slope with rigid foundation

Junlong Hu* & Yao Xie
CCCC Fourth Harbor Engineering Institute Co., Ltd, Guangzhou, Guangdong, China
Key Laboratory of Environment and Safety Technology of Transportation Infrastructure Engineering, CCCC, Guangzhou, Guangdong, China

Jing Wang & Deyong Wang
CCCC Fourth Harbor Engineering Institute Co., Ltd, Guangzhou, Guangdong, China
Key Laboratory of Environment and Safety Technology of Transportation Infrastructure Engineering, CCCC, Guangzhou, Guangdong, China
Southern Marine Science and Engineering Guangdong Laboratory (Zhuhai), Zhuhai, Guangdong, China

ABSTRACT: Given the current situation that the existing high embankment slopes are designed to cover a wide area and have a large number of fills, which are likely to cause damage to the ecological environment in the mountains, this paper takes a high-filled embankment on the Guangzhou–Lianzhou Expressway as an example and uses the software to establish the corresponding numerical values. The analysis model is used to simulate the settlement of filling construction and post-construction settlement. The results show that the relative influence of the embankment slope width with the slope height change on the settlement of the subgrade working area is an important factor causing the settlement difference. This paper proposes a zoning design method that divides the embankment slope into a settlement control area and a strength control area and further proposes a land-saving design method by steepening the slope rate in the strength control area.

1 INTRODUCTION

With the development of the economy and society, the number of line engineering projects in mountainous areas has increased year by year, resulting in a large number of high-fill embankments. The height of the side slope of the high-fill embankment is more than 20 m. The high embankment slope design is carried out according to the current standard design method, which has the characteristics of a wide area and a large number of fills. The excessive area is easy to encroach on the limited cultivated land resources in the mountainous area. When the line passes through an ecologically sensitive area, the large-scale filling is limited, and the filling excavation is also likely to cause soil erosion and ecological damage. To build a green and sustainable highway project, it is necessary to reduce the road construction land from the design source, which objectively gave birth to the concept of land-saving design.

The settlement of embankment is a problem of soil consolidation and compression. Based on different consolidation theories and combined with engineering practice, scholars have proposed a variety of settlement calculation methods. Among the many calculation

*Corresponding Author: hjunlong@cccc4.com

methods, the layered sum method is widely used in the calculation of settlement. However, because it adopts a single compressive modulus, it cannot reflect the complexity of the soil. Therefore, many scholars have proposed a variety of correction methods considering the variable modulus. Zheng Mingxin and Zhang Zhanrong (Zheng et al. 2015; Zhang et al. 2010, 2011) proposed an improved layered sum method based on the secant modulus of soil in calculating the settlement of layered filling. He Siming and Cao Wengui (Cao 2013; He 2003) proposed different buried methods based on the idea of hierarchical loading. They modified the layered sum method of the deformation modulus of deep foundation soil. Pantelids (2020) combined the advantages of classical elastic theory and the Schmertmann semi-empirical method and proposed the strain-affected zone method. The finite element correlation analysis method is based on computer technology combined with the relevant theory of soil constitutive model, divides the heterogeneous and anisotropic soil into grid elements, summarizes the displacement of each element and node, and calculates the embankment settlement. Zhang Yan (Zhang & Fei 2010) used FLAC to simulate the vertical settlement and deformation of the high embankment during the construction period and verified that the settlement of the high embankment under the action of graded loading has the law that the middle is large and the two sides are small. Jiang et al. (2021) used PLAXIS finite element software to analyze the settlement characteristics of soft soil foundation under a wide embankment and obtained that the embankment surface settlement curve of a wide embankment is roughly W-shaped, and the maximum settlement occurs near the toe of the embankment, while the settlement of narrow embankment is a V shape, the maximum settlement is always located at the centerline of the embankment.

Therefore, this paper uses software to simulate the settlement during the filling construction period and after the construction to explore the range that significantly affects the pavement settlement in the embankment slope area on the premise of ensuring that the pavement settlement meets the requirements of the specifications, further study the zoning design method of dividing the embankment slope into settlement control area and strength control area, and provide a new design concept for land saving design.

2 MODEL ESTABLISHMENT AND PARAMETER VALUES

Subgrade settlement is mainly divided into subgrade filling settlement and foundation settlement. In this paper, a high slope of the Guanglian Expressway is used as a prototype for analysis. The foundation is strongly weathered granite with high stiffness, which can be regarded as a rigid foundation. The subsidence part of the foundation is not considered.

The embankment slope model is established according to the slope rate and symmetrical embankment recommended by the specification, as follows: the slope rate of grade 1 is 1:1.5, the grade 2~3 is 1:1.75, and the grade 4~5 is 1:2; the height of the graded slope is 8 meters, the platform is 2 meters; the width of the road surface is 34 meters; considering the symmetry of the subgrade shape, a half-width subgrade is taken, and the embankment height is designed to be 40 meters. The calculation model is shown in Figure 1.

The model assumes that the foundation soil and embankment fill are elastic–plastic materials, and the Mohr–Coulomb constitutive model is used. The calculation and analysis process is divided into two stages. The first stage simulates the layered filling process during the construction period. Due to the rapid settlement in this stage, it can be regarded as elastic deformation. After the soil parameters of the 100 kPa area are calculated, 500 steps are calculated as the construction settlement of filling a layer, and then calculated layer by layer to the top of the subgrade as the settlement during the entire subgrade construction period. For the calculation of the second stage, refer to the secant modulus method and assign different soil parameters according to four different stress states, as shown in Table 1. When the unbalanced force ratio reaches 10-5, the calculation is stopped to simulate the post-construction settlement.

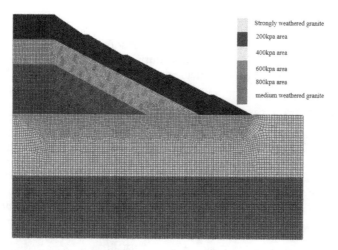

Figure 1. Slope calculation model diagram.

Table 1. Model parameter values.

Soil Physical Parameters	Elastic Modulus (MPa)	Poisson's ratio	Density (g/cm³)	Cohesion (kPa)	Friction angle (°)
Strongly weathered granite	2,000	0.23	1.92	20.5	28.5
Mediumly weathered granite	41,800	0.21	1.91	25.8	30.2
100 kPa area	15	0.28	2.01	35	26
200 kPa area	22	0.28	2.04	35	26
400 kPa area	26	0.28	2.06	35	26
600 kPa area	29	0.28	2.07	35	26

Set up a monitoring line on the center line of the embankment, and set up monitoring points 1#, 2#, and 3# on the center line of the embankment 20m below the road surface, under the shoulder, and the foot of the first-class slope, respectively, to monitor the settlement during the construction period. The location of each monitoring point is shown in Figure 2.

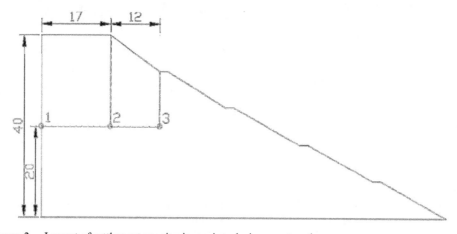

Figure 2. Layout of settlement monitoring points during construction.

3 ANALYSIS OF CALCULATION RESULTS

Import the embankment slope model built into the software for calculation, analyze the settlement data of the embankment and slope during the construction period and after the construction, and discuss the law of settlement change.

3.1 *Analysis of settlement results during construction*

Since the settlement of the slope is mainly controlled by the height of the fill, the settlement of the subgrade working area is larger than that of the slope area, and the height of the maximum settlement will be in the center of the fill height. The calculation process also found that when the construction settlement of the embankment slope is 55% of the maximum settlement of the subgrade working area, there is a special phenomenon that although the fill height of the embankment slope is different, the height of the maximum settlement is the same (Figure 3). Therefore, it is necessary to analyze further the influence of the filling area on the settlement of different slope parts. To this end, a five-level embankment settlement analysis model, as shown in Figure 4, is established.

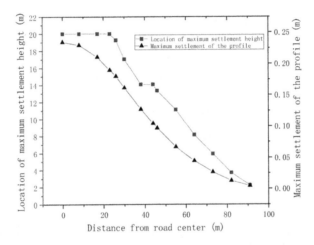

Figure 3. Cloud map of settlement relationship.

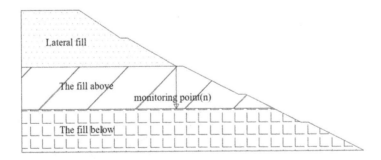

Figure 4. Settlement analysis model diagram.

For the convenience of analysis, the center of the embankment slope was observed at the midpoint between the filling height of 1m to 20m, and 20 monitoring midpoints were arranged (Figure 5). The settlement caused by the filling load σ_c of the fill above the lateral direction of the monitoring midpoint is recorded as s_c, and the settlement caused by the filling load σ_z of the fill directly above is recorded as s_z. The settlement amount s_z caused by the soil load σ_z can be obtained from the relationship between the increment of s_z and the filling height of the embankment slope (Figure 6). It can be seen from Figure 6 that in the range of No. 1–14 monitoring points, the settlement increment has a good linear correlation with the increase of the embankment slope filling height. Since the height of the embankment is 40m, the height of the embankment slope at the No. 14 measuring point is 28m (14*2 = 28m). Therefore, the No. 14 measuring point is equivalent to 0.7 times the height of the embankment (28/40 = 0.7), indicating that 0.7 times the embankment height. The fill settlement s_z in the embankment slope area below the height is greatly affected by the fill load below the embankment slope and has good uniformity.

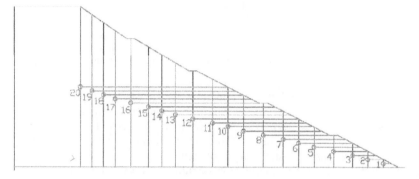

Figure 5. The specific location map of the monitoring median point (n).

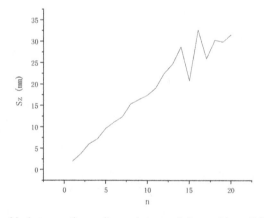

Figure 6. The relationship between the median point s_z and the position of the slope.

The s_c/s_z ratio of each monitoring median point (No. 1-20) can be obtained by analyzing the change of the cumulative settlement of the embankment filling to the top surface of the slope after the completion of filling at the bottom of each median point during the subgrade filling process. Variation with slope position (Figure 7). It can be seen from Figure 7 that the s_c/s_z ratio is a flat section in the middle area of the roadbed slope (that is, the range of monitoring midpoints 8–13), and the peak value of the flat section appears approximately at 2/3 of the embankment height (measured the slope height of point 13 is 26m, 26/40 = 0.65 times), which indicates that the influence of lateral fill load σ_c on the construction settlement of the slope is limited to the part of the embankment slope greater than 0.65 times.

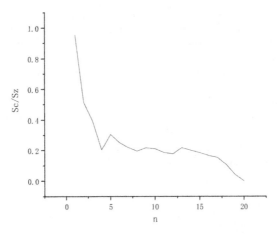

Figure 7. The relationship between the s_c/s_z ratio of the site and the position of the slope.

From this, it can be inferred that the main influence of the fill load in the subgrade working area on the settlement of the embankment slope is in the higher slope area greater than 0.65 times the height of the embankment, while the settlement at the lower slope area less than 0.65 times the height of the embankment. It is mainly controlled by the fill in the slope area. Therefore, based on the analysis of settlement data during the construction period, the slope of the high embankment is divided into the upper settlement control area close to the road surface (subgrade work area) and the lower strength control area away from the road surface (non-pavement work area) (Figure 8).

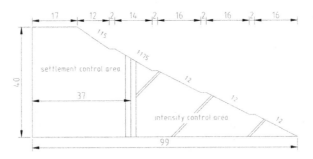

Figure 8. Schematic diagram of the zoning design of the fifth-level embankment.

Taking a high-filled embankment of Guanglian Expressway as an example, the length of the embankment is 437.2 m, the maximum center fill height is 37.04 m, and the maximum embankment slope height is 46.92 m.

Slope steepening design: use the zoning design method to design the section of the high embankment slope and use the parameters in Table 1 for the model parameters. The zoning design method of the high embankment slope is divided into three specific design steps:

1) Design area division: Take 2/3 of the embankment height (H) as the division boundary, and divide the high embankment slope into the upper settlement control area and the lower strength control area. The upper half of the first and second-grade slopes belong to the upper settlement control area, and the lower half of the second-grade slope, the third, fourth, and fifth-grade slopes belong to the lower strength control area;

2) Carry out filling design for grade 1 and grade 2 slopes according to the standard method of roadbed design;
3) According to the conditions to ensure the stability of the subgrade slope, the land-saving design is carried out for the 3rd, 4th, and 5th-grade slopes;
4) The specific process of the land section design is as follows: the lower strength control area is gradually closed from top to bottom, and the stability check is carried out until the stability coefficient reaches 1.35.

Taking a high embankment of Guanglian Expressway as an example, the embankment slope on one side of the embankment slope section can be reduced by 14 meters, and the amount of earth filling can be reduced by 20,000 m^3 per 100 linear meters of the embankment. The less land area is 1,400 m^2, and the less slope protection area is 1,211 m^2.

Based on the above data, it can be seen that the land-saving design of the high embankment slope by using the settlement zoning law can save engineering land, reduce the amount of filling earthwork and the damage to the environment caused by excavation, and achieve the land-saving design purpose. Considering the influence of post-construction load and rainfall, to meet the needs of anti-scour damage on the slope, the steep slope can be wrapped with geogrid to ensure the normal use of the slope.

4 CONCLUSION

In this paper, a conventional grading design model of grade 5 high embankment slope is calculated using FLAC3D software, and the settlement data of the embankment and slope during and after construction are analyzed, and the following conclusions are obtained:

1. Based on the settlement characteristics of the high embankment slope during construction and post-construction, this paper proposes a zoning design method, which divides the high embankment slope into the upper part greater than 2/3 of the embankment height and lower strength control areas less than 2/3 the height of the embankment by taking 2/3 of the embankment height (i.e., 2/3H) as the division boundary,
2. The lower strength control area is gradually closed from top to bottom, and the stability check is carried out until the stability coefficient reaches 1.35.
3. Taking the grade 5 high-fill embankment slope of the Guanglian expressway as an example, the land-saving design is carried out in sections. Since the divisional land-saving design takes the whole slope in the traditional subgrade design as the settlement control area and reduces it to the upper settlement control area, it not only ensures that the pavement settlement control meets the specification requirements but also saves the construction compaction cost and shortens the subgrade filling construction period. At the same time, through the land-saving design of the lower strength control area of the high embankment slope, the embankment filling volume and the slope surface area can be significantly reduced. It is an optimization design method worthy of further study.

REFERENCES

Cao Wengui, Deng Xiangjun and Zhang Chao. Discussion on the Analysis Method of Foundation Settlement Layered Summation Based on the Duncan-Chang model. *Chinese Journal of Geotechnical Engineering*, 2013,35(04): 643–649.

He Siming. Modified Layered Sum Method Based on Elastic-plastic Theory. *Geotechnical Mechanics*, 2003, (1): 88–92.

Jiang X., et al. (2021). "Analysis of Settlement Behaviour of Soft Ground Under Wide Embankment." *The Baltic Journal of Road and Bridge Engineering* 16(4): 153–17

Pantelidis L. (2020). "Elastic Settlement Analysis for Various Footing Cases Based on Strain Influence Areas." *Geotechnical and Geological Engineering* 38(4): 4201–4225.

Zhang Yan. and Fei Shijiang. FLAC Simulation of Settlement and Deformation of High-fill Embankment During Construction. *Journal of Liaoning University of Science and Technology*, 2010, 33(3): 268–271.

Zhang Zhanrong, Liu Qinghui and Yang Yanshuang, et al. Analysis of Settlement Calculation Method of High-fill Embankment. *Railway Standard Design*, 2011, (2): 5–8.

Zhang Zhanrong, Sheng Qian and Zhu Zeqi, et al. Research on Modified Layered Summation Method for Embankment Settlement Analysis. *Journal of Yangtze River Academy of Sciences*, 2010, 27(3): 50–53.

Zheng Mingxin, Yuan Qian and Tu Wenjing, et al. Calculation Method of Settlement Correction Considering Layered Filling of Embankment. *Chinese Journal of Civil Engineering*, 2015, 48(S2): 274–278.

Evaluation of the construction effect of the Three-North Shelterbelt in Chaoyang City, China

Hongge Li*

School of Resource and Environmental Sciences, Wuhan University, Wuhan, China

ABSTRACT: The Three-North Shelterbelt Program represents a large-scale ecological program of planted forests constructed in the northeast, north, and northwest of China, which purpose is to alleviate environmental problems such as drought and Wind-sand Hazards, improve the ecological environment fundamentally, and free 100 million people from long-term poverty. This paper evaluates the construction results of the Three-North Shelterbelt Program in Chaoyang City. With Landsat series, remote sensing data, NDVI, and linear regression were used for the vegetation evolution process analysis of the Three-North Shelterbelt Program from 1985 to 2020. After that, the construction effect was evaluated. Results show that: (1) the NDVI in Chaoyang City generally shows an overall increasing trend, and the vegetation in southwestern Chaoyang City is generally better than in northeastern. (2) The forest land area showed an apparent increasing trend from 1985 to 2020. Their abnormally low values appeared in 2000 and 2010. (3) Regional differences exist for the vegetation coverage in Chaoyang City, with the distribution characteristics of high in the southwest and low in the northeast. The poor forest-covered areas are mainly concentrated in Longcheng District and Shuangta District. (4) There was a decline in vegetation during 1990–2000 and a significant increase after 2000.

1 INTRODUCTION

The northeast, north, and northwest of China are called the Three-North. The Three-North regions account for more than 40% of China's land, and once most of the regions were covered by arid and semi-arid lands (Peng *et al.* 2016). The Three-North are ecologically fragile areas which have been affected by ecological disasters such as soil erosion, sandstorm, and drought for a long time (Yang *et al.* 2005). The severe environmental conditions in this area restrict the economy's development and the improvement in the condition of the people living there. To slow down the process of desertification and soil erosion in this region, from 1978 onwards, the Chinese government has been engaged in an extended reforestation program in the Three-North zone, the program known as the Three-North Shelterbelt Program. The program consists of three stages and eight periods, with the key objective being to increase regional forest coverage, slow or reverse desertification trends and improve the environment. 1978–2000 is the first stage, divided into three scheduled periods. 1978–1985 is the first period, 1986–1995 is the second period, and 1996–2000 is the third period. 2001–2020 is the second stage, divided into two scheduled periods. 2001–2010 is the fourth period, and 2011–2020 is the fifth period. 2021–2050 is the third stage, divided into three scheduled periods. 2021–2030 for the sixth period, 2031–2040 for the seventh period, and 2041–2050 for the eighth period (Li *et al.* 2012).

---

*Corresponding Author: honggeli@whu.edu.cn

The program covers an area of approximately 4,480 km east-west and 560–1,460 km north-south. The region of this program includes 13 provinces in China: Heilongjiang, Jilin, Liaoning, Hebei, and Shanxi. The total area is about 4,069,000 square kilometers, accounting for 42.39% of China's land area. The size of the program is so huge that it can be one of the most significant environmental programs in the world. In the fourth and the fifth scheduled period, the Chinese government divided the whole shelterbelt program into four parts: Northeast North China Plain, the Loess Plateau gully region, the sandy area, and the Northwest desert area. Construction of the shelterbelt in Chaoyang City, Liaoning Province, belongs to the first part. The purpose of the afforestation in this part is to prevent wind and sand, maintain soil and water, and protect farmland.

There have been many studies in China on using remote sensing to evaluate the construction results of the Three-North Shelterbelt Program(Peng *et al.* 2016; Qiang *et al.* 2014; Yu *et al.* 2021; Zhang *et al.* 2016), but few studies focus on the municipal level to show the construction results from a smaller scale. Since the third period of the Three-North shelterbelt program, the construction of the shelterbelt system in Chaoyang City has been going on for more than 20 years. This paper aims to evaluate the construction achievements of the shelterbelt in Chaoyang City as a whole. Based on the Landsat series remote sensing data and the method of NDVI and linear regression, the vegetation evolution process of the Three-North Shelterbelt from 1985–2020 was analyzed, and the construction effect was evaluated.

2   RESEARCH AREA

Chaoyang City is one of the critical areas for constructing the Three-North Shelterbelt Program. This city is located in the northwest of the Liaoning province, ringing from 39°49'N to 40°5'N, and 116°21'E to 116°38'E (Figure 1). The area of Chaoyang City is about 19,699 km², and the population is about 2.84 million. The topography is higher in the northeast and northwest, and lower in the east. This region has a Northern temperate continental monsoon climate with a yearly average temperature of 5.4–8.7°C, yearly rainfall of

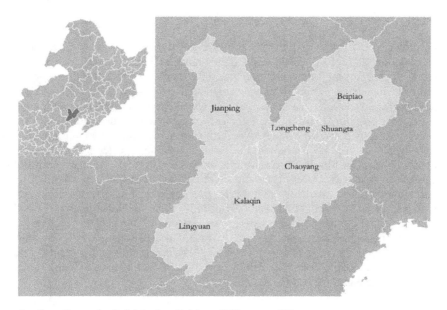

Figure 1.   Location and administrative division of Chaoyang City.

450–580 mm, and annual sunshine duration of 2,850–2,950 h. The aridity of Chaoyang City increases from south to north, and the vegetation type of Chaoyang City transitions northward to the semi-arid temperate deciduous broadleaf forest of the arid steppe type. The southern part of Chaoyang City has better vegetation conditions and is characterized by the flora of northern China; the northern part has poorer ecological functions and more arid-type plants. The overall forest coverage rate of Chaoyang City is 30% (2022). With the continuous progress of the Three-North Shelterbelt Program in Chaoyang City, the forest coverage rate in this city is increasing continuously.

Chaoyang City has six different counties and cities under its jurisdiction. Detailed administrative divisions are shown in Figure 1.

3 METHODS

3.1 Remote sensing data

The Landsat program is a joint NASA / USGS program, the longest-running enterprise for acquiring satellite imagery of Earth. The Landsat image usually has a high spatial resolution and is generally used to calculate the standardized normalized difference vegetation index (NDVI). For more than 40 years, these data have been extensively utilized in a variety of disciplines, such as ecology, phenology, biology, hydrology and botany, and more. These data have also been widely used in different research areas, including vegetation detection, and have a broad application prospect in constructing the Three-North Shelterbelt Program (Liu & Hong 2005). Due to the high spatial resolution of Landsat data, it is suitable for research in the small-scale range (Bullock *et al.* 2018; Grinand *et al.* 2013).

3.2 The normalized difference vegetation index

The normalized difference vegetation index (NDVI) is a broadly used index by remote sensing and is known as the best indicator of plant growth status and spatial distribution density of vegetation. It can also show the changes in forest land cover clearly (Wang *et al.* 2011). NDVI is a rate parametric using this formula:

$$NDVI = (NIR - R)/(NIR + R) \qquad (1)$$

Where R indicates the red band and *NIR* indicates the near-infrared band.

NDVI is more sensitive to changes in soil context, and it eliminates the influence of topography to a large extent, increasing the sensitivity of vegetation detection. So it can accurately reflect many parameters related to green vegetation, like photosynthesis and metabolic rates of the vegetation, as well as seasonal and annual variations. NDVI values can be used as a criterion for the presence and growth status of vegetation (Sellers 1992; Tucker *et al.* 1985, 2005).

3.3 The linear regression

The linear regression method is simple and practical to reveal the climate and vegetation change trend. It is used to study the movement of the vegetation area change(Wang *et al.* 2011).

The trend of area change can be calculated by the linear regression of one variable for a specific time. A one-dimensional linear regression equation of vegetation area versus time and equation is established as follows:

$$x_i = a + bt_i, \ i = 1, 2, 3, \ldots, n \qquad (2)$$

$$a = x^- - bt^- \qquad (3)$$

$$b = \frac{\sum_{i=1}^{n} x_i t_i - \frac{1}{n}\left(\sum_{i=1}^{n} x_i\right)\left(\sum_{i=1}^{n} t_i\right)}{\sum_{t=1}^{n} t_1^2 - \frac{1}{n}\left(\sum_{i=1}^{n} t_i\right)} \qquad (4)$$

Where x indicates the forest land area, n is the total number of years under observation, and t indicates the corresponding year.

3.4 Data processing

3.4.1 Data acquisition

In this study, the Landsat image collation 2 level 2 dataset is used for NDVI analysis. Combined with the construction of protective forests and related documents, the study period was selected as a total of 35 years from 1985 to 2020. The images covering the study area were selected every five years. The photos were taken from the end of August to the beginning of September of the year, as there were less cloudy and the vegetation was more luxuriant during this period. From 1985 to 2010, landsat5 TM images were selected from 2015 to 2020, and the landsat8 OLI images were also used (Yu et al. 2021).

3.4.2 NDVI calculation

The Landsat image collation 2 level 2 dataset has been generated by high-precision radiation, geometric, and atmospheric correction, which are used to calculate the NDVI. As for Landsat5 TM images, the NIR band is the 4th band, while the R band is the 3rd band; for Landsat8 OLI images, the NIR band is the 5th band, while the R band is the 4th band.

The upper limit of NDVI for each year is uniformly around 0.5, and the lower limit is set to −0.2. The obtained results are shown in the time series maps in Figure 1.

3.4.3 The NDVI threshold method and the extraction of forest area

Based on the NDVI image histogram combined with the existing forest land area statistics, the NDVI threshold is set to 0.22, and the region with NDVI higher than this value is set as forest land(Ding et al. 2018). The number of forest pixels is counted to calculate the area.

$$Area = P * (x^2)/1000000$$

Where P is the number of pixels, x is the spatial resolution with the resolution of the current image of 30 meters, and the area unit is km^2.

A series of line charts show the vegetation changes in different counties (Figure 2). The linear regression was used to analyze the vegetation changes in different counties.

4 RESULTS AND DISCUSSION

4.1 Trend analysis of vegetation changes

The results directly displayed by NDVI on the time series maps clearly show that NDVI in all counties of Chaoyang City shows an increasing trend (Figure 2).

In the spatial dimension, the vegetation in southwestern Chaoyang City is generally better than in the northeastern. In the temporal dimension, the vegetation condition in Chaoyang has generally shown a continuous improvement over the past 35 years.

4.2 Temporal distribution characteristics of vegetation

The quantitative metrics of the forest land area obtained from the NDVI threshold method show that the forest land area in all counties has fluctuated but showed an apparent upward

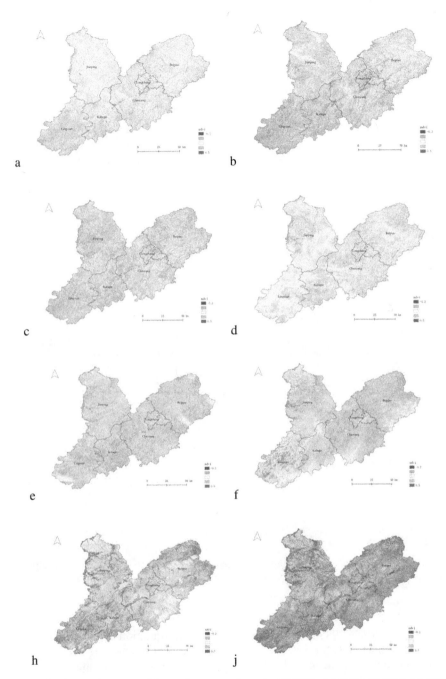

Figure 2. The time series maps of the study area to show the NDVI in (a) 1985; (b) 1990; (c) 1995; (d) 2000; (e) 2005; (f) 2010; (g) 2015; (h) 2020.

trend over the past 35 years. The linear regression method was used to analyze the vegetation NDVI in Chaoyang City. The variation trend of vegetation NDVI is shown in Figure 3.

According to them, the NDVI value has typically displayed a moderately increasing trend with an annual average linear change trend of 260.4 km^2 per year. The forest proportion

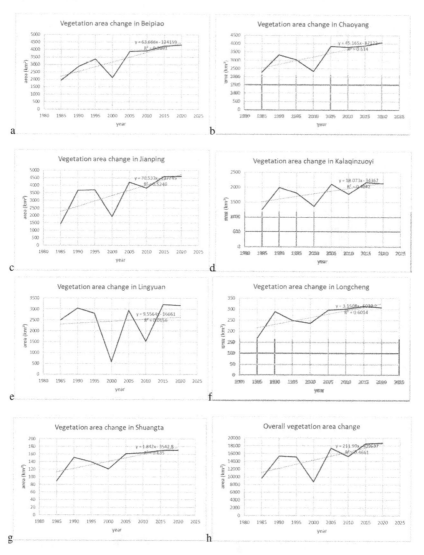

Figure 3. The line charts of the vegetation changes in (a) Beipiao; (b) Chaoyang; (c) Jianping; (d) Kelaqinzuoyi; (e) Lingyuan; (f) Longcheng; (g) Shuangta; (h) overall change trend.

increased from 49% in 1985 to 92% in 2020. Detailed information on changes in forest area by county is shown in Table 1. If the current conditions of the natural and artificial environment are maintained, the forest land area in Chaoyang City should continue to increase in the foreseeable future.

Results show that there are also some outliers though the forest land area generally showed an increasing trend. In 2000, due to the influence of image quality and the severe drought in this area, the vegetation area declined in all counties. In 2010, some areas of the city, especially the southwestern part, also had decreased vegetation. Checking the relevant information, we can see that there was also a widespread drought in Liaoning Province in 2009, and the effects on vegetation may have continued into the following year. Besides, due

Table 1. Change in forest land area and Forest proportion (1985–2020).

Year	Shuangta	Longcheng	Lingyuan	Kelaqin	Jianping	Chaoyang	Beipiao	Total	Forest proportion/%
2020	170.24	307.90	3172.50	2130.69	4614.83	4063.03	4299.29	18758.47	0.95
2015	169.91	313.89	3205.67	2163.23	4593.64	3871.33	4241.28	18558.94	0.94
2010	163.63	301.21	1530.55	1766.13	3826.01	3792.53	3921.03	15301.08	0.78
2005	161.56	297.09	2946.04	2106.66	4218.47	3850.88	3873.59	17454.30	0.89
2000	121.13	236.99	582.99	1372.37	1921.46	2341.96	2129.92	8706.83	0.44
1995	139.73	248.59	2815.83	1801.94	3706.46	3034.59	3378.67	15125.82	0.77
1990	150.93	288.46	3054.64	1994.87	3674.36	3335.18	2872.05	15370.49	0.78
1985	89.28	168.15	2493.73	1256.12	1418.88	2276.49	1938.89	9641.54	0.49
Annual change/km^2	2.31	3.99	19.39	24.99	91.31	51.04	67.44	260.48	
Average area/km^2	145.8014625	270.283725	2475.243113	1824.00165	3496.7646	3320.750475	3331.841513	14864.68654	

to the impact of human activities, the ecological vulnerability of Chaoyang City deteriorated during this time.

4.3 Spatial distribution characteristics of vegetation

The overall distribution of forest land in Chaoyang City is relatively uniform but shows a specific spatial variation, reflected in the gradual increase of forest area from northeastern Chaoyang city to southwestern. The map of the average forest land area share by counties is shown in Figure 4.

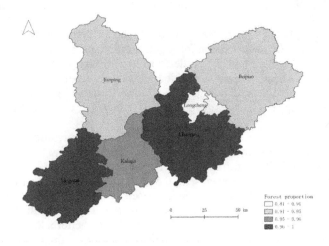

Figure 4. The map of the average forest land area.

The northwestern part of Chaoyang City is located on the southern edge of the horqin sandy area, the climate is dry all year round, and the wind and sand hazards are serious. Southwestern Chaoyang City is part of the North and Northeast China Plain, and the soil and water conditions are significantly better than those in the northeast. So the northwestern part is the leading construction area of the shelterbelt, and the primary purpose of planting trees in the southwestern part is to protect agricultural land.

By county, it can be seen that Chaoyang County and Lingyuan County have a relatively high percentage of forest land, which means the construction of the shelterbelt program in these counties is effective. In contrast, Longcheng District and Shuangta District have a relatively low percentage of forest land, which means the construction of the shelterbelt program in these counties still needs to be strengthened.

4.4 Vegetation changing detection

According to the research results and our research situation, the vegetation cover grade is determined according to the different values taken by NDVI (Cao et al. 2017, Shen et al. 2017). The vegetation cover grade is divided into three levels, the low level with NDVI < 0.3, the medium level with NDVI between 0.3 and 0.6, and the high level with NDVI > 0.6 (Table 2).

Table 2. The vegetation cover grade classification.

NDVI range	Vegetation level
<0.3	low
0.3–0.6	medium
>0.6	high

Through the vegetation cover grade, most of Chaoyang City has a low and medium vegetation level. After entering 2010, the fifth period of the shelterbelt program, some high-level areas appear.

According to the phased construction plan of the shelterbelt program, four-time points in 1990, 2000, 2010, and 2020 were chosen for vegetation changing detection. During a selected period, a change in vegetation cover grade from low to high is considered an increase in vegetation, and from high to low is regarded as a decrease in vegetation. The variation between the four-time points and the overall variation is shown in Figure 5. The number of image pixels, the occupied area, and the percentage of different variation trends are shown in Table 3.

It can be seen that there was a significant decline in vegetation in the 1990–2000 interval, which may be a combination of factors such as the low investment in the construction of the shelterbelt program in the early stage and the severe drought that occurred in 2000 in Northeast China. However, with the construction of the fourth and fifth periods of the shelterbelt program, the forest area increased again. Specifically, the forest area in northeastern Chaoyang city has grown more than that in southwestern Chaoyang city between 2000 and 2010 (during the fourth period of the shelterbelt program), while the forest area in southwestern Chaoyang city has grown more than that in northeastern between 2010 and 2020 (during the fifth phase of the shelterbelt program). In general, the forest land area in Chaoyang City showed a significant upward trend over the past 35

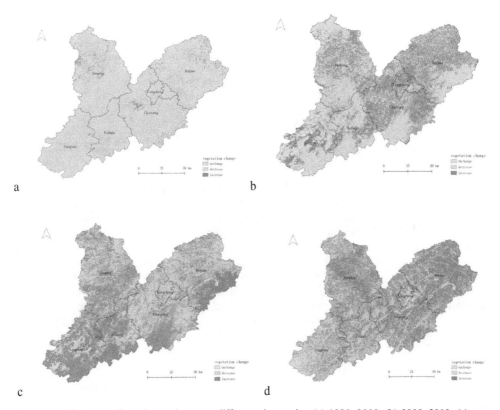

Figure 5. The vegetation change between different time points (a) 1990–2000; (b) 2000–2010; (c) 2010–2020; (d) 1990–2020.

Table 3. The vegetation change between different time points.

period	Increase/ km^2	Proportion/ %	Decrease/ km^2	Proportion/ %	Unchanged/ km^2	Proportion/ %
1990–2000	580.43	0.03	6183.63	0.31	12,944.71	0.66
2000–2010	6,110.76	0.31	567.63	0.03	12,975.13	0.66
2010–2020	9,610.38	0.49	479.98	0.02	9,562.99	0.49
1990–2020	9,759.94	0.50	644.26	0.03	9,301.51	0.47

years, and there was more forest land increase in northeastern Chaoyang city than in southwestern.

4.5 *Analysis of the effectiveness of the shelterbelt construction*

Based on the above study, there have been outstanding achievements since the implementation of the program, and the forests are in good condition in most areas. Table 4

Table 4. Comparison of actual and measured reforestation area in Chaoyang City.

Shelterbelt construction period	Actual reforestation area/km^2	Measured reforestation area/km^2
1985–1995	5040.83	5484.28
1996–2001	5293.46	6418.99
2002–2011	7298.07	6594.25
2012–2020	6160.21	3457.39

shows the comparison between the actual reforestation area (Fan *et al.* 2012; Jia 2019; Ma 2019; Wang *et al.* 2019) and the increase in vegetation area calculated in this study. It is obvious that although there are differences between them, generally, they coincide with each other.

Since the construction of the Three-North Shelterbelt Program in Chaoyang, the forest coverage rate and the environmental quality has been significantly improved; the ecological vulnerability of the Chaoyang area has been reduced, and the environment has tended to develop steadily. The area of desertified land and soil erosion has been significantly reduced, desertification control has been effective, and soil conservation has been enhanced (Jia 2019; Ma 2019; Wang *et al.* 2019).

5 CONCLUSION

This study analyzes and evaluates the effect of the Three-North Shelterbelt Program's implementation in Chaoyang City. The conclusions are as follows.

1. The NDVI map indicates that the NDVI in Chaoyang City generally shows an overall increasing trend, the vegetation in southwestern Chaoyang City is generally better than in the northeastern.
2. The forest land area in all counties has fluctuated but showed an apparent increasing trend over the past 35 years from 1985 to 2020. The annual average linear change trend was 260.4 km^2 per year. The forest proportion increased from 49% in 1985 to 92% in 2020. The forest land area generally showed an increasing trend, but there are abnormally low values that appeared in 2000 and 2010.
3. The overall distribution of forest land in Chaoyang City is relatively uniform but shows a specific spatial variation, which is reflected in the gradual increase of forest area from northeast to southwest of Chaoyang. It can also be seen that the proportion of forest land is higher in Chaoyang County and Lingyuan County and relatively lower in Longcheng District and Shuangta District.
4. According to the NDVI, the vegetation was divided into low, medium, and high levels. Most areas in Chaoyang City have low and medium vegetation levels. After entering 2010, some high-level areas appeared. Four-time points of 1990, 2000, 2010, and 2020 were selected for vegetation change detection. There was a decline in vegetation during 1990–2000 and an increase in forest area after 2000. between 2000–2010, the forest area in northeastern Chaoyang City increased more than that in southwestern Chaoyang City, while between 2010–2020, the forest area in south-western Chaoyang City increased more than that in northeastern Chaoyang City. Overall, there has been a clear upward trend in forest area in Chaoyang over the past

35 years, with more forest area growth in northeastern Chaoyang City than in southwestern.
5. Overall, outstanding achievements have been made since the implementation of the shelterbelt program, and the vegetation conditions in most areas have been significantly improved. Since the construction of the Three-North Shelterbelt Program in Chaoyang City, the forest coverage rate has increased significantly and the ecological fragility of the Chaoyang area has been significantly reduced. For areas with relatively low vegetation proportions, local governments should continue actively implementing shelterbelt programs to promote the healthy and sustainable development of local ecological construction.

REFERENCES

Bullock E.L., Woodcock C.E. and Olofsson P. 2018. *Monitoring Tropical Forest Degradation Using Spectral Unmixing and Landsat Time Series Analysis*. Remote Sensing of Environment.

Cao Y., Xiaorui L.I. and Zhang L. 2017. *Analysis of Dynamic Evolution Characteristics of Vegetation in Liaoning Province from 2000 to 2014*. Water Resources and Hydropower Engineering.

Ding Y., Cao C.H., Cheng L.X., Wang N. and Wen L.J. 2018. Monitoring of Enteromorpha Proliferation in the Yellow sea with MODIS Image Based on Linear Mixing Model and NDVI Threshold. *Chinese Journal of Ecology*, 37, 3480–3486.

Fan G., You Y., Jin Z., Zhao S., Hou H. and Dong A. 2012. The Effectiveness of the Construction of the Fourth Period of The Three-North Shelterbelt Program in Liaoning Province. *Journal of Liaoning Forestry Science & Technology*, 6.

Grinand C., Rakotomalala F., Gond V., Vaudry R. and Vieilledent G. 2013. Estimating Deforestation in Tropical Humid and Dry Forests in Madagascar from 2000 to 2010 Using Multi-date Landsat Satellite Images and the Random Forests Classifier. *Remote Sensing of Environment*, 139, 68–80.

Jia D. 2019. *Effectiveness and Experience of the Mid-term Construction of the Fifth Periods of the Three-North Shelterbelt Program in Liaoning Province*. Protection Forest Science & Technology, 2.

Li M.M., Liu A.T., Zou C.J., Xu W.D., Shimizu H. and Wang K.Y. 2012. An Overview of the "Three-North" Shelterbelt Project in China. *Forestry Studies in China*, 14, 70–79.

Liu B. and Hong J.Y. 2005. *Application of Using Landsat-7 ETM + Remote Sensing Image in Forest Resources Investigation of County Level in the Three North Shelterbelt Project*. Protection Forest Science & Technology.

Ma C. 2019. *Effectiveness of The Three-North Shelterbelt Program in Liaoning Province and Suggestions for Development*. Protection Forest Science & Technology, 3.

Peng D., Wu C., Zhang B., Huete A., Zhang X., Sun R., Lei L., Huang W., Liu L., Liu X., Li J., Luo S. and Fang B. 2016. *The Influences of Drought and Land-Cover Conversion on Inter-Annual Variation of NPP in the Three-North Shelterbelt Program Zone of China Based on MODIS Data. PLoS One*, 11, e0158173.

Qiang W., Bo Z., Zhiqiang Z., Xifeng Z. and Shengpei D. 2014. The Three-North Shelterbelt Program and Dynamic Changes in Vegetation Cover. *Journal of Resources and Ecology*, 5, 53–59.

Sellers P.J. 1992. Canopy Reflectance, Photosynthesis, and Transpiration. *International Journal of Remote Sensing*, 6, 1335–1372.

Shen L., Sun Y., Yang Y. and Jing Y. 2017. *Spectrum Characteristic of Vegetation Coverage Change Based on NDVI in the Three-North Shelter Forest Program*. Environmental Science & Technology, 40, 9.

Tucker C.J., Townshend J.R. and Goff T.E. 1985. *African Land-Cover Classification Using Satellite Data. Science*, 227, 369–375.

Tucker C., Pinzon J., Brown M., Slayback D., Pak E., Mahoney R., Vermote, E. and El Saleous N. 2005. An Extended AVHRR 8-km NDVI Dataset is Compatible with MODIS and SPOT Vegetation NDVI data. *International Journal of Remote Sensing*, 26, 4485–4498.

Wang X., Piao S., Ciais P., Li J., Friedlingstein P., Koven C. and Chen A. 2011. Spring Temperature Change and its Implication in the Change of Vegetation Growth in North America from 1982 to 2006. *Proceedings of the National Academy of Sciences of the United States of America*, 108.

Wang Y., Ge J., Han D. and Wang G. 2019. Research on the Effectiveness and Problems of The Three-North Shelterbelt Program Construction in Liaoning–Take Chaoyang City as an Example. *Journal of Green Science & Technology*, 4.

Yang X., Zhang K., Jia B. and Ci L. 2005. Desertification Assessment in China: An overview. *Journal of Arid Environments*, 63, 517–531.

Yu T., Liu P., Zhang Q., Ren Y. and Yao J. 2021. Detecting Forest Degradation in the Three-North Forest Shelterbelt in China from Multi-Scale Satellite Images. *Remote Sensing*, 13.

Zhang Y., Peng C., Li W., Tian L., Zhu Q., Chen H., Fang X., Zhang G., Liu G., Mu X., Li Z., Li S., Yang Y., Wang J. and Xiao X. 2016. Multiple Afforestation Programs Accelerate the Greenness in the 'Three North' region of China from 1982 to 2013. *Ecological Indicators*, 61, 404–412.

Research and analysis of the distribution of greenhouses in Jiangsu Province

Jikun Zhao* & Chaowei Deng
College of Information Management, Nanjing Agricultural University, Nanjing City, Jiangsu Province, China

ABSTRACT: The vigorous development of protected horticulture is one of the important symbols of modern agriculture, and the application of greenhouses in large areas is an important means and carrier to improve the quality of agricultural products, increase farmers' incomes and realize rural revitalization. This paper took the development of the greenhouse industry in Jiangsu Province as the research object and used such research methods as field research and comparative analysis to deeply analyze and elaborate the distribution of facilities, the development of scales, and the industrial characteristics of the greenhouse industry in Jiangsu Province. From a practical point of view, tomatoes, cucumbers, and eggplants, the three common and representative vegetables were selected for the cost-benefit research, and then such relevant problems were found a low level of mechanization and the difficulties in land transfer in the greenhouse industry. Based on this, the author drew lessons from foreign development experience, combined with the actual development situation of the greenhouse industry in Jiangsu Province, and put forward six suggestions for industrial development given the main problems existing in the greenhouse industry, including increasing investment in greenhouse facilities, improving the level of mechanization, increasing investment in science and technology, building a long-term quality and safety control mechanism, optimizing the mode of agricultural production and operation, and strengthening the macro-oriented role of the government, to provide a reference for the development of the greenhouse industry.

1 INTRODUCTION

Protected horticulture refers to environment-controlled agriculture in the areas or seasons that are not suitable for the growth of crops through the construction of specific protection facilities, the use of Internet of Things technology, automation technology, and modern management technology to artificially create an environment suitable for the growth of horticultural crops, to achieve the production of high-quality, high-yield and stable agricultural products (Guo 2012). On October 18, 2017, the report of the Nineteenth National Congress of the Communist Party of China proposed to implement the rural revitalization strategy, adhere to the priority development of agriculture and rural areas, make agriculture a promising industry, and accelerate the structural reform of the agricultural supply side. The greenhouse industry of protected horticulture is within the realm of national key support. It not only meets the needs of China's agricultural industrial upgrading and transformation but also is an important symbol of the level of agricultural modernization in a region (Li 2019). It can increase agricultural efficiency, increase farmers' incomes and help rural revitalization.

*Corresponding Author: zhaojikun@njau.edu.cn

According to the statistics of the Department of Agricultural Mechanization, Ministry of Agriculture and Rural Affairs of the People's Republic of China, as shown in Figure 1, by the end of 2018, the total area of greenhouse cultivation in China has increased to 1.894 million hm², including 54,000 hm² of multiple greenhouses, 577,000 hm² of solar greenhouses and 1.263 million hm² of plastic greenhouses. The total scale of greenhouses accounts for more than 80% of the world's protected horticulture area. Correspondingly, the production efficiency is far lower than that of developed countries, and there are many problems, such as the low level of mechanization and the difficulties in land transfer. According to the statistics of each caliber, the greenhouse industry in Jiangsu Province is highly developed and representative. Therefore, the investigation and analysis of the greenhouse industry in Jiangsu Province have strong practical significance in finding out the main problems existing in the current situation and drawing lessons from foreign development experience to put forward targeted strategies and suggestions for the upgrading and transformation of China's agricultural industry.

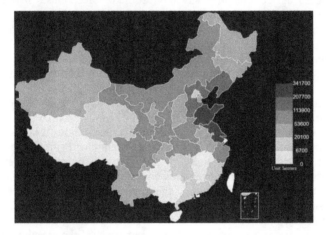

Figure 1. The distribution map of the greenhouses' area of China's protected horticulture.

2 THE DISTRIBUTION OF GREENHOUSE FACILITIES IN JIANGSU PROVINCE

According to the data of the papers of the National Institute of Facility Agriculture, the scale of the greenhouse planting area (covering small and medium-sized arch sheds) in China is about 3.7 million hm². In comparison, the data of the Department of Agricultural Mechanization Management of the Ministry of Agriculture and Rural Affairs in the same year are 1.89 million hm² (Li 2019); the sampling statistics of scientific research units and professional associations are between 4.0 million and 4.5 million hm². The statistical data of the Jiangsu Provincial Department of Agriculture in 2015 show that the greenhouses' area of protected horticulture in Jiangsu Province is about 800,000 hm². According to the data of the third agricultural census in Jiangsu Province in 2016, the total area of greenhouses is only 120,000 hm² (Mu 2017); according to the caliber data of the Department of Agricultural Mechanization, the greenhouses' area of Jiangsu Province in 2016 is roughly 340,000 hm² (2017).

As the study mainly focuses on the three kinds of multiple greenhouses, solar greenhouses, and plastic greenhouses, it is feasible to use the statistical data of the Department of Agricultural Mechanization Management. Since it is sampled by province, there is no more specific data on the level of the city, and the difference value between the greenhouse area of

Jiangsu Province in 2016 and the latest area in 2018 is relatively small (only 1,375 hm^2). For this reason, it is proposed to use the proportion of greenhouses in each city in the third agricultural census (2016), multiplied by the latest greenhouse data from the Department of Agricultural Mechanization in 2018, to obtain the current distribution of greenhouse facilities in Jiangsu Province, which is the local optimal solution as a scheme. The data results are as follows:

Table 1. Distribution table of greenhouse facilities in Jiangsu Province (Unit: hectare).

	Multiple Greenhouses	Solar Greenhouses	Plastic Greenhouses	Total Amount of Greenhouses	Proportion
Jiangsu Province	19,687	25,176	294,541	339,404	100%
Nanjing City	845	1,080	15,258	17,183	5.06%
Wuxi City	576	737	10,851	12,165	3.58%
Xuzhou City	7,880	10,077	79,305	97,263	28.66%
Changzhou City	319	408	6,425	7,152	2.11%
Suzhou City	841	1,076	18,227	20,143	5.93%
Nantong City	2,109	2,697	41,558	46,365	13.66%
Lianyungang City	2,145	2,743	6,815	11,703	3.45%
Huai'an City	1,171	1,497	18,608	21,276	6.27%
Yancheng City	1,524	1,949	58,040	61,513	18.12%
Yangzhou City	443	567	6,997	8,007	2.36%
Zhenjiang City	495	633	10,245	11,373	3.35%
Taizhou City	430	551	11,205	12,186	3.59%
Suqian City	908	1,161	11,007	13,076	3.85%

In the distribution of greenhouse facilities in Jiangsu Province, the total amount of greenhouses and the area of plastic greenhouses in northern Jiangsu (Xuzhou, Lianyungang, Huai'an, Yancheng, and Suqian) accounts for about 60%, and the ones in central Jiangsu (Nantong, Yangzhou, and Taizhou) and southern Jiangsu (Nanjing, Wuxi, Changzhou, Suzhou, and Zhenjiang) account for roughly 20%, respectively. In the total area of multiple greenhouses and solar greenhouses, northern Jiangsu accounts for approximately 70%, and central and southern Jiangsu each account for around 15%. Among all the cities in Jiangsu Province, Xuzhou has the largest scale and the largest area of the greenhouse industry, accounting for 28.66% of the total of this province, while Changzhou has the smallest industrial scale and the smallest area, accounting for only 2.11% of the whole province.

3 THE DEVELOPMENT OF THE GREENHOUSE SCALE IN JIANGSU PROVINCE

Given the statistics of the total amounts of greenhouse facilities, plastic greenhouse facilities, solar greenhouse facilities, and multiple greenhouse facilities in Jiangsu Province over the years, according to the caliber of the Department of Agricultural Mechanization Management of the Ministry of Agriculture and Rural Affairs, the figures are shown in Figure 2:

In the total amounts of greenhouse facilities and plastic greenhouse facilities, their area scales increased exponentially from 53,854 hm^2 to 29,756 hm^2 and from 51,423 hm^2 to 260,609 hm^2 between 2008 to 2014, respectively. Thereafter, from 2015 to 2018, their area scales nearly reached saturation, maintaining their fluctuations between

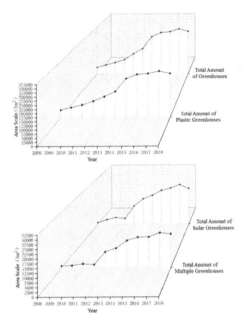

Figure 2. The area map of the greenhouse facilities in Jiangsu Province over the years.

330,705 hm^2 and 359,008 hm^2, and between 288,940 hm^2 and 310,803 hm^2, respectively. The total amount of area scales of greenhouse facilities and solar greenhouse facilities fluctuated between 1,200 and 2,500 hm^2 and between 1,100 and 4,800 hm^2, respectively, before 2011. After 2011, the scale of the two developed at a relatively rapid speed. From 2011 to 2017, their area scales expanded from 2,017 hm^2 to 20,422 hm^2 and from 4,089 hm^2 to 27,783 hm^2, respectively. Thereafter, in 2018, their scales were reduced by 735 hm^2 and 2,607 hm^2, respectively.

According to Figure 2, the analysis is made based on the curve trends of the total amount of greenhouses and the total amount of each kind of greenhouse facility. Before 2014, with the improvement of agricultural productivity and the development of science and technology in Jiangsu Province, the area of plastic greenhouses increased exponentially. Subsequently, due to the constraints of the demand side of agricultural products, the scale reached saturation and fluctuated within a certain range between 2015 and 2018. Due to their high cost, the scales of solar greenhouses and multiple greenhouses did not expand significantly in the early development stage of protected horticulture in Jiangsu Province. However, after 2011, with the government's attention to the "agriculture, rural areas, and farmers" issues and a large number of funds invested in agriculture, the areas of the two began to gradually expand, reaching their maximums in 2017. From 2008 to 2018, the proportion of plastic greenhouse area in total greenhouses in Jiangsu Province decreased from 95.5% to 86.8%; the proportion of greenhouse area and solar greenhouse area in total greenhouses in Jiangsu Province increased from 2.3% to 5.8%, and from 2.2% to 7.4%, respectively. During the ten years, although the proportion of plastic greenhouses has declined, the current scale still dominates; although the proportions of multiple greenhouses and solar greenhouses have increased, their current area scales are still small. Based on the current development level of protected horticulture, the scale of greenhouses in Jiangsu Province in the future is expected to remain at the current level of fluctuation, but there will be a transformation in the types of facilities. The proportion of plastic greenhouses will gradually decrease, while the proportion of solar greenhouses and multiple greenhouses with a relatively higher level of facilities will gradually expand.

4 MAIN DEVELOPMENT CHARACTERISTICS OF THE GREENHOUSE INDUSTRY IN JIANGSU PROVINCE

4.1 *The saturated area scale and the reasonable location distribution*

From the perspective of the scale of the greenhouse industry in Jiangsu Province, after a substantial increase in 2008–2015, the production area of greenhouses has maintained between 330,000 hm^2 and 350,000 hm^2 in recent years, and the scale tends to be saturated. In the next few years, due to the constraints of the demand side of agricultural products, the area scale will remain at the current level with merely a narrow fluctuation. After a long period of natural selection of the ecological environment, the market scale, and the socio-economic level, in terms of the location distribution, all cities in Jiangsu Province have had a greenhouse industry, and the industrial scale of northern, central and southern Jiangsu is roughly in a 6:2:2 ratio. Based on the consideration of the industrial structure and the economic development level, cities in northern Jiangsu have vigorously developed the greenhouse industry. The areas of multiple greenhouses and solar greenhouses account for more than 70% of the whole province, and the upgrading and transformation of the agricultural industry are promoted through high-level protected horticulture. Since their secondary and tertiary industries are relatively more developed and their industrial and commercial strength is stronger, the scale of greenhouses in central and southern Jiangsu is lower than that in northern Jiangsu. From the overall perspective of the greenhouse industry in Jiangsu Province, the location distribution tends to be reasonable.

4.2 *The prominent industry drive and the increasing income of farmers who are getting rich*

The greenhouse industry is a modern agricultural system based on the film chemical industry, the building materials industry, the steel metallurgy industry, and the commercial logistics industry (Contemporary Horticulture 2011). According to the calculation, the consumption of materials in the upstream and downstream industries driven by the greenhouse industry in Jiangsu Province is 462,000 tons of agricultural plastic films, 16.38 million seedling trays, 1,218 billion bamboo poles in the greenhouse skeletons, 63 million steel pipes in the greenhouse skeletons, 67.2 million straw mats, 588,000 tons of cement, 4.074 million squares of sands and a considerable number of other materials, which directly or indirectly drives the expansion and progress of these industries. At the same time, millions of tons of greenhouse fruits and vegetables and a large number of flower products directly promote the rapid growth of business and the logistics industry. According to the government's official research, a single labor force can operate 1000–1350 m^2 of greenhouse production to exchange help among farmers' neighbors (Zhang 2010). The 339,000 hm^2 planting scale of the greenhouse industry in the whole province can solve the employment of at least 2.53 million people and can drive the development of upstream and downstream industries to create 1.45 million jobs, which plays a key role in properly arranging returning migrant workers and alleviating the employment pressure in urban and rural areas. At present, compared with open-field crop cultivation, greenhouses can greatly improve the output value and output benefit of crops per mu by artificially controlling the microclimate in the greenhouses and driving farmers to increase income and get rich.

5 ANALYSIS OF THE PRODUCTION COST PER MU OF GREENHOUSES IN JIANGSU PROVINCE

Based on the field investigation of the greenhouse industry in Nanjing Geguan Ecological Park, combined with part of the data of the vegetables in Jiangsu Province of the document assembly of the cost benefits of national agricultural products, this paper focused on the standardized plastic greenhouses in the process of agricultural production and made a comparative analysis of the direct costs, the indirect costs and labor costs of tomatoes, cucumbers and eggplants, the three kinds of common and representative vegetables, planted in open fields and greenhouses.

5.1 Analysis of the total production cost per mu of the tomatoes, cucumbers, and eggplants planted in facilities in Jiangsu Province

As shown in Table 2 below, the average total production costs per mu of tomatoes, cucumbers, and eggplants in greenhouses in Jiangsu Province is higher than that in open fields in China. The difference value is the highest between the total cost of tomatoes planted in greenhouses and that in an open field, reaching 4,545.27 yuan. Regarding the cost ratio, no matter what planting method is adopted, the labor costs account for the largest proportion of the total production costs. The labor costs of tomatoes and cucumbers account for more than 60%, and the labor costs of eggplants fluctuate around 50%. At the same time, the indirect costs of greenhouse planting are higher than those of open-field planting because the depreciation cost and sales cost of greenhouse planting are significantly higher than those of open-field planting.

Table 2. Production costs table of tomatoes, cucumbers, and eggplants per mu (Unit: yuan).

Item	Tomatoes Open Field	Greenhouses	Cucumbers Open Field	Greenhouses	Eggplants Open Field	Greenhouses
1. Material and Service Costs per mu	**1,234.93**	**2,919.94**	**1,421.63**	**1,971.08**	**1,878.57**	**2,470.57**
(1) Direct Costs	**1,141.52**	**2,258.30**	**1,319.82**	**1,506.76**	**1,739.59**	**1,853.64**
1. Seed Cost	204.07	365.48	199.22	216.45	143.41	332.87
2. Fertilizer Cost	285.55	336.45	287.46	218.61	286.68	279.23
3. Farm Manure	170.29	309.62	299.38	208.08	863.06	268.84
4. Pesticide Cost	138.74	263.70	167.09	182.68	145.77	193.87
5. Film Cost	85.26	594.38	79.17	383.78	76.56	531.68
6. Lease Operating Cost	111.06	144.07	124.58	149.97	122.65	131.50
Mechanical Operation Cost	64.00	100.77	78.99	99.03	90.61	95.77
Irrigation and Drainage Cost	45.12	43.30	41.75	50.94	26.64	35.73
Of which: Water Cost	11.86	1.07	7.96	3.46	5.14	2.33
Storage Cost	1.94		3.84		5.40	
7. Fuel Power Cost	24.81		16.85	14.82	21.44	
8. Technical Service Cost	16.34	2.23	15.81	3.29	33.20	2.54
9. Tool Material Cost	100.14	215.69	121.93	116.43	39.58	93.93
10. Maintenance and Repair Cost	5.26	26.68	8.33	12.65	7.24	19.18
(2) Indirect Costs	**93.41**	**661.64**	**101.81**	**464.32**	**138.98**	**616.93**
1. Depreciation of Fixed Assets	14.90	350.59	18.12	385.05	21.64	292.28
2. Insurance Cost		54.98	0.28	37.77	0.39	51.07
3. Management Cost	3.24	25.01	9.24	41.50	20.46	24.68
4. Financial Cost	2.71		5.43		15.24	
5. Sales Cost	72.56	231.06	68.74		81.25	248.90

(*continued*)

Table 2. Continued

Item	Tomatoes Open Field	Greenhouses	Cucumbers Open Field	Greenhouses	Eggplants Open Field	Greenhouses
2. Labor Costs per mu	**2,360.42**	**5,220.68**	**2,672.80**	**3,213.11**	**1,744.08**	**3,351.85**
1. Family Employment Discounts	1,653.32	4,607.83	1,725.47	1,912.23	1,081.16	2,538.30
Family Employment Days	19.48	54.28	20.33	22.53	12.74	29.90
Labor Day Price	84.89	84.89	84.89	84.89	84.89	84.89
2. Employment Cost	707.10	612.85	947.33	1300.88	662.92	813.56
Employment Days	5.83	7.97	7.65	14.70	5.31	11.48
Labor Price	121.29	76.90	123.83	88.50	124.84	70.87
3. Total Costs per mu	**3,595.35**	**8,140.62**	**4,094.43**	**5,184.19**	**3,622.65**	**5,822.42**
4. Proportion of Direct Costs	31.75%	27.74%	32.23%	29.06%	48.02%	31.84%
5. Proportion of Indirect Costs	2.60%	8.13%	2.49%	8.96%	3.84%	10.60%
6. Proportion of Labor Costs	65.65%	64.13%	65.28%	61.98%	48.14%	57.57%

Note: The material is from *Document Assembly of the Cost Benefits of the Agricultural Products in China*, of which the planting areas of tomatoes, cucumbers, and eggplants in Jiangsu Province are relatively small, and the statistical data are incomplete, so the national average data are taken to be compared.

5.2 Analysis of the direct costs per mu of the tomatoes, cucumbers, and eggplants planted in facilities in Jiangsu Province

The ratio of the seed cost, the chemical fertilizer and farmyard manure cost, the pesticide cost, the agricultural film cost, the rental operation cost, the technical service cost, the tool material cost, the maintenance and repair cost, and other direct costs of tomatoes, cucumbers, and eggplants in open field planting and those in greenhouse planting in Jiangsu Province to the total production costs are calculated respectively, and the corresponding strip diagram is drawn as shown in Figure 3:

5.2.1 Seed cost

The seed cost of the tomatoes, cucumbers, and eggplants planted in open fields and greenhouses accounts for a relatively low proportion of the total production costs, fluctuating between 3.96% and 5.72%. The direct seeding of seeds is mostly used in open-field planting, while the plantation of seedlings in trays is mostly used in greenhouse planting. Relatively speaking, the seed cost per mu of the greenhouse planting is higher than that of the open field planting. The maximum difference value of eggplants is 189.46 yuan, and the minimum difference value of cucumbers is 12.23 yuan. The main reasons for the cost difference are that the price of the special seedling varieties for greenhouses is higher than that of the general seedling varieties for open fields and the amount of plug seedlings per unit area is higher than that of conventional seedling methods, and so on.

5.2.2 Chemical fertilizer, farmyard manure, and other fertilizer cost

The fertilizer costs of the greenhouse planting fertilizer and the farmyard manure account for 7.94%–9.41% of the total production costs. The fertilizer cost of tomato planting in open fields accounts for 12.68% of the total production cost, that of cucumber planting 14.33%, and that of eggplant planting 31.74%. As shown in Figure 3, the fertilizer and farmyard manure cost of eggplants is extremely high. Since the cost of the open-field farm manure is obtained from the national average data, the reason for the high cost is that the cost of the farm manure in Fujian Province is 1,406.31 yuan, which greatly increases the national

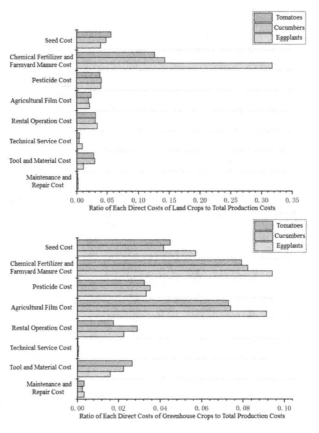

Figure 3. Ratio of the direct costs of open field planting and greenhouse planting to total production costs.

average level. After excluding the specific value, the cost of the open-field eggplant fertilizer accounts for 10.29% of the total production costs. In a general view of the categories, the proportion of the greenhouse fertilizer cost is slightly lower than that of the open field fertilizer cost. The fertilizer cost of both plantings accounts for about 10% of the total production costs, and the proportion is relatively large, which partly reflects that in the current agricultural production, the extensive production and management mode leads to excessive fertilization.

5.2.3 *Pesticide cost and agricultural film cost*
The pesticide cost of the tomatoes, cucumbers, and eggplants planted in open fields and greenhouses accounts for 3.24%–4.08% of the total costs, with little difference. The film cost of planting in open fields accounts for 1.93%–2.37% of the total costs, while the proportion of the film cost in the greenhouse planting is 7.30%–9.13%. The proportion and value of the film cost in the greenhouse planting are significantly higher than those in the open field planting. The main reason is that there is a large amount of agricultural film loss in greenhouses every year, while open field planting only replaces plastic films with less loss.

5.2.4 *Rental operation cost*
The rental operation costs mainly include the mechanical operation cost, the irrigation and drainage cost, and the storage cost (the discount of the farming livestock operation). The

rental operation cost of the tomatoes, cucumbers, and eggplants planted in open fields accounts for 3.04%–3.39% of the total costs, while the rental operation cost of the greenhouse planting accounts for 1.77%–2.89%, which is slightly lower than the former. The main reasons are that, on the one hand, the supply of small machinery suitable for greenhouse production is insufficient for supply, and on the other hand, the difficulties of land transfer lead to the decentralized operation of individual farmers, and the large-scale mechanical operation barriers and the overly high costs. The low proportion of the rental operation cost intuitively reflects the low mechanization level of the greenhouse industry in Jiangsu Province.

5.2.5 *Technical service cost*
The technical service cost mainly includes technical training, consultation, and guidance in the production process. The technical service costs of the open field planting and the greenhouse planting account for a very small proportion of the total production cost, both less than 1%. The low technical service cost intuitively reflects the overall low scientific and technological contents of the greenhouse industry in our province, the disjunction of the front-end agricultural scientific research and the back-end planting and production operation, the poor application effects, and the lack of technical guidance for relevant personnel.

5.2.6 *Tool and material cost*
The tool and material cost mainly includes the cost of the agricultural tools and trays needed in the planting process. The cost of tools and materials for the tomatoes and cucumbers cultivated in open fields and greenhouses accounts for 2.25%–2.98% of the total production costs. In contrast, the tool material cost of eggplants ranges from 1.09% to 1.61%. The difference of cost mainly comes from the different number of agricultural tools and trays needed to produce different crops.

5.2.7 *Maintenance and repair cost*
The maintenance and repair cost mainly includes the repair cost of fixed facilities such as greenhouses and mechanical equipment. The maintenance cost of greenhouse planting is higher than that of the open field, mainly because of the maintenance of greenhouses. At the same time, the maintenance and repair cost of the tomatoes, cucumbers, and eggplants planted in greenhouses accounts for 0.24%–0.33% of the total production costs. The reason for the extremely small proportion is that the cost of the greenhouse itself is low, and there is no relevant high-end equipment. In addition, daily maintenance is mostly to replace the skeletons and support materials of the greenhouses, which cannot produce high costs.

5.3 *Analysis of the indirect costs per mu of the tomatoes, cucumbers, and eggplants planted in facilities in Jiangsu Province*

The ratio of the depreciation of fixed assets, the insurance cost, the sales cost, and other indirect costs of tomatoes, cucumbers, and eggplants in open field planting and those in greenhouse planting in Jiangsu Province to the total production costs are calculated respectively, and the corresponding strip diagram is drawn in Figure 4:

5.3.1 *Depreciation of fixed assets*
The depreciation cost of fixed assets for the tomatoes, cucumbers, and eggplants planted in open fields mainly includes the depreciation of the tools and machinery used for more than one year in production, which accounts for a very low proportion of the production costs per mu, being less than 1%. The depreciation of the fixed assets of the greenhouse planting is mainly the depreciation of the greenhouse facilities, with a large proportion of costs. According to the annual depreciation rate of 8%, the depreciation cost of planting tomatoes, cucumbers, and eggplants accounts for 4.31%–7.43% of the total production costs per mu.

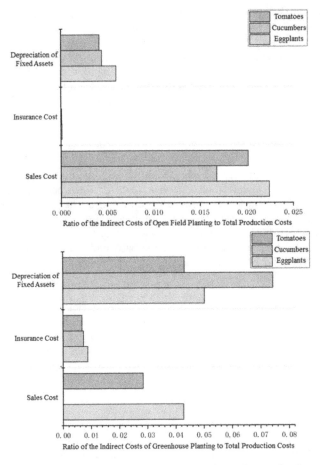

Figure 4. Ratio of the indirect costs of open field planting and greenhouse planting to total production costs.

From the depreciation cost of fixed assets, it can be calculated that the cost of the greenhouse used to grow tomatoes, cucumbers, and eggplants are within the range of 3,000 and 5,000 yuan, indicating that the greenhouse facilities in Jiangsu Province are mainly greenhouses of simple structures.

5.3.2 *Insurance cost*

The insurance cost per mu of the tomatoes, cucumbers, and eggplants planted in open fields can almost be ignored. According to production habits, farmers rarely cover insurance for their cultivated crops in their fields, and insurance companies rarely have suitable insurance for them. However, the insurance of greenhouse crops is an industry consensus, for greenhouse production tends to be greatly affected by extreme weather. Once affected, crops would be damaged, and the greenhouse facilities invested in the early stage would be destroyed. Therefore, the greenhouse planting of tomatoes, cucumbers, and eggplants will generate about 30–50 insurance costs per mu. Expenditure on the insurance cost reflects that the level of greenhouse facilities in this province is generally low, the performance of load strength and insulation capacity is weak, and it is greatly affected by extreme weather such as cold damage and frost damage.

5.3.3 Sales cost

The sale costs are mainly composed of the packaging, handling, transportation, traveling, and advertising costs generated in selling agricultural products. The sales cost per mu of the tomatoes, cucumbers, and eggplants planted in the open fields accounts for 1.68%–2.24% of the total production costs. In addition to the lack of sales of facilities cucumbers in Jiangsu Province, the sales of facilities tomatoes account for 2.84%, and the sales of facilities eggplants account for 4.25%, all of which are higher than open field planting. The main reason is that the greenhouse off-season marketing costs are higher.

5.4 Analysis of the labor costs per mu of the tomatoes, cucumbers, and eggplants planted in facilities in Jiangsu Province

The ratio of the depreciation of the family employment discounts, the employment cost, and other labor costs of tomatoes, cucumbers, and eggplants in open field planting and those in greenhouse planting in Jiangsu Province to the total production cost is calculated respectively, and the corresponding strip diagram is drawn in Figure 5:

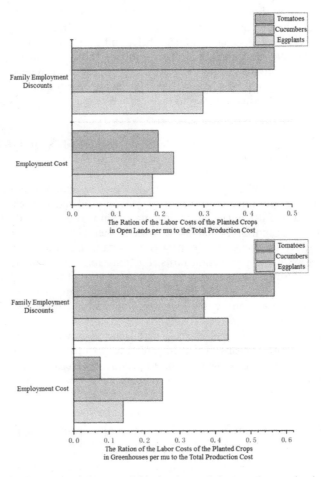

Figure 5. Ratio of labor costs of the open field planting and the greenhouse planting to total production cost.

5.4.1 Family employment discounts

As shown in Figure 5, the family employment discounts for the tomatoes, cucumbers, and eggplants planted in open fields and greenhouses account for a very large proportion of the production costs, of which the highest proportion of the production costs of greenhouse tomatoes is 56.6%, and the lowest proportion of the production costs of open field eggplants is 29.84%. In the case of the equal daily labor price, the family employment discounts are mainly linearly related to the number of days of family employment, and the number of days of family employment depends on the production law and density of the planted crops. The number of family labor days for greenhouse planting in Jiangsu Province is significantly higher than that of open field planting, which is mainly due to the higher planting density per unit area of the greenhouse planting than that of the open field, increasing labor days. At the same time, the household labor discount cost of greenhouse production is high, which directly reflects the current situation of greenhouse production, that is the new agricultural business entities and agricultural production enterprises are few, the land transfer is difficult, and the production and operation are mainly performed by individual farmers.

5.4.2 Employment cost

The labor costs are affected by the labor price and the number of employment days. The market determines the labor price, and the labor price of open-field planting is significantly higher than that of greenhouse planting. The number of employment days is related to the amount of work, excluding family employment. It can be seen from Table 2 that the number of employment days for the tomatoes, cucumbers, and eggplant planted in greenhouses is significantly greater than that planted in the open field. The employment days of tomatoes, cucumbers, and eggplants in greenhouses are long, which hence reflects the low level of mechanization and low production efficiency of the greenhouse industry as a whole, and the manual operation of individual household farmers and employees is the main one.

6 ANALYSIS OF THE PER MU PRODUCTION BENEFITS OF GREENHOUSES IN JIANGSU PROVINCE

In the accounting system of the production efficiency of agricultural products, the benefits obtained by planting agricultural products are generally reflected by economic indicators such as the output value per mu, the cash income per mu, and the retained profits per mu. The output value is the sum of the income that the farmer earns by selling the products and the income that the farmer may receive through the retained products. It does not take into account any factors of the production costs, but only reflects the actual total income of farmers by growing crops. Cash income refers to the balance of the output value of the crop products subtracting all the cash and physical expenses that are generated during the crop planting cycle. It does not subtract the family employment discounts in labor costs and the self-employment land rent in land costs, and it is the balance of the output value of a kind of crop product subtracting the incomplete cost within the crop cycle, which reflects the actual income of farmers' planting crops. Retained profits refer to the balance of the output value of the crop products subtracting the costs of all production factors such as cash, materials, labor, and land that are invested within the crop planting cycle, which reflects the net return of all the resources consumed in the crop planting cycle (Jie 2019).

6.1 Analysis of the output value per mu of the tomatoes, cucumbers, and eggplants in facilities in Jiangsu Province

As shown in Table 3, the average yields per mu of the tomatoes, cucumbers, and eggplants planted in greenhouses in Jiangsu Province are 4,192.95 kg, 5,310.05 kg, and 3,331.78 kg, respectively. The average yields per mu of the tomatoes, cucumbers, and eggplants planted

Table 3. Output value table of tomatoes, cucumbers, and eggplants per mu.

Items	Tomatoes Open Fields	Tomatoes Greenhouses	Cucumbers Open Fields	Cucumbers Greenhouses	Eggplants Open Fields	Eggplants Greenhouses
Yield per mu(kg)	3,288.20	4,192.95	3,182.44	5,310.05	2,733.08	3,331.78
Unit price (Yuan)	2.2476	3.2658	2.0468	2.0764	1.9554	3.1686
Output Value per mu (Yuan)	7,390.29	13,693.51	6,514.09	11,026.25	5,344.31	10,556.95

in open fields in China are 3,288.20 kg, 3,182.44 kg, and 2,733.08 kg, respectively. From the perspective of yield, planting vegetables in greenhouses can effectively improve the yield of crops per unit area. The highest yield of cucumbers in greenhouses is 167% of the open field, while the lowest yield of eggplants in greenhouses is 122%.

In terms of product prices, greenhouse cucumbers and open-field cucumbers have little difference in their supply-side sales unit prices, but greenhouse tomatoes and greenhouse eggplants are significantly higher than open-field tomatoes and open-field eggplants in sales prices. This indirectly proves that greenhouse crop products not only have better quality but also can sell for a good price.

After a careful consideration of the product output and the sales unit price, the average output values per mu of greenhouse tomatoes, cucumbers and eggplants are CNY 13,693.51, CNY 11,026.25, and CNY 10,556.95, and those of open field tomatoes, cucumbers, and eggplants are CNY 7,390.29, CNY 6,514.09 and CNY 5,344.31. The average output value per mu of greenhouse crops is significantly higher than that of open-field planting. The average output value per mu of greenhouse tomatoes is 185% of that of the open field planting, the average output value per mu of greenhouse cucumbers is 169% of that of the open field planting, and the average output value per mu of greenhouse eggplants is 198% of that of the open field planting.

6.2 Analysis of the cash income per mu of the tomatoes, cucumbers, and eggplants in facilities in Jiangsu Province

The cash income per mu mainly depends on the output value per mu and the cash cost per mu. As shown in Table 4, the cash costs per mu of tomatoes, cucumbers, and eggplants in greenhouses are CNY 3,806.91, CNY 3,716.79, and CNY 3,589.56, respectively. The average cash incomes per mu are CNY 9,886.60, CNY 7,309.46, and CNY 6,967.39, respectively. The cash costs per mu for tomatoes, cucumbers, and eggplants are CNY 1,973.71,

Table 4. Cash income statement for tomatoes, cucumbers, and eggplants per mu.

Items	Tomatoes Open Fields	Tomatoes Greenhouses	Cucumbers Open Fields	Cucumbers Greenhouses	Eggplants Open Fields	Eggplants Greenhouses
Yield per mu (Yuan)	7,390.29	13,693.51	6,514.09	11,026.25	5,344.31	10,556.95
Cash Cost per mu (Yuan)	1,973.71	3,806.91	2,402.03	3,716.79	2,570.20	3,589.56
Cash Income per mu (Yuan)	5,416.58	9,886.60	4,112.06	7,309.46	2,774.11	6,967.39

CNY 2,402.03, and CNY 2,570.20, respectively. The average cash incomes per mu are CNY 5,416.58, CNY 4,112.06, and CNY 2,774.11, respectively. The cash income per unit area of the greenhouse planting is significantly higher than that of the open field planting. The cash income of greenhouse eggplants is 251% of that of open-field eggplants, the cash income of greenhouse tomatoes is 183% of that of open-field tomatoes, and the cash income of greenhouse cucumbers is 178% of that of open-field cucumbers.

6.3 Analysis of the retained profits per mu of the tomatoes, cucumbers, and eggplants in facilities in Jiangsu Province

The retained profits per mu mainly depend on the total output value and the total costs per mu, of which the total costs per mu include the production cost and the land costs, and the land costs include the transfer land rent and the self-employment land rent. As shown in Table 5, the total costs per mu of tomatoes, cucumbers, and eggplants in greenhouses are CNY 8,552.60, CNY 5,698.78, and CNY 6,247.65, and the retained profits per mu are CNY 5,140.91, CNY 5,327.47 and CNY 4,309.30. The total costs per mu of tomatoes, cucumbers, and eggplants are CNY 3,797.36, CNY 4,373.28, and CNY 3,876.68, and the obtained profits per mu are CNY 3,592.93, CNY 2,140.81, and CNY 1,467.63. The retained profits per unit area of the greenhouse planting are significantly higher than that of the open field planting. The retained profits of greenhouse eggplants are 294% of those of open-field eggplants, the retained profits of greenhouse cucumbers are 249% of those of open-field cucumbers, and the retained profits of greenhouse tomatoes are 143% of those of open-field tomatoes.

Table 5. Retained profits statement of tomatoes, cucumbers, and eggplants per mu.

Item	Tomatoes Open Fields	Tomatoes Greenhouses	Cucumbers Open Fields	Cucumbers Greenhouses	Eggplants Open Fields	Eggplants Greenhouses
Yield per mu (Yuan)	7,390.29	13,693.51	6,514.09	11,026.25	5,344.31	10,556.95
Total Cost per mu (Yuan)	3,797.36	8,552.60	4,373.28	5,698.78	3,876.68	6,247.65
Production Cost	3,595.35	8,140.62	4,094.43	5,184.19	3,622.65	5,822.42
Land Cost	202.01	411.98	278.85	514.59	254.03	425.23
Retained Profits per mu (Yuan)	3,592.93	5,140.91	2,140.81	5,327.47	1,467.63	4,309.30

Note: In calculating the retained profits per mu, the tax rate is not considered, and the agricultural producers are exempted from tax according to the national regulations.

7 THE ANALYSIS CONCLUSION OF THE PRODUCTION COSTS AND BENEFITS OF GREENHOUSES IN JIANGSU PROVINCE

7.1 Low-cost greenhouses dominate

Although the total scale of greenhouses in Jiangsu Province is huge, greenhouses of a simple structure (bamboo and mixed structure, etc.) with a relatively low cost occupy an absolute dominant position. Through the field investigation of Nanjing Geguan Industrial Park, it is found that according to different crops, farmers' investment in greenhouse facilities per mu fluctuates between 3,000 and 4,000 yuan. At the same time, according to the 8% depreciation of fixed assets in the document assembly of the cost-benefit of national agricultural products, the average cost of eggplant greenhouses in Jiangsu Province is about CNY 3,600, the average cost of tomato greenhouses is about CNY 4,300, and the average cost of cucumber greenhouses is about CNY 4,800. From many angles, the conclusion can be confirmed that greenhouses of a relatively lower cost are dominant.

7.2 *Labor costs remain the main costs of the greenhouse production*

As can be seen from Table 2 and Figure 5 above, the labor costs (family employment discounts + the employment cost) of the tomatoes, cucumbers, and eggplants planted in greenhouses in Jiangsu Province account for about 60% of the total production cost, which is the largest expenditure of the greenhouse production. The family employment discounts account for more than 60% of the labor costs, indicating that the current production and management of greenhouses in Jiangsu Province are mostly based on families as the main bodies, and the labor costs are mainly the labor discounts of farmers' crops.

7.3 *Greenhouse planting can effectively improve crop yield and quality*

As shown in Table 3, the yield per mu of the tomatoes, cucumbers, and eggplants planted in greenhouses in Jiangsu Province is significantly higher than that planted in open fields, which proves that greenhouse planting can effectively increase yield. At the same time, the price of greenhouse vegetable products per kilogram is higher, indirectly indicating that the quality of the agricultural products planted in greenhouses is better. When the yield and the quality are significantly improved, greenhouse planting crops can greatly improve the output value per mu.

7.4 *Higher benefits per mu of greenhouse products*

From the indexes in Tables 4 and 5, it can be seen that the output value per mu, the cash income per mu, and the retained profits per mu of the tomatoes, cucumbers, and eggplants planted in greenhouses in Jiangsu Province are higher than those planted in open fields. Although the production costs and the cash costs of open-field planting products are lower than those of greenhouse planting, the latter has a higher yield per mu and output value per mu, which can hence improve the benefit per mu of planting crops. Among them, compared with those of the open field, the cash incomes and the retained profits per mu of greenhouse eggplants increase to the greatest level.

8 MAIN PROBLEMS IN THE DEVELOPMENT OF THE GREENHOUSE INDUSTRY IN JIANGSU PROVINCE

8.1 *Investment in greenhouse facilities is much lower than that in developed countries and the level of facilities is low*

Based on the statistical data and field investigation of all aspects, the greenhouse facilities in Jiangsu Province are mainly made of bamboo-wood structures, mixed structures, and steel frame structures of a low cost, and the average fixed asset investment is less than 7.5 yuan/m^2. The Israeli modern intelligent-control greenhouses need an investment of 500 yuan/m^2 (Zeng 2017), and the polycarbonate rigid plastic sheets covering the U.S. facility greenhouses need an investment of 190 yuan/m^2 (Sun 2019). In contrast, the investment in greenhouse facilities in Jiangsu Province is much lower than that in developed countries. Corresponding to low inputs, the load intensity of the greenhouse structure is low, the environmental regulation ability is weak, and the thermal insulation performance is poor, resulting in relatively frequent cold damages and freezing damages in the process of crop planting and production and the huge non-productive risks. Most greenhouses of simple structures lack the necessary environmental control equipment, and their facility level is low. They cannot regulate the temperature, humidity, light, O_2, and CO_2 concentrations in the greenhouse. The labor productivity is low while the intensity is high, and the crops are always in a sub-health state for a long time.

8.2 The level of mechanization is low, and the greenhouse production operations mainly rely on human inputs

At present, the mechanization level of greenhouse planting in Jiangsu Province has been far lower than that of field planting. According to the field investigation on the planting situation of farmers in Nanjing Geguan Ecological Park, there is little mechanized equipment used in production. As to the greenhouse supporting machinery and equipment, there are only small pumps and a drip irrigation pipeline system, while other production mainly relies on human inputs. There are two main reasons for the low mechanization level of greenhouse production in Jiangsu Province. First, the low level of facilities and the small planting scale are not conducive to production under mechanization. Since the greenhouses of bamboo-wood structures, hybrid structures, and steel frame structures need a large number of pillars in their spans, the narrow distance between columns makes it difficult to apply a large number of agricultural machinery. At the same time, due to the difficulties in land transfer between farmers and enterprises, the production and operation of greenhouses are mostly based on families, resulting in scattered fields and the high costs of large-scale mechanical operations. (Shu 2018) Second, the crops are vast in varieties, and the supply of small machinery special for greenhouse production is insufficient. Compared with bulk food crops, the planting period of fruits and vegetables is shorter while the stubble is more, and the cultivation laws of various crops differ. The complex production and management process leads to the blankness of small-scale operating machines in the links of planting, tillage management and harvesting, and so on.

8.3 The industry as a whole has low technological content, weak basic research, and poor application effects

Because the greenhouse facilities in Jiangsu Province are mainly greenhouses of simple structures and low cost, there is a huge gap between Jiangsu Province and the developed countries with advanced agriculture in terms of environmental control technology, Internet and Internet of Things technology, and cultivation and management technology. The overall scientific and technological contents of the greenhouse industry are low, the scale of high-level modern intelligent glass greenhouses is small, and the popularization rate of advanced technologies such as soilless cultivation and digital agriculture is low. Upstream agricultural seed enterprises lack specific greenhouse fruit and vegetable varieties with independent intellectual property rights. The breeding level of high yield, high quality, pest resistance, and other compound resistance is far lower than those of agriculturally developed countries. The quality of domestic greenhouse fruit and vegetable seeds is poor, resulting in a low penetration rate and market share. The application scale and area of the soilless cultivation technology are small, accounting for a very small proportion of greenhouse crop cultivation in the province. The related researches in physiological and biochemical aspects and the growth of crops in greenhouses are not deep and systematic enough, and the research on environmental impact factors lacks relevant quantitative indicators. The weak basic research leads to the lack of scientific theoretical basis in the process of crop planting, and the extensive production causes a huge waste of water and fertilizer resources. Most of the relevant production technologies of greenhouse crops are of the nature of scattered experience, while there are few systematic operating technical specifications, and there are only poor application effects.

8.4 Soil salinization, continuous cropping obstacles and pests, and diseases restrict the development of the greenhouse industry

The phenomenon of the dependence of greenhouse planting on heavy water and fertilizer in Jiangsu Province is common, but the corresponding resource utilization rate is only about 10%–20%, while the phenomenon of excessively using pesticides and fertilizers blindly is very serious. In some main production areas of protected horticulture, a large number of inorganic fertilizers such as urea and ammonium nitrate are used in greenhouses, resulting in soil hardening. Artificial watering is given priority, and less rain leaching causes the secondary salinization of the soil, and the decline of the product quality. Due to the relatively single-crop species planted in greenhouses, the repeated cropping of vegetables and eggplants in actual production is serious. In addition, the extensive use of pesticides and the limited level of soil management technology have led to the change in soil microbial population, the proliferation of pathogens, and the increase of continuous cropping obstacles year by year, which have become a major bottleneck for the sustainable and efficient utilization of facility soil. The soil salinization and the continuous cropping obstacles lead to the phenomena that the salt contents of the cultivated lands are more than ten times higher than that of open fields for vegetables, that the pH value decreases to be acidic, and the lack of soil trace elements, such as calcium, magnesium, boron, and molybdenum, causes more and more serious crop diseases and insect pests. It is estimated that there are more than 100 diseases and insect pests of facility crops in the province all year round, leading to nutrient imbalance and inhibiting plant growth. The poor growth and development of crops and the serious insect pests and diseases lead to the excessive use of fertilizers and pesticides by farmers, forming a vicious cycle that seriously restricts the healthy development of the greenhouse industry.

8.5 Production and management are performed by individual farmers, the cultural quality is relatively low, and inflows of talents lack

At present, the production and management of greenhouses in Jiangsu Province have still been dominated by small-scale farmers, and there have been few new agricultural operators such as family farms, farmers' professional cooperatives, and production enterprises. The phenomenon of small-scale decentralized operation of an individual household is very common, and it is difficult to combine various production factors and connect with the market effectively. The levels of intensification, industrialization, and organizational scale of the agricultural production are low, the employees are senior in age with low cultural quality, and the proportion of employees with educational backgrounds below junior high school accounts for 83.95%, all of which result in low labor efficiency. The existing agricultural cooperatives are small in scale, weak in strength, and limited at the technical level. The objectives of unified agricultural procurement, unified seedling cultivation, unified pest control, unified product grading, and unified brand sales are far from being achieved. At the same time, greenhouse enterprises are mostly distributed in rural areas far from the city center, and poor living, medical and transportation conditions, high work intensity, and low-profit rate of the industry feature these areas. It is difficult for operators to pay relatively higher wages, and they are in an unfavorable situation in their competition with talents in other popular industries, resulting in the lack of inflowing agricultural talent. According to the actual investigation, it is found that most of the modern multiple greenhouses are developed and designed based on computers and the environmental control technology of the Internet of Things, which has high requirements for agricultural professional knowledge and the operation of the computer system by enterprise employees. As shown in Figure 6, the Venlo glass greenhouse projects of Nanjing Xitian Ecological Park and Pukou Geguan Ecological Park, which have been built for several years, have not been put into production and are only used for tourism. The lack of high-end compound agriculture-related talents

Figure 6. Real view of modern glass numerical control greenhouse in Nanjing geguan ecological park.

has caused the dilemma of the completed construction and the difficulty in putting them into the production of the modern numerical control greenhouses, and the talent gap has seriously restricted the development of the greenhouse industry in Jiangsu Province.

8.6 *Land transfer is difficult, facility subsidies are low in proportion and narrow in scope, and technical guidance is inadequate*

The large-scale contiguous greenhouse facilities are conducive to the mechanized operations of production and can reduce the cost of greenhouses per mu and improve the production and utilization capacity of greenhouses. The success or failure of land transfer directly determines the degree of scale aggregation of the greenhouse industry. At present, land transfer in Jiangsu Province is performed mostly between farmers, and only a small part of the transfer is to cooperatives and enterprises. In the actual implementation process, the "land-treasuring" complex of the farmers is serious, making it quite difficult the performance of the transfer work. According to the Subsidy List of Agricultural Machinery Purchased in Jiangsu Province in 2020, issued by the Jiangsu Provincial Department of Rural Affairs, the subsidies of the greenhouse facilities listed in the table only include hot stoves and sterilization equipment for edible fungi. The proportion of subsidies for greenhouse facilities and equipment is very low and the scope is narrow. At the same time, the connection among agricultural research institutions, agricultural education institutions, and agricultural extension institutions in the province is not in place. More than 60% of farmers indicate that agricultural technicians have not come in one year, 80% of farmers learn planting and pest control technology from sales personnel of seeds and pesticides, and the technical guidance of government agencies for farmers is not in place.

9 SUGGESTIONS ON THE DEVELOPMENT OF THE GREENHOUSE INDUSTRY IN JIANGSU PROVINCE

9.1 *Increasing investment in greenhouse facilities and gradually completing the upgrading of greenhouses*

The purpose of developing the greenhouse industry is to improve agricultural production efficiency and resource utilization and promote the upgrading and transformation of the agricultural industry. Based on the actual situation of the greenhouses of simple structures in

Jiangsu Province, there is still a long distance from the target. Currently, the level of greenhouse facilities in the province is generally low, with the greenhouses of bamboo-wood structures, mixed structures, and steel frame structures as the main ones. Daily production mainly depends on human inputs, and there is still much room for production efficiency to be improved. In foreign countries with developed greenhouse industries, the precise and automatic control of environmental factors such as light, water, fertilizer, air, and temperature in greenhouses can be realized through mechanization, automation, and intelligent technologies. It can not only greatly improve production efficiency and crop yield, but also significantly improve the appearance of agricultural products and maintain the uniformity of output crops. Therefore, by drawing on the experience of the developed countries, the greenhouse industry in Jiangsu Province will also catch up with that of foreign countries in the future. It is necessary to gradually increase the investment in greenhouse facilities, improve the level of facilities in greenhouses, especially the environmental control systems and so on, and gradually complete the transition from simple-structure greenhouses to modern intelligent greenhouses.

9.2 *Promoting the standardized development of the greenhouse industry and improving the mechanization level*

Although Jiangsu Province has made some progress in the research, construction, and application of greenhouses, the relevant industrial standards have not been widely used in greenhouse design, construction and mechanical research and development, and so on. The construction standards of greenhouses advocated by local governments are quite different, and the mechanical research and development standards of different manufacturers of agricultural equipment are not unified, which hinders the development of the greenhouse industry to some extent. To change the current situation, the first thing is to implement unified standards for greenhouse facilities and mechanical research and development, standardize the construction of greenhouses and further improve the applicability of mechanical equipment. Given the production laws of different types of fruits and vegetables, the mechanical research and development and application should be strengthened from the sowing of cultivated lands, the irrigation and fertilization, and the pest control of the planting stage to the picking and grading of mature products, the packaging and transportation, and other links. In particular, the research and development and promotion of small-scale tillage machines, precision seeders, and automatic water-and-fertilizer integration systems should be strengthened, replace the large labor consumption in the production and planting process and effectively improve the mechanization level of the greenhouse industry in the province.

9.3 *Increasing investment in science and technology and focusing on basic research and the application of results*

The modern greenhouse industry is a new high-tech industry that integrates agricultural biotechnology, mechanical automation technology, and Internet of Things technology. To improve the overall level of the greenhouse industry, it is necessary to increase investment in science and technology, enhance innovation capability, and pay attention to basic research and the application of achievements. In the level of facilities, the transfer to modern greenhouses should be gradually practiced. In mechanical research, unified standards and development according to local conditions should be performed with precise targets. In biotechnology, the collection, research, breeding, rejuvenation, and purification of new varieties suitable for horticultural planting in the Jiangsu area should be focused on. In basic research, the quantitative indicators of environmental impact factors should be formulated to understand the internal mechanism affecting crop growth. In the application of the results, the trinity of production, learning, and research should be performed, and the popularization and application of new science and technology, new research, and new achievements should be paid attention to. The state and governments at all levels should ensure cash investment in the scientific research of the greenhouse industry, the breeding test of new varieties, the research and development of soilless cultivation technology, and other projects. Funds for core links, such as the basic research of crops and the development of greenhouse environmental control equipment, should be given priority to avoid the obstruction of the greenhouse industry development due to insufficient investment in science and technology and uneven capital distribution.

9.4 *Changing the production concept and establishing the long-term quality and safety control mechanism*

The excessive use of pesticides, caused by pests and diseases in greenhouse production, further leads to soil salinization. The unscientific planting of continuous cropping and the lack of soil management technology lead to increasing continuous cropping obstacles year by year. To fundamentally solve this problem, it is necessary to change the concept of production completely and to transform from the past extensive planting and treatment after the emergence of the disease to fine production and operation and prevention first. The concept of green agricultural development should be established, the mode of agricultural development should be changed, the agricultural pollution products should be controlled and dealt with, and the long-term control mechanism of quality and safety should be constructed. The reasonable selection of crop planting and socket arrangement in actual production should be performed. The types of pests and diseases that may occur should be analyzed by collecting the environmental parameters in the greenhouses for early prevention and control. Ecological cultivation techniques and highly efficient pesticides of low toxins should be promoted, and the use of fertilizers and pesticides should be strictly controlled. The comprehensive prevention and control mode combining biological control, ecological control, and physical control, should be carried out. Emphasis on soil improvement and management should be laid on, with the concept of sustainable development and timely restoration of the damaged lands. The whole process should attach great importance to the quality and safety of agricultural products, the emissions of pollutants should be controlled in the plant cultivation and production, and the standardized crop production and planting process should be practiced with the concept of being environmentally friendly and resource-saving, and the problems of pesticide, bacteria and heavy metal residues in agricultural products should be solved.

9.5 *Optimizing the mode of agricultural production and operation and cultivating new professional farmers and talent teams*

The development of the greenhouse industry must be based on the benefits of the scale. It is difficult for the traditional and decentralized individual management mode to adapt to the current market competition environment, and this mode is in a disadvantageous situation in procurement, planting, sales, and other aspects. The agricultural sector should rationally ordinate and plan, optimize the layout of the agricultural industry, comprehensively consider the regional environment and climate, agricultural resources and planting traditions, and other factors, focus on the development of the greenhouse horticultural planting by local conditions and maximize the benefits with industrial clusters. The decentralized management mode should be transformed into the centralized management one with the new agricultural management subjects and farmers' cooperative organizations as the core forces, and the cultural quality and professional knowledge training of agricultural practitioners should be strengthened to improve the organization degree of the greenhouse industry. It should be insisted to develop agriculture through science and education and strengthen agriculture through talent as the major strategy and core driving force to support the development of the greenhouse industry. According to the requirements of modern agricultural production and management, the demonstration base of greenhouse equipment, the training base of production management and system operation, and the incubation base of joint personnel training should be established to realize the re-education of individual farmers and to cultivate new professional farmers. At the same time, the government should allocate certain funds to subsidize agricultural practitioners, and form a wage payment model of "business entities + government subsidies," which fundamentally solves the low-income situation of agricultural practitioners, attracts talent inflows, and enables college students to come in, stay here and work for a long time.

9.6 *Strengthening the macro-oriented role of the government and increasing support for preferential agricultural policies*

The development of the greenhouse industry is a long-term process which requires state investment and social participation, while policy support is the guarantee for the healthy development of the industry. Governments at all levels in Jiangsu Province should systematically plan and guide the direction of industrial development based on the actual situation of the region and introduce strong laws and regulations, and policies to guide the macro industry based on the market and centering around the benefits. The orderly transfer of the rights of land contractual management can be realized through subsidizing the transfer price, providing jobs, and implementing pension insurance and other measures. The regional capital, technology, and talent resources should be effectively integrated, the early warning mechanism of the demand and supply of agricultural products should be improved, the blindness of industrial development and the information gap should be reduced, and the policy atmosphere and conditions for the formation of industrial clusters should be created. The series of central government's agricultural policies to strengthen agriculture and benefit farmers should be implemented, the scope and proportion of subsidies for greenhouse construction and machinery purchase should be expanded, and the guidance and effectiveness of subsidies and support should be increased. Financial investment should be increased. Financial capital and social capital should be guided and leveraged to flow in, and the enthusiasm of different levels and different market players should be fully mobilized to participate in the greenhouse industry. The production and management information files for difficult households should be established, researchers should be encouraged to lead projects and technologies into the production line of greenhouses, and the technical guidance for production and management of difficult households should be strengthened.

10 CONCLUSIONS

In this study, the data on greenhouse area distribution in Jiangsu Province were collected from government websites, industry associations, statistical yearbooks, and CNKI papers. Through field research and literature analysis, this paper expounds on the development status of the greenhouse industry in Jiangsu Province and summarizes the facility distribution, scale development, and industrial characteristics. From a practical point of view, focusing on the plastic greenhouse, which is the most widely used in the production process, three common and representative vegetables, tomato, cucumber, and eggplant, are selected to analyze the total cost, direct cost, indirect cost, labor cost, average output value per mu, cash income and net profit in the production process, Then the valuable economic benefit analysis conclusion is obtained.

Finally, based on the development experience of foreign countries, combined with the actual situation of the development of the greenhouse industry in Jiangsu Province, the author puts forward the main problems existing in the development of the greenhouse industry in Jiangsu Province and puts forward relevant suggestions. Due to the limited data, the author failed to conduct more detailed research and Analysis on the planting situation and area distribution of greenhouse crops in Jiangsu Province but only gave a rough overview. For the proposed industrial development proposals, all sectors of society need to work together to achieve. In the future, it is expected that government departments and industry associations can establish a greenhouse industry database as soon as possible for social sharing to track the development status of the greenhouse industry in real-time and provide more scientific and effective decision-making for the development of the greenhouse industry.

ACKNOWLEDGMENTS

The study was supported by the Special Fund of Basic Scientific Research Operations of Central Universities of China (Grant No. KYZ201664), the Agricultural Machinery Foundation of Jiangsu Province (Grant No. GXZ2014003), and Key Laboratory of Modern Agricultural Equipment, the Ministry of Agriculture of China (Grant No. 201601002). The financial support is gratefully acknowledged. The authors thank the Associate Editor and anonymous reviewers for their helpful and insightful comments.

REFERENCES

Guo S.R., Sun J. and Shu S. An Analysis of the Development Overview, Characteristics and Trend of Foreign Protected Horticulture. *Journal of Nanjing Agricultural University*. 2012 Sep. 30; 32-1148/S; 43–52.

Jie R., Liu J.B. and Huang ZhY. *Study on the Income of Solanaceous Vegetables in Nanjing Under Different Cultivation Conditions. Rural Economy and Science-Technology*. 2019 Feb. 20; 42-1374/S; 55–58.

Li B.G., Huang C.L. and Chen L.C. Opportunities and Challenges of the Protected Horticulture Industry in Jiangxi province. *Northern Horticulture*. 2019 Jan. 15; 23-1247/S; 171–177.

Li W.L. *China Agricultural Machinery Industry Yearbook*. Beijing: China Machine Press; 2019.

Li W.L. *China Agricultural Machinery Industry Yearbook*. Beijing: China Machine Press; 2017.

Mu G.Y. *Jiangsu Almanac*. Nanjing: Jiangsu Yearbook Magazine; 2018.

Research Group on Development Strategy of Protected horticulture in Ministry of Agriculture. A Study on the Development Strategy of the Facility Horticulture Industry in China. *Contemporary Horticulture*. 2011 Apr. 25; 36-1287/S; 13–16.

Shu S., Kang Y.Y., Wang Y. Development Overview, Characteristics and Trends of the Facility Horticulture in the World. *China Vegetables*. 2018 Jul. 1; 11-2326/S; 1–13.

Sun J., Gao H.B., Tian J. Development Status and Trend of Facility Horticulture in China. *Journal of Nanjing Agricultural University*. 2019 Apr. 17; 32-1148/S; 594–604.

Zeng X.P., Chen Y.S., Gu L.T. Development Status and Suggestions for the Production Mechanization of Facility Vegetables in Jiangsu Province. *Journal of Changjiang Vegetables*. 2017 Mar. 8; 42-1172/S; 10–13.

Zhang Z.H., Chen Q.Y., Gao L.H. A Research of the Development Countermeasures of the Facility Vegetable Industry in China. *Vegetables*. 2010 May 15; 11-2328/S; 1–3 + 6.

Biomaterial equipment and metallurgical engineering

Analysis on mechanical properties of prefabricated pipe laying with fabricated machine-made sand concrete

Hua Mao, Fang Geng & Suna Bai
State Grid Tianjin Electric Power Company, Tianjin, China

Zhipeng Xiong*
Tianjin Electric Power Design Institute, Tianjin, China

Jipeng Tang, Xiangyang Fang, Tao Qin & Bingran Shao
State Grid Tianjin Electric Power Company, Tianjin, China

ABSTRACT: In order to explore the application of prefabricated pipe laying with machine-made sand concrete instead of cast-in-situ ordinary concrete as a fabricated structure in practical projects, it is necessary to conduct a mechanical analysis. The mechanical properties of machine-made sand concrete under different replacement rates (0%, 40%, 60%, 80%, and 100%) are analyzed, and the optimal replacement rate is selected for the preparation of prefabricated pipes of machine-made sand concrete. Test finite element numerical simulation analysis of the deflection and stress change of the prefabricated bent pipes made of machine-made sand. The prefabricated bent pipes made of machine-made sand can be used for temporary fabricated structures, and its finite element model is effective, which can effectively predict and calculate the subsequent complex working conditions.

1 INTRODUCTION

Green grid construction is the new mission of the power grid in the construction field under the new situation. In the construction link, how to achieve low carbon, low loss, low pollution, and low ecological disturbance design and construction is the focus of research in the construction design and construction field. As a substitute for natural sand, the development and application of machine-made sand in practical projects have effectively solved the problem of natural sand shortage. A large number of studies have shown that different replacement rates of machine-made sand will change various properties of concrete (Duan *et al.* 2022; Ke *et al.* 2019; Maisarah Ali *et al.* 2015), and the workability (Cortes *et al.* 2008) and mechanical properties (Chen *et al.* 2015) of machine-made sand concrete are better than natural sand concrete under certain conditions. For temporary cables, small-scale pipe laying is generally adopted. However, the on-site pouring construction method adopted by the traditional pipe-laying method makes it impossible to excavate and completely remove the cable pipe laying and other underground structures after the transition (José-Vicente Valdenebro 2019; Mander 1988; Wang *et al.* 2018), and achieve recycling. The resulting waste or scrap not only affects the environment but also causes investment waste (Bentz 2010; Goldston 2016).

---

*Corresponding Author: zhipeng.xiong@tepdi.cn

DOI: 10.1201/9781003433644-37

In this paper, machine-made sand with different replacement rates is used to replace natural sand to mix concrete, and its basic working performance and mechanical properties are studied. At the same time, prefabricated pipe-laying segments of machine-made sand concrete are prepared with the optimal replacement rate. Through the loading of the component, the deflection deformation and the development of steel strain are observed to understand the actual working performance of the entire component. According to the comparative analysis of the test results and theoretical calculation, verify and optimize the calculation parameters and methods, and optimize and improve the components. Suggestions are put forward for the construction of prefabricated cable duct laying with machine-made sand concrete to replace the traditional cast-in-place ordinary concrete duct laying in engineering practice.

2 RAW MATERIALS AND TEST METHODS

2.1 Raw materials

Cement: 42.5 ordinary Portland cement (P·O 42.5) produced by Tangshan Jidong Cement Co., Ltd. Coarse aggregate: 5–20mm continuously graded crushed stone, with an apparent density of 2731kg/m^3, bulk density of 1583kg/m^3, and mass ratio of 5–10mm and 10–20mm particles of 3:7. Fine aggregate: machine-made sand and natural sand (medium sand). See Table 1 for a comparison of various parameters of machine-made sand; The natural medium sand is continuously graded from 0 to 4.75mm, the apparent density is 2620kg/m^3, the bulk density is 1620kg/m^3, and the fineness modulus is 2.41. Water-reducing agent: JM-HPC3 high-efficiency retarding water-reducing agent, with a water reduction rate of 18%.

Table 1. Properties of manufactured sand.

Fineness modulus	Stone powder content/%	MB/ (g/kg)	Apparent density/(kg/m^3)	Bulk density/ (kg/m^3)	Light-matter content/%	Crushing index/%
3.01	6.7	1.2	2675	1690	0.1	21

2.2 Concrete mix proportion

According to the Specification for Mix Proportion Design of Ordinary Concrete (JGJ 55-2011), the concrete with C30 strength grade shall be prepared with machine-made sand at different replacement rates, and the concrete shall be grouped according to the replacement rates of 0%, 40%, 60%, 80%, and 100% (MR represents the replacement rates of machine-made sand, namely MR0, MR40, MR60, MR80, and MR100). See Table 2 for mixed proportions.

Table 2. Mix proportions of manufactured sand concrete (unit: kg/m^3).

Code	Cement	Sand Machine-made sand	River Sand	Stone	Water	Water reducing agent
MR0	376.00	0.00	709.00	1157.00	158.00	4.51
MR40	376.00	283.60	425.40	1157.00	158.00	4.51
MR60	376.00	425.40	283.60	1157.00	158.00	4.51
MR80	376.00	567.20	141.80	1157.00	158.00	4.51
MR100	376.00	709.00	0.00	1157.00	158.00	4.51

2.3 Test method

2.3.1 Mechanical property test of machine-made sand concrete

The mechanical property test shall be carried out according to the Standard for Test Methods of Physical and Mechanical Properties of Concrete (GB/T 50081-2019). The size of the cube specimen for the compressive strength test is 150mm × 150mm × 150mm, and the size of the specimen for the bending strength test is 150mm × 150mm × 600mm, the size of the specimen for the elastic modulus test is 150mm × 150mm × 300mm. After the casting is completed and the test piece is formed, it shall be placed in the water tank for curing at room temperature for 28 days.

2.3.2 Mechanical property test of prefabricated pipe row made of machine-made sand concrete

Through the loading of the component, observe the development of deflection deformation and reinforcement strain, and understand the actual working performance of the whole component. According to the comparative analysis of the test results and theoretical calculation, verify and optimize the calculation parameters and methods, and optimize and improve the components. Considering the convenience of hoisting, the prefabricated pipe laying shall be 3m/section. In this test, 6-hole prefabricated pipes are prepared according to Figure 1. The pipe laying section is prepared with machine-made sand concrete with a 60% replacement rate and reinforced with HPB300 rebar with a diameter of 6 mm and HRB400 rebar with a diameter of 12 mm.

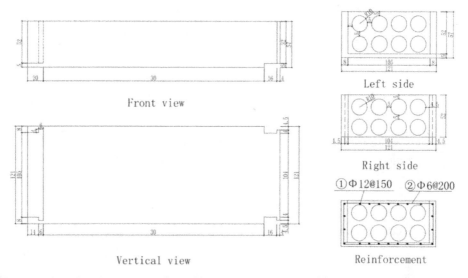

Figure 1. Section and reinforcement of prefabricated pipe arrays.

The positive position test consistent with its actual working state shall be adopted for the test structural members, and the load test shall be carried out by splicing 4 prefabricated segments with a length of 3m. In addition to the dead weight of the pipe and the pipe inside the pipe, the test load on the upper part of the pipe shall be applied from both sides to the middle of the span in turn according to 20kN/m^2, as shown in Figure 2, and the number is working condition 1-6.

The deflection value of a simply supported beam is an index that can best reflect its comprehensive performance in the measured data, and the most important is to measure the

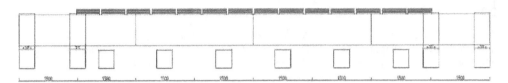

Figure 2. Loading diagram of load test.

maximum deflection value in the beam span. In order to obtain the true deflection, considering the settlement of the bearing, the deflection measuring points are symmetrically arranged along both sides of the component as shown in Figure 3.

Measure the strain caused by bending and arrange measuring points on the section with the maximum positive and negative bending moments or the section with sudden changes in bending moments. For flexural members, first arrange measuring points along the section height on the section with the largest bending moment, and each section should not be less than two; when it is necessary to measure the strain distribution along the section height, the number of measuring points should not be less than five; strain measuring points shall be arranged on the main reinforcement in the tensile area of the same section, and the arrangement position of the strain gauge of the prefabricated bent tube reinforcement is shown in Figure 4. According to the analysis of the data of each strain gauge, the concrete strain value of the prefabricated segment under a load of each working condition is obtained, and the concrete stress at the corresponding position is obtained through conversion.

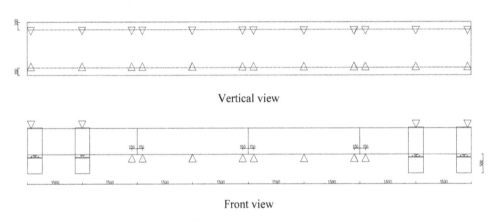

Figure 3. Layout of deflection measuring points.

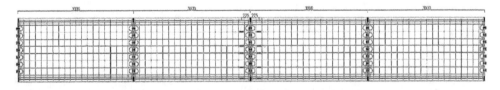

Figure 4. Layout of reinforcement strain gauge (Vertical view).

2.3.3 *Finite element simulation analysis of prefabricated pipe laying of machine-made sand concrete*

According to the layout of the test, the finite element analysis model of the test manifold is built with ABAQUS software. Concrete adopts a solid element, and ordinary reinforcement and prestressed steel strands adopt a truss element. The overall model has 35220 nodes and 27370 elements, including 20527 solid elements and 6843 truss elements, as shown in Figure 5. The external load shall be applied gradually according to the test conditions.

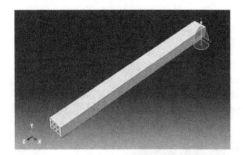
Concrete simulation model

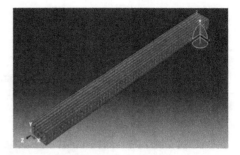
Reinforcement simulation model

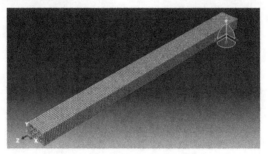
Grid division diagram

Figure 5. Finite element model of prefabricated pipe arrays.

3 RESULTS AND DISCUSSION

3.1 *Mechanical properties of machine-made sand concrete under different replacement rates*

The mechanical properties of machine-made sand concrete with different replacement rates are shown in Table 3.

According to the table, the mechanical properties of concrete with a 60% replacement rate of machine-made sand are the best. Compared with ordinary concrete, its cube compressive

Table 3. Mechanical properties of manufactured sand concrete.

Code	Cube Strength/MPa	Flexural strength/MPa	Elastic modulus/GPa
MR0	32.58	5.28	22.49
MR40	34.86	5.52	22.96
MR60	43.62	6.48	28.33
MR80	39.91	6.18	25.91
MR100	35.64	5.64	23.48

strength is 33.89% higher, flexural strength is 22.7% higher, and elastic modulus is 25.97% higher. Compared with the machine-made sand concrete with a 100% replacement rate, the cube compressive strength is 22.39% higher, the flexural strength is 14.89% higher, and the elastic modulus is 20.65% higher. Prefabricated pipe-laying segments of machine-made sand concrete are prepared with a replacement rate of 60%.

3.2 *Mechanical property analysis of prefabricated pipe laying with machine-made sand concrete*

The mid-span deflection and the mid-span concrete stress changes of the prefabricated bent pipe of machine-made sand concrete under various working conditions are shown in Figure 6. Through calculation, the bending moment caused by the external load and the self-weight of the member is close to the ultimate bending moment that 7 HRB400 bars with a diameter of 16 can bear.

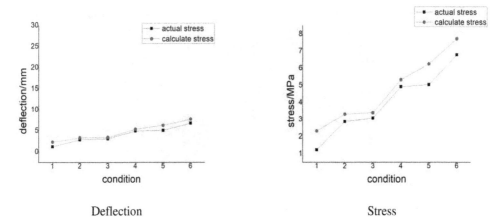

Deflection   Stress

Figure 6. Deflection and stress changes of prefabricated pipe arrays under different working conditions.

For the deflection change curve, the deflection change is approximately proportional before Condition 4. After Condition 4, the deflection curve increases slowly with the increase of load. There is no obvious direct proportional relationship between stress change and load. In practical projects, the prefabricated pipe laying of machine-made sand concrete can be used as a temporary fabricated structure instead of the ordinary cast-in-place concrete pipe laying. In the case of long-term structures, further analysis of the connection nodes is required.

Through the finite element analysis, the deflection and stress change of the corresponding position of the test row pipe under each working condition is obtained. The calculated values of the principal stress and displacement under each working condition are greater than the corresponding measured values, and the corresponding change laws are similar. The model can be used for the subsequent research and analysis of prefabricated row pipes made of machine-made sand.

4 CONCLUSION

1. The replacement rate of machine-made sand will affect the mechanical properties of concrete. The mechanical properties of machine-made sand concrete with a replacement

rate of 60% are better than those of machine-made sand concrete with other replacement rates. The prefabricated pipes of machine-made sand concrete are prepared with a replacement rate of 60%.
2. The mechanical properties of prefabricated pipe laying with machine-made sand are better, which can effectively replace the traditional cast-in-place concrete pipe laying. Prefabricated pipe laying with fabricated machine-made sand can effectively save the exploitation of natural sand and can be reused after the temporary transition period, which is environmentally friendly and economical.
3. The finite element simulation model of prefabricated pipe laying with machine-made sand is effective, which can effectively predict and calculate the temporary fabricated pipe laying with different burial depths under the weak soil layer. The joint of the precast segment involves uneven settlement. For the mechanical properties of the joint, the simulation model can be further used in subsequent research to calculate and test.

ACKNOWLEDGMENT

This work was supported by State Grid Tianjin Electric Power Company Science and Technology Project. "KJ22-1-75 Research and application of transmission line recycling technology".

REFERENCES

Chen Zhengfa, Zhu Hehua, Yan Zhiguo, Peng Gaojv. *The Open Civil Engineering Journal*, 2015, 9 (1).
Cortes D.D., Kim H.-K., Palomino A.M. *et al. J. Cement and Concrete Research*, 2008, 38 (10): 1142–1147.
Duan Yun, Wang Qicai, Yang Zijiang, Cui Xiaoning, Liu Fei, Chen Hai. *Construction and Building Materials*, 2022, 315.
Evan C. Bentz and Laurent Massam and Michael P. Collins*Journal of Composites for Construction*, 2010, 14 (6): 637–646.
Goldston M., Remennikov A. and Neaz Sheikh M. *Engineering Structures*, 2016, 113: 220–232.
Guoju Ke, Jiaqian Wang, Bo Tian. *ACI Materials Journal*, 2019, 116 (3).
José-Vicente Valdenebro and Faustino N. Gimena and J. Javier López. *Tunnelling and Underground Space Technology Incorporating Trenchless Technology Research*, 2019, 89: 38–49.
Maisarah Ali, Muhammad Hariz Nordin, Siti Asmahani Saad.. *Advanced Materials Research*, 2015, 4043 (1115–1115): 160–165.
Mander J.B., Priestley M.J.N. and Park R. *Journal of Structural Engineering*, 1988, 114 (8): 1804–1826.
Tianyu Wang *et al. Tunnelling and Underground Space Technology incorporating Trenchless Technology Research*, 2018, 76: 92–106.

Research on key technologies and standards of waste plastics recycling in China

Yanxin Gao, Shuang Ding*, Dongfeng Gao, Yi Zhu & Rui Zhang
China National Institute of Standardization, Beijing, China

ABSTRACT: China is a major producer and consumer of plastics and attaches great importance to the control of waste plastic pollution. This paper systematically summarized the key technologies and standards of waste plastics recycling, analyzed the advantages and disadvantages of different technologies, and proposed the application prospects and main research directions of waste plastics recycling technologies. Besides, this paper also analyzed the problems in the standardization of waste plastics recycling, which would provide a reference for choosing proper technologies along the whole chain management of plastic pollution by means of standardization.

1 INTRODUCTION

As necessary materials for people's daily life, improper use of plastics in production and consumption results in a large number of waste plastic products (Zhang *et al.* 2021). The Chinese government attaches great importance to the prevention and control of waste plastic pollution. In recent years, China has issued a series of policy documents on the prevention and control of waste plastic pollution. In December 2018, The General Office of the State Council issued the Pilot Work Plan for the Construction of "Waste-free Cities," which limits the production, sale, and use of disposable non-degradable plastic bags and plastic tableware and increases the application scope of biodegradable plastic products. In January 2020, the National Development and Reform Commission and the Ministry of Ecology and Environment issued "Opinions on Further Strengthening the Control of Plastic Pollution," making a comprehensive plan for the control of plastic pollution. In September 2021, the National Development and Reform Commission and the Ministry of Ecology and Environment issued an action plan on controlling plastic pollution during the 14th Five-Year Plan period (2021–2025) to improve further the plastic pollution control system along the whole chain. The implementation of policies related to the prevention and control of plastic pollution has continuously promoted the control of plastic pollution from the aspects of production, use, recycling, disposal, and cleaning, which effectively curbs the environmental pollution caused by plastic waste.

According to data from the report released by the China Materials Recycling Association, nearly 60 million tons of waste plastics were generated in 2020, and the overall recycling rate of waste plastics was only 26.7%. Nearly 50 million tons of waste plastics are generated in domestic waste every year, which would emit about 160 million tons of CO_2 if all of them were incinerated. However, the disposal of waste plastics by landfill would also cause pollution to the environment. If waste plastics accumulate in landfills and natural environments, it will result in long-term environmental pollution (Geyerr *et al.* 2017). Reasonable recycling

*Corresponding Author: dings@cnis.ac.cn

of waste plastics can control environmental pollution and convert waste into resources, resulting in good environmental and economic benefits (Shuai 2017). This paper analyzed key technologies and standards for the recycling of waste plastics, summarized the advantages and disadvantages of recycling technologies on plastic waste, as well as the current status of relevant technical standards, in order to provide a reference for the selection of technologies for plastic pollution along the whole chain.

2 KEY TECHNOLOGIES FOR RECYCLING WASTE PLASTICS

Based on the concept of circular economy, waste plastics recycling technologies can be divided into physical recycling technologies and chemical recycling technologies (Table 1). Physical recycling technologies include simple regeneration technology and physically modified regeneration technology. Chemical recycling technologies include chemical cracking technology, supercritical oil/water separation technology, heat energy utilization technology (incineration gasification technology, blast furnace injection technology), and co-coking technology.

Table 1. Advantages and disadvantages of key technologies on waste plastic recycling (Tang 2021; Zheng et al. 2014).

S/N		Technical types	Advantages	Disadvantages
1	Physical recycling technology	Simple regeneration technology	Simple process; Low investment cost; Wide range of application	Unstable quality of regenerated products; Low performance; Easy to become brittle; Not suitable for producing high-grade plastic regenerated products. Narrow application scale.
2		Physical modified regeneration technology	The mechanical properties of regenerated plastics products are optimized, which can be used to make high-grade regenerated plastic products	Special equipment is needed, and the processes are more complicated
3	Chemical recycling technology	Chemical cracking technology	Less content of spoilage organic matter in the pyrolysis residue; Less air pollution; High discharge density with compact structure.	The material sources for treatment are single The equipment investment is large The process and operation are complex It is difficult to realize large-scale production
4		Supercritical oil/water separation technology	High decomposition reaction rate; Less secondary pollution No catalyst is needed in the reaction Easy to separate the reaction products	The reaction needs to be carried out under the conditions of high temperature and high pressure; Large equipment investment;

(*continued*)

Table 1. Continued

S/N	Technical types		Advantages	Disadvantages
5	Heat energy utilization technology	Incineration gasification technology	Heat energy from incineration is recovered and reused	High operation cost; Corrosion and salt blockage problems in the reaction process limit the industrial application Easy to produce secondary pollution; High equipment investment cost; High equipment loss and maintenance operation cost.
6		Blast furnace injection technology	The waste plastics can be used in the current steel manufacturing equipment based on blast furnaces. Low production cost; Good economic benefit, Fully utilization of energy; Less toxic and harmful gases.	Waste plastic needs to be processed into a certain size of bulk injection into the blast furnace, resulting in high costs.
7		Co-coking technology	A simple process by plastic and coal mixing technology; Large treatment scale; Large equipment investment; Short the construction period; Coke oven treatment of chlorine-containing waste plastic	The catalyst has a great influence on the liquefaction effect, and it is easy to reduce the recovery of tar

From the perspective of the actual application scenarios of waste plastics recycling, modified recycling technologies dominated the physical recycling technologies. And modified regeneration technology is widely used because it adds modifiers to optimize the mechanical properties of recycled plastic products, enhances the use value of recycled plastic products, and can produce high-grade plastic recycled products.

Chemical recycling technologies are mainly applied by chemical cracking technology. Chemical cracking technology is the thermal cracking of plastic polymers into small molecular chains of petrochemicals, with the main processes of pyrolysis and distillation (Al-Salem et al. 2010). The waste plastics are pyrolyzed at 450°C in a pyrolysis furnace and settled to produce a recombinant fraction of oil. The lighter fraction will enter the condenser as primary fuel oil, and the primary fuel oil is again turned into gas in the distillation furnace after it is condensed and filtered through the condenser to give the petrochemical product fuel oil (Wang et al. 2022). With China's goal of carbon peaking and carbon neutrality, chemical cracking technology dealing with waste plastics is widely used due to its advantages of smaller CO_2 emissions and less secondary air pollution during the reuse of energy in the chemical cycle.

In summary, the recycling of waste plastics can effectively improve the efficiency of the comprehensive utilization of resources and reduce the pollution of the ecological environment by waste plastics, and the application of waste plastics recycling technology has broad prospects. Currently, recycled plastic products are mainly embodied in household appliances, office equipment, computers, etc. The future development trend is to shift from low-quality and high-energy consumption processes to high-quality and low-energy consumption, multi-species, fine classification, and high technology, with the main research directions focusing on the following aspects:

1. Development of automated sorting technology and equipment for a variety of waste mixed plastics in order to provide a pre-treatment process for subsequent recycling technology treatment;
2. Development of environmentally biodegradable plastics through molecular design research and accelerated development of technologies for alloying biodegradable plastics or common plastics with starch, cellulose, or inorganic material fillers to achieve high-quality alloys of recycled plastics;
3. Drawing on the development of standardization of waste plastics recycling in foreign countries, combine China's waste plastics recycling technology and its products, and formulate relevant technical standards or technical specifications to promote the high-quality development of the waste plastics recycling industry.

3 CURRENT STATUS OF STANDARDS WASTE PLASTICS RECYCLING IN CHINA

According to statistics, there are 29 standards related to waste plastics recycling in China, including 13 national standards, six industrial standards, and ten local standards. The national standards include two mandatory national standards and 11 optional national standards (Table 2). The industry standards include three environmental protection industry standards, one commercial industry standard, one commodity inspection industry standard, and one safety industry standard. The local standards include one local standard from Henan Province, two local standards from Hunan Province, three local standards from Hebei Province, one local standard from Guangdong Province, one local standard from Fujian Province, one local standard from Jilin Province and one local standard from Hainan Province.

In recent years, China has gradually attached importance to the development of standardization of waste plastics recycling and has issued and implemented a series of national standards, industry standards, and local standards, focusing on technical contents including waste plastics classification and grading, recycling, biodegradation, collaborative disposal, recycling processing, environmental labelling, and other aspects. The following problems still exist in the standardization of the recycling of waste plastics in China:

1. The standard system for recycling waste plastics is not perfect
   The standard system for recycling waste plastics is the basis and foundation for guiding and coordinating the standard making and revision work. Due to the late start of waste plastics recycling and resource utilization in China, the theoretical and practical basis of waste plastics recycling is weak, and the technical conditions for the establishment of the standard system are insufficient. As China's green low-carbon cycle development system continues to improve, chemical recycling as an environmentally-friendly new industry and an important part of the national plastics recycling economy, the standard system

Table 2. Waste plastics recycling standards in China.

S/N	Standard No.	Name of Standard	Standard Type
1	GB 25936.4-2010	Plastics and rubber machines – Size reduction machines – Part 4: Safety requirements for agglomerators	Mandatory National Standard
2	GB 30485-2013	Standard for pollution control on co-processing of solid wastes in cement kiln	Mandatory National Standard
3	GB/T 30760-2014	Technical specification for co-processing of solid waste in cement kiln	Optional National Standard
4	GB/T 32662-2016	Complete set of pyrolysis equipment for waste rubber and waste plastic to oil	Optional National Standard
5	GB/T 37547-2019	Classification and code of waste plastics	Optional National Standard
6	GB/T 37821-2019	Technical specifications for recycling of waste plastics	Optional National Standard
7	GB/T 39171-2020	Technical specification for waste plastics recycling	Optional National Standard
8	GB/T 18006.3-2020	General requirement of degradable disposable tableware	Optional National Standard
9	GB/T 21661-2020	Plastic shopping bags	Optional National Standard
10	GB/T 29646-2013	Modified biodegradable polyester used for blown film	Optional National Standard
11	GB/T 38082-2019	Biodegradable plastic shopping bags	Optional National Standard
12	GB/T 41008-2021	Biodegradable drinking straws	Optional National Standard
13	GB/T 41010-2021	Biodegradable plastics and products degradation performance and labeling requirements	Optional National Standard
14	HJ 364-2022	Technical specification for pollution control of plastic waste	Environmental protection industry standard
15	HJ 662-2013	Environmental protection technical specification for co-processing of Solid wastes in cement kiln	Environmental protection industry standard
16	HJ/T 231-2006	Technical requirement for environmental labeling products made from recycled plastics	Environmental protection industry standard
17	SB/T 11149-2015	Technical specifications of waste plastics collection and sorting	Commercial industry standard
18	SN/T 2928.1-2011	Method for identification type of waste polymer materials. Part 1:Waste plastics	Commodity inspection industry standard
19	AQ 4232-2013	Safety specification for dust explosion protection and prevention in the plastic processing system	Safety industry standard
20	DB41/T 2084-2020	Technical specification for construction of waste plastic compound modified asphalt pavement	Local Standard from Henan Provincial
21	DB43/T 551-2010	Waste plastic recycling standards-part 1:waste PVC-U of recovery rating and regeneration powder	Local Standard from Hunan Provincial
22	DB43/T 551.2-2014	Specifications for Recycling of waste plastics Part2: The recovery of polyethylene plastic and recycled polyethylene plastics	Local Standard from Hunan Provincial

(continued)

Table 2. Continued

S/N	Standard No.	Name of Standard	Standard Type
23	DB13/ 1082-2009	Technical specification for reprocessing and recycling of waste plastics	Local Standard from Hebei Province
24	DB13/T 5361-2021	Technical specification for pollution control during collection and recycling of waste plastics	Local Standard from Hebei Province
25	DB13/T 2471-2017	General technical requirements for oxidized biodegradable plastic bags	Local Standard from Hebei Province
26	DB44/T 2216-2019	Environmental management specification for containing copper waste and scrap plastic recycling utilization agglomeration park	Local Standard from Guangdong Province
27	DB35/T 998-2010	Starch-based biodegradable plastic master material	Local Standard from Fujian Province
28	DB22/T 2645-2017	General technical requirements for biodegradable plastic retail packaging bags	Local Standard from Jilin Province
29	DB46/T 505-2020	General technical requirements for all biodegradable plastic products	Local Standard from Hainan Province

construction work will become more important. Domestic market development trends are from the control of plastic waste recycling and resource treatment technology, biodegradable plastic technology to improving the quality of plastic recycled product control technology, carrying out standard making and revision work, and gradually improving the recycling of waste plastics standard system.

2. Lack of key technical standards for recycling waste plastic resources

In recent years, under the constraints of national energy-saving and low-carbon and environmental protection objectives, as well as the guidance of relevant planning and policy documents, China has made great progress in the standardization of waste plastics recycling. China has issued the Opinions on Further Strengthening the Control of Plastic Pollution, the Action Plan for the Control of Plastic Pollution in the 14th Five-Year Plan, and other guidance documents, as well as the implementation of relevant standards, effectively promoting the development of the plastic recycling industry. However, some key technical standards remain gap, especially in new industrial fields such as biodegradable plastic technology, green design of plastic products, plastic waste homogenization, and high value-added utilization technology, which restrict the scale development of the plastic recycling industry.

3. Integration of standards and policies needs to be improved

There is some disconnection between China's industrial policies on the resource utilization of plastics and the formulation and revision of standards, resulting in a low implementation rate of standards. The coordination mechanism between plastic pollution prevention and management departments and standardization authorities is insufficient, which restricts the effect of standard implementation. Policy implementation has a guiding function. If the policy development process lacks the articulation of high-standard indicators, it may affect market development. Therefore, the coordination between plastic resource utilization policies and technical standards in the future should be improved, and the simultaneous development and release of policies and supporting standards should be promoted to improve the standard support for green development policies.

4 CONCLUSION

The production and consumption of plastic products have brought great convenience to people's lives, but improper treatment and disposal will bring serious environmental pollution problems. This paper summarized the current status of waste plastics recycling technologies and standards, compared the advantages and disadvantages of different technologies, and also pointed out the current situation and problems of waste plastic resource utilization standards, so as to provide a reference for the selection of technologies for plastic pollution along whole-chain treatment.

ACKNOWLEDGMENTS

This work was financially supported by Dean's Foundation Project "National Technical Committee for the Standardization of Product Recycling Basis and Management-Research on Standardization of Circular Carbon Reduction (2022)" (No. 542022Y-9375)

REFERENCES

Al-Salem S.M., Lettieri P. and Baeyens J. The Valorization of Plastic Solid Waste (PSW) by Primary to Quaternary Routes: From re-use to Energy and Chemicals. *Progress in Energy and Combustion Science*, 2010, 36 (1):103–129.

Geyerr R., Jambeck J.R., Law K.L. Production, Use, and Fate of all Plastics Ever made. *Science Advances*, 2017, 3 (7): el700782.

Jian Tang. Management and Development Status of Waste Plastics Recycling. *Plastics Additives*, 2021 (01):71–75, 43.

Qiming Shuai. The Recycling and Regeneration of Waste Plastics. *China Resources Comprehensive Utilization*, 2017, 35 (10):51–53.

Yang Wang, Yifan Gu, Yufeng Wu, et al. Comprehensive Performance Evaluation of Typical Waste Plastic Recycling Technologies in South China. *Environmental Engineering*, 2022, 40 (2):184–190.

Yang Zheng, Zongpei Li, Chuanhua Liao. Research Progress of Recycle Utilization of Waste Plastic. *Plastics Additives*, 2014 (02):11–16, 25.

Zhang F., Zhao Y.T. and Wang D.D et al. Current Technologies for Plastic Waste Treatment: a Review. *Journal of Cleaner Production*, 2021, 282:124523.

N-doping porous carbon with CoP loading for hydrogen evolution reaction

Yuelong Xu* & Shasha Wang
Institute of Energy Resources, Hebei Academy of Sciences, Shijiazhuang, China
Hebei Engineering Research Center for Water Saving in Industry, Shijiazhuang, China

Zhi Tian
Hebei Baoli Engineering Equipment Group Co. Ltd., Hengshui, Hebei Province, China

ABSTRACT: Because of clean-burning, highly efficient, and abundant resources, hydrogen has attracted more and more attention. To develop new technologies for hydrogen production, electro-catalysis and photocatalysis are applied to the hydrogen production field. The catalyst plays a vital role in the electro-catalysis process. Recently, transition metal phosphides with high catalytic performance, low electrochemical impedance, and simple preparation methods have been widely reported for hydrogen evolution reaction applications. In this work, N-doping porous carbon with CoP loading is obtained through a sol-gel method. Phytic acid is used to phosphate the metal compounds and to dissolve the chitosan for N-doping porous carbon synthesis. The as-prepared catalyst exhibited an outstanding catalytic performance with a low overpotential, 120 mV at 10 mA cm^{-2}, and a small Tafel slope value, 105 mV dec^{-1}. Meanwhile, this catalyst also kept good stability for a long time test. This result indicates that the sol-gel method adopting biomass and phytic acid can prepare novel catalysts to improve the catalytic performance for hydrogen evolution reactions.

1 INTRODUCTION

The energy crisis has attracted more and more attention, and the environmental problem also has influenced social development. The demand for clean energy has been urgent. Clean and environmental-friendly hydrogen has been identified as the next-generation energy substitute for social development (Graciela *et al.* 2019; Lai *et al.* 2021; Sun *et al.* 2017). With rich resources and low cost, water splitting for clean hydrogen production has been widely investigated and reported. Electrochemical water splitting includes two half-reactions: hydrogen evolution reaction (HER) in the cathode and oxygen evolution reaction (OER) in the anode. The theoretical electrochemical water splitting potential is 1.23 V to obtain clean hydrogen and oxygen, the over-potential is necessary. The lower the over-potential value is, the poorer the energy loss. Therefore, efficient and stable catalysts have become needed.

Traditional electrochemical catalysts for hydrogen production are mainly noble metal compounds, such as Pt, Ir, Ru, and RuO$_2$ (Li *et al.* 2021; Zhang *et al.* 2022). Because of *d*-orbital, the noble catalysts can facilitate the H adsorption and reduce the reaction Gibbs

---

*Corresponding Author: xudalong.cool@163.com

DOI: 10.1201/9781003433644-39

free energy to realize a low over-potential for water splitting. Liu et al. reported a facile method to prepare Ir single-atom catalyst for HER (Liu et al. 2022). They adopted a polyhexaphenylbenzene material with intrinsic holes to prepare amorphous carbon support, which could be beneficial for ion transport and accelerate the catalytic reaction. The prepared catalysts exhibited a low over-potential, 17 mV at 10 mA cm^{-2}, with good stability. The density functional theory (DFT) results indicated that the d-band center of PBN-300-Ir is lower than other catalysts, which was attributed to the amorphous carbon around to reduce the energy hydrogen adsorption. Ultra-small Ru nanoparticles highly dispersed on sulfur-doped graphene were obtained by Sun et al. (2020). The Ultra-small Ru nanoparticles showed an obvious electron density decrease caused by the S-doped graphene. This result was good for the electron release and facilitated H$_2$O and H-OH bond breakage. The over-potential at 20 mA cm^{-2} was 14 mV, and the tafel slope was 60 mV dec^{-1}.

Because of high cost and scarce resources, noble catalysts application has been hindered. To develop low cost and abundant resources, transition metal compounds played a vital role for HER. Recently, transition metal sulfides, selenides, carbides, phosphides, and nitrides have been widely reported for hydrogen evolution reactions. These catalysts possessed Pt-like d-orbital, which can be beneficial for H adsorption. Wu et al. have synthesized Ni$_2$P catalyst with S doped for HER (Wu et al. 2022). The obtained materials exhibited a porous structure, which benefited the ion transport and reduced the electrochemical impedance. When S doped content was 10 wt%, the corresponding catalyst showed a low over-potential, 290 mV at mA cm^{-2}. In this work, N-doping porous carbon with CoP loading is obtained through a sol-gel method. Phytic acid is used to phosphate the metal compounds and to dissolve the chitosan for N-doping porous carbon synthesis.

2 EXPERIMENT

2.1 *Materials*

The materials used in this work were all purchased from Aladdin Reagent Co. and were all used without further purification.

2.2 *Synthesis of N-doping porous carbon with CoP loading*

The catalysts were prepared through a sol-gel process, and the preparation details were as follows: chitosan (5.0 g), Co(NO$_3$)$_2$ (1.2 g), pyrrole (10.0 mL) and phytic acid solution (100 mL, 3.0 wt%) were added into an agate pot and ground for 12 h to obtain a black gel. The obtained materials were freeze-dried for 72 h. Then, the materials were carbonized at 900°C under an N$_2$ atmosphere. N-doping porous carbon with CoP loading was named CN/CoP, and the material without CoP loading was named CN.

2.3 *Characterization*

The prepared catalysts were characterized by SEM, TEM, XPS, XRD, and Raman spectrum. SEM images were obtained through a TESCAN MAIA3 microscope, TEM images were observed by a JEOL JEM-2100F microscope, XPS analysis was executed in a PHI5600 Physical Electronics instrument, XRD analysis was investigated in Rigaku Ultima IV X-ray diffractometer with Cu Kα radiation (λ = 1.54 Å), and Raman spectrum was obtained from Renishaw microscope.

2.4 Electrochemical measurements

The as-prepared catalysts were mixed with Nafion solution (5 wt%), DI water, and ethanol and then drop-wised into a working electrode. Carbon paper was used as the counter electrode; SCE was used as the reference electrode. LSV curves were obtained in 1.0 KOH solution, and the potential window was from −1.6 V to −0.8 V. In this work, the experimental potential value was changed into a reversible hydrogen potential (RHE) value, and the converted equation was E (vs. RHE) = E (vs. SCE) + 0.224 V + 0.059 * pH.

3 RESULTS AND DISCUSSION

The morphologies of the as-prepared catalyst were observed through a TESCAN MAIA3 microscope, and the images are shown in Figure 1. As shown in Figure 1, CN/CoP exhibited a 3D network cross-linking structure. The plentiful porous structure was beneficial for CoP loading and the ions transport, which reduced the electrochemical impedance and facilitated the hydrogen evolution reactions.

Figure 1. SEM Images of CN/CoP.

The morphologies of CN/CoP were obtained from TEM, and the corresponding images were presented in Figure 2. Obviously, the loading metal compounds could be seen in the porous carbon from Figure 2a, which indicated that N-doping porous carbon with CoP loading was successfully prepared through the aforementioned method. The lattice fringes can be clearly seen in Figure 2b, and the lattice distance was 0.29 nm and 0.19 nm, which correspond to (011) and (211) crystal planes of CoP.

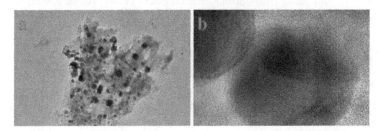

Figure 2. TEM Images of CN/CoP.

The crystal structure was investigated, and the corresponding result is presented in Figure 3. Figure 3 shows two obvious peaks at 24° and 42° could be observed, which

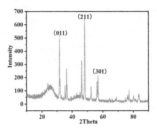

Figure 3. XRD Pattern of the CN/CoP.

corresponded to amorphous carbon. The peaks at 31.6°, 48.1°, and 56.8° were signed to the crystal plane of (011), (211), and (301) from the CoP crystal structure. This analysis result proved that CoP nanoparticles were successfully loaded into porous carbon.

The graphitization degree of as-prepared materials was studied through the Raman spectrum, and the corresponding result is shown in Figure 4. As seen in Figure 4, two obvious peaks at 1360 cm^{-1} and 1590 cm^{-1} could be obtained, which corresponded to amorphous carbon and graphite carbon. The intensity ratio (I_D / I_G) of amorphous carbon and graphite carbon could indicate the graphitization degree. The I_D / I_G values of CN and CN/CoP were 1.53 and 1.67, respectively, which indicated that CoP loading could improve the defect structure, enhancing the catalytic performance.

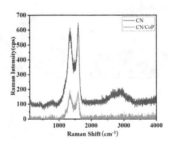

Figure 4. Raman spectra of CN and CN/CoP.

The chemical composed of as-prepared catalysts was investigated through XPS spectra, and the result is presented in Figure 5. As shown in Figure 5 (a), C, N, O, Co, and P could be obtained, which were located at 286 eV, 400 eV, 533 eV, 799 eV, and 134 eV, respectively. Co $2p_{3/2}$ and $2p_{1/2}$ and the corresponding satellite peaks could also be found, which proved the presence of Co.

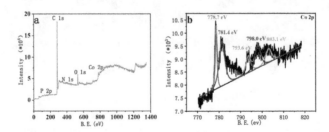

Figure 5. XPS survey spectra for CN/CoP (a) and Co 2p spectra (b).

The electrochemical performance was investigated through LSV curves and the corresponding Tafel slopes, and the results are presented in Figure 6. As shown in Figure 6 (a), the catalysts all had excellent catalytic performances. The over-potentials at 10 mA cm^{-2} were 180 mV, 450 mV, and 220 mV for CN/CoP, CN, and CoP, respectively. This result demonstrated that CoP loading obviously improved the catalytic performance of N-doping porous carbon. The Tafel slope values of CN/CoP, CN, and CoP were 64 mV dec^{-1}, 61 mV dec^{-1}, and 125 mV dec^{-1}, respectively. The lower Tafel slope value indicated good catalytic reaction kinetics.

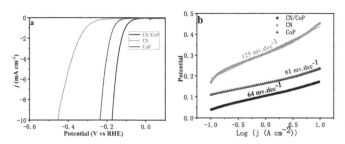

Figure 6. LSV Curves of catalysts (a) and Tafel slopes (b).

4 CONCLUSION

This paper adopted the sol-gel method to prepare N-doping porous carbon with CoP loading, and the electrochemical catalytic performance for HER was systematically investigated. The main conclusions can be summarized as follows: (1) the sol-gel method provided a novel strategy to obtain HER catalysts; (2) the over-potentials at 10 mA cm^{-2} was 180 mV; (3) the Tafel slope value of the as-prepared catalyst was 64 mV dec^{-1}. In terms of future work, the sol-gel method and transition metal phosphide loading should be carried out to enhance the catalytic performance for HER.

ACKNOWLEDGMENTS

This work was financially supported by the science and technology projects of the Hebei Academy of Sciences (21706 and 21711).

REFERENCES

Graciela A., Roxana C. and Liliana D. (2019) Ni-Mo Alloy Electrodeposited over Ni Substrate for HER on Water Electrolysis. *Electrocatalysis*, 10:17–28.

Lai W., Ge L., Li H., Deng Y., Xu B., Ouyang B. and Erjun K. (2021) In situ Raman Spectroscopic Study Towards the Growth and Excellent HER Catalysis of Ni/Ni (OH) 2 Heterostructure. *Int. J. Hydrogen Energ.*, 46: 26861–26872.

Li H., Dai S., Dinesh B., Alice H., Chou J. and Chen T. (2021) Interfacial Atomic Ni Tetragon Intercalation in a NiO2-to-Pd Heterostructure Triggers Superior HER Activity to the Pt Catalyst. *J. Mater. Chem. A*, 9: 12019–12028.

Liu C., Pan G., Liang N., Hong S., Ma J. and Liu Y. (2022) Ir Single Atom Catalyst Loaded on Amorphous Carbon Materials with High HER Activity. *Adv. Sci.* 9: 2105392.

Sun H.M., Xu X.B., Yan Z.H., Chen X., Cheng F.Y., Weiss P.S. and Chen J. (2017) Porous Multishelled Ni2P Hollow Microspheres as an Active Electrocatalyst for Hydrogen and Oxygen Evolution. *Chem. Mater.*, 29: 8539–8547.

Sun X., Gao X., Chen J., Wang X., Chang H., Li B., Song D., Li J., Li H. and Wang N. (2020) Ultrasmall Ru Nanoparticles Highly Dispersed on Sulfur-Doped Graphene for HER with High Electrocatalytic Performance. *ACS Appl. Mater. Interfaces.* 12: 48591–48597.

Wu Y., Chen X., Su L., Wang Q. and Ren S. (2022) A Sulfur-doped Ni2P Electrocatalyst for the Hydrogen Evolution Reaction. *New J. Chem.* 46: 7675–7681.

Zhang J., Lian J., Jiang Q. and Wang G. (2022) Boosting the OER/ORR/HER Activity of Ru-doped Ni/Co Oxides Heterostructure. *Chem. Eng. J.*, 439: 135634.

Discussion on shear strength parameters of rock mass

Yong Yang*
Northwest Research Institute of Engineering Investigation and Design, China
School of Geological Engineering and Geomatics in Chang'an University, China

Wen Fan*
School of Geological Engineering and Geomatics in Chang'an University, China

Zhangjian Xu*, Zhihai Zhao* & Haifeng Zhang*
Northwest Research Institute of Engineering Investigation and Design, China

ABSTRACT: Rock mass contains many structural planes, which is a typical discontinuous medium. Its strength characteristics show anisotropy and size effect. Therefore, when discussing the mechanical property index of rock mass, it should be carried out on different scales. Firstly, this paper discusses the division of large, medium, and small scales and reviews the previous research on the size effect of rock mass strength. Secondly, the practical application of the Hoek Brown strength criterion on a large scale is discussed, and some other empirical formulas are introduced. Finally, according to the principle of slope limit equilibrium, a formula of equivalent internal friction is deduced and combined with the test results of the slope in the South exposed sky of the Jinduicheng molybdenum mine and the influence effects of various factors in the formula are discussed.

1 DISCUSSION ON THE RESEARCH SCALE OF ROCK MASS STRENGTH

Rock mass contains many structural planes and is a typical discontinuous and anisotropic medium. The mechanical properties of rock mass show anisotropy, which is reflected in the properties of rock materials and the structure of rock mass. At the same time, as an engineering research object, rock mass scale often exceeds the scale that the conventional structural effect of rock mass needs to consider. Moreover, the occurrence conditions of rock mass vary greatly from one project to another and cannot be generalized. Therefore, when discussing the mechanical property index of rock mass, it should be carried out on different scales according to different environments.

A large number of engineering practices show that under the overall stability of the rock slope, there are a large number of wedge failures, falling blocks, slumping failures, etc., locally. Certainly, the strength index of rock mass reflected by this local failure is not the same as that reflected by the overall stability of the slope. It can be seen from this that the objectively existing strength index is not an invariable inherent characteristic. Therefore, we believe that the mechanical indexes of high and large rock slopes should be discussed at least on three scales. The concept of this scale is shown not only in the volume of the research object but also in the stress environment of the research object.

---

*Corresponding Authors: 28610419@qq.com, fanwen@chd.edu.cn, xzjxbzk@126.com, zhaozhihai601@163.com and 983460979@qq.com

The first scale is the small scale, also known as the test scale. The size of rock mass in this scale range ranges from several centimeters to several meters. The indoor test of rock block and the in-situ test of rock mass are applicable in this scale range, and the rock mass is basically in an unconfined condition. The mechanical indexes of rock mass are strongly affected by structural planes, and the size effect is particularly obvious.

The second scale is the medium scale, where the rock mass size ranges from several meters to tens of meters, and general rock slopes are applicable. In this scale range, the stability of the rock slope is controlled by the dominant structural plane or composite structural plane, and the rock mass strength index is mainly reflected in the structural plane strength in engineering applications.

The third scale is the large scale. The rock mass size in this scale range ranges from tens of meters to hundreds of meters or even larger. In this scale range, the anisotropy of structural planes is further weakened. Rock block materials and a large number of structural planes are considered as a whole, and rock mass materials can be treated as homogeneous materials.

2 ROCK MASS STRENGTH INDEX AT MEDIUM AND SMALL SCALES

In medium and small scales, the strength of rock mass is greatly affected by the structural plane. On the size effect of rock mass strength, predecessors have done a lot of research: Liu Baochen, Zhang Jiasheng, *et al* (1998) studied the uniaxial compressive strength test of seven different rocks, and believed that the size effect of rock compressive strength can be better reflected by exponential function; Zhou Huoming, Xu Gaowei, *et al* (2001), based on the rock test results of the Three Gorges Permanent Shiplock Slope Project and the Qingjiang Shuibuya Water Control Project, considered that the deformation parameters of the rock mass were in a power function relationship with its section size; Xu Gaowei, Bai Shiwei, *et al.* (2004); (2006) respectively used exponential function, logarithmic function, power function, and hyperbolic function to fit the elastic moduli of seven kinds of rocks with different degrees of softness and hardness. They believed that the size-effect ratio of fitting the elastic moduli of hard rocks with the exponential function, logarithmic function, and power function was ideal, and that of fitting the elastic moduli of soft rocks with the exponential function and logarithmic function was ideal.

Sun Guangzhong (2011) summarized the influencing factors of the structural plane on the mechanical properties of the rock mass into seven aspects, namely: the combination of the structural plane, the filling situation, the morphological characteristics of the structural plane (roughness, rise), the extensibility (connectivity) of the structural plane, the density of the structural plane, the occurrence of the structural plane, and the number of structural plane groups. It can be summarized into three rules, namely, the mechanical effect of climbing angle, the size effect, and the anisotropic mechanical effect. After normalizing the collected test data, the normalization curve and strength formula of rock mass ultimate compressive strength are obtained, as shown in Formula 1.

$$R_m = R_0 + \frac{a}{V^b} \tag{1}$$

where R_m represents the mechanical parameters of a rock block of a certain size, R_0 represents the mechanical parameters of rock mass of a certain size, a is the attenuation value of rock mass failure strength, V is the engineering rock mass volume, and b is the structure effect index.

Liu Shungui, Chi Yongxiang, *et al.* (2009) studied the size effect of shear strength of column jointed basalt rock mass in combination with indoor direct shear test and on-site large shear test and believed that the shear strength is exponentially related to the sample size. The representative unit sizes of cohesion C and internal friction coefficient f are determined, which are 7.96 m and 0.67 m, respectively, indicating that cohesion C is more sensitive to the specimen size.

The above research shows that the strength index of rock mass is negatively related to the size of the specimen in the range of its characterization unit in the medium and small scale range. When the size of the specimen increases, its strength index no longer increases with the specimen size but tends to a certain value.

3 ROCK MASS STRENGTH INDEX UNDER LARGE-SCALE CONDITIONS

In the practical application of a high slope, the scale of rock mass is very large, and the confining pressure of rock mass is greatly exerted. The huge structural planes distributed in rock mass no longer play a controlling role in the overall stability evaluation of slope, and the anisotropy of rock mass strength is further weakened. If the rock mass is assumed to be an ideal layered block divided by the structural plane, it can be known that the shear strength of the rock mass is the minimum when it is sheared along the structural plane (shear strength of the structural plane), while the cross-cutting structural plane is the maximum (similar to the shear strength of the rock block). When it is destroyed along the composite shear plane, its strength is between the two. The shear strength envelope of the rock mass is shown in Figure 1.

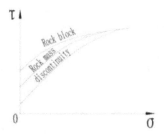

Figure 1. Envelope diagram of rock mass shear strength.

It can be seen from Figure 1 that when the stress is low, the strength of the rock mass changes in a large range. With the increase of stress, the range of change gradually decreases. When the stress increases to a certain extent, the rock mass strength is not affected by the structural plane and tends to be isotropic.

The strength index of rock mass depends more on in-situ tests or experience. On the other hand, the in-situ test of rock mass is costly and time-consuming, and the variability of test results is also large. The selection and application of indicators also depend on experience. In China's practical application, various manuals and specifications also provide empirical values of various strength indicators of various rock masses based on experience. At present, there are two main calculation methods for strength parameters of fractured rock mass: one is the empirical formula method based on Hoek Brown strength criterion, and the other is the empirical formula method based on rock mass integrity coefficient, longitudinal elastic wave velocity and other parameters (collectively referred to as quasi rock mass strength in this paper). In general, these methods are more dependent on tests or engineering experience.

3.1 Hoek Brown empirical formula method

This method is based on the Hoek Brown empirical strength criterion of nonlinear failure of jointed rock mass, which is derived, fitted, and expanded. This method is recommended in

Technical Code for Non-coal Open-pit Mine Slope Engineering (GB51016). (GB 51016-2014) Hoek Brown strength criterion is a modified formula of the empirical strength criterion proposed by Hoek and Brown in 1980 on the basis of tests. After practical application and modification, Hoek and Brown proposed the modified formula in 2002. The strength formula is:

$$\sigma_1 = \sigma_3 + \sigma_c \left(m_b \frac{\sigma_3}{\sigma_c} + S \right)^a \tag{2}$$

$$m_b = m_i \exp\left(\frac{GSI - 100}{28 - 14D}\right) \tag{3}$$

$$S = \exp\left(\frac{GSI - 100}{9 - 3D}\right) \tag{4}$$

$$a = \frac{1}{2} + \frac{1}{2}(e^{-GSI/15} - e^{-20/3}) \tag{5}$$

where σ_C is the uniaxial saturated compressive strength of rock block; m_i is Hawke Brown constant of intact rock; D is rock mass disturbance parameter, D = 0~1; m_b is the material constant of broken rock mass, dimensionless, reflecting the hardness of rock; S is a parameter related to the characteristics of rock mass, dimensionless, reflecting the degree of fragmentation of rock mass; a is the constant representing jointed rock mass, dimensionless.

In this method, the structural characteristics of rock mass, the height of the slope, the material characteristics of rock, and the influence of blasting are considered when calculating the shear strength index of the rock mass.

Based on the rock test results of the Jinduicheng Molybdenum Mine South Open pit High Slope Project, the shear strength indexes of 6 rock masses under different slope heights are calculated by using Hoek Brown empirical formula, and the relationship between them and the slope height is discussed. The general physical and mechanical property indexes, RMR indexes, and GSI indexes of 6 kinds of rock masses are summarized in Table 1.

Table 1. Statistics of physical and mechanical indexes of 6 type rock masses.

Stratum	Rock Mass Densityr (kN/m3)	Uniaxial Compressive Strength σc (MPa)	Rock Constantmi	Quality IndexRMR	Strength IndexGSI
Metaquartz Sandstone 2	2.64	19.1	20	57	52
Metaquartz Sandstone 3	2.55	41.0	20	64	59
Slate	2.77	25.5	10	59	54
Quartzite	2.58	29.3	21	69	64
Andesitic Porphyrite	2.86	27.3	27	64	59
Granite	2.61	29.7	32	66	61

According to the calculation results, scatter plots of shear strength indexes (cohesion, internal friction angle) calculated for various rock masses under different slope heights are drawn, as shown in Figures 2 and 3.

It can be seen from the figure that the shear strength indexes of rock mass have a good power correlation with the slope height. The value of c increases nonlinearly with the slope height h. On the contrary, the value of φ decreases nonlinearly with the slope height h.

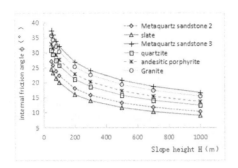 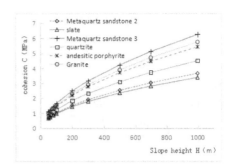

Figure 2. Scatter diagram of φ—h.   Figure 3. Scatter diagram of c—h.

3.2 Quasi rock mass strength (other empirical formula methods)

1) In 1970, Japan's Ikeda proposed the relationship between the uniaxial compressive strength of rock mass and the longitudinal wave velocity of rock mass and rock block:

$$\frac{\sigma_{cm}}{\sigma_{ci}} = \left(\frac{V_p^m}{V_p^i}\right)^2 = K \tag{6}$$

where σ_{Cm} is the uniaxial compressive strength of rock mass; σ_{Ci} is the uniaxial compressive strength of rock block; V_p^m is the longitudinal wave velocity of rock mass; V_p^i is the longitudinal wave velocity of the rock block.

2) In 1996, Aydan proposed a formula to estimate the uniaxial compressive strength of weak rock mass by using the elastic wave velocity of rock mass:

$$\sigma_{cm} = \left(5V_p^m - 7\right)^{1.43} \tag{7}$$

3) In 1996, Ito proposed a formula to estimate the uniaxial compressive strength of rock mass by using the elastic wave velocity of rock mass when excavating tunnels in mudstone and muddy rock:

$$\sigma_{cm} = \left(\frac{V_p^m}{1.6}\right)^{6.9} \tag{8}$$

4) In 1995, Barton et al. proposed a formula to estimate the uniaxial compressive strength of rock mass based on the elastic wave velocity of rock mass:

$$\sigma_{cm} = 10^{\frac{V_p^m + 0.28}{3}} \tag{9}$$

5) In 1982, Agapoiso and Hardy proposed the following empirical formula:

$$\sigma_{cm} = \sigma_{ci}\left(\frac{V_i}{V_m}\right)^a \tag{10}$$

where V_i is the volume of rock specimen in the laboratory; V_m is the volume of in-situ rock mass; a is the volume reduction coefficient (0.12, 0.08, and 0.06 for coal, oil shale, and hard quartzite, respectively).

6) In 1993, Singh proposed the relationship between the uniaxial compressive strength of rock mass and Q value:

$$\sigma_{cm} = 0.7\gamma Q^{\frac{1}{3}} \quad (11)$$

where γ is the weight of rock mass; Q is the classification index value of rock mass.

7) In 1995, Kalamaras and Bieniawski proposed a formula to determine the uniaxial compressive strength of rock mass based on the rock mass classification system index RMR:

$$\frac{\sigma_{cm}}{\sigma_{ci}} = 0.5\frac{(RMR-15)}{85} \quad (12)$$

8) In 1997, Arid Palmstrom put forward the following empirical formula, which took into account the factors of alteration degree, roughness, continuity, and average volume of the rock mass.

$$\sigma_{cm} = \sigma_c \cdot JP = \sigma_c \cdot 0.2\sqrt{JC} \cdot V_b^{0.37JC^{-0.2}} \quad (13)$$

$$JC = JL \cdot JR/JA$$

where JP is the strength reduction coefficient of rock mass; JA is the score of rock joint alteration; JR is the scoring value of rock joint roughness factor; JL is the rock mass joint size and continuity factor score; V_b is the average volume of rock block.

4 EQUIVALENT INTERNAL FRICTION ANGLE OF ROCK MASS

The equivalent angle of internal friction is an imaginary angle of internal friction taking into account the cohesion of the rock, also known as the quasi internal friction angle or the comprehensive internal friction angle. As the equivalent internal friction angle of rock mass reflects the shear strength of rock mass, its index is single, its concept is clear, and its application is simple and intuitive, especially in judging the overall stability of the slope, it can be directly compared with the slope rupture angle. According to the General Code for Engineering Investigation, the equivalent internal friction angle of slope rock mass must be provided for slope engineering.

There are many methods to calculate the equivalent internal friction angle of rock mass, but two basic theories are widely used: one is the equivalent internal friction angle calculated under the condition of equal earth pressure, which is generally used in the design of retaining walls. The method is based on Rankine's basic formula of active earth pressure (assuming that the wall back is smooth, vertical and the filling surface is horizontal), and the active earth pressure of cohesive rock and soil is equivalent to Rankine's active earth pressure under the condition of non-cohesive rock and soil. The formula is as follows:

$$\varphi_d = 90° - 2\arctan\left(\tan\left(45° - \frac{\varphi_d}{2}\right) - \frac{2c}{h\gamma}\right) \quad (14)$$

This method can be applied only when the active earth pressure is greater than zero. In addition, as an extension of this method, the equivalent internal friction angle is also calculated according to the equivalent moment of Rankine active earth pressure to the wall toe. Another basic principle for calculating the equivalent internal friction angle is based on the condition that the shear strength is equal, which is mainly used in slope stability evaluation and design. This method starts from the Mohr-Coulomb strength formula and reduces the cohesion C value of the rock to the internal friction angle of the rock. The formula is as follows:

$$\varphi_d = \arctan\left(\tan\varphi + \frac{2c}{h\gamma\cos^2\theta}\right) \quad (15)$$

It can be seen from the foregoing that the basic principles and formulas for calculating the equivalent internal friction angle have strict assumptions and application limitations. Based on the fact that the equivalent internal friction angle is mainly used for slope stability analysis and evaluation in this study, we directly derive the formula for calculating the equivalent internal friction angle of slope rock mass from the basic principles and methods of slope limit equilibrium analysis (Figure 4) as follows:

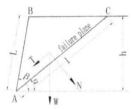

Figure 4. Diagram of the limit equilibrium method.

Limit equilibrium conditions:

$$F_s = \frac{cl + W\cos\alpha\tan\varphi}{W\sin\alpha} = \frac{cl}{W\sin\alpha} + \frac{\tan\varphi}{\tan\alpha} \quad (16)$$

$$W = \frac{h^2\gamma\sin(\beta-\alpha)}{2\sin\alpha\sin\beta} \quad (17)$$

$$l = \frac{h}{\sin\alpha} \quad (18)$$

$$\Rightarrow F_s = \frac{\tan\varphi}{\tan\alpha} + \frac{2c\sin\beta}{h\gamma\sin(\beta-\alpha)\sin\alpha} = \frac{\tan\varphi_d}{\tan\alpha} \Rightarrow \tan\varphi_d = \tan\varphi + \frac{2c\sin\beta}{h\gamma\sin(\beta-\alpha)\cos\alpha} \Rightarrow \varphi_d$$

$$= \arctan\left(\tan\varphi + \frac{2c\sin\beta}{h\gamma\sin(\beta-\alpha)\cos\alpha}\right) \quad (19)$$

It can be seen that the factors affecting the equivalent internal friction angle include not only the rock shear strength but also the slope height, slope angle, and fracture angle.

We let $F_s = 1$, according to Formula (16):

$$c = \frac{h\gamma\sin(\beta-\alpha)(\sin\alpha - \cos\alpha\tan\varphi)}{2\sin\beta} = \frac{h\gamma}{2} \cdot \frac{\sin(\beta-\alpha)\sin(\alpha-\varphi)}{\sin\beta\cos\varphi} \quad (20)$$

We let:

$$\frac{dc}{d\alpha} = \frac{h\gamma}{2\sin\beta\cos\varphi}\sin(\beta+\varphi-2\alpha) = 0$$

$$\Rightarrow \alpha = (\beta+\varphi)/2 \quad (21)$$

We assume: $\beta = 90$, $\alpha = 45 + \varphi/2$ then:
$\varphi_d = \arctan(\tan\varphi + \frac{2c}{h\gamma\cos^2(45+\varphi/2)})$, the formula for calculating the equivalent internal friction angle is effectively unified with the formula calculated according to the principle of equal shear strength.

According to the formula derived in this paper, using the rock test results of the Jinduicheng Molybdenum Mine South Open pit High Slope Project, the variation of equivalent internal friction angle of 6 kinds of rock masses with slope height under different slope angle conditions is discussed. The shear strength index of the rock block is used for calculation, and the integrity coefficient method is used to modify the calculation results. The results of the indoor shear test strength of 6 kinds of rock blocks are summarized in the following table:

Table 2. Shear strength indexes of 6 kinds of rock blocks.

Stratum	C (MPa) Maximum	Minimum	Average	Standard	Φ (°) Maximum	Minimum	Average	Standard
Metaquartz Sandstone 2	5.1	1.3	3.6	2.9	44.7	41.9	43.2	42.4
Metaquartz Sandstone 3	13.7	4.2	8.4	6.4	44.3	42.6	43.4	43.0
Slate	9.0	1.7	4.9	3.6	42.9	39.0	41.4	40.5
Quartzite	10.0	2.8	6.3	4.9	44.7	43.0	44.1	43.7
Andesitic Porphyrite	8.6	1.3	3.9	2.7	44.7	43.0	44.2	43.8
Granite	5.2	2.9	3.9	3.4	44.7	42.4	43.8	43.3

According to the previous analysis, the internal friction angle comprehensively reflects the contribution of the cohesion (C) and friction strength (f) of the rock mass to the stability of the rock mass slope. Regarding the concept of quasi-rock mass strength, the equivalent internal friction angle of the rock mass is discounted by the integrity coefficient of the rock mass ($\frac{\sigma_{cm}}{\sigma_{ci}} = (\frac{V_p^m}{V_p^i})^2 = K$), which comprehensively reflects the reduction of the rock mass structure to the rock mass shear strength.

According to the calculation results, the scatter diagram of the equivalent internal friction angle of typical andesitic porphyrite and quartzite under different slope angles varying with the slope height is drawn, as shown in Figures 5 and 6.

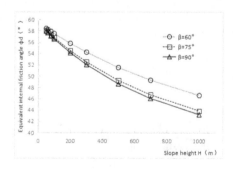

Figure 5. Φd-H scatter diagram of Andesite.

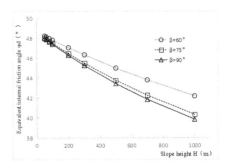

Figure 6. φd-H scatter diagram of Quartzite.

It can be seen from Figures 5 and 6 that the equivalent internal friction angle of rock mass decreases nonlinearly with the slope height. At the same time, when the slope angle is small, the equivalent internal friction angle is relatively large, and this effect gradually increases with the slope height.

5 CONCLUSION

1. The strength index of rock mass/rock block should be discussed and selected on three different scales according to the difference of test or research objects.
2. The shear strength indexes of rock mass calculated by Hoek Brown empirical formula have a good power correlation with the slope height. The c value increases nonlinearly with the slope height, and the φ value decreases nonlinearly with the slope height.
3. According to the basic principle of slope stability limit equilibrium, the formula for calculating the equivalent internal friction angle is derived. The formula takes the slope angle into account, and the calculation result is closer to the field practice.
4. The equivalent internal friction angle of rock mass decreases nonlinearly with the slope height. At the same time, when the slope angle is small, the equivalent internal friction angle is relatively large, and this effect gradually increases with the slope height.

ACKNOWLEDGMENTS

This work was supported by Jinduicheng Molybdenum Industry Co., Ltd. and Northwest Research Institute of Engineering Investigation and Design.

REFERENCES

Liu Baochen, Zhang Jiasheng, et al. Size Effect on Compression Strength of Rock. *Chinese Journal of Rock Mechanics and Engineering*, 1998,17(6):611–614.
Liu Shungui, Chi Yongxiang, et al. Size Effect on Shear Strength of Basalt Rock Mass with Columnar *Joints. Journal of Engineering Geology*, 2009,17(3):367–370.
National Standards of the People's Republic of China. *Technical Code for Non-coal Open-pit Mine Slope Engineering (GB 51016-2014)*. Beijing: China Planning Press, 2014.

Sun Guangzhong and Sun Yi. *Principles of Rock Mass Mechanics*. Beijing: Science Press, 2011.

Xu Gaowei and Bai Shiwei. Fit Analysis on Size Effect Modulus of Elasticity of Rock Mass. *Copper Engineering*, 2006,(3):17–20.

Zhou Huoming, Shen Qian, et al. Numerical Simulation Test on Macro-mechanics Parameters of Layered Rock Masses. *Chinese Journal of Rock Mechanics and Engineering*, 2004,23(2):289–292.

Zhou Huoming, Shen Qian, et al. Size Effect Analysis on Macro-mechanics Parameters for the Rock Mass of Ship-lock Slope of TGP. *Chinese Journal of Rock Mechanics and Engineering*, 2001,20(5):661–664.

Simulation of typical odor of automotive materials

Yalin Liu*, Chen Cui, Siwei Zheng, Ke Wang, Jiayong Fu, Yi Zheng & Xiaojing Zhu
CATARC Automotive Component Test Center (Ningbo) Co., Ltd.1, Ningbo, Zhejiang, China

ABSTRACT: The volatile organic compounds in the foaming materials for automotive seats were determined by low-temperature purge and trap gas chromatography-mass spectrometry, and various compounds were screened and sorted. The compounds and their contents that mainly reflect the foaming odor characteristics in the sample were determined. Finally, the typical gases representing the foaming materials were prepared with corresponding chemical reagents, and the simulation of the foaming material gas was realized. The method of simulating and restoring the typical odor of automotive materials is summarized to facilitate the research on odor-type construction and odor optimization of automotive materials.

1 INTRODUCTION

The problem of interior automotive odor is one of the key issues in the automobile industry at present. It is not only a model for health evaluation but also an important factor for evaluating vehicle comfort. In the automotive industry, the evaluation of odor in the vehicle is mainly subjective. Recently, automobile enterprises and scientific research institutions have carried out a lot of research work on automobile odor, such as optimization of evaluation methods, odor improvement, development of intelligent sniffing and identification equipment, etc. Zhu Daye (2021) proposed a method to evaluate the odor of parts and vehicles and to improve the odor of vehicles. Xu Shuangying (2019) traced the source of the vehicle odor by using the method of gas chromatography-mass spectrometry (GC-MS)/odor identification synchronous analysis. And based on the odor substances of various characteristic materials in the vehicle, such as foam, leather, rubber and so on, their odor properties cannot be studied without the reduction and simulation of odor substances. It can be seen from the literature that there is no research on typical odor simulation of materials in the industry at present.

The foaming smell is the most common typical smell in the car, through qualitative and quantitative analysis of a kind of foam material in the car, then we can screen the typical foaming odor substances in the foaming materials. And through calculation and screening, the representative odor substances with significant influence on foaming are locked, then the typical odor of foaming was trial produced by using an odor preparation device. According to the subjective evaluation of odor evaluators, the odor prepared can reflect the typical odor characteristics of foaming materials. In accordance with the above steps, we have summarized a typical odor preparation method for automotive materials to simulate the characteristics of typical odor substances of materials. The typical odor gases prepared can be used not only for the improvement of odor substances and the construction of basic data of

*Corresponding Author: liuyalin@catarc.ac.cn

intelligent odor recognition equipment but also for the odor training of odor evaluators, as well as for the optimization and development of odor types.

2 DETERMINATION OF TYPICAL ODOR SUBSTANCES AND CONTENTS

The evaluation of interior automotive odor and consumers' visual feedback are mainly based on normal temperature odor. However, during the analysis of odor substances in materials, as the odor substances in materials emit slowly at room temperature, in most cases, it will be considered to increase the temperature to accelerate the emission of odor substances. There are many methods to detect odorous substances in materials. For example, Tang Ting (2021) used the sample to heat in the airbag and then collected the gas to determine the odorous substances in the vehicle leather by using thermal desorption gas chromatography-mass spectrometry, and Yang Yuelu (2018) used headspace gas chromatography-mass spectrometry to determine the odor substances in polyurethane sponge for textiles. Through experimental comparison, it is found that the emission of odorous substances at high temperatures is significantly different from that at normal temperatures, whether from the type of substances or the number of compounds emitted. In order to ensure that the characteristics of odor substances can be well restored, this experiment needs to determine the types of odor substances and ensure the concentration ratio of odor substances. In this experiment, the method of low-temperature purging and trapping (Gu et al. 2021) combined with gas chromatography-mass spectrometry is used to ensure that the volatilization of odorous substances in materials is increased while the release of compounds at extraordinary temperatures is reduced, so as to facilitate the determination of typical odorous substances.

3 EXPERIMENTAL PARAMETERS AND STEPS

The experimental steps are as follows:

(1) Selecting the seat foam samples that have been offline for 7-14 days, and pre-treating them for 24 h at 23°C, humidity 50% RH without volatile solvents and odors before the experiment.
(2) Taking 5 g of the sample, and using scissors cut the sample particles with a mass range of 10-25 mg into a 40 ml sample vial.
(3) Purging and trapping conditions: the sampling mass is 5 g, the purging temperature is 25°C, and the purging time is 30 minutes.
(4) The analysis conditions of GC-MS were set according to HJ/T 400-2007 "Determination of Volatile Organic Compounds and Carbonyl Compounds in Cabin of Vehicles".

4 SCREENING OF TYPICAL SUBSTANCES

The screening of typical substances was confirmed from two aspects: concentration of compound and response coefficient of compound odor.

After qualitative and quantitative analysis of VOCs analyzed by low-temperature purge and trap gas chromatography/mass spectrometry, we select compounds with content greater than 10 ug/L for further screening, as we can see in the following Table 1 for the results:

For the list of detected compounds, there may be most compounds, some of which are high in content, but they are not necessarily the main influence substances of odor. Different compounds have different effects on odor. The odor activity value (Wu 2017) reflects the response intensity of the odor of different compounds by the ratio of the concentration of the odor-causing compound to the odor threshold of the substance. Therefore, for the screening of compounds, it is necessary to further consider the odor influence of compounds, and combine the odor concentration and influence to determine typical odor substances.

Table 1. Volatiles of foaming materials.

No.	Substance	CAS No.	Content C_I (ug/L)
1	Triethylenediamine	000280-57-9	317
2	Dimethylaminoethyl ether	003033-62-3	169
3	Decane	000124-18-5	85
4	Hexamethylcyclotrisiloxane	000541-05-9	30
5	Dodecane	000112-40-3	21

The odor intensity curve (Liu et al. 2021) is used to confirm typical odor substances, and the formula is as follows:

$$A = \lg c * a \quad (1)$$

where A represents the odor simulation intensity; C represents the content of compounds. The content of each compound is shown in Table 1. A represents the response coefficient of compound concentration and odor intensity. The response coefficient of the compound is calculated from the above formula as shown in Table 2 below.

Table 2. Response factors of each compound.

No.	Substance	Response Coefficient a
1	Triethylenediamine	1.04
2	Dimethylaminoethyl ether	1.30
3	Decane	0.85
4	Hexamethylcyclotrisiloxane	1.09
5	Dodecane	0.86

Formula ① is used to obtain the odor simulation intensity A_I of each compound which can be seen in Table 3, and rank A_I.

Table 3. Odor simulation intensity of compounds.

No.	Substance	Substance concentration C_I (ug/L)	Odor intensity A_I
1	Triethylenediamine	317	2.601102
2	Dimethylaminoethyl ether	169	2.896253
3	Decane	85	1.640006
4	Hexamethylcyclotrisiloxane	30	1.610062
5	Dodecane	21	1.137109

We set the odor intensity level of 2.0 as the odor threshold. After removing compounds with odor intensity of less than 2.0, the remaining substances are typical odor substances.

5 PREPARATION METHOD

As the volatile compounds that are easy to volatilize and smell under normal temperature are generally volatile substances with low boiling points, these odor compounds cannot be prepared with volatile and odorous solvents, because they need to be gasified and diluted with high-purity reagents to prepare single or mixed typical gases.

The following two factors are considered when using high-purity reagents to gasify and prepare gas:

(1) Determining the heating temperature according to the boiling point of the compound
To ensure that compounds are fully gasified when heated in the gasification equipment, the heating temperature of the equipment shall be higher than the boiling point of the compounds, but the expansion volume of liquid gasification caused by excessive temperature shall not exceed the gasification heating area. We query the boiling point of the compound to be gasified, set the heating temperature of the gas preparation instrument to 20°C above the maximum boiling point, and gasify according to the order of the amount of compound injection from more to less°C

(2) Considering the gasification efficiency and liquefaction possibility of the solution.
The gasification efficiency and liquefaction possibility of the solution should be fully considered when the solution is converted to room temperature for use and storage. Because the reagent is gasified at high temperature, and then collected and used at room temperature, it is necessary to calculate whether there is a possibility of gas liquefaction at the target volume through the saturated vapor pressure of various reagents.

5.1 Calculation of compound concentration

We set the preparation volume of simulated gas as V1 (unit: L), and calculate the volume of pure compound added v (unit: mL) in combination with the normal odor culture state of the physical sample.

$$v = c_I * V_1 / \rho \qquad (2)$$

where c_I represents the detected content of compounds in Table 1 (ug/L); V1 means that the preparation volume of analog gas is V_1(unit: L); ρ is the density of superior pure compound (g/ml).

According to the compound concentration in Table 4 and the saturation vapor pressure, the actual partial pressure of each compound is calculated as follows:

$$p_x = p_{total} n_x / n_{total} \qquad (3)$$

Table 4. Calculation of preparation volume and scaling amount.

Substance	Preparation Volume	Scaling Amount (ml)
Triethylenediamine	50 L	0.014
Dimethylaminoethyl ether	50 L	0.009

where p_x represents the actual partial pressure of compound x in the mixture; p_{total} represents the total pressure of the mixed gas; n_x represents the amount of compound x in the mixture; n_{total} always represents the total amount of substances in the mixture.

The saturated vapor pressure and other data of each compound were obtained by querying MSDS of the compound, as shown in Table 5 below.

By comparing p_x and p_m, if $p_x \leq p_m$, it indicates that the gasification component will not be liquefied at the corresponding temperature, and the gas can be used normally. If this condition is not met, it is necessary to consider increasing the release volume.

To calculate the purge gas volume of each compound from each p_x, where v_x represents the volume of compound x in the mixture; p_x represents the partial pressure of compound x in the mixture; P is the total pressure of mixed gas; v is the total volume of mixed gas. The

Table 5. Saturation vapor pressure data of compounds.

Substance	Molecular Formula	CAS No.	Temperature	Density	Saturation Vapor Pressure	Boiling Point
Triethylenediamine	$C_6H_{12}N_2$	280-57-9	25°C	1.14	1.2 mmHg	174.0 ± 0.0 °C at 760 mmHg
Dimethylaminoethyl ether	$C_8H_{20}N_2O$	3033-62-3	25°C	0.9	0.4 mmHg	194.8 ± 15.0 °C at 760 mmHg

partial pressures of the compounds in this experiment are lower than the saturated vapor pressure under their temperature, as shown in Table 6 below.

$$v_x = p_x/P * v \qquad (4)$$

Table 6. Purge volume of each compound.

Substance	Partial Pressure	Purging Volume (L)
Triethylenediamine	0.052 mmHg	36.4
Dimethylaminoethyl ether	0.020 mmHg	13.6

5.2 Preparation

After determining the type, order, amount, heating temperature and purging volume of the compounds, the heating gasification device can be used to vaporize the high-grade pure reagents of various compounds in turn, and the Teflon airbag that has been cleaned at high temperature and has no odor can be used for collection. In actual use, the content can be increased according to the proportion of the compound (the configuration part needs to be recalculated) or used after dilution, as shown in Table 7 below.

Table 7. Preparation parameters.

No.	Order of Addition	Scalar Quantity	Heating Temperature	Purging Volume (L)
1	Triethylenediamine	0.014	200 °C	36.4
2	Dimethylaminoethyl ether	0.009	220 °C	13.6

5.3 Odor subjective evaluation

The prepared gas was subjectively evaluated by five odor evaluators with blind samples, and the results are shown in Table 8 below.

Table 8. Subjective evaluation results of gas.

Personnel No	Describe
1	Foaming
2	Foaming and greasy
3	Foaming
4	Foaming taste
5	Foaming and amine

From the feedback results, the subjective evaluation results of odor are all foaming, indicating that the selection and preparation of odor substances can reflect the odor characteristics of samples. Because this experiment is only aimed at the foaming material, more accurate results need to be obtained through parameter optimization when it is applied to other materials. In addition, after obtaining typical odor substances, typical material odors with different odor characteristics can also be prepared according to the proportion of substance content.

6 SUMMARY AND OUTLOOK

At present, the development of the intelligent olfactory instrument in the automobile industry has always been the most concerned problem in the whole industry. The accumulation of data on the relationship between odor intensity and concentration of odor substances at the material level can help odor detection and research. The method of determining typical substances proposed in this experiment can lock key compounds, and further research on the relationship between odor intensity and concentration can be carried out by preparing gases. Later, the accumulated data can be used for the development of intelligent olfactory discrimination instruments, which will help to realize the olfactory evaluation work of automatic instruments instead of human beings.

In addition, through the determination of typical odor substances of automobile materials and the preparation of gas, further research on typical odor substances is possible. Through the subsequent adjustment of the proportion of typical odor substances, different odor types can also be obtained, so as to improve the odor in the vehicle.

ABOUT THE AUTHOR

Liu Yalin (1983), male, senior engineer, research direction: automobile VOC detection, automobile odor evaluation, and automobile hazardous substances detection. Email: liuyalin@catarc.ac.cn.

REFERENCES

Gu Juanhong, Yan Min, Liu Yan and Xu Zhendong. Determination of Various Odors in Textiles by Purge and Trap Gas Chromatography/mass Spectrometry. *Printing and Dyeing Auxiliaries*, 2021,38 (04): 55–59

Liu Yalin, Yao Qian, Wang Yanmeng, Li Chuanjie, Li Lixuan and Hu Junyan. The Application of Odor Intensity Curve in Vehicle Odor Control. *Automotive Technology and Materials*, 2021 (03): 34–37. DOI: 10.19710/j.cnki.1003-8817.20200071

Tang Ting and Wang Bin. Traceability and Improvement of Vehicle Leather Smell. *Proceedings of the Annual Meeting of the Chinese Society of Automotive Engineers* (2). 2021:373–377. DOI: 10.26914/c.cnkihy.2021.027201

Wu Chuandong. *Research on Odor Activity Value Coefficient Method and its Application in Odor Evaluation of Waste Dump*. Beijing University of Science and Technology, 2017

Xu Shuangying and Chen Sihang. Research on the Application of Gas Chromatography-mass spectrometry/olfactory Discrimination in Vehicle Odor Traceability. *Automotive Technology and Materials*, 2019 (06): 52–58. DOI: 10.19710/J.cnki.1003-8817.20180340

Yang Yuelu, Wang Xiaoning and Liao Qing. Composition Analysis of Polyurethane Sponge Odor. *Journal of Beijing Institute of Clothing Technology (Natural Science Edition)*, 2018, 38 (03): 22–31. DOI: 10.16454/j.cnki.issn.1001-0564.2018.03.005

Zhu Daye, Wu Feng and Zhao Xingfu. Evaluation of a New Car Odor and its Improvement Method. *Auto Parts*, 2021 (08): 59–62. DOI: 10.19466/j.cnki.1674-1986.2021.08.013

Risk identification and evolution analysis of comprehensive urban river management based on WBS - RBS - ISM

Guofa Li, Liu Yang* & Shutian Li
School of Civil Engineering and Architecture, Xi'an University of Technology, Xi'an, Shaanxi, China

Xin Wang & Yan Li
Building and Installing Engineer Co., Ltd. of China Railway 12th Bureau Group, Taiyuan, Shanxi, China

ABSTRACT: Comprehensive Management of Urban Rivers belongs to the field of public infrastructure construction, and the risk identification and evolution analysis of comprehensive management projects are the basis for effective risk management throughout the project life cycle. It starts from four aspects: politics and law, economy and finance, construction and technology, and operation and maintenance. 18 key risk factors were selected, and a WBS - RBS - ISM-based risk identification and evolution model for urban river comprehensive governance was constructed. The research and analysis were carried out in combination with the second phase of a river environmental comprehensive governance project in Xi'an. Based on the whole life cycle perspective of the urban river comprehensive management project, six main types of risk links of urban river comprehensive management are analyzed. In combination with key risks and risk transmission paths, four countermeasures and suggestions are proposed to provide a reference for risk identification and evolution analysis of similar river comprehensive management projects.

1 INTRODUCTION

Urban rivers are an important part of the national economic infrastructure, and river management plays an important role in flood prevention and disaster management and in safeguarding regional economic development (Zhu et al. 2021). Comprehensive urban river management is an important part of urban construction, a practical way to safeguard the water ecology, and an effective way to seek a healthy river ecosystem.

Peng Bei (2021) used the hierarchical analysis method to study the risk management of the construction process of the water conservancy project for the management of the Gu River in R city. Ma Li (2011) used the system level fuzzy evaluation method to conduct a post-evaluation study on the impact of an urban section of an urban area comprehensive management project and assessed the construction performance of the waterfront landscape. Zhang Linbo (2018) conducted an investigation and research on the risk management of a city's water environment comprehensive improvement EPC project by using the AHP method. Li Qingxue and Dong Tianyu (Li et al. 2022) evaluated the characteristics and risks of antibiotic pollution in typical northern urban rivers. The above incomplete search results show the results of risk analysis and research on urban river comprehensive management, river ecological management and river environmental management projects by some scholars from a single stage or all entry points.

---

*Corresponding Author: yangliu0414@163.com

Integrated urban river management faces different types and degrees of risks, therefore, it is particularly important to summarise the risk categories, distinguish the levels of risk factors and clarify the risk evolution path from the perspective of the whole project life cycle. This paper uses the WBS-RBS method to identify and modify the possible risks of integrated urban river management projects from four aspects: political and legal, economic and financial, construction technology, and operation and maintenance, and establishes and analyses the ISM risk model.

2 RISK IDENTIFICATION AND DETERMINATION

2.1 WBS-RBS initial risk source identification

Based on the project management perspective, the river comprehensive management project risk identification process with the help of the WBS-RBS method (Zheng et al. 2021), can improve not only the efficiency of risk identification but also the orderly identification of risk collection, and the standardized operation makes the induction process is not easy to appear risk factors omission.

2.1.1 WBS work breakdown tree

Regarding the management procedures of water conservancy construction projects, the whole life cycle of an integrated urban river management project is divided into the investment decision stage, the survey and design stage, the procurement and construction stage and the delivery and use stage. Through the decomposition of work activities, the work activities W_i.

2.1.2 RBS risk structure decomposition

The keywords "urban river management", "comprehensive river management" and "river management" were searched through different databases such as Web of Science and CNKI. In order to ensure the relevance of the retrieved literature to this study, 20 relevant papers were finally selected. The risk factors of integrated urban river management projects were categorised according to four attributes: political and legal, economic and financial, construction technology and operation management, and various initial risk sources were obtained by using the RBS risk decomposition structure method.

2.2 WBS-RBS coupling risk factor correction

2.2.1 Construction of WBS-RBS coupling matrix

The WBS-RBS coupling matrix facilitates the identification of key typical risks. The elements of the coupling matrix represent the mapping relationship between integrated river management work activities and the risk factors faced (Li et al. 2020), with the number of rows and columns increasing with the level of detail in the decomposition, where i - is the risk source serial number, j - represents the work activity serial number.

Fill the work activity Wi in the work breakdown tree in the first row of WBS-RBS coupling matrix, and the initial risk source H_j in the first column. In order to further extract the risk factors of comprehensive urban river management, this study, based on the perspective of stakeholders, invites an expert from the designer and construction party to conduct interviews and fill in the coupling matrix element A_{ij}. After negotiation, the WBS-RBS coupling matrix of urban river comprehensive management risk is obtained. If there is a strong mapping relationship between the engineering activity Wi and the risk factor H_j, the expert fills in the number 1 at the cross square, otherwise fills in 0.

2.2.2 Risk factor correction results

According to the WBS-RBS coupling matrix, the risk factors were screened by combining the mapping relationship between work activities and risk factors of the urban river comprehensive management project with expert opinions, the risk item H_j with the value of A_{ij} is 0 does not meet the screening requirements, and the risk item H_j with the value of A_{ij} is 1 is selected to establish the risk factor set M={M_1, M_2, M_3, ... , M_{18}}, M_1-M_{18} are the risk factor secondary index codes, and the risk index system of the urban river comprehensive management project is established as shown in Table 1.

Table 1. Risk factor correction results.

Tier 1 Indicators	Name of Risk Factor	Tier 1 Indicators	Name of Risk Factor
Political & Law	National Political M_1	Construction & techniques	Quality/safety risk M_{10}
	Inappropriate choice of design standards/specifications M_2		Materials, equipment supply M_{11}
Economy & Finance	Project finance risk M_3		Subcontractor Selection M_{12}
	Contract Management Risk M_4		Human Resource Management M_{13}
	Investment decision risk M_5	Operations & Maintenance	River Governance Orientation Change M_{14}
Construction & techniques	Delay in river training M_6		River Management Project Information Management M_{15}
	Inappropriate Governance M_7		Acceptance of completion of river training works M_{16}
	Supplier Choice M_8		Impact on the effectiveness of integrated river management M_{17}
	Organizational coordination risk M_9		Supervisory/consulting risk M_{18}

3 CONSTRUCTION OF THE ISM MODEL AND RISK EVOLUTION ANALYSIS

3.1 *ISM model construction*

ISM interpretative structural model is a system analysis method developed for analyzing complex systems (Zhang 2022). The implementation process includes element identification and correlation analysis, expert assignment to establish the adjacency matrix, and the reachability matrix obtained through the Boolean operation. Then the reachability matrix is summarized to obtain the antecedent (antecedent) set and reachable set of each risk factor. Finally, the risk link transmission is analyzed according to the element hierarchy diagram, and relevant suggestions are put forward accordingly.

3.1.1 *Creating adjacency matrix $C_{18 \times 18}$*

To establish the ISM model of the risk impact of integrated urban river management, it is necessary to judge the interrelationship between the risks, combining the modified set of risk factors M={M_1, M_2, M_3, ..., M_{18}} obtained in 1.3. to establish the adjacency matrix $C_{18 \times 18}$. The adjacency matrix is a square matrix with diagonal elements of 0, implying that the risk factors M_i themselves have no interrelationship. If risk factor M_i has a direct influence on risk factor M_j, the value is assigned to 1, otherwise, the value is assigned to 0.

It can be seen that: risk factor M_1 is defined as "national politics", which, after consultation with the experts, is classified as a root cause and there is no risk factor that affects it. M_{17} is set as "the effect of comprehensive river management", that is, the final effect of comprehensive urban river management, which can also be understood as the final risk, and will not have a direct impact on the key risk factors screened. However, by summing up the scores of experts, there are factors M_6, M_7 and M_{16} that have a direct impact on factor M_{17}, indicating that M_{17} is a risk item that occurs later in the order, so it is different from the final risk of the ISM model. The adjacency matrix is transformed into a table form to obtain Table 2.

Table 2. Adjacency matrix $C_{18 \times 18}$ transformation table.

Factors	Influencing Factors	Factors	Influencing Factors	Factors	Influencing Factors
M_1	M_3 M_7	M_7	M_6 M_{17}	M_{13}	M_7
M_2	M_{10}	M_8	M_4 M_6	M_{14}	M_7 M_8
M_3	M_{14}	M_9	M_6	M_{15}	M_6
M_4	M_7	M_{10}	M_{16}	M_{16}	M_6 M_7 M_{17}
M_5	M_{18}	M_{11}	M_6	M_{17}	–
M_6	M_{16} M_{17}	M_{12}	M_9	M_{18}	M_6

3.1.2 Calculating the reachability matrix

The calculation of the adjacency matrix requires the application of Boolean rules based on the 0-1 correlation of the risk factors given in the adjacency matrix(Xu et al. 2022), and the choice of the concatenated multiplication method to solve the reachable matrix, using the matrix form to describe the degree of influence that can be achieved by the risk factor Mi after a certain path. The kth order reachable matrix Dk of the adjacency matrix $C_{18 \times 18}$ (C_{18}) is calculated as shown in equation (1).

$$(C_{18} - E_{18}) \neq (C_{18} - E_{18})^2 \neq \cdots \neq (C_{18} - E_{18})^{k-1} = (C_{18} + E_{18})^k = D_k \tag{1}$$

3.2 Risk evolution analysis

3.2.1 Reachable sets and prior sets

It is easy to see from Table 2 that, based on the nature of C18x18, there are no factors in the table that directly affect *M1, M2, M5, M11, M12, M13* or *M15*, so such factors are generally used as the source of a particular risk link.Calculation of reachable/priority sets by computer software.According to the hierarchical division method, it can be obtained that when the prior set Q and the intersection set A satisfy Q(M_i) = Q(M_i) ∩ A(M_i), the risk factor M_i is the element of the layer (Li 2012). From the Table 3 below, we can get Q(M_1) = Q(M_1) ∩ A(M_1),

Table 3. Reachable/Prior set of tier 1 risk factors.

Factors	Up to Pool P	Advance Assembly Q	Intersection A = M ∩ Q
M_1	1,3,4,6,7,8,14,16,17	1	1
M_2	2,6,7,10,16,17	2	2
M_3	3,4,6,7,8,14,16,17	1,3	3
M_4	4,6,7,16,17	1,3,4,8,14	4
M_5	5,6,7,16,17,18	5	5
M_6	6,7,16,17	1,2,3,4,5,6,7,8,9,10,11,12,13,14,15,16,18	16,6,7
M_7	6,7,16,17	1,2,3,4,5,6,7,8,9,10,11,12,13,14,15,16	16,6,7
M_8	4,6,7,8,16,17	1,3,8,14	8
...	...	...	...
M_{14}	4,6,7,8,14,16,17	1,3,14	14
M_{15}	6,7,15,16,17	15	15
M_{16}	6,7,16,17	1,2,3,4,5,6,7,8,9,10,11,12,13,14,15,16	16,6,7
M_{17}	17	1,2,3,4,5,6,7,8,9,10,11,12,13,14,15,16,17,18	17
M_{18}	6,7,16,17,18	5,18	18

so the first layer of risk is $L_1 = \{M_1\}$. Remove M_1 from the reachable matrix to get a new reachable matrix D_{17}, continue the above steps, and so on for the second level of risk as $L_2=\{M_3\}$, the third level of risk as $L_3=\{M_{14}\}$, the fourth level of risk as $L_4=\{M_2, M_5, M_8, M_{12}\}$, the fifth level of risk as $L_5=\{M_4, M_9, M_{10}, M_{11}, M_{13}, M_{15}, M_{18}\}$, and the sixth level of risk as $L_6=\{M_6, M_7, M_{16}\}$ and the seventh level of risk is $L_7=\{M_{17}\}$.

The risk hierarchy was divided, categorizing M_1, M_3, and M_{14} as Basic influencing factors, M_6, M_7, and M_{16} as direct influencing factors, M_{17} as top-level risk factors, and the rest as indirect influencing factors.

3.2.2 Reachable sets and prior sets

Based on the adjacency matrix, the reachability matrix and the hierarchy of risk factors made for integrated urban river management, the project risk factors and their evolutionary risk chains can be obtained.

From the evolution of project risks in Figure 1, it can be seen that changes in river management orientation, inappropriate selection of design standards/specifications, investment decision risks, subcontractor selection, river management project information management, material and equipment supply, human resource management, etc. are the source risks that cause poor performance of integrated river management in urban river management projects in the final risk, and each source risk will, in turn, be along the corresponding risk transmission chain.

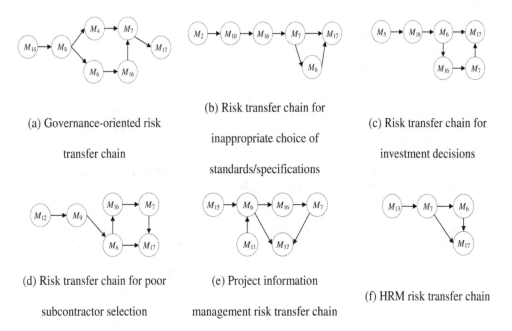

(a) Governance-oriented risk transfer chain

(b) Risk transfer chain for inappropriate choice of standards/specifications

(c) Risk transfer chain for investment decisions

(d) Risk transfer chain for poor subcontractor selection

(e) Project information management risk transfer chain

(f) HRM risk transfer chain

Figure 1. Risk evolution of integrated urban river management projects.

4 COUNTERMEASURES AND RECOMMENDATIONS

In order to make the integrated urban river management project more standardized and safe to carry out, it can effectively respond to the risks faced in the management process to achieve water safety, manage the water environment and safeguard the water ecology (Wang et al. 2022). This paper makes the following recommendations.

(1) Grasping the need of integrated river management. Urban river management projects should be people-oriented, undertake a new management concept, fully grasp the actual management needs at the beginning of the project decision, and fully consider the socio-economic and livelihood development.
(2) Systematically and comprehensively consulting design standards and specifications. An effective measure to reduce governance risks arising from inappropriate design and standard selection is to systematically and comprehensively review river governance standards and specifications when carrying out comprehensive urban river management design.
(3) Strengthening construction safety and project quality supervision. In the process of integrated river management, a quality risk monitoring mechanism is set up to control the safety and quality of the project in advance, and to control the process afterward by using the PDCA cycle principle to improve risk response.
(4) Selection of subcontractors and suppliers. The design, procurement and construction stages of the traditional engineering project management mode are independent of each other. The EPC mode adopts design, procurement and construction general contracting (Lin 2022), which largely avoids the risks brought about by the construction party sub-contracting each stage of the project separately.

5 CONCLUDING REMARKS

(1) Based on the perspective of urban river comprehensive management project management, the ISM model of urban river comprehensive management risk is constructed by sorting out multiple risks from four aspects: political and legal, economic and financial, construction technology, and operation and maintenance.
(2) The WBS–RBS coupling matrix was used to identify and revise the risk factors for integrated urban river management, giving the elements of the coupling matrix mapping relationships to avoid errors due to subjective consciousness to a certain extent. 18 key risks were systematically analyzed and collated, and a $C_{18\times 18}$ adjacency matrix was established in this way.
(3) Combined with the characteristics of the second phase of a river environmental comprehensive management project in Xi'an, the risks of the urban river comprehensive management project were identified and analyzed for evolution, and the reachable matrix D_k reachable set, prior set and their intersection were calculated and analyzed to obtain a 7-layer (L_1-L_7) risk hierarchy.
(4) According to the $C_{18\times 18}$ adjacency matrix, combined with D_k reachability matrix calculation results and visual risk hierarchy diagram, six types of risk links were sorted out, and four countermeasures and suggestions for typical risks and risk links were put forward.

ACKNOWLEDGMENTS

This work was supported by the Key Scientific Research Program of Shaanxi Provincial Department of Education (20JT056).

REFERENCES

Li W., 2012 *Study on Risk Management of International Hydropower Project General Contracting*. Dalian University of Technology.

Li Q.X., Dong T.Y., Sun W.R., Liu H.Y., Wu Li N., & Wang Q. 2022. A Typical Northern City Rivers Antibiotics Pollution Characteristics and Risk Evaluation, *Journal of Ecological Toxicology*: pp1–15.

Li Q., Qian H., Pei J.J., *et al* 2020 Safety Risk Analysis of Bridge Rhombic Hanging Basket Construction Based on WBS-RBS and Rough Set Theory, In IOP Conference Series: Materials Science and Engineering vol 780 pp 072033. IOP Publishing.

Lin L. 2022. *Discussion on the Thinking and Analysis of the Modernization and Fine Construction of Water Conservancy Project Construction Management Shaanxi Water Resources*, vol 9 pp 177–178.

Ma L. 2011 *Study on Post-impact Evaluation of Comprehensive Management Project in Laiwucheng Section of Muwen River*, Shandong Agricultural University.

Peng B. 2021 *Research on Risk Management of Water Conservancy Project Construction Process of Guhe River in R City*, Shandong University.

Wang K., Ruan P.G., Huang Y.F., Gui D.M. 2022. *Analysis of EPC General Contracting Mode of Water Conservancy Projects Yangtze River Technology and Economics*, vol 6(04) pp 62–65.

Xu Y.Q, Wen X.M., Ma S.J., *et al.* 2022 Analysis of Obstacles to the Implementation of ISM-based Whole Process Engineering Consulting Mode, *Construction Economics*, vol 43(10) pp 81–89.

Zhang J. 2022 *Analysis of Influencing Factors of New Rural Community Construction Based on ISM Method Agriculture and Technology*, vol 42(15) pp 168-172.

Zhang L.B. 2018 *Study on Risk Management of EPC Project of S City Water Environment Comprehensive Remediation*, Nanchang University.

Zheng Z., Chen Q.W., Zhang T.C., *et al* 2021 Construction Risk Analysis of Water Environment Treatment Project Based on WBS-RBS and AHP in Flood Period–Take the EPC Project of Comprehensive Management of Water Environment in the East of a City as an Example In E3S Web of Conferences. *EDP Sciences* vol 236 pp 04025.

Zhu J.W., Wang J.R., Liu Y.Y. 2021 Performance Evaluation of Urban River Ecological Governance Projects During Operation Period Based on COWA-grey Fixed-weight Clustering Method, *Chinese Journal of Water Resources and Water Engineering*, vol 32(01) pp 14–21.

Civil Engineering and Energy-Environment – Gao & Duan (Eds)
© 2023 the Author(s), ISBN 978-1-032-56057-1

A novel method of synthesizing high thermal stability of $Ce_{0.37}Zr_{0.53}(LaY)_{0.10}O_2$ by introducing sulfate ligands

Zheng Zhao, Yongqi Zhang*, Yongke Hou*, Meisheng Cui, Weixin Zhao, Qingping Zhang, Juanyu Yang, Zongyu Feng & Xiaowei Huang
National Engineering Research Center for Rare Earth, GRINM Group Corporation Limited, Grirem Advanced Materials Co., Ltd., Beijing, China
Griem Hi-tech Co. Ltd., Langfang City, Hebei, China
Rare Earth Functional Materials (Xiong' an) Innovation Center Co. Ltd., Baoding City, Hebei, China

ABSTRACT: Ceria-zirconia-based compound oxides (CZs) have been attracting great interest in the fields of environmental catalysis, but enhancing its thermal stability remains a great challenge. Here, a simple method was reported to synthesize SO_4^{2-} modified $Ce_{0.37}Zr_{0.53}(LaY)_{0.10}O_2$ (SO/CZLY) with high thermal stability. Various molar concentrations of SO_4^{2-} ligands were introduced in the co-precipitation process as a coordination agent. Based on the structural characterization of SO/CZLY and CZLY, we found that the smaller grain size and better particle dispersion can be achieved by introducing SO_4^{2-}. The thermal stability of SO/CZLY can be improved. Compared with the traditional co-precipitation method without SO_4^{2-} ligands, SO/CZLY has a larger specific surface area (SSA). In addition, the SO/CZLY-0.3 (molar concentrations of SO_4^{2-} = 0.3 mol/L) aged sample has the highest SSA (23.1 m^2/g-1100°C/10 h) and oxygen storage capacity (326.1 μmol O_2 g-1).

1 INTRODUCTION

CZs have been attracting great interest in the fields of environmental catalysis energy, such as three-way catalysts (TWCs) (Montini, Melchionna, Monai, Fornasiero 2016) and solid oxide fuel cells (Esch et al. 2005). Nevertheless, CZs are used in high temperatures (>90°C) (Haneda et al. 2010). It is easy to be sintered above that temperature, causing the attenuation of SSA and oxygen storage capacity (OSC), further reducing the catalytic activity of TWCs. Thus, the synthesis of high SSA and OSC of CZs materials is of great significance for their practical applications.

Interestingly, the introduction of a dopant is one of the useful methods to improve the SSA and OSC of CZs. Moreover, metal elements are considered good accelerants (Guo et al. 2013; Yang et al. 2015; Zhou et al. 2018). When metal accelerants such as La, Y, Ca, and Mg, the SSA of CZs will increase due to the increase in structural stability. At present, the modulation of metal and metal-related components in CZs has attracted much attention to improving SSA and OSC. Moreover, in the process of co-precipitation synthesis, a variety of organic compounds can be used as coordination agents to form a rare earth ion buffer system (Feng et al. 2010; Si et al. 2007; Wang et al. 2010). However, enhancing the thermal stability (1100°C/10 h) of CZs remains a great challenge.

In this work, the high thermal stability of $Ce_{0.37}Zr_{0.53}(LaY)_{0.10}O_2$ was synthesized by a simple method. SO_4^{2-} was introduced to regulate the precipitation kinetic of $ZrO2+$. It was found that SO/CZLY-0.3 (SO_4^{2-} molarity=0.3 mol/L) has the largest SSA (23.1 m^2/g).

---

*Corresponding Authors: zcrise@163.com and hyongke@126.com

Furthermore, the SO/CZLY-0.3 sample has the highest OSC of 326.1 m²/g, indicating an enhanced CZs material for TWCs.

2 EXPERIMENTAL DETAILS

2.1 *Preparation of CZs*

The sulfate-aided co-precipitation method was used to prepare $Ce_{0.37}Zr_{0.53}(LaY)_{0.10}O_2$ samples, where the SO_4^{2-} ligand was introduced in the co-precipitation process as a coordination agent. Cerium nitrate, zirconium oxynitrate, lanthanum nitrate, and yttrium nitrate solutions at the different molarity of SO_4^{2-} were precipitated with ammonia. The different molar concentrations of SO_4^{2-} were set as 0.1~0.5 mol/L with an interval of 0.1 mol/L. The sample of CZs was further calcined at 800°C for 3 h. Afterward, the SO/CZLY-a aged samples can be obtained by heating treatment at 1100°C/10 h.

2.2 *Characterizations*

Powder XRD of $Ce_{0.37}Zr_{0.53}(LaY)_{0.10}O_2$ was characterized using a diffraction instrument working at 40 kV and 40 mA, using Cu Kα radiation by setting λ = 0.15418 nm. The XRD patterns were collected from 10° to 90° (2θ) with a 0.02° step size. The SSA of $Ce_{0.37}Zr_{0.53}(LaY)_{0.10}O_2$ fresh and aged samples was characterized by Quadrasorb SI-KR/4MP. The microstructure of $Ce_{0.37}Zr_{0.53}(LaY)_{0.10}O_2$ fresh and aged samples was characterized by high-resolution TEM.

3 RESULTS AND DISCUSSIONS

3.1 *The phase structure and dispersion properties*

The phase structure of the sample was characterized by XRD. As given in Figure 1 (a), $Ce_{0.37}Zr_{0.53}(LaY)_{0.10}O_2$ has four broad diffraction peaks near 29.67°, 34.40°, 49.39° and 58.81°, which belongs to <111>, <200>, <220> and <311> crystal planes. There is no significant difference in XRD spectra, indicating that the phase structure of Ce0.37Zr0.53(LaY)0.10O2 is slightly affected by the addition of SO_4^{2-} with different molar concentrations. In addition, the peak is more obvious as shown in Figure 1 (b), indicating that the high crystallinity can be obtained by the aging process. According to the Debye Scherrer equation

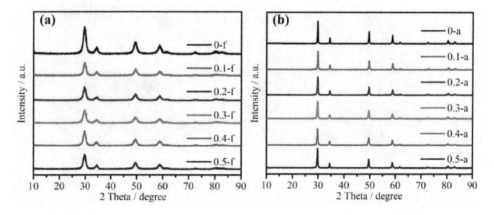

Figure 1. XRD spectrum of $Ce_{0.37}Zr_{0.53}(LaY)_{0.10}O_2$-f (a) and $Ce_{0.37}Zr_{0.53}(LaY)_{0.10}O_2$-a samples.

(Otwinowski & Minor 1997), the grain size (GS) can be calculated as shown in Table 1. It can be found that the grain size of SO/CZLY-0.3 fresh (6.5 nm) and aged (30.0 nm) samples is smaller than that of other CZs samples.

Table 1. The GS of $Ce_{0.37}Zr_{0.53}(LaY)_{0.10}O_2$ Samples.

Samples	0-f	0.1-f	0.2-f	0.3-f	0.4-f	0.5-f
Grain Sizes(nm)	6.9	7.5	7.0	6.5	7.7	7.7
Samples	0-a	0.1-a	0.2-a	0.3-a	0.4-a	0.5-a
Grain Sizes (nm)	45.9	44.2	36.5	30.0	36.2	39.5

Figure 2 (a–f) shows the TEM images of SO/CZLY-0-a, SO/CZLY-0.1-a, SO/CZLY-0.2-a, SO/CZLY-0.3-a, SO/CZLY-0.4-a, SO/CZLY-0.4-a, and SO/CZLY-0.5-a. It can be found that, compared with other samples, SO/CZLY-0.3-a has better dispersion performance. The high dispersion of SO/CZLY-0.3-a is caused by introducing SO_4^{2-}, which regulates the precipitation kinetic of $ZrO2^+$ (Li & Li 2002). In addition, the particle size of the SO/CZLY-0.3-a sample is more uniform, indicating that SO/CZLY-0.3-a has better particle dispersion. Therefore, it can be concluded that SO/CZLY-0.3-a has better dispersion performance, which is conducive to increasing the SSA.

Figure 2. TEM images of SO/CZLY-0-a (a), SO/CZLY-0.1-a (b), SO/CZLY-0.2-a (c), SO/CZLY-0.3-a (d), SO/CZLY-0.4-a (e), and SO/CZLY-0.5-a (f) samples.

3.2 Thermal stability and OSC

To investigate the thermal stability of $Ce_{0.37}Zr_{0.53}(LaY)_{0.10}O_2$ with different molar concentrations of SO_4^{2-}, Figure 3 (a) gives the SSA of $Ce_{0.37}Zr_{0.53}(LaY)_{0.10}O_2$. It can be found that the dependence of the SSA on the different molar concentrations of SO_4^{2-} is not a monotonic change, but experiences two different stages. The SSA increases monotonically firstly. Then, it begins to decrease at specific molar concentrations of SO_4^{2-} SSA of SO/CZLY-0.3, which has the largest SSA (23.1 m^2/g), 2.13 times higher than SSA of SO/CZLY-0. Moreover, the OSC of SO/CZLY-0-a, SO/CZLY-0.1-a, SO/CZLY-0.2-a, SO/CZLY-0.3-a, SO/CZLY-0.4-a, and SO/CZLY-0.5-a was further characterized. As shown in Figure 3(b), the OSC of SO/CZLY-0.3-a (326.3 μmol O_2 g^{-1}) was larger than SO/CZLY-0-a (282.1 μmol O_2 g^{-1}). In a word, SO/CZLY-0.3-a has higher thermal stability and OSC.

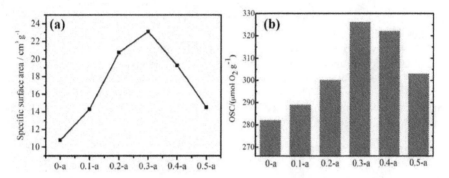

Figure 3. The SSA of $Ce_{0.37}Zr_{0.53}(LaY)_{0.10}O_2$ aged samples (a); The histogram image of the OSC for $Ce_{0.37}Zr_{0.53}(LaY)_{0.10}O_2$ aged samples (b).

3.3 Mechanism analysis

In order to understand the sulfate effect on co-precipitation of $Ce_{0.37}Zr_{0.53}(LaY)_{0.10}O_2$, its mechanism was further analyzed. As shown in Figure 4(a), FTIR of $Ce_{0.37}Zr_{0.53}(LaY)_{0.10}O_2$ indicates the existing SO_4^{2-} in the surface. Therefore, the performance improvement can be explained by the action of SO_4^{2-} as shown in Figure 4 (b). SO_4^{2-} can decrease the

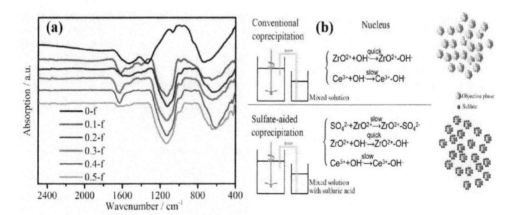

Figure 4. The FTIR of $Ce_{0.37}Zr_{0.53}(LaY)_{0.10}O_2$ fresh samples (a); The sulfate-aided mechanism during precipitation (b).

precipitation rate of ZrO^{2+} and achieve homogeneous precipitation of ZrO^{2+}, Ce^{3+}, and other RE. When the molar concentration of SO42- increases to 0.3 mol/L, the introduction of sulfate ions in the mixed solution can make Zr and Ce precipitate more uniformly, which can improve the dispersion of nanoparticles and the particle size. Therefore, it is in favor of improving thermal stability and OSC. The further detailed mechanism has been analyzed in our previous work (Chen et al. 2021).

4 CONCLUSION

In a word, a simple method was reported to synthesize SO_4^{2-} modified $Ce_{0.37}Zr_{0.53}(LaY)_{0.10}O_2$ with high thermal stability and OSC. Various molar concentrations of SO_4^{2-} ligands were introduced in the co-precipitation process as a coordination agent. It is found that the performance of $Ce_{0.37}Zr_{0.53}(LaY)_{0.10}O_2$ could be adjusted by the molar concentrations of SO4^{2-}. With this strategy, the SSA of SO/CZLY-0.3 has the largest SSA (23.1 m^2/g), which is 2.13 times higher than that of SO/CZLY-0. Moreover, the OSC of SO/CZLY-0.3-a was obviously improved to 326.3 μmol O2 g-1 from 282.1 μmol O2 g^{-1} for SO/CZLY-0-a. The sulfate-aided mechanism was further analyzed. SO_4^{2-} can decrease the precipitation rate of ZrO^{2+} and achieve homogeneous precipitation of ZrO^{2+}, Ce^{3+}, and other RE, which is beneficial for increasing the TS and OSC. Our results suggest that TS and OSC of CZs can be tuned by molar concentrations of SO$_4$$^{2-}$, which is critical for guiding the experimental preparation of high-performance CZs.

ACKNOWLEDGMENTS

This work was financially supported by the National Key Research and Development Program (2021YFB3503201, 2021YFB3503203), National Natural Science Foundation of China (52204376), Youth Foundation of Hebei Province (E2022103007), High tech Zone Science and Technology Project of Yanjiao (YJXM211211), Youth Fund Project of GRINM (G12620223129035), and Young Elite Scientists Sponsorship Program by CAST.

REFERENCES

Chen S., Hou Y. and Wang H. (2021). Enhanced Thermal Stability of Ce0. 33Zr0. 55 (LaNdY) 0.12 O2 Mixed Oxides Prepared by Sulfate-aided Co-Precipitation Method. *Journal of Rare Earths.*, 39(5): 587–595.
Esch F., Fabris S., Zhou L., Montini T., Africh C., Fornasiero P., Comelli G. and Rosei R. (2005) *Electron Localization Determines Defect Formation on Ceriasubstrates, Science.*, 309, 752-755.
Feng W., Sun L.D., Zhang Y.W. and Yan C.H. (2010) Synthesis and Assembly of Rare Earth Nanostructures Directed by the Principle of Coordination Chemistry in the Solution-based Process. *Coord. Chem. Rev.*, 254(9–10): 1038.
Guo J., Shi Z., Wu D., Yin H., Gong M. and Yaoqiang C. (2013) Study of Pt–Rh/CeO$_2$–ZrO$_2$–M$_x$O$_y$ (M=Y, La)/Al$_2$O$_3$ Three-way Catalysts. *Appl. Surf. Sci.*, 273:527.
Haneda M., Houshito O., Sato T., Takagi H., Shinoda K., Nakahara Y., Hiroe, K. and Hamada H. (2010) Improved Activity of Rh/CeO2–ZrO2 Three-way Catalyst by High-temperature Aging. *Catal. Commun.*, 11, 317–321.
Li C. and Li M. (2002) UV Raman Spectroscopic Study on the Phase Transformation of ZrO2, Y2O3-ZrO2, and SO42-/ZrO2. *J. Raman Spectrosc.*, 33:301.
Montini T., Melchionna M., Monai M. and Fornasiero P. (2016) Fundamentals and Catalytic Applications of CeO2-based Materials. *Chem. Rev.*, 116, 5987–6041.
Otwinowski Z. and Minor W. (1997) Processing of X-ray diffraction data collected in oscillation mode. *Methods Enzymol.*, 276(97):307.

Si R., Zhang Y.W., Wang L.M., Li S.J., Lin B.X., Chu W.S. (2007) Enhanced Thermal Stability and Oxygen Storage Capacity for CexZr1-xO2 (x= 0.4–0.6) Solid Solutions by Hydrothermally Homogenous Doping of Trivalent Rare Earth. *Phys. Chem. C.*, 111, 787.

Wang Q.Y., Zhao B., Li GF., Zhou R.X. (2010) Application of Rare Earth Modified Zr-based Ceria-zirconia Solid Solution in the three-way catalyst for Automotive Emission Control. *Environ. Sci. Technol.*, 44(10): 3870.

Yang X., Yang L., Lin S. and Zhou R. (2015) Investigation on Properties of Pd/CeO$_2$-ZrO$_2$-Pr$_2$O$_3$ Catalysts with Different Ce/Zr Molar Ratios and its Application for Automotive Emission Control. *J. Hazard. Mater.*, 285:182.

Zhou Y., Xiong L., Deng J., Wang J., Yuan S. and Lan L. (2018) Facile Synthesis of High Surface Area Nanostructured Ceria-Zirconia-Yttria-Lanthana Solid Solutions with the Assistance of Lauric Acid and Dodecylamine. *Mater. Res. Bull.*, 99:281.

Effect of different dosing of fly ash and silica fume on the mechanical properties of coral concrete

Wei Liu*

No.3 Engineering Company Ltd. of CCCC Second Harbor Engineering Company Ltd. Jiangsu, China

ABSTRACT: To investigate the effect of different amounts of fly ash and silica fume on the mechanical properties of coral concrete, this paper was conducted to examine the effect of various amounts of fly ash and silica fume on the mechanical properties of coral concrete. The optimum mechanical properties of coral concrete were tested in the previous study. Then different amounts of fly ash and silica fume (5%, 10%, and 15%) were added to the coral concrete, and the specimens were tested for their compressive strength after curing. Finally, the internal structure of hydration products of coral concrete with different doses of fly ash and silica fume were compared and analyzed by SEM electron microscopy to analyze the effect of fly ash and silica fume on the compressive strength of coral concrete from a microscopic point of view. The final results show that the compressive strength of the coral concrete cured for 28d increases with the increase of the admixture when the fly ash admixture is inevitable and the silica fume admixture is between 5% and 10%, while the compressive strength of the coral concrete is the opposite when the silica fume admixture is between 10% and 15%. Secondly, when the silica fume admixture is 15%, and the fly ash admixture is between 5% and 15%, the compressive strength of the coral concrete increases with the increase of fly ash admixture and decreases. When silica fume admixture is 5% and 10%, the compressive strength of coral concrete grows linearly in the interval of 5%-10% of fly ash admixture and decreases linearly in the gap of 10%-15% of fly ash admixture. The structure of the hydration product of fly ash admixture with 10% of silica fume is the best, and the strength of coral concrete is the highest at this time.

1 INTRODUCTION

With the increasing rise of marine engineering, coral concrete is gradually increasing. To further extend the service life of coral concrete, a lot of research has been conducted on the durability of coral concrete, the most typical of which is the study of the mechanical properties of coral concrete (Cheng et al. 2017; Wang et al 2014; Wang 2016). Through a large number of studies, it was found that the addition of fly ash and silica fume in concrete is a critical way to improve the performance of concrete. Adding the appropriate amount of silica fume to concrete can play an excellent capillary filling effect and reduce the porosity of concrete, which can significantly improve the strength and durability of concrete. Incorporation of the appropriate amount of fly ash in concrete can reduce the cost of the project and enhance the compatibility and pumpability of concrete, reduce the heat of hydration of concrete, reduce the hazards caused by an alkali-aggregate reaction in concrete, and to a certain extent, can effectively improve the impermeability and frost resistance of the structure (Jalal et al. 2015; Liu 2011; Safiuddin & Zain 2005). Therefore, it is essential to study the specific different admixtures of fly ash and silica fume on the mechanical properties of coral concrete.

---

*Corresponding Author: 421651201@qq.com

The efficient use of fly ash and silica fume has resulted in significant cost savings in construction projects. Therefore a lot of research has been carried out on fly ash and silica fume by every pair of people. Among them, Chung (Chung et al. 2010) studied the effect of fly ash and silica fume on the frost durability of concrete. The results showed that the incorporation of fly ash and silica fume reduced the chloride ion permeability coefficient of concrete specimens after 300 freeze-thaw cycles, where the concrete with silica fume had the smallest chloride ion permeability coefficient and the best durability, and the concrete with fly ash also showed better frost resistance. Hariharan A R (Hariharan et al. 2011) studied the effect of different doses of fly ash and silica fume on the strength of high-strength concrete. The results showed that adding different proportions of fly ash and silica fume usually exhibited excellent hardening characteristics because the combination of the two had some synergistic effect. The addition of silica fume exhibited early strength growth characteristics, while fly ash exhibited late strength growth characteristics. Through the above studies, it is easy to find that most of the existing studies focus on how adding fly ash to ordinary concrete can improve its workability and adding silica fume can improve the compactness of concrete, while the combination of fly ash and silica fume applied to coral concrete is focused on by very few scholars. Therefore, it is important to investigate the compressive strength of coral concrete with different amounts of fly ash and silica fume and to provide a solid basis for further understanding the effects of fly ash and silica fume on the mechanical properties of coral concrete.

In this paper, the changes in the compressive strength of coral concrete at different composition ratios are studied by selecting the best mechanical property ratio of coral concrete and adding different amounts of fly ash and silica fume according to the best composition ratio of mechanical properties. Then the effects of various parts of fly ash and silica fume on the mechanical properties of coral concrete are comprehensively analyzed. Finally, the structure of internal hydration products of coral concrete with different amounts of fly ash and silica fume is compared and analyzed by SEM scanning electron microscope. Then the effect of fly ash and silica fume on the compressive strength of coral concrete is studied from a microscopic perspective.

2 EXPERIMENTAL MATERIALS AND METHODS

The performance parameters of fly ash and silica fume used in the tests in this paper are shown in Tables 1 and 2.

Table 1. Parameters of fly ash.

Burning Loss/%	Density/ g/cm^3	Ratio Table/ m^2/g	Fineness/ %	SO$_3$ Content/ %	Water Content/ %	Water Demand Ratio/%	Adequacy/ mm
≤ 8.0	—	≥ 15	≤ 25	≤ 3	≤ 1.0	≤ 105	≤ 5.0
3.7	2.16	17.2	8.7	0.8	0.5	98	2.0

Table 2. Parameters of silica.

Burning Loss/%	Density/ g/cm^3	Ratio Table/ m^2/g	Fineness/ %	SO$_3$ Content/ %	Water Content/ %	Water Demand Ratio/ %	Adequacy/ mm
≤ 6.0	—	≥ 15	≤ 10	≤ 85	≤ 1	≤ 125	≤ 105
2.5	2.7	17.2	2.4	90.2	0.7	121	109

Through the previous research, we determine the optimal ratio of mechanical properties of poured coral concrete, and the specific data are shown in Table 3 below. In this paper, we study the effect of different amounts of fly ash and silica fume on their mechanical properties based on the optimal ratio of mechanical properties.

Table 3. Mix ratio of coral concrete with optimal mechanical properties.

Water-to-glue Ratio	Water (kg/m^3)	Total Cementitious Material (kg/m^3)	Coral Sand (kg/m^3)	Coral Reefs (kg/m^3)	Water Reducer (kg/m^3)
0.35	195	557	749	749	4

Checking the literature (Ghutke & Bhandari 2014), it is known that the admixture of silica fume in concrete should be controlled at 5%-15%. At the same time, the compressive strength of the concrete is reduced if too much fly ash is added. Therefore, in this work, the admixture of fly ash and silica fume is limited to 5-15%. The compressive strength of coral concrete with a different admixture of fly ash is compared by comparing the compressive strength of coral concrete with a foreign admixture of fly ash under the premise of quantitative silica fume admixture and the compressive strength of coral concrete with a different admixture of fly ash under the premise of quantitative assumption and by comparing the compressive strength of coral concrete with different dosages of silica fume. For the comparison, the specimens required for the test were cast under the above conditions. After the specimens were released and stored in the standard curing room for 28 days, they were tested for compressive strength. The effects of different amounts of fly ash and silica fume on the mechanical properties of coral concrete were analyzed by comparing the compressive strength values. Finally, the effect of fly ash and silica fume on the compressive strength of coral concrete was analyzed by SEM electron microscopy of coral concrete with different amounts of fly ash and silica fume from a comparative microscopic view.

3 TEST RESULTS AND ANALYSIS

3.1 *Compressive strength test of coral concrete with different amounts of fly ash and silica fume*

After repeated tests, in order to make the effect of fly ash and silica fume on the compressive strength of coral concrete more illustrative, we analyze the following two cases.:

1. When the amount of fly ash is kept constant, the compressive strength test data for coral concrete are shown in Table 4 below.

It can be seen from the above table that the compressive strength of coral substantially changes as the amount of silica fume changes when the addition of fly ash is safe, and the effect curve is shown in Figure 1.

As seen from Figure 1, when the amount of fly ash was less than 5%, the compressive strength of the 28d cube of coral concrete increased with the amount of silica fume. When the amount of fly ash was 10%, the compressive strength increased and then decreased, with a maximum compressive strength of 28d of 45 MPa at 10% silica fume content. The compressive strength of the cubes also showed a trend of first increasing and then decreasing with the increasing addition of silica fume, with a maximum compressive strength of 28d of 38.9 MPa at 10% silica fume content. There are two main reasons for presenting the above law, one is the physical effect of silica fume, namely the particle filling impact, whereby the fine

Table 4. Results of cube compressive strength test 1.

Specimen Number	Fly Ash Content %	Silica Fume Content %	28d Compressive Strength (MPa)
TS1	5	5	38.7
TS2		10	39.5
TS3		15	42.7
TS4		5	41.9
TS5	10	10	45.0
TS6		15	40.4
TS7		5	35.8
TS8	15	10	38.9
TS9		15	37.6

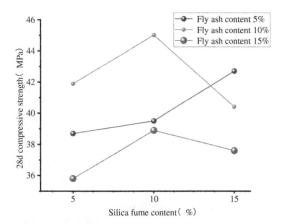

Figure 1. Influence of silica fume content on compressive strength of coral concrete.

particles of silica fume are uniformly dispersed between cement particles and improve the particle size distribution of cementitious materials. It improves the particle size distribution of cementitious materials, the compaction of cement mortar, the compaction of coral aggregate and cement paste, and the bond strength of the coral aggregate-cement paste interface. On the other hand, the effect of silica fume volcanic ash: silica fume is very active at room temperature, and the SiO_2 of silica fume reacts with the calcium hydroxide produced by cement hydration to form calcium silicate gel (Ren 2017), which can improve the strength of all-coral concrete.

However, the compressive strength of coral concrete tended to decrease when the proportions of fly ash and silica fume exceeded 10% and 10%, respectively. At the same time, the compressive strength of coral concrete also showed a tendency to decrease when the proportions of fly ash and silica fume exceeded 15% and 10%, respectively. The main reason for this phenomenon is the tendency for the mix's amount of fly ash and silica fume to increase. Excessive amounts of silica fume increase the mass loss of coral concrete and ultimately reduce the strength of the concrete, as large quantities of excess silica fume combine with water to form a silica-rich gel, which absorbs large amounts of water and reduces the compatibility of the concrete.

(2) When the amount of silica fume mixing is certain, the compressive strength test data of coral concrete are organized as shown in the following Table 5.

Similarly, observation of the above table shows that when the amount of silica fume admixture is certain, the compressive strength of coral concrete varies with the amount of fly ash admixture, and its influence curve is shown in Figure 2.

Table 5. Results of cube compressive strength test 2.

Specimen Number	Fly Ash Content %	Silica Fume Content %	28d Compressive Strength (MPa)
TS1	5	5	38.7
TS4		10	41.9
TS7		15	35.8
TS2		5	39.5
TS5	10	10	45.0
TS8		15	38.9
TS3		5	42.7
TS6	15	10	40.4
TS9		15	37.6

From the above figure, it can be seen that: when silica fume dosing is 5%, coral concrete 28d cubic compressive strength with the increase of fly ash dosing shows a trend of first increase and then decrease, when fly ash dosing is 10%, 28d compressive strength maximum is 41.9 MP; when silica fume dosing is 10%, coral concrete 28d cubic compressive strength also with the increase of fly ash dosing shows a trend of first increase and then decrease; when the amount of fly ash admixture is 10%, 28d compressive strength maximum is 45 MPa. With a 15% addition of silica fume, the cubic compressive strength of coral concrete with the addition of fly ash shows a decreasing trend, and the tendency of decreasing strength is more evident due to this law of strength variation. The addition of fly ash, which partially replaces cement, improves the concrete's fluidity, compressibility, and adhesion.

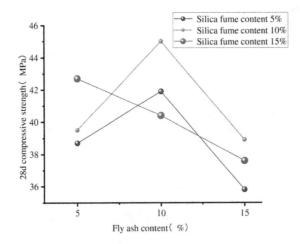

Figure 2. Influence of fly ash content on compressive strength of coral concrete.

The combined effect of the active and micro-aggregate effects of fly ash is that the active SiO_2 and Al_2O_3 of fly ash react with the cement hydrate $Ca(OH)_2$ to form calcium silicate hydrate and aluminate hydrate, reducing the number of crystals in the concrete and filling voids in the concrete. Thus This increases the compressibility of the concrete. However, increasing the amount of fly ash in the mix leads to an excess of fly ash after the reaction of the active SiO_2 and Al_2O_3 in the fly ash with the cement hydrate $Ca(OH)_2$, producing a matrix mortar (Wang et al. 2020) and reducing the compressive strength of the coral concrete.

3.2 Microstructural analysis

The hydration products and the microstructure of the cement after mixing with fly ash and silica fume were investigated by scanning electron microscopy (SEM) to further analyze the effect of fly ash and silica fume on the mechanical properties of the corroded concrete, whose specific microstructure is shown in the following figures.

Figure 3 (a) shows the microscopic morphology of the hydration products of the fly ash-free and silica fume-free coral concrete. It shows that the main product is dense C-S-H, along with a large number of calcium hydroxide crystals, which are thought to affect the formation of adhesive strength in the transition zone at the interface between the aggregate and silica fume, reducing the overall strength of the coral concrete. However, when the cement mortar penetrates the pores of the coral aggregate and binds tightly to the cement matrix surrounding the aggregate, some of these hydration products form (Qi & Ba 2000), increasing the bond strength at the interface. This embedded structure results in a higher strength in the transition zone between the aggregate and mortar in coral concrete than in conventional concrete.

Figures 3 (b) to 3 (j) show the hydrated coral concrete mixed with fly ash and silica fume. Observation (e) in Figure 3 shows that the microscopic morphology of the transition zone between coral aggregate and mortar changes significantly after mixing fly ash and silica fume. In the absence of fly ash and silica fume, the transition zone between the coral aggregate and the mortar interface is mainly composed of hydrates infiltrated into the pores of the coral aggregate. However, Figure 1 (e) shows that thin calcium hydroxide flakes are present at the aggregate-solution interface, filling the voids between the hydration products and the aggregates. Therefore, the aggregate, together with the calcium hydroxide filled the interfacial zone (Sarkar et al. 1992), reducing the porosity and improving the pore structure, increasing the density and improving the properties of the coral concrete.

Observations (b)-(j) show that when fly ash and silica fume were mixed, the hydrated calcium silicate gel was also predominantly in dense form. But due to the reaction of the volcanic ash, the fly ash and silica fume reduced the number and size of calcium hydroxide crystals, increased the content of hydrated calcium silicate and calcium aluminate, increased the content of calcium aluminate, and improved the macroscopic strength of the coral concrete. In particular, Figure (f) shows that there are few flaky calcium hydroxide crystals and that fibrous and cloudy cohesive hydrated silicates appear in addition to the dense hydrated silicate gel form, indicating that the different C-S-H gel forms combine to form a homogeneous dense cross-linked structure. As a result of the continuous hydration reaction, the initial water-filled spaces are gradually replaced by hydration products, with a consequent increase in the density of the system, ultimately leading to a significant increase in the strength of the coral concrete, so that the structure of the hydration products ranging from a 10% silica fume to a 10% fly ash mix is optimal in obtaining the highest strength coral concrete.

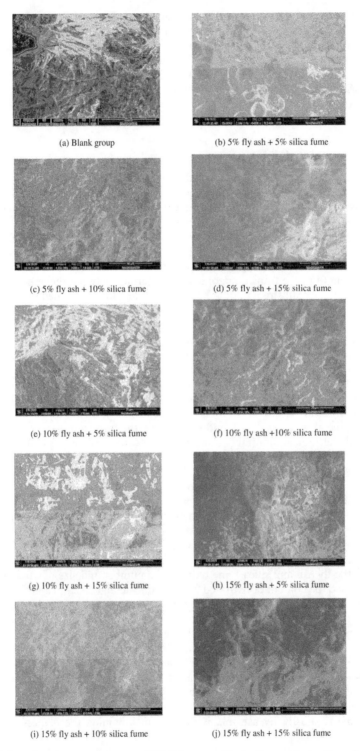

Figure 3. 9 Scanning electron microscope (SEM) images of hydration products of coral concrete with different silica fume content of fly ash.

376

4 CONCLUSION

In this paper, after experimental analysis, we have chosen the optimal mechanical properties of coral concrete ratio as the basis, comparing and analyzing the effect of different doping amounts of fly ash and silica fume on the mechanical properties of coral concrete obtained some conclusions as follows.

(1) When the amount of fly ash is certain, the compressive strength of coral concrete cured for 28d when the amount of silica fume is between 5% and 10% increases with the increase of the amount of the mixture, while the compressive strength of coral concrete does not increase with the increase of the amount of the mix when the amount of silica fume is between 10% and 15%.
(2) When the silica fume admixture is 15% and fly ash admixture is between 5% and 15%, coral concrete's compressive strength decreases with the increase of fly ash admixture. When the silica fume admixture is 5% and 10%, the compressive strength of coral concrete increases linearly in the interval of 5% to 10% of fly ash admixture and decreases linearly in the gap of 10% to 15% of fly ash admixture.
(3) The structure of the hydration product of fly ash mixed with 10% of silica fume is the best, and the strength of coral concrete is the highest at this time.

REFERENCES

Cheng S., Shui Z., Sun T. et al. Effects of Fly Ash, Blast Furnace Slag and Metakaolin on Mechanical Properties and Durability of Coral Sand Concrete. *Applied Clay Science*, 2017, 141(JUN.):111–117.

Chul-Woo.Chung, Shon Chang-Seon and Young-Su Kim. Chloride Diffusivity of Fly Ash and Silica Fume Concretes Exposed to Freeze-thaw cycles. *Construction and Building Materials*, 2010(2).

Ghutke V.S., Bhandari P.S. Influence of Silica Fume on Concrete. *IOSR Journal of Mechanical and Civil Engineering*, 2014.

Hariharan A.R., Santhi A.S., Ganesh G.M. Study on Strength Development of High Strength Concrete Containing Fly ash and Silica Fume. *International Journal of Engineering Science & Technology*, 2011.

Jalal M., Pouladkhan A., Harandi O.F. et al. Comparative Study on Effects of Class F fly ash, Nano Silica and Silica Fume on Properties of High-performance Self-compacting Concrete. *Construction and Building Materials*, 2015, 94:90–104.

Liu B.Y., Kai L.I., Zhao S.C. Study of Effects on Chloride Resistance to Ion Penetration and Frost of Concrete Mixed with Fly Ash and Silica Fume. *Concrete*, 2011.

Qi J.Y. and Ba H.J. Research on Lightweight High-Performance Concrete. *New Building Materials*, 2000,9(6): 19–21

Ren Y.Y. *Experimental Research on Attack and Freeze-thaw Properties for Silica Fume Fly Ash Concrete Under Seawater Environment*. Shandong University of Science and Technology, 2017.

Safiuddin M. and Zain M. Effects of Silica Fume and Fly Ash on the Properties of High-performance Concrete[C] *The 33rd Annual General Conference of the Canadian Society for Civil Engineering*. 2005.

Sarkar S.L, Chandra S. and Berntsson L. Interdependence of Microstructure and Strength of Structural Lightweight Aggregate Concrete. *Cement and Concrete Composites*, 1992, 14(1):239–248

Tiao Wang, Tetsuya Ishida and Rui Gu. A Study of the Influence of Crystal Components on the Reactivity of Low-calcium Fly Ash in Alkaline Conditions Based on SEM-EDS. *Construction and Building Materials*, 2020,243.

Wang L., Liu C.P., Xiong Z.J. Study Test on Mechanical Property of Sisal Fiber Reinforced Coral Concrete. *Journal of Henan Polytechnic University (Natural Science)*, 2014.

Wang Q. Mechanical Properties and Microstructure of Portland Cement Concrete Prepared with Coral Reef Sand. *Journal of Wuhan University of Technology-Materials Science Edtion*, 2016.

Research on QC achievement problems and countermeasures of water project safety production based on high-quality development

Qian Fu*
River And Lake Protection, Construction and Operation Safety Center, Haihe River Water Conservancy Commission, MWR, Tianjin, China

Hui Tan*
Center Of Construction Management & Quality & Safety Supervision, Ministry of Water Resources, Beijing, P.R. China

Zhenyu Bai
Tianjin Institute of Science and Technology Information, Tianjin, China

Mengting Huang
CHN Energy Dadu Rive Repair & Installation Co., Ltd, Sichuan, China

ABSTRACT: In 2016-2021, the number of production safety accidents in the field of water project construction accounted for an average proportion of 82.52% of industrial accidents. During the same period, safety QC (quality control) results accounted for only 2.38% of the total 2858 results of the water project, in contrast to the proportion of accidents. With the expansion of construction in 2022, reducing accidents with quality work methods is an urgent need. The QC results creation of safety production is highly in line with the "fifteen measures of safety production", which is an effective way to develop high-quality safety work in the water project. This study analyzes the problems and causes of QC results, proposes suggestions for improvement, and fills the gaps.

1 INTRODUCTION

On June 17, 2022, Shanzhong Wei, Vice Minister of Water Resources, said at a press conference, "In terms of this year, the country is going to finish investing more than 800 billion yuan in water construction." The expansion of the scale of construction of the water project increases the probability of accidents. At the same time, new technologies and new methods used in the intelligent construction of the water project may also increase non-traditional production safety risks. It can be seen that the pressure on safe production work in the field of water project construction is rising, and high-quality development methods are urgently needed to deal with it.

1.1 The proportion of safety accidents in the field of water project construction is as high as 82.5%

From 2016 to 2021, the production safety accidents of water project construction accounted for 82.5% of the total accidents in the industry (as shown in Figure 1). It can be seen that the ability to prevent and resist accidents and disasters in the field of water project construction

*Corresponding Author: fq400@sohu.com

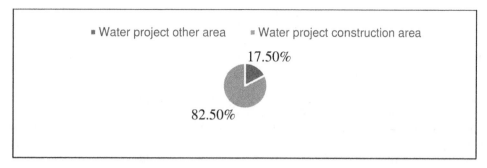

Figure 1. Statistical analysis of production safety accidents in the water project industry from 2016 to 2021.

is still fragile. Using high-quality development methods to reduce the proportion is the top priority of the industry's safety work, and the task is arduous.

1.2 *The QC results creation of safe production for the water project is an effective way of high-quality development*

1.2.1 *Concept*

Water project organization refers to the enterprises and institutions engaged in water project construction and operation management activities, including project legal person, survey, design, construction, supervision, consultation, manufacturing (including supply), bidding agency, quality inspection, operation management, maintenance and training (An *et al.* 2017). The organization also includes project companies such as water project PPP, BOT, construction management, as well as water project EPC general contractors, enterprises and institutions involved in related intelligent construction.

QC results of water project safety production refer to the results report formed by the employees of the production, service and management positions of the water resources engineering organization around the business strategy, policy objectives and safety production problems that exist on the site of the project under construction, after using the quality management theory to carry out and achieve the desired goals of the activities and then after a systematic sorting process. It is also known as engineering safety QC results. The purpose of the report is to solve problems, improve the quality of safety work and improve the human manner and safety benefits.

The above concepts show that the QC results of safety production for the water project are methods that combine the concept of quality management and have the attributes of high-quality development.

1.2.2 *The QC results creation of safety production for the water project as a high-quality development method is highly compatible with the implementation of the "Fifteen Measures for Safe Production"*

1.2.2.1 The fifteen measures for safety production

The State Council combed through relevant laws and regulations, practical initiatives and effective measures taken in recent years in response to new situations, and then developed fifteen measures to further strengthen the implementation of safety production responsibilities and resolutely prevent serious accidents. On March 31, 2022, the national television and telephone conference on production safety was released to mobilize the efforts of all parties to solve the outstanding problems of not solid safety development concept, not in place for the implementation of responsibility, poor investigation and rectification of hidden dangers, and do a good job of safety prevention.

The main content of the fifteen measures for safe production: 1. Strictly implementing the responsibility of local party committees for production safety 2. Strictly implementing the responsibility of local governments for production safety 3. Strictly implementing departmental responsibility for safety supervision; 4. Seriously pursuing leadership and supervisory responsibility; 5. The main person in charge of the enterprise must strictly enforce the responsibility of the first responsible person; 6. Immediately carrying out an in-depth national production safety inspection. 7. Firmly ensuring the safety standards of project approval; 8. Severely punishing illegal contracting-out, subcontracting and affiliating; 9. Effectively strengthening the safety management of labor dispatch and flexible workers. 10. Severe to carry out a crackdown on illegal production and operation activities; 11. Resolutely rectifying the problem of lax law enforcement and inspection; 12. Focusing on strengthening the construction of safety supervision and law enforcement team. 13. Rewarding to stimulate the reporting of hidden production safety hazards 14. Seriously punishing the concealment, false reports, late reports and omission of accidents 15. Integrating economic development, epidemic prevention and control and production safety work (Fifteen measures of safety production 2020).

1.2.2.2 The safety QC results creation of the water project and safety production of the fifteen measures are highly compatible with the requirements.

The fifteen measures for safe production are based on the system theory, starting from the leadership, management, and operation layers, and from the perspectives of people, machines, materials, and environments, which are used to continuously eliminate the inability to implement responsibilities, weakening execution, the occurrence of hidden dangers and other problems in safety management, to reduce the overall risk of accidents (Editor,s note 2022). The traditional method is difficult to achieve strict implementation of each article. The mass characteristics of safety QC results creation, the method of fishbone diagram analysis and the logical analysis process are highly compatible with the 15 measures for safe production, which are high-quality development methods to help the implementation of measures.

Firstly, the mass characteristics of safety QC results show that this is one of the main forms of safety work quality innovation with full participation. Through the creation of "full staff, the whole process and all-round" achievements, the quality and innovation ability of safety work for the water project will be improved, and the safety management network will be densely constructed, which will help to solve safety problems in an all-round way. For example, the quality management innovation of water project organizations should be considered from these three aspects, of which full participation is the first (An *et al.* 2018). Secondly, the cause analysis program of the creation process uses the Fishbone Diagram method to find the core causes of safety problems from the perspectives of "man, machine, material, environment, method, and measurement". Figure 2 shows a fishbone diagram of why safety hazards occur in culvert construction. Then, we will go through the procedure, including identifying the main causes, developing countermeasures, implementing countermeasures, checking the results, developing enhanced measures, and summarizing and planning the next steps (An *et al.* 2018) to eliminate the symptoms of insufficient risk identification. It can be seen that QC results creation strictly follows the PDCA procedure (Plan-Do-Check-Adjust procedure), which is one of the four pillars of total quality management (Qi 2013). The activities insist on using data to illustrate facts and use scientific statistical methods to analyze and solve problems (An *et al.* 2018), which is fully integrated into the concept of quality management of new methods of production safety management.

Therefore, the creation of safety QC results of the water project and safety production of the fifteen measures is highly compatible with the requirements. It is a method to implement high-quality development.

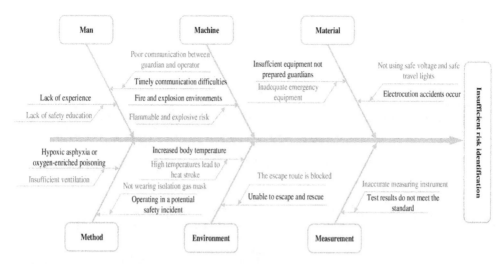

Figure 2. Fishbone diagram of safety core cause analysis.

1.3 *The research on the QC results creation of safety production for the water project is still blank*

The author used the keyword "water project safety production QC group results" to search on Baidu with no results. The search in China Knowledge Network also has no results, indicating that the relevant provisions, specific methods and research are in a blank state. Therefore, this study has important practical significance.

2. RESEARCH PURPOSE

By analyzing the data since the evaluation of the results of the excellent safety production QC group of water project from 2016, the overall situation of the creation of results and the problems in the use of technology were found. Then the reasons were analyzed and suggestions were made for QC results creation to better play a role in the high-quality development of safety production for the water project.

3 RESEARCH SAMPLE

The study is based on the total of 2858 achievements of China Water Engineering Association's 2016–2021 excellent quality management team as samples for categorical statistical analysis. The results cover the categories of engineering quality, schedule, safety, environmental protection, cost management, intelligent construction and so on. Therefore, this study has typical significance.

4 PROBLEMS

4.1 *Quantitative aspects: QC results in the safety category are not adequately and coherently carried out leading to outstanding problems*

Among the total 2858 QC results compiled by the author from 2016 to 2021, there are only 68 safety production items. Although the number of results has increased, the average percentage is only 2.38% (Table 1, Figure 3), which is in sharp contrast to the 82.5% proportion of production safety accidents in the field of water project construction during the same

Table 1. 2016-2021 Water project QC results in the statistics table.

Project	2016	2017	2018	2019	2020	2021	Total
Number of Results in the Safety category	1	8	14	13	15	17	68
Total Results	115	314	432	522	701	774	2858
Total Results Growth Rate		173.04%	37.58%	20.83%	34.29%	10.41%	**55.23%**
Percentage of Results in the Safety Category	0.87%	2.55%	3.24%	2.49%	2.14%	2.20%	**2.38%**

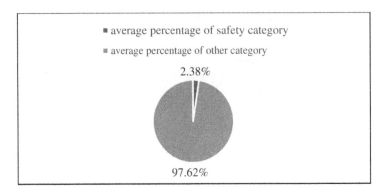

Figure 3. Statistical chart of QC results the percentage of safety production in the water project from 2016 to 2021.

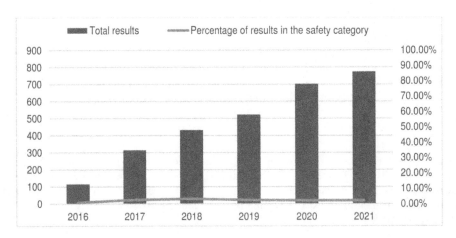

Figure 4. QC results annual percentage analysis of safety production in water project from 2016 to 2021.

period (Figure 1). The average annual growth rate of total results in the same period amounted to 55.23% (Table 1, Figure 4). Obviously, the results of the production safety class are not carried out adequately and coordinated leading to outstanding problems. Improving the proportion is the top priority of the QC group creation for the water project.

4.2 Category: Nearly 60% in the category of hidden danger investigation and treatment, and less in other categories

The author conducted a statistical analysis of a total of 68 results in the safety category from 2016 to 2021 and plotted Figure 5. Of the seven categories of the water project safety management process, there is the highest percentage of 58.82% in the category of hidden danger investigation and treatment, 13.24% in the category of technical management, and 10.29% in the category of safety management system. The hazard identification and risk level evaluation category accounted for 7.35%, the process control category accounted for 5.88%, and the flood safety and emergency management category accounted for 4.41%. This means that except for the category of hidden danger investigation and management, the proportions of other categories are relatively small, and the accident management category has not yet appeared.

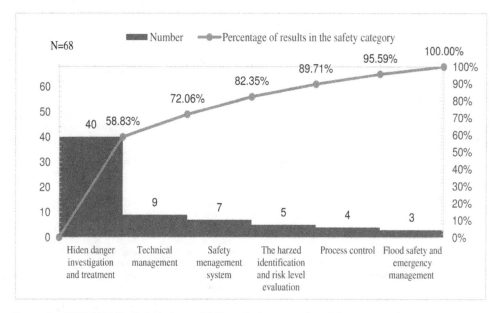

Figure 5. 2016-2021 Statistical chart of QC results in categories of the water project.

4.3 Activities procedural aspects

The author selected five representative results in terms of result creation procedures for specific analysis (see Table 2 for details).

5 RECOMMENDATION

5.1 In terms of evaluation policy, the QC results of the safety category for the water project are evaluated as a separate category and attention shall be paid to it. Its unique advantage of extensive mass is used. And the basic network of safety management will be densely constructed.

5.2 Management has helped in the bidding regulations to direct more resources to address the unbalanced and insufficient development due to the stark contrast between the percentage of safety results and the percentage of accidents.

Table 2. Statistical table of QC results in the problem of safety production in the water project from 2016 to 2021.

Results No.	1	2	3	4	5
Enterprise category	Construction companies	Construction companies	Construction companies	Construction companies	Construction companies
Topic category	Problem solving	Problem solving	Problem solving	Problem solving	Problem solving
Problem Category	Risk management	Hidden danger investigation and treatment	Hidden danger investigation and treatment	Hidden danger investigation and treatment	Hidden danger investigation and treatment
Problem Status	The risk value for silt removal in a culvert with limited space is D = 126	Fire alarm controller failure times 16 times per year	Distributed photo-voltaic power station box-type transformer communication ailure rate of 85.7%.	7.5% incidence of hidden dangers in culvert construction	The first wiring pass rate of the electric cable connection terminal in the power distribution cabinet is 80%
Crux of reason	High C value for risk level	1. Main power failure 2. System failure	The high temperature of the measurement and control module	Inaccurate hazards identification	1. Irregularities Contact Crimping 2. Wrong cable crimping
Confirm the main reasons	1. High content of toxic gases 2. Too many operators 3. Too long working hours	1. Lightning interference 2. Smoke probe with sundries inside	Fewer exhaust fans	1. Insufficient ventilation 2. Not using safe voltage and safe travel lights	1. Crimping pliers and terminals do not match 2. Wiring operation is not standardized
Take countermeasures	1. Increase ventilation equipment or replace high-powered ventilation equipment 2. Add a suction sewage truck with manual dredging	1. Install a surge protection device 2. Replace the smoke detectors with an insect-proof design	Self-designed external air circulation device for box-type transformers	1. Add ducts for ventilation fans 2. Use 12 V low voltage lamps	1. Purchase multifunctional crimping pliers 2. Assessment of termination success rate
Problem during implementation	1. No requirements are listed for the selection of topics 2. the concept of risk rate is not explained 3. Lack of data support for setting targets 4. the Wrong choice of statistical tool for causality analysis, fishbone diagram or system diagram should be used, not an association diagram	1. the title should be modified to reduce the incidence of fire alarm failure in the booster station 2. The status investigation is not stratified, such as device failure and external failure should be analyzed separately. The two are not the same hierarchical problem, and the staffer should continue the hierarchical analysis of device failure in depth.	1. Cause analysis system diagram should not use 5M1E analysis but should be selected from the logical relationship 2. Lack of data support for "confident to solve the problem of high temperature of measurement and control module" in the target feasibility demonstration	1. The safety problem characteristics are not described in "cross work and rainy season construction" in Table 5–1 of the target feasibility study. 2. No data support for "Control the safety hazard rate of other problems at 14.3%" in Table 5.2 of the target feasibility study	1. No data support for the "complete elimination of terminal crimping irregularities and cable crimping errors" in the current survey. 2. Consolidation measures are not listed in the specific content of the Management System of Rewards and Punishments for Distribution Cabinet Wiring

5.3 The guidelines about the QC results creation of safety category for the water project and industry training materials are published, which fully reflects its creation characteristics and supports the creation of standardized results.

5.4 Relevant departments should do a good job of data mining the results, discovering its common patterns and problems, and solving the existing problems in time.

5.5 Relevant departments complete inter-professional integration training, such as carrying out special training for QC creation of safety production personnel to cultivate composite talents.

5.6 The selected topics cover the whole chain of safety management as far as possible to help the higher-quality development of water project safety management.

6 CONCLUSION

This paper conducts an empirical study on the problems existing in the QC results creation of the water project safety category from 2016 to 2021 and finds that there are many problems, such as a small number of results, unbalanced topic selection, and improper use of creation procedures. The study concludes that the QC results creation for the safety production of the water project is an effective way for high-quality development, and it is highly consistent with the implementation of the 15 measures for safe production. The authors suggest improving the top-level design from the evaluation policy, bidding regulations, training materials formulation and so on, which will help to solve the difficulties and better play a unique role in reducing safety accidents in the water project construction by creating safety QC results. In the future, the authors will carry out research on the characteristics, difficulties and countermeasures of creating QC results of safety production in the water project to improve the application value of the results and promote high-quality development of safety production in the water project.

REFERENCES

Editor's note. High-Quality Development with High Level of Safety-Observation on the Implementation of the 15 measures of Production Safety. (2022) *China Emergency Management*. 5, pp.21.

Fifteen Measures of Safety Production. (2020). http://www.gov.cn/xinwen/2022-04/10/content_5684337.htm

Weiming Qi. (2013) *Theory and Method of the Quality Management Group*. China Quality and Standards Publishing & Media Co., Ltd. Beijing. pp.15.

Zhongren An, Hongyuan Dong, Yi Yuan. (2018) *Activity Guideline of Quality Management Group Creation of Water Project*. China Water & Power Press.Beijing. 4(3), pp.13.

Zhongren An, Hongyuan Dong and Yi Yuan. (2017) *Activity Guideline of the Quality Management Group of the Water Project*. China Water & Power Press.Beijing. pp.1.

Simulation research on fire emergency evacuation based on Pathfinder

Bei Wu*, Zhen Ma*, Yuhe Zhao, Ming Wang & Yunjun Yang
Department of Economics and Management, Tianjin Renai College, Tianjin, China

ABSTRACT: In recent years, the proportion of building fires in various types of fires in China is increasing year by year. Once a building fire occurs, the scene of escape is chaotic and the situation is relatively special and complex. How to effectively and safely carry out personnel evacuation is a key problem affecting the rapid development of social security. To solve this problem, based on the actual situation of the project and software simulation parameters, this paper uses Pathfinder to conduct simulation research on fire and safety evacuation, simulating evacuation time of personnel in different areas, combining with the actual engineering cases and fire scene simulation design. To effectively understand the various factors affecting the escape when a building fire occurs, and the general law of building fire development and evacuation situations. Combined with various factors and research conclusions, the possible fire hazards of the research project are obtained. This paper has important reference value for the general development law of public buildings in case of fire and the simulation analysis of escape based on the characteristics of public buildings.

1 INTRODUCTION

In the process of urbanization, informationized, intelligent, and industrialized buildings will become the trend of the development of modern buildings, but in the process of the rapid development of the construction industry, fire hazard has become one of the important factors that endanger people's life safety and cause property losses. Faced with this situation, we will combine Building Information Modeling (BIM) technology with fire dynamics and other scientific theories to explore how to evacuate when a fire occurs in a Building. We simulate the real evacuation route of personnel under the condition of a sudden building fire and the time for people in different areas to reach the environment to ensure their own safety. Pathfinder uses visual modeling and simulation technology to visually simulate the movement of individual units in a building, analyzing evacuation processes and the utilization of escape routes (Cui & Lv 2017). With the help of Pathfinder simulation calculation of the personnel evacuation software, this paper selected a hospital in Shenzhen as the research object, focusing on the development law of smoke diffusion in the process of fire. Through the combination of practical experience and theoretical research, the purpose of this paper is to use software technology to study the fire spread of buildings and analyze the optimal evacuation route.

---

*Corresponding Authors: beiwu@tjrac.edu.cn and 948829906@qq.com

2 INTRODUCTION TO SIMULATION METHODS

2.1 Introduction to fire simulation methods

Because the construction of modern buildings diversifies and the building layout is not unity, a conventional real evacuation drill will be alone when a fire broke out in a complex situation completely restore, for ensuring the personnel can be quickly away from fire hazards. To ensure the safety of their own place, people escape simulation schemes and result comparison is very necessary. According to the special structure and different characteristics of all kinds of buildings, an accurate fire simulation model is established to simulate all kinds of possible fire situations parameterized, so as to carry out scientific and reasonable fire rating evaluation of buildings and fire prevention and control programs. In this paper, Pathfinder is used to visualize and simulate all individual movements in buildings. With individual characters as the basic unit of simulation, the 3D time course simulation with high precision visualization is used to establish visual Windows and kanban to reflect the evacuation of dense people on the floor (He *et al.* 2016).

3 MODEL BUILDING

3.1 Introduction to the Pathfinder model

Pathfinder simulates the evacuation of people in both routine and emergency. Pathfinder supports two simulation models, one of which is the "Steering" mode, in which the evacuee uses the Steering system to move and interact with other personnel. This model restores the real behavior and movement of humans in the face of fire with maximum possibility. The other is the SFPE model. This simulation model ignores the collision between people and provides designers with a visual scheme comparison by limiting and calculating the flow of people at the exit of each room and counting the escape situation at each escape intersection. The two simulation methods can be switched freely and flexibly according to needs.

3.2 Hospital building overview

A hospital in Luohu District, Shenzhen, has a total construction area of 73246.86 square meters, covering an area of 24903.45 square meters, with an overhead green area of 1759.71 square meters, seismic fortification intensity of seven degrees, and building fire resistance rating of one level. Its above-ground part is each treatment room and the clinic, with 10 floors of inpatient building, 8 floors of the administrative research building, an underground garage, equipment room, belonging to a class of high-rise hospital buildings. The reasonable selection of steel structure and fireproof materials in the project is under the premise of meeting the standards as far as possible to reduce the number of materials.

4 SETTING OF FIRE SIMULATION PARAMETERS

4.1 Software functions

Pathfinder relies on computer graphics and motion simulation technology. It is the simulation of the specific parameters of the moving process of each individual and group to escape and simulate the interaction between functions. It combines the technology of computer technology and data statistics personnel in the building evacuation escape simulation visualization application software. The software simulates by the individual to the whole. Visual analysis of the escape process can be realized from single to global (Lyu *et al.* 2019).

4.2 Fire scene setting

In this paper, the typical situation of fire in large hospitals is simulated by virtual fire simulation. The fire scene is set to a transfusion area of labor-intensive characteristics on fire caused by a diffused flammable liquid, with some disadvantages to imitating the fire scene. An against-a-fire situation was simulated, with the fire simulation representing a rapid-fire growth type. The source is based on ISO/TS16733, the fire safety engineering part 4: Setting fire scenarios and setting fire options.

4.3 Fire simulation results and analysis

Parameters such as visibility and carbon monoxide mass fraction distribution at corresponding time points in the process of fire development were simulated in the Pathfinder software. Under the premise of not affecting the simulation results, the distribution of each parameter is more intuitively displayed, and the unnecessary part of the model is hidden.

4.3.1 General rules of smoke spreading

The general law of this smoke simulation is as follows: After the fire occurs, as shown in Figure 1, the fire source is used as the smoke release source, the smoke keeps gathering in the room, and the temperature keeps rising. Figure 2 shows the smoke spreads to the corridor through the partition door with the continuous improvement of the smoke concentration. In the experiment, the measuring point of smoke height after the fire occurred was set in the hallway, and the height of the smoke layer was determined to drop to the dangerous value of 2 m at about 75 s, and the fire situation reached the dangerous value when 261 s reached the evacuation staircase. A general rule can be drawn from the simulation results: when a fire occurs and it is difficult to control it in a short time, the smoke first accumulates in a large number in the ceiling, and when the smoke density reaches a certain amount, it gradually diffused downward until it spills out of the room where the fire is located. The results of this study can effectively guide the personnel to determine the correct escape route and avoid the inhalation of large amounts of toxic gases during evacuation injury.

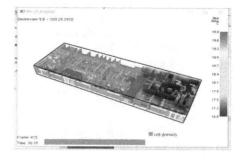

Figure 1. Schematic diagram of the fire origin.

Figure 2. Fire simulation - Fire spread diagram.

4.3.2 Simulation of comprehensive influencing factors of visibility and CO concentration

Visibility and carbon monoxide concentration are important indicators to evaluate the safety of public buildings after a fire. As the smoke generated in the fire blocks the line of sight, visibility will be reduced, thus affecting the speed of escape of the trapped people and the rescue effect of the fire personnel. Carbon monoxide accumulation concentration is one of the most important indexes to evaluate building safety (Qin & Li 2021). Therefore, in the crowd evacuation simulation study, visibility, temperature, and carbon monoxide concentration after a fire are important indicators to determine whether people can evacuate to safe areas.

As shown in Figure 3, the top view of the smoke spreads in the natural exhaust state. When the fire broke out in 90 s, it could be observed from the figure that the smoke occupied a small proportion of the whole fire zone and the smoke was very thin. Due to the short time of the fire, the temperature at the ignition point had not reached the peak level. In the 270 s, the top view is full of thick smoke, part of the partition of the flue gas has landed on the ground floor, and the visibility is less than 9 m. In the 270 s to 360 s period, it is filled with smoke in the whole and interior areas, and the visibility is less than 3 m. If the fire to this period, it will bring a lot of field rescue operations personnel to work harder. At the same time, the speed of evacuation of trapped people and the difficulty of entering the rescue personnel will also be affected. To sum up, in the period of fire at the early stage, until the strongest fire, smoke spreads most of the time. As the fire increases, visibility will gradually decline. CO due to the thermal effect and its density properties will be filled with the top of the indoor area, then gradually spread down, until all diffuse to the interior area. So when a fire broke out, it is sure to extinguish the fire in time, determine whether to strengthen ventilation to ensure normal indoor oxygen supply conditions after the cause of the fire, improve indoor air conditions while evacuating personnel, reduce the risk factor, and strive for precious time for the evacuation of all hospital personnel.

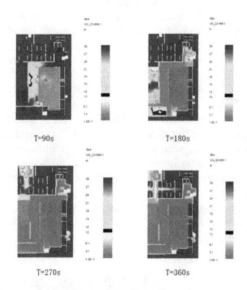

Figure 3. Top view of fire smoke spreading.

5 PERSONNEL EVACUATION SIMULATION

5.1 *Model processing and methods*

Model processing and method are based on the Revit-built model, and it is exported to a DWG format file. In the Pathfinder software, the model is processed to build the Pathfinder model, and the number of personnel is set according to the characteristics and functions of buildings and the actual situation of the fire evacuation drill, and the simulation study of emergency evacuation is carried out (Song *et al.* 2018). Two different evacuation modes are set up in Pathfinder. One is for people to evacuate to the designated safety exit according to the shortest evacuation path, which is also the default evacuation method. The other is for people to evacuate according to the orderly number of people set up in the evacuation channel. That is, the software is used to calculate and analyze the number of people accommodated by each exit in the case of ensuring that evacuees leave the burning building safely within the shortest time. When the number of evacuees reaches a peak at a specific exit, the rest of the people choose other safety exits. These two methods complement each other, and reasonable use of the two methods before the beginning of the evacuation process can provide a good visual effect for a single on-site fire evacuation drill. Based on fire simulation and result analysis, pathfinder software defines the parameters of each person (number of people, walking speed, and distance from the fire point) to simulate the optimal escape path. The escape path map is placed in a prominent place in each ward to ensure the safety of patients.

5.2 Simulation of evacuation path for personnel escape

Through the actual simulation and reading of relevant data, the fire response warning time was set at 126 s, the personnel response time was set at 130 s, and the personnel evacuation mode was adopted in the Steering mode. At the beginning of the evacuation simulation, the evacuation time of the personnel in each stairwell to reach the safe place was obtained, the corresponding evacuation fire door was placed at each escape passage, and the opening and closing state of the fire door was randomly set. As shown in Figure 4, the personnel distribution and evacuation situation of each evacuation channel was simulated. Due to the complexity and particularity of the hospital environment, the age span of the people accommodated is large, and the evacuation speed also has a great relationship with the gender and age of the people. According to a large number of simulated data, in the case of rapid fire diffusion, the average escape speed of men and women is 2.57 m/s and 1.96 m/s, respectively, and the escape speed of the elderly and children is relatively slow compared with these two groups of data.

For the hospital's environment variety and complexity, most distribution rooms are in the middle place. At the same time, considering exhaustion due to factors such as illness, the danger is the slowest part of the evacuation, therefore, escape simulation analysis has to be set separately in this special case, as shown in Figure 5, to ensure the reduction of the real scene when the fire broke out. In addition, due to a large number of people in the hospital and a large number of flammable items, it is necessary to set up an automatic fire alarm system, which can be considered that the difference between fire detection and alarm time is 0 s. Due to the large space of the hospital, it takes a certain amount of time for the detector to detect the fire. According to conservative estimation, the fire detection time is 25–34 s, and the personnel response time is about 27 s. Finally, it is calculated that the necessary time for the safe evacuation of personnel is 205.3 s.

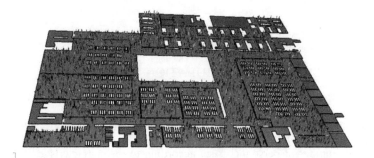

Figure 4. Evacuation distribution diagram.

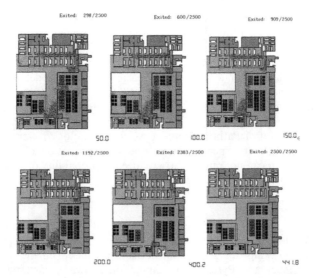

Figure 5. Personnel distribution and evacuation in different periods.

The use of Pathfinder personnel evacuation simulation software and Pyrosim smoke flow analysis software is for building fire data calculation and evacuation process simulation. According to the simulation results, as shown in Table 1 for details, exit 1 has the largest number of people choosing to escape, resulting in congestion and the longest evacuation time compared with other exits. However, the utilization rate of exit 2 and exit 3 is relatively low, and the number of evacuees is small, so it can be concluded that the evacuation time of exit 2 and exit 3 is short. Part of the medical staff and patients on the second floor are divided into areas. Different exits are used by people in different areas for evacuation, which to some extent reduces the time they spend in exit queuing, improves evacuation efficiency, improves the utilization rate of other exits, and shortens evacuation time (Wang & Li 2020).

Table 1. Number and time of evacuation at different exits.

Export Position	Number of Evacuees/Persons	Time/s
Export 1	299	204
Export 2	147	124
Export 3	118	124
Export 4	220	160
Export 5	196	154

Through evacuation simulation results, we can see that, for the hospital in this particular scenario, age, and sex are the factors influencing the evacuation speed most obviously. At the same time, as all aspects of the limiting factors lead to that doctors and patients had little chance of evacuation exercise together, only through a place marked indication evacuation, and the use of monitoring facilities and radio guidance for evacuation, fire in time to open a variety of safe escape channels, taking fire prevention, and fire extinguishing measures, all personnel can be guaranteed safe evacuation. In order to prevent fire control accidents, the hospital shall also be equipped with emergency materials, emergency fire control equipment, and professional rescue teams. It is necessary to increase the number of firefighting equipment, strengthen the inspection and management of firefighting equipment, and train medical staff, in the event of a fire, on the premise of ensuring their own safety to take good care of the lives and health of patients. If the building architecture and structural complexity are not high, it is a good choice to use BIM + Pathfinder technology to complete the modeling work first and then simulate the established information model. In the case of firefighting in hospitals and buildings with complex professional structures, the huge workload will bring pressure on professionals to a certain extent. However, due to the complexity of the hospital environment, it is not feasible to conduct real personnel escape simulations. Therefore, the application of Pathfinder and Pyrosim technology is very necessary for the security management of some special places, and the application of the emergency fire escape simulation system can not only greatly reduce the probability of fire, but also make a contribution to the daily security management.

6 CONCLUSION

In this paper, BIM modeling technology and Pathfinder are effectively applied to a hospital project in Shenzhen. Taking this project as an example, based on the mutual integration technology of Pathfinder and Pyrosim fire simulation software, corresponding simulation research is successfully achieved. The simulation study includes the influence of different conditions on escape time and the best escape route for evacuation under limited conditions. At the same time, I learned that the fire escape simulation based on Pathfinder has great development potential and outstanding advantages. For example, it can restore the most real escape route and analyze the best escape route, which greatly avoids the waste of manpower and material resources spent in real scene drills (Yan *et al.* 2021). Through simulation, the life and property safety of medical personnel and medical staff can be guaranteed to a great extent. In addition, the management unit should improve people's safety awareness and ensure the normal use of the automatic alarm system, fire hydrant system, fire shutter, and other firefighting facilities in the building, to help people in the event of a fire, for a safe escape for precious time.

ACKNOWLEDGMENTS

This work was financially supported by the Teaching Reform Project of Tianjin Renai College in 2021 (2021-3-5), and the Innovation and entrepreneurship training program for college students of Tianjin (202114038044).

REFERENCES

Cui Y.Y. and Lv P. (2017) Safety Evacuation Based on FDS and Pathfinder. *Design*, 37: 58–60.
He X., Chang L., Xie F., Song W.H. and Li L. (2016) Study on the Safety Evacuation of the Shopping Mall Building Based on the Revit and Pathfinder. *J. Nankai Univ. (Nat. Sci. Ed.)*, 49: 14–20.
Lyu X.K., Bai J.J. and Chen Y. (2019) Metro Station Fire Simulation Based on BIM and Pyrosim Software. *Urban Mass Transit*, 22: 147–151.
Qin R.Q. and Li X.J. (2021) Study on the Grid Selection of Block Scale PyroSim Fire Simulation. *Urban. Archit*, 18: 107–109.
Song Y., Chen S.G., Lan S.J. and Yang K. (2018) *Simulation Study on Fire Evacuation from the Airport Terminal. China Safety Sci. J.*, 28: 31–37.
Wang Z.T. and Li Y.J. (2020) Research on Building Entrance and Stair Optimization Based on Pathfinder Simulation. *Security*, 9: 16–21.
Yan W., Zhang R., Liu J., Zhang Y. and Sun W. (2021) Study on Fire Evacuation of University Library Based on Pathfinder. *J. Shenyang Jianzhu Univ. Nat. Sci.,* 37: 627–633.

Stress state study of atmospheric pressure storage tanks with corrosion defects

Lijian Zhou, Donglin Zhu*, Shouye Dong & Xinjie Yu
Northeast Petroleum University, Daqing, Heilongjiang, China

ABSTRACT: Orthogonal analysis method was used to study the stress state of the vertical storage tank with corrosion pits, and the influence of the main factors of corrosion defects on the stress was explored to provide a reference for the maintenance and safe operation of storage tanks. A 1000 cubic meter storage tank with corrosion defects was established using ABAQUS finite element software, and the influence of geometric parameters of corrosion defects on the stress state of the tank wall was calculated by the orthogonal test method. The results show that the equivalent stress distribution of the tank wall without corrosion defects is relatively uniform. The closer the tank wall with corrosion defect is to the defect, the greater the change of equivalent stress is, and the maximum equivalent stress increases with the increase of defect depth. The depth of the defect has the greatest influence on the equivalent stress of the tank wall, followed by the length and width of the defect. The research results provide a theoretical basis for the safe operation and maintenance of storage tanks.

1 INTRODUCTION

Corrosion caused by the tank crater directly affects the safe use of storage tanks, the knowledge of elastic mechanics know that irregular corrosion at the crater is prone to stress concentration, and the stress value at a certain point may exceed the permissible stress of steel, resulting in corrosion of the perforated part of the tank, greatly endangering the safety of storage tanks. The corrosion of oil storage tanks and storage tanks overturn, and fire accidents frequently occur, which greatly endanger the safety of the state and the people's property. A lot of research has been conducted at home and abroad on the corrosion strength of storage tanks, the American Petroleum Institute issued API579 guidelines, and China has developed a standard "in use with pit defects pressure vessel safety assessment." This provides a systematic method for evaluating the safety suitability of pressure vessels and atmospheric storage tanks as well as oil and gas pipelines for corrosion defects during use.

In recent years, domestic and foreign scholars have also researched this. Hossain (Hossain & Seshadri 2010) *et al.* used the m-tangent method to represent the stress gradient changes in the corrosion site, considering the decay length and reference volume, and other parameters, and the authors used the method to estimate the strength of the pressure vessel. Genel (2007) and other bending fatigue experiments were to explore the fatigue performance of high-strength aluminum alloy, and it was found that the presence of pitting corrosion reduced the fatigue strength of the aluminum alloy by about 60%. Zhang Hongcai (Zhang *et al.* 2003) studied cylindrical shell pressure vessels containing crater defects of different sizes using limit analysis and analyzed the ultimate load of the pressure vessel and concluded that the edge

---

*Corresponding Author: 316696193@qq.com

stress effect has little effect on the ultimate load. Broggi (Broggi & Schuëller 2011) et al. studied the initial geometric defects of cylindrical shells and the static properties of cylindrical shell-like structures, respectively, which made the theory of cylindrical shell statics increasingly mature. Wu Mei (2015) used ANSYS to perform a finite element simulation of crude oil storage tanks to study the stress variation at corrosion pits and the effect of corrosion on the remaining strength. Chen Zijing (2009) performed a finite element simulation of storage tanks containing pitting corrosion defects and investigated the effect of single and multiple corrosion on the remaining strength of the tanks. Most of the research on tank wall corrosion is in the finite element simulation, and the research method is relatively concentrated. Therefore, this paper is based on the previous paper using the orthogonal test method to establish a finite element model while using the specification to determine the correctness of the model to study the corrosion of atmospheric pressure vertical storage tanks under the action of static force corrosion defects of the geometric parameters of the corresponding corrosion at the tank stress state.

2 MODELING OF TANKS CONTAINING CORROSION

The model of the storage tank is relatively large, and the division of the mesh is relatively complex because the tank wall is relatively thin compared to the storage tank, which usually uses shell cells to define the tank wall. But this paper is the study of corrosion of the tank wall, so the tank wall modeling uses solid cells, the application of solid cell modeling, and the use of 6-facet division of the mesh. Tank material selected Q235 steel, and the specific properties of Q235 steel are as follows: density of 7850, modulus of elasticity 2.06e11, Poisson's ratio of 0.3, yield strength of 3.58e8, shear modulus of 2.15e9, tank wall corrosion for rectangular type external corrosion, defined corrosion pit along the tank circumferential corrosion length is l/mm, corrosion width is d/mm, and corrosion depth is t/mm. The tank wall is subjected to a hydrostatic pressure equivalent to the pressure and considers the role of the tank itself gravity, such as the latter Figure 4 for the tank wall without corrosion defects by hydrostatic pressure and gravity analysis results, the normal tank by hydrostatic pressure, the tank wall to bear the maximum stress in the lower part of the tank, and thus defines the corrosion of the tank wall in the distance from the tank bottom plate near 1.2 m high. Because the static force is applied only to the tank wall to study the stress changes at the tank corrosion pit, the boundary conditions are defined as the bottom of the tank by using a fixed constraint. The subsequent analysis can not consider the impact of the tank foundation and then directly apply a fixed constraint in the bottom of the tank to simplify the analysis model. At the same time, according to the actual situation, we know that the conventional large storage tank for the tank wall is an unequal thickness structure. Still, due to the study of specific parts of the static situation, this paper tentatively takes the maximum stress part of the tank wall thickness modeling and simplifies the model while facilitating the calculation of the subsequent model tank wall by using a uniform thickness.

To determine whether a material has failed, the US API 590 code (Zhuo 2008) is generally used to determine. In the specification specified in the water pressure test at room temperature, the allowable stress of the material is generally (3/4 σ_s, 3/7 σ_b), where σ_s is the yield strength of the material, σ_b is the tensile strength of the material. The tensile strength of Q235 steel is known to be 375 Mpa, and the permissible stress of steel is 161 Mpa. When the maximum stress at the corrosion exceeds the permissible stress of steel, it can be considered a steel failure.

The model meshes and the effect of dividing different mesh densities on the model results cannot be ignored (Yang et al. 2021), and the number of meshes is analyzed to determine the number of meshes suitable for the model. And since the effect of the tank foundation plate can be temporarily disregarded, different cell models of the tank without the foundation plate are established. This is shown in Table 1 and Figure 1.

Table 1. The number of cells and corresponding mises values (Self-drawn).

Number of Units (size)	Mises (Mpa)
1706	91.88
2104	93.79
2312	94.71
2532	95.5
2736	97.92
3208	98.2
4184	98.84
4910	98.79

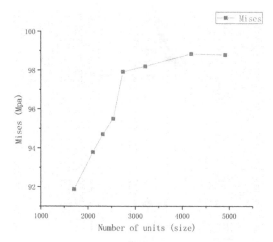

Figure 1. The relationship between the number of different elements and Mises stress (Self-drawn).

As shown in Figure 1, when the number of units reaches 3208, the Mises stress value curve trend is relatively flat, and the stress value is stable at about 97 Mpa. So the number of units selected for this model is 3208. On the basis of this unit, the tank containing wall corrosion is simulated. Because it is the stress analysis of the tank wall, the subsequent simulation will not consider the impact of the tank foundation. Through the above information, Figures 2 and 3

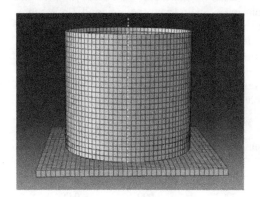
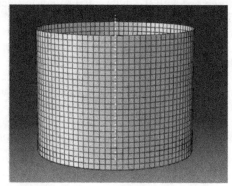

Figure 2. Storage tank model.　　　　　　Figure 3. Simplified model of storage tank.

are established for the tank analysis model and subsequent analysis of the simplified model, respectively.

3 MODEL VERIFICATION

The force and displacement clouds of the normal storage tank are established under hydrostatic pressure, as shown in Figures 4 and 5.

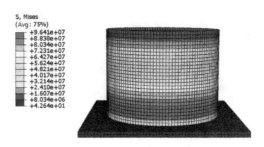

Figure 4. Hydrostatic pressure stress cloud diagram of normal storage tank (Self-drawn).

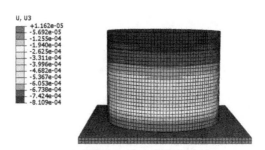

Figure 5. Cloud diagram of hydrostatic pressure displacement of normal storage tank (Self-drawn).

Before performing the model calculation, the correctness of the model should be verified first. The commonly used validation method is based on the theory of elastodynamics and combined with the differential equation calculation of cylindrical shell (Jiao 2021; Wang & Tang 2001; Yu 2012; Zhu 2000), and the accuracy of the model is verified by the theoretical results. The parameters of the present model are brought into the differential equations and calculated to obtain the theoretical values of the radial displacement of the tank at different heights, as shown in Table 2.

The radial displacement magnitudes of the tanks in Figure 5 above at 1 m, 2 m, 3 m, and 4 m were extracted separately, as shown in Table 3.

Table 2. Theoretical radial displacement (Self-drawn).

Tank Wall Height	1	2	3	4
Radial Displacement	0.000161	0.000270	0.000391	0.000396

Table 3. Actual radial displacement (Self-drawn).

Tank Wall Height	1	2	3	4
Radial Displacement	0.000154	0.00025	0.000368	0.000364

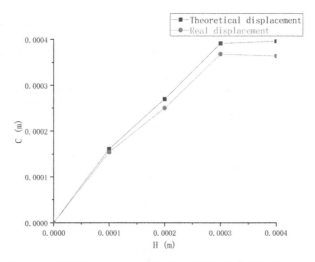

Figure 6. Comparison of radial displacement of tank wall.(C) Radial displacement; (H) Tank wall height (Self-drawn).

The theoretical values of the radial displacement of the tank wall were also compared with the actual displacement values of the tank wall from the finite element simulation, as shown in Figure 6.

From Figure 6, it can be seen that the results of the finite element calculation of the displacement of the tank wall do not differ much from the displacement results obtained from the specification, and the overall error is within 10%, which is in line with the test conditions required in this paper. In addition, the reasonableness of the calculation results is guaranteed.

4 EXAMPLE CALCULATION

4.1 Orthogonal experimental design

The test uses nonlinear finite element simulation. The lengths of corrosion pits, corrosion width, and corrosion depth are selected as orthogonal test factors (respectively, with A, B, and C). These three factors can take the corresponding level, taking into account the actual situation of tank wall corrosion, determined as four levels of orthogonal combination as shown in Table 4.

The number of trials was reduced as much as possible to avoid affecting the results when conducting orthogonal tests. The frequency of occurrence of different numbers in each column in the orthogonal table was consistent (Zhang et al. 2015). Therefore, a minimum of 16 trials were determined based on the combination of levels and factors collocation, and the average of the results of each trial was taken as test data. The test results are shown in Table 5.

Table 4. Level table of orthogonal factors. (Self-drawn). (l) Corrosion length; (b) Corrosion width; (c) Corrosion depth.

Level	Al/mm	Bb/mm	Cd/mm
1	10	6	1
2	20	9	2
3	30	12	3
4	40	15	4

Table 5. Orthogonal test table. (Self-drawn) (l) Corrosion length; (b) Corrosion width; (c) Corrosion depth.

Test Number	Al/mm	Bb/mm	Cd/mm	mises/Mpa
1	1(10)	1(6)	1(1)	96.8
2	1(10)	2(9)	2(2)	97.2
3	1(10)	3(12)	3(3)	106.3
4	1(10)	4(15)	4(4)	134.9
5	2(20)	1(6)	2(2)	99.5
6	2(20)	2(9)	1(1)	95.5
7	2(20)	3(12)	4(4)	124
8	2(20)	4(15)	3(3)	108
9	3(30)	1(6)	3(3)	106.7
10	3(30)	2(9)	4(4)	120.7
11	3(30)	3(12)	1(1)	98.6
12	3(30)	4(15)	2(2)	99.1
13	4(40)	1(6)	4(4)	124.5
14	4(40)	2(9)	3(3)	103.4
15	4(40)	3(12)	2(2)	97.7
16	4(40)	4(15)	1(1)	94.5

4.2 Experimental results and their analysis

In order to facilitate comparative analysis, the test was divided into four groups, of which tests No. 1~4 were the first group, and so on to test No. 16 to obtain the second, third, and fourth groups, respectively. As the stress effect of test No. 1 and test No. 2 is not obvious, the stress cloud diagram of the more representative test model results of No. 3 and No. 4 in Table 2 is extracted, as shown in Figure 4.

As shown in Figure 7, the stress distribution of the storage tank under hydrostatic pressure is uniform, and the maximum stress on the tank wall in the center of the corrosion pit and

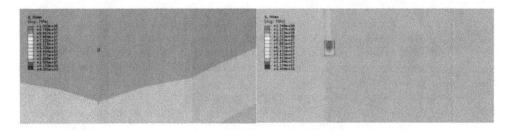

No.3　　　　　　　　　　　　　　No.4

Figure 7. Stress cloud of No.3 and No.4 test models (Self-drawn).

along the corrosion center to both sides of the trend gradually decreases. In the area far from the corrosion center of the tank wall stress size and no corrosion tank under hydrostatic pressure tank wall, stress size is not much different. In the top of the tank, stress is generally small, and subsequently, stress gradually becomes larger with the increase in water depth, in line with the law of stress distribution under hydrostatic pressure. With the increase in corrosion depth and width, the Mises stress of the tank wall increases, with the maximum stress reaching 134.9 Mpa until it is close to the permissible stress of steel. At this point, the tank should take emergency remedial measures to prevent the tank from perforating and leaking. In the tank wall corrosion near the uncorroded area, the tank wall Mises stress with the corrosion depth and corrosion width increasing also gradually becomes larger. It can be seen that the depth of corrosion and width of the tank wall changing in the size of the stress on the tank has a certain impact. As the second and third groups of tests in the corrosion length, corrosion width, and corrosion depth of the change do not have a certain law, the stress analysis results are not convincing, so this will not be discussed.

Similarly, the stress clouds of model results for the fourth group of tests (test 13 and test 14) are extracted according to Table 2, as shown in Figure 5.

As shown in Figure 8, the stress distribution on the tank wall with the closer the distance from the corrosion pit gradually increases in a step distribution. The maximum stress point in the center of the corrosion pit area stress concentration phenomenon, with the corrosion depth and corrosion width decreasing, the stress at the corrosion gradually decreases. Around the farther away from the corrosion area of the stress, with the corrosion depth decreasing, also has the trend of decreasing. At the same time, it can be seen that in test 14, away from the corrosion of the tank wall under hydrostatic pressure without the corrosion tank, the stress size difference is very small, basically negligible. But the test 13 corrosion pit depth is 4 mm, and the corrosion of the stress at the size of 124.5 Mpa basically reached the steel allowable stress of 161 Mpa. The tank, in this case, is more dangerous, and very easy to produce perforation phenomenon. This time should be timely and focused maintenance of storage tanks. In the area far from the corrosion pit, stress change is not large. By comparing the stress of other parts of the fourth group, it is found that the tank wall in different corrosion conditions far from the corrosion pit tank wall had a small change in stress. The middle of the tank wall away from the corrosion pit area had a stress of generally around 6.7 Mpa, which was not much different from the hydrostatic pressure in the corrosion-free storage tank area stress size in Figure 1, further proving the model to be rational.

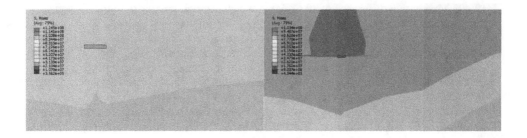

No.13　　　　　　　　　　　　　　　　　　No.14

Figure 8.　Stress cloud images of test models 13 and 14 (Self-drawn).

5 RESULTS AND DISCUSSION

5.2 Analysis of extreme differences

The use of extreme difference analysis of the tank corrosion model test results for numerical calculations and data analysis results are shown in Table 6 for the extreme difference analysis table.

Table 6. Range analysis table (Self-drawn).

Projects	1A	2B	3C
K1	435.2	427.5	385.4
K2	427	416.8	393.5
K3	425.1	426.6	424.4
K4	420.1	436.5	504.1
k1	108.8	106.88	96.35
K2	106.8	104.2	98.38
K3	106.28	106.65	106.1
K4	105	109.13	126.03
R	3.8	4.93	29.68

According to the calculation principle of the extreme difference analysis method, the sum of simulation results of each factor corresponding to the same level of stress magnitude is expressed by K1, K2, K3, and K4, where κ_1, κ_2, κ_3, and κ_4 denote the average value corresponding to each level, respectively. R is the extreme difference between the sum of each simulation result data, and the magnitude of R reflects the degree of influence of each factor on the test results (Chen & Li 2019; Ma et al. 2015).

From the results of Table 3, an extreme difference analysis can be seen, with R3 > R2 > R1. The size of the impact of these three factors can be described as follows: Corrosion depth has the most significant impact on the maximum stress corrosion, followed by corrosion width, and corrosion length has the smallest impact on the maximum stress corrosion.

(1) When the tank wall corrosion length is constant at 10 mm, with the increase in corrosion width, the stress change at the corrosion is not obvious. Corrosion width from 6 mm to 15 mm in the process of increasing the average value of the maximum stress at the corrosion of the tank wall is 3.8 Mpa, and the stress change is not obvious. When the corrosion depth changes from 1 mm to 4 mm in the process, the average value of the stress at the corrosion of the tank wall changes more obviously, from 96.35 Mpa to 126.03 Mpa with a difference of 29.68 Mpa, which is much greater than the difference of corrosion length and corrosion width, and the value fluctuates greatly. At this point, the corrosion of the tank wall is very easy to occur as the consequences of perforation, seriously affect the safety of the tank. This shows that the corrosion width of the tank wall corrosion at the stress changes has a certain impact on the corrosion depth of the tank wall, which is more obvious when the corrosion depth is 3 mm. It needs to use the storage tank to focus on testing and maintenance.

(2) When the corrosion defect corrosion length increases from 10 mm to 40 mm, the maximum stress in Table 3 changes from 104.2 Mpa to 109.13 Mpa on average, and the difference is only 4.93 Mpa. It can be seen that the corrosion at the stress change is not obvious. But when the corrosion width is more than 12 mm, corrosion at the maximum stress changes significantly. At this time, the tank wall has a certain risk of perforation. It can be seen that when the corrosion width is controlled within 12 mm, and corrosion depth within 3 mm, the tank's operating condition is relatively safe. The corrosion depth

is 3 mm when the actual project will need to repair the storage tank to prevent the risk of perforation.
(3) When the corrosion length is 40 mm, with the corrosion width increasing and corrosion depth decreasing, the maximum stress at the corrosion shows a decreasing trend, and the change in corrosion width is not enough to affect the change in the maximum stress at the corrosion. Corrosion at the average value of the maximum stress from 96.36 Mpa to 126.03 Mpa occurs a more obvious increase. In the same case, the corrosion depth of the corrosion at the maximum stress plays a decisive role, while the corrosion width and corrosion length only produce a small impact. When the corrosion depth is 1 mm, along with the corrosion length and corrosion width changing, corrosion at the maximum stress average value is 96.6 Mpa, and in the hydrostatic pressure, tank wall under the size of the stress is not much difference, indicating that in the actual project depth of 1 mm, minor corrosion only needs to be simply maintained. When the corrosion depth is more than 3 mm, it needs to pay special attention. Especially, when the corrosion depth is 4 mm, it is necessary to timely repair the tank to prevent accidents.

6 CONCLUSION AND OUTLOOK

The orthogonal test method is used to study the stress state of the tank containing corrosion defects, finite element modeling based on Abaqus, and error analysis by cylindrical shell theory to verify the reasonableness of the model. Different corrosion states were analyzed, and the following conclusions can be made.

(1) Corrosion length, width, and depth will affect the stress state of the tank wall. With the increase of the corrosion length, width, and depth, corrosion at the maximum stress correspondingly increased, while there is a certain amount of security risk. Corrosion depth of corrosion at the size has the most obvious impact of stress, corrosion width is the second, and the corrosion length of the tank stress size has the least obvious impact. At the same time, corrosion depth is the main consideration in the tank for testing and maintenance.
(2) When the corrosion depth is 1 mm, the tank corrosion at the stress size and the stress size of the tank without corrosion is not too different, the stability of the tank is good, and the subsequent only needs simple maintenance. When the corrosion depth reaches 3 mm or more, the safety of the tank is under certain threat, and then the tank needs to be repaired to ensure the safe operation of the tank.
(3) To better determine the corrosion parameters for the impact of the tank wall stress, subsequent research should consider the cold conditions in the tank and the complex loading effect of the stress changes in the corrosion of the tank wall. At the same time, because of the limitations of finite element simulation, subsequent research should use more experimental methods to improve the integrity of the results data.

REFERENCES

Broggi M., Schuëller G.I. Efficient Modeling of Imperfections for Buckling Analysis of Composite Cylindrical Shells. *Engineering Structures*,2011,33(5):

Chen C., Li W. Inspection Test of Buried Pipeline Corrosion Protection Layer Based on Polar Difference Analysis Method. *Total Corrosion Control*, 2019, 33(8):5.

Chen Z.J. *Evaluation of Residual Strength of Crude Oil Floating Roof Tanks Containing Pitting Defects*. China University of Petroleum, 2009.

Genel K. *The Effect of Pitting on the Bending Fatigue Performance of High-strength Aluminum Alloy*. Scripta Materialia, 2007.

Hossain M.M., Seshadri R. Simplified Fitness-for-service Assessment of Pressure Vessels and Piping Systems Containing Thermal Hot Spots and Corrosion Damage. *International Journal of Pressure Vessels & Piping*, 2010, 87(7):381–388.

Jiao P. *Research on Flexural Behavior and Design Methods of Thin-walled Cylindrical Shell Structures Under Local Axial Compression*. Zhejiang University, 2021.

Ma C.Q., Zhang S.C., Ma Y., et al. Optimal Design of Medium Ratio Speed Pump Without Overload Based on Orthogonal Design Method. *Fluid Mechanics*, 2015, v.43;No.520(10):42–46

Wang Z.J., Tang B.X. Finite Element Analysis of a 20,000m^3 Double-hung Valve Tank. *Journal of Changzhou Branch of Hohai University*, 2001, 15(4):5.

Wu M. *Analysis of Corrosion Defect Stress and Reliability of Suizhong 36-1 Terminal Crude Oil Storage Tank*. Southwest Petroleum University,2015.

Yang Y.H., Gu X.T., Zhang X., et al. Residual Strength Study of Senior X100 gas Transmission Pipeline Containing Double Point Corrosion Defects. *Corrosion and Protection*, 2021,42(04):48–53.

Yu D.L. *Experimental Study and Numerical analysis of Axial Compression Elasticity and Plastic Buckling of Welded Cylindrical Shells*. Zhejiang University, 2012.

Zhang H.C., Li P.N., Chen, D.Q. Limit Load Analysis of Craters at Structural discontinuities on the Spherical Head. *Petrochemical Equipment*, 2003, 32(6):3.

Zhang X.W., Jin X.Y., Zhou Z.Z. et al. Study of Sliding Friction Performance Based on Orthogonal Test Design. *Lubrication and Sealing*, 2015, 40(4):5.

Zhu E.C., Call C. Stability Analysis of Uniform Axially Compressed Cylindrical thin Shells. *Journal of Harbin University of Architecture*, 2000, 33(4):4

Zhuo Z. *Chemical Vessels and Equipment*. China Petrochemical Press, 2008.

Experimental study on comprehensive recovery of bismuth smelting slag by hydrometallurgy

Tengyue Gao*, Guangsheng Li, Xingfu Zhu & Qiang Ji
Metallurgical Laboratory Branch of Shandong Gold Mining Technology Co., Ltd., China

ABSTRACT: Taking the bismuth smelting slag from the silver separation furnace as the research object, the comprehensive recovery test of bismuth and copper was carried out by adopting the hydrometallurgy process and the NaCl-H_2SO_4 leaching system. The effects of the dosage of reagents and the pH value of hydrolysis on the recovery of bismuth and copper were investigated. The results show that the valuable elements in the bismuth smelting slag can be effectively recovered by using the NaCl-H_2SO_4 leaching system, and the recovery rates of bismuth and copper in the obtained products are up to 90%, which realizes the comprehensive recovery and utilization in the bismuth smelting.

1 INTRODUCTION

In the process of comprehensive recovery of lead anode slime by pyrometallurgy, bismuth smelting slag will be produced in the later stage of oxidation refining of the silver separation furnace (He 2017). The treatment process of the smelting slag can be roughly divided into two categories: pyrometallurgy and hydrometallurgy. Among them, the pyrometallurgy process is more complicated, the yield of copper smelting products is low, and the vacuum separation process of silver bismuth alloy is greatly affected by impurities (Xu *et al.* 2015). According to the different kinds of acid used for leaching, the hydrometallurgy process can be divided into the HCl system and NaCl-H_2SO_4 leaching system (Tan *et al.* 2016; Zou *et al.* 2018). Among them, the leaching rate of the HCl system is fast, but the concentration of industrial hydrochloric acid is only about 30%, so the amount of wastewater in this system is large, and the production cost is high. The reagent cost of the NaCl-H_2SO_4 system is low, and most lead smelting enterprises have convenient conditions for producing sulfuric acid (Liu *et al.* 2014; Wang *et al.* 2014).

In this study, the NaCl-H_2SO_4 system was selected for the comprehensive recovery of bismuth smelting slag. The effects of reagent dosage and leaching potential on the leaching effect of bismuth and copper were investigated, and the washing process of leaching slag was studied. At the same time, hydrolysis precipitation of bismuth and replacement of copper recovery was carried out with NaOH and reduced iron powder. The optimum technological conditions for the wet recovery of bismuth smelting slag were determined, and the comprehensive recovery of valuable metals in the slag was realized.

2 EXPERIMENT

2.1 *Raw materials*

The high bismuth slag used in this test is taken from a leading smelting enterprise in Hunan. The multi-element analysis results are shown in Table 1. Bi, Cu, Pb, and Ag in the high

---

*Corresponding Author: gaotengyue@sd-gold.com

Table 1. Analysis of main elements of high bismuth slag.

Au (g/t)	Ag (%)	Bi (%)	Cu (%)	Pb (%)	Fe (%)	Sb (%)
0.11	1.30	43.10	9.70	22.92	0.89	0.57

bismuth slag are the main recovered valuable metal elements. Among them, Bi and Cu need to be recovered as separate products, while Pb, Ag, and trace Au can be returned to the anode slime smelting process with the leaching slag for treatment. According to the XRD and process mineralogical analysis, the bismuth element in the high bismuth slag mainly exists in the form of bismuth lead slag and bismuth oxide slag, and the copper element mainly exists in the form of cuprous oxide. The XRD analysis pattern and process mineralogy phase composition analysis results are shown in Figure 1 and Table 2, respectively.

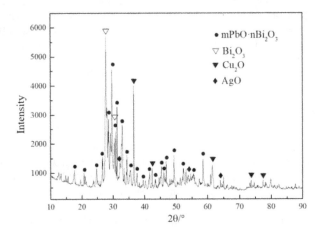

Figure 1. XRD analysis of high bismuth slag.

Table 2. Analysis of main phase composition in high bismuth slag.

NO.	Phase Composition	Main Elements	Relative Content (%)
1	Bismuth lead slag	Bi Pb O	49.83
2	Bismuth slag	Bi O	20.26
3	Bismuth lead antimony slag	Pb Sb Bi O	12.52
4	Copper slag	Cu O	9.52
5	Lead slag	Pb O	2.73
6	Silver slag	Ag O	2.09
7	Antimony copper slag	Sb Cu O	0.90
8	Other phases	Fe Mg Ca O *else*	2.15
Total	—	—	100.00

2.2 *Test method*

The leaching experiment of high bismuth slag was carried out by using a constant temperature magnetic stirrer and water bath heating. The leaching potential was measured by Shanghai Instrument Electric ORP electrode, and the stability of the leaching potential was maintained by NaClO3. After the leaching, the filtrate is taken, and the magnetic stirrer is used to conduct the hydrolysis and bismuth precipitation test. NaOH is used to adjust the hydrolysis pH value, and the pH meter is used to detect the pH value change in the hydrolysis process. After hydrolysis, the residual liquid was replaced by iron powder for copper recovery.

3 RESULTS AND DISCUSSION

3.1 *Effect of sulfuric acid dosage on leaching effect*

Figure 2 shows the effect of initial sulfuric acid concentration on the leaching rate of Bi and Cu when NaCl concentration is 4 mol/L, the leaching temperature is 80°C, and the liquid-solid ratio is 5:1. It can be seen from Figure 2 that when the initial H2SO4 concentration in the leaching solution is 150 g/L, the leaching effect of Bi and Cu in the later slag is the best, the leaching rate of Bi reaches 96.42%, and the leaching rate of Cu reaches 99.44%. If the concentration of H2SO4 continues to be increased, the salting out action will lead to the crystallization of NaCl in the leaching solution, and a too-high concentration of H2SO4 will lead to the dissolution of Sb in the leaching process. Therefore, it is appropriate to maintain the initial H2SO4 concentration in the leaching solution at 150 g/L.

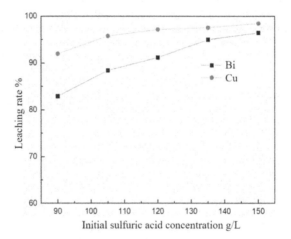

Figure 2. Effect of initial sulfuric acid concentration on the leaching rate of Bi and Cu.

3.2 *Effect of NaCl dosage on leaching effect*

Under the condition of an initial H2SO4 concentration of 150 g/L, the effect of NaCl concentration on the leaching rate of Bi and Cu was investigated. It can be seen from Figure 3 that when the NaCl concentration is 4 mol/L, the leaching rate of Bi reaches the maximum value. With the decrease in NaCl concentration, the leaching rate of Bi decreases significantly. This is because the solubility of Bi is affected by the concentration of Cl- and pH value. When the concentration of Cl- in the leaching solution is too low, the concentration of Bi in the solution will reach saturation, so the leaching of Bi cannot be carried out normally. Thus, it is determined that the initial NaCl concentration of the leaching solution is 4 mol/L, and under the test conditions, the NaCl solution of 4 mol/L is nearly saturated, and its concentration cannot be further increased.

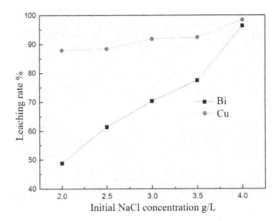

Figure 3. Effect of initial NaCl concentration on the leaching rate of Bi and Cu.

3.3 *Experimental study on leaching residue washing*

In the following, clean water, sulfuric acid solution (pH=0), and 4 mol/L NaCl solution (pH=0) are used as washing water, respectively, to investigate the influence of washing water type and amount on the washing effect of leaching residue. It can be seen from Figure 4 that the washing efficiency is the highest when 4 mol/L NaCl solution (pH=0) is used. When the amount of washing water is 200 ml, the washing rate of Bi reaches 95%. When washing with clean water, the pH value and Cl- concentration drop sharply, resulting in the hydrolysis of Bi and precipitation, resulting in a low washing rate. Washing with the sulfuric acid solution with a pH value of 0, although the influence of pH value is weakened, the influence of Cl- concentration still exists. Therefore, 4 mol/L NaCl solution (pH=0) has the best washing effect. In addition, if the pH value of washing water is too high, it will cause the dissolution of Sb in the leaching residue, so the optimal pH value of washing water should be consistent with the pH value of the leaching endpoint.

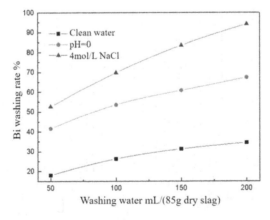

Figure 4. Test results of leaching residue washing.

3.4 *Experimental study on bismuth deposition*

In this study, 40% NaOH solution was used to adjust the pH value of the leaching solution, and the effect of pH value on hydrolysis precipitation of bismuth was investigated, as shown in Figure 5. Since the residual Bi in the solution after hydrolysis cannot be recycled, the hydrolysis process must maximize the recovery of Bi. When the hydrolysis pH value is 2.5, the hydrolysis recovery rate of Bi is high. At this time, the Bi content in the hydrolysis product reaches 68.21%, and the residual Bi content in the solution decreases to 0.32 g/L. Considering the reagent cost and the impurity content of the hydrolysate, it is appropriate to control the hydrolysis pH at about 2.5.

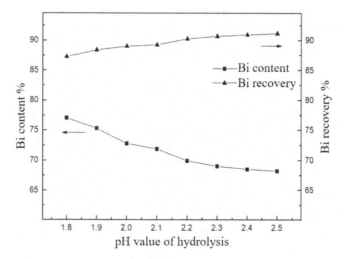

Figure 5. Effect of pH value on hydrolysis of Bi.

3.5 *Experimental study on displacement copper deposition*

The following is an experimental study on the replacement and recovery of copper by using the residual solution after hydrolysis with a Cu content of about 15 g/L and a pH value of 2.5 to investigate the effect of the amount of reduced Fe powder on the replacement process. It can be seen from Figure 6 that when the amount of reduced Fe powder is 1.2 times as much as the theoretical amount, the content of Cu in the obtained replacement product is relatively high, and the content of Fe is low. This is because excessively reduced Fe powder can inhibit the formation of Fe3+ in the solution, thus avoiding the generation of Fe(OH)3 precipitation. Therefore, the Fe content in the replacement product is relatively low. It is determined that it is appropriate to add 1.2 times as much as the theoretical amount of reduced Fe powder.

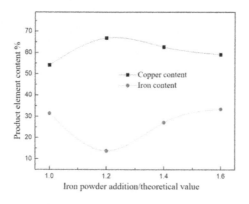

Figure 6. Effect of the amount of reduced Fe powder on the replacement process.

4 CONCLUSION

The valuable elements in the high bismuth slag mainly exist in the form of oxides. Under the optimal parameter conditions, the content of Bi in the hydrolysate is 68.21%, the content of Cu in the replacement product is 66.46%, and the recovery rate is 90%. The hydrolysate can be washed efficiently by using the acidic NaCl solution. Therefore, the leaching hydrolysis precipitation bismuth replacement copper recovery process can realize the comprehensive recovery and utilization of high bismuth slag.

REFERENCES

He Yulong, Xu Ruidong, He Shiwei, et al. Research Development of Lead Anode Slime Treatment Technology. *Nonferrous Metals Science and Engineering*, 2017, 8(5): 40–51.

Liu Wei, Jiang Xunxiong, Jiang Wei, et al. Recovery and Preparation of Bismuth Oxide from Hydrochloric Acid Leaching Solution of Silver-separation Slag. *Nonferrous Metals(Extractive Metallurgy)*, 2014, (11): 60–62.

Tan Daidi, Jiang Chaojin, Yang Yuexin, et al. Recovery of Copper and Bismuth from Bismuth Slag. *Mining and Metallurgical Engineering*, 2016, 36(6): 100–103.

Wang Chao, Jiang Xunxiong, Jiang Wei, et al. Recovery of Bismuth and Antimony from Silver-separation Slag of copper Anode Slime. *Nonferrous Metals(Extractive Metallurgy)*, 2014, (9): 16–19.

Xu Shuai, Song Bingyi, Jiang Wenlongi, et al. Recycling of Silver from Lead-Silver-Copper Alloy by Vacuum Distillation. *Chinese Journal of Vacuum Science and Technology*, 2015, 35(8): 1011–1016.

Zou Xiangyu, Luo Qingwei, Xu Feng, et al. Leaching Mechanism and Process of Lead-silver and Antimony From Silver Separated Residue. *Journal of Materials and Metallurgy*, 2018, 17(1): 32–37.

Aluminate-based flocculant from fly ash for dye wastewater treatment with flue gas neutralization

Guoqiang Zhong, Zhaohui Ren, Haixin Zheng, Jinyun Xu, Minjing Li & Di Zhao
School of Chemical Engineering, Tianjin Key Laboratory of Green Chemical Technology and Process Engineering, State Key Laboratory of Separation Membrane and Membrane Processes, Tiangong University, Tianjin, China

Xudong Hu
School of Materials Science and Engineering, Key Laboratory of Advanced Ceramics and Machining Technology, Ministry of Education, Tianjin University, Tianjin, China

Xiangyin Cheng, Jianing Guo, Guanwei Yao & Chunming Zheng*
School of Chemical Engineering, Tianjin Key Laboratory of Green Chemical Technology and Process Engineering, State Key Laboratory of Separation Membrane and Membrane Processes, Tiangong University, Tianjin, China

Xiaohong Sun*
School of Materials Science and Engineering, Key Laboratory of Advanced Ceramics and Machining Technology, Ministry of Education, Tianjin University, Tianjin, China

ABSTRACT: This work prepared an aluminate water flocculant from fly ash by using sodium bicarbonate and calcium carbide slag. Aluminum salt was extracted under the optimized condition of reactant mass ratio (fly ash, sodium bicarbonate, and calcium carbide slag, 1:0.7:1.2) and calcination temperature of 850°C at 2 h. The present method saves the consumption of inorganic acid, which achieves the purpose of waste recycling at a low cost. The maximum removal efficiency reaches 95% for the methylene blue of the dye wastewater. The possible reaction mechanisms are also discussed. The enhanced flocculant efficiency of synthesized products might rely on the destruction of mullite and quartz phases and the extraction of aluminum ions released from fly ash.

1 INTRODUCTION

Currently, the recovery and recycling of printing and dyeing wastewater have become a hot issue of widespread concern in environmental management [1]. The discharged wastewater contains a large amount of hard-to-degrade organic substances, dye molecules, etc., and if the wastewater with pollutants is discharged into the environment without treatment, it will seriously endanger plants and animals, the safety of water bodies, and human health. Adsorption is one of the common techniques used in wastewater treatment today [1] [2]. By adsorption and flocculation (or coagulation), suspended particles, etc. in printing and dyeing wastewater can be effectively treated.

Fly ash contains large amounts of silicon and small amounts of aluminum and iron, which can be used to prepare adsorbents, catalysts, and flocculation adsorbents. The extraction of alumina from fly ash has become a hot research topic in recent years. In order to extract

---

*Corresponding Authors: zhengchunming@tiangong.edu.cn and sunxh@tju.edu.cn

alumina from fly ash [3], ammonium sulfate can be added to fly ash for activation, while a highly active adsorbent can be obtained. Aluminum chloride crystals can also be obtained by adding hydrochloric acid to the fly ash leachate for crystallization, solid-liquid separation, and washing, and these crystals are calcined to produce metallurgical-grade alumina. However, waste acid is generated during the sintering and calcination activation process [3], and the gas produced also causes serious pollution to the environment, which requires further research to complete the recycling of waste acid. In contrast, alumina in fly ash exists as amorphous and mullite phases, which could be extracted by a suitable heat treatment followed by acid leaching [4]. During the modification of fly ash with sodium bicarbonate and calcium carbide slag, the mullite and quartz phases in the fly ash are dissolved by these alkaline agents, thus releasing aluminum ions from the fly ash that participate in the adsorption of dyes in the wastewater [5].

In this article, bicarbonate and calcium carbide slag are used to activate fly ash, and the resulting product is used as an adsorbent to treat dye wastewater, which has the characteristics of cheap raw materials, easy availability, and easy scaling up of the preparation process. This method could not only effectively prevent fly ash pollution, but also turn waste into treasure, giving new use value to waste and achieving the purpose of resource recycling.

2. EXPERIMENTAL

2.1 *Chemicals*

Bicarbonate (AR, > 99.9%), methylene blue (AR, > 98.5%), and polyacrylamide (cPAM, >99%) were commercially purchased from Aladdin Bio-Chem Technology, Shanghai. Industrial coal fly ash was collected from Inner Mongolia Erdos Thermo&Electric Co. Ltd. All chemicals were used without further purification, and deionized water was used throughout this study.

2.2 *Preparation of flocculant and flocculation processes of dye wastewater*

In the process of preparing the aluminate-based flocculant, a certain amount of sodium bicarbonate and calcium carbide slag were added to 5 g of fly ash. The mixture was calcined at different temperatures (700–1000°C) and at different times (1–5 h), respectively. After the calcination was completed, the samples were cooled to room temperature naturally. Then, the samples were taken out as an adsorption agent for dye wastewater treatment (methylene blue). The removal experiment was carried out as follows: 0.03 g/L methylene blue solution and 1 g/L polyacrylamide (PAM) solution were used, and methylene blue was degraded with the prepared aluminate water treatment flocculant; 0.3 g of aluminate water treatment flocculant was added to the prepared methylene blue solution, the solution was stirred to dissolve for 0.5 h, and 1 mL of the prepared PAM solution was added. After the precipitation was complete, a spectrophotometer (UV1800PC) was used to measure the absorbance after degradation and before degradation, and the removal rate was calculated.

Removal rate = (initial absorbance - absorbance after removal) / initial absorbance.

The experiment can eliminate methylene blue by more than 90%.

2.3 *Characterization*

The precipitation of dye wastewater was characterized by X-ray diffraction with Cu Kα radiation (0.154 nm) as the X-ray source. Scanning electron microscopy (SEM) was done on a Hitachi S-4800. Transmission electron microscopy (TEM) was done on a JEOL JEM-2100. Energy dispersive X-ray spectroscopy (EDX) was done on an X-flash 6130.

3. RESULTS AND DISCUSSION

3.1 *SEM of fly ash and carbide slag*

Scanning electron microscope images of the original fly ash and calcium carbide slag are shown in Figure 1. From Figure 1 (a) and (b), it can be seen that the fly ash sample is composed of many spherical crystals, hollow spheres, and irregular unburnt materials that are mainly composed of mullite and quartz. Spherical crystals have relatively smooth surfaces. This further shows that the chemical stability of fly ash is not only related to its crystal size, but also to its crystal structure. It is necessary to break the Si-O-Al bond in the mullite structure to reduce the hardness of fly ash, thereby forming new species to prepare new aluminate-based flocculants. Figure 1 (c) and (d) are SEM images of carbide slag at different magnifications. It can be clearly seen that the structure of calcium carbide slag is composed of many cubic block crystals, with a small number of spherical particles embedded in it. When we combine the XRD pattern of calcium carbide slag, we can see that the cubic crystals are calcium hydroxide, and the spherical crystals are calcium carbonate.

Figure 2 (a) shows the EDX results of the original fly ash. Based on the EDX results, silicon, aluminum, calcium, and iron can be detected in fly ash. Figure 2 (b) shows the

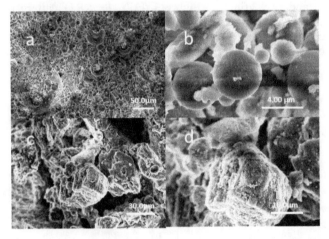

Figure 1. SEM images of original fly ash and calcium carbide slag; (a, b) fly ash at different magnifications as it is; (c, d) carbide slag at different magnifications.

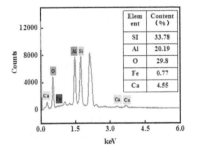 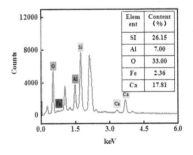

Figure 2. EDS spectrum of fly ash and aluminum leaching slag.

EDS spectrum scan of the aluminum leaching slag. Compared with the original fly ash energy spectrum, after being modified by sodium bicarbonate and calcium carbide slag, the aluminum content decreased from 20.19% to 7%. It further shows that the aluminum is obviously successfully leached (the leaching rate reaches about 65%), and the aluminum has changed from the original crystalline phase to a free state to form an aluminosilicate flocculating water treatment agent, which could enhance its adsorption performance.

3.2 XRD of fly ash and calcium carbide slag.

According to the XRD characterization results in Figure 3 (a), most of the XRD spectrum of fly ash is a dispersion peak, which indicates that the composition of fly ash is an amorphous phase. Sharp diffraction peaks appear at an angle of 20°–35°. The main crystalline phases in this range are mullite and quartz. Through XRD analysis, it can be concluded that alumina mainly exists in the mullite crystal phase. And there is almost no free alumina phase in fly ash. Figure 3 (b) is similar to the XRD pattern of low-temperature fly ash from the XRD pattern calcined at 1000°C in the muffle furnace, indicating that the crystal form of fly ash will not change due to high temperature. Compared with sodium carbonate modification, sodium bicarbonate will decompose and release water vapor and carbon dioxide during the calcination process, resulting in low product strength and easy grinding. Figure 3 (c) is the XRD pattern of dried calcium carbide slag, it can be concluded that after crystal structure analysis, calcium hydroxide slag is mainly composed of calcium hydroxide, and there is also a small number of diffraction peaks of calcium carbonate.

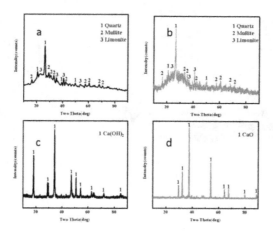

Figure 3. (a) The original sample of fly ash; (b) 1000°C roasted fly ash; (c) Calcium carbide slag; (d) 1000°C roasted calcium carbide slag.

3.3. TEM diagram of fly ash and modified fly ash

Figure 4 shows the TEM comparison between the original fly ash and the modified fly ash. It can be seen there are spherical crystals of different sizes in the fly ash. After modification, the spherical crystals disappear and form a block material with a basic uniform shape. This result is consistent with SEM.

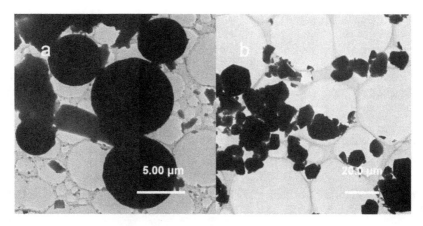

Figure 4. (a) TEM of fly ash as is; (b) TEM of modified fly ash.

3.4 *Removal efficiency with different synthesis conditions*

According to Figure 5, fly ash, in the presence of sodium bicarbonate and calcium carbide slag, extracts aluminum and prepares a silicoaluminate brine treatment agent. Different comparative experiments have been done, and only fly ash, calcium carbide slag, sodium bicarbonate and fly ash, calcium carbide slag and fly ash and sodium bicarbonate, calcium carbide slag, and fly ash are compared. The results show that the removal efficiency of methylene blue is better than that of only sodium bicarbonate, better than that of only calcium carbide slag, and better than that of fly ash in the presence of sodium bicarbonate and calcium carbide slag.

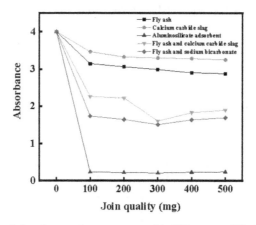

Figure 5. Comparison of absorbance after treatment with different modified adsorbents.

4 CONCLUSIONS

In summary, this work uses sodium bicarbonate and calcium carbide slag to extract aluminum salts from fly ash, the mullite and quartz phases in fly ash are destroyed, and the aluminum ions in the phases are released to finally prepare the silica-aluminate adsorbent. This method can avoid the disadvantages of the traditional acid extraction method to prepare aluminate water treatment adsorbent from fly ash, thus reducing the consumption of inorganic acid and alkali, lowering the cost of raw materials, and finally achieving the purpose of high-value recycling of waste, without producing any waste acid. The results showed that the removal efficiency of methylene blue was better under combined sodium bicarbonate and calcium carbide slag modification conditions than under sodium bicarbonate or calcium carbide slag modification conditions alone; however, there is still room for improvement, and future research should focus on reducing the temperature of calcined fly ash, thus reducing energy consumption.

ACKNOWLEDGMENTS

This work was supported by the State Scholarship Fund of the China Scholarship Council (201709345012).

REFERENCES

[1] Ma W., Yao B., Zhang W., He Y., Yu Y., Niu J. and Wang C. (2018) A Novel Multi-flaw MoS2 Nanosheet Piezocatalyst with Superhigh Degradation Efficiency for Ciprofloxacin, *Energy Environ. Sci.*, 5(12): 2876–2887.
[2] Miao C.G., Wang X.Q. and Zhang H. (2011) Flocculation of Harmful Algal Blooms by Modified Fly Ash, *Adv. Mater. Res.*, 347–353: 2090–2093.
[3] Shemi A., Mpana R.N., Ndlovu S., van Dyk L.D., Sibanda V. and Seepe L. (2012) Alternative Techniques for Extracting Alumina From Coal Fly Ash, *Miner. Eng.*, 34: 30–37.
[4] Tripathy A.K., Behera B., Aishvarya V., Sheik A.R., Dash B., Sarangi C.K., Tripathy B.C., Sanjay K. and Bhattacharya I.N. (2019) Sodium Fluoride Assisted Acid Leaching of Coal Fly Ash for the Extraction of Alumina, *Miner. Eng.*, 131: 140–145.
[5] Yao Z.T., Xia M.S. Sarker P.K. and Chen T. (2014) A Review of the Alumina Recovery From Coal Fly Ash, With a Focus in China, *Fuel*, 120: 74–85.

Study on the mechanical characteristics of red-bed mudstone in Southwest China under point load and uniaxial compression and tensile

Yao Cui*
Chongqing Survey Institute, Chongqing, China
State Key Laboratory for the Coal Mine Disaster Dynamics and Controls, Chongqing University, Chongqing, China
Chongqing Research Center of Geotechnical Engineering Technology, Chongqing, China

Siyu Qi
Chongqing Survey Institute, Chongqing, China

Pengyu Zhu, Rui Wang & Yongneng Feng
Chongqing Survey Institute, Chongqing, China
Chongqing Research Center of Geotechnical Engineering Technology, Chongqing, China

ABSTRACT: Red-bed mudstone is difficult to be made into a standard specimen with high water content because it is easily disintegrated in water. As a result, one of the important means to calculate its strength parameters is by point loading test. This paper carried out point loading tests under three water contents, uniaxial compression tests, and Brazilian splitting tests under two water contents on four typical red-bed mudstones in southwest China. The effects of water content, clay mineral content, and test method on the uniaxial compressive and tensile strength converted from point loading strength were explored. The results show that the higher the water content or clay mineral content is, the less discrete the data of the point loading test is. In addition, the point loading test data obtained by the axial test has the smallest discreteness, and the irregular rock sample test has the largest. From the comparative analysis of the converted strength and the measured strength, it is found that the results obtained by the axial test are closer to the true value, while the irregular rock sample test has a larger error. Besides, the higher the clay mineral content is, the closer the converted value of uniaxial compressive strength is to the measured value, while it is the opposite for the uniaxial tensile strength. Based on the test results, the conversion formula of point loading strength is derived again, and the saturated uniaxial compressive strength and tensile strength of red mudstone are calculated.

1 INTRODUCTION

The red bed refers to the continental clastic deposit strata formed since the Mesozoic, which is mainly red and purple in appearance. In this stratum, mudstone is the most common [1]. Red-bed mudstone is characterized by low strength, easiness to disintegrate in water, and easiness to be weathered [2], while engineering geological disasters such as subgrade settlement and landslide caused by the special engineering characteristics of red-bed mudstone are very common in civil engineering construction in southwest China [3]. Uniaxial compressive strength and uniaxial tensile strength are important parameters to determine the bearing

*Corresponding Author: stephentsui@qq.com

capacity of the foundation, slope stability, and classification of the rock mass. The two parameters need to be obtained through the uniaxial compression test and Brazilian splitting test, which have high requirements on the size and shape of specimens. However, standard test specimens with high water content cannot be obtained from red-bed mudstone, which is easily disintegrated in water [4] [5]. Therefore, it is of great practical significance and engineering value to infer the uniaxial compressive and tensile strength of red-bed mudstone by a simple and efficient-point loading test.

Scholars have done a lot of research on how to infer mechanical parameters such as the uniaxial compressive and tensile strength of rocks more accurately through the point loading test [6] [7]. Broch and Franklin [8] first conducted the radial concentrated force loading tests based on cylindrical specimens and developed a point loading strength calculation method that took the square of the shortest distance between loading points as the bearing area of specimens, and ISRM developed a test method of point loading strength on the basis of this method [9]. Sabatakakis [10] carried out a point-loading test and uniaxial compression test on three kinds of rocks with different strengths and found that if the strength of rocks is different, the conversion coefficient is also different. Zhang and Li [11] tested the uniaxial compressive strength and point loading strength of six common rocks in mines and found that the uniaxial compressive strength and point load strength show a highly linear positive correlation. The conversion of point loading strength to the uniaxial compressive and tensile strength of red-bed mudstone is affected by many factors. Chen and Wei [12] carried out three different loading tests on sandstone, mudstone, and limestone in Chongqing, and found that the more irregular the specimens are, the less accurate the uniaxial compressive strength calculated by the empirical formula is. Mo [13] conducted point-loading tests on weathered red-bed mudstone in southern Sichuan and found that the bedding structure of red-bed mudstone had a great influence on the calculation results. Wu et al. [14] conducted dry-wet cycle tests on the red-bed mudstone in the Badong formation in the Three Gorges Reservoir area and found that the reciprocating change of water content of red-bed mudstone has a great influence on the conversion accuracy of point loading strength to uniaxial tensile strength.

The above research results show that the conversion accuracy between point loading strength and uniaxial compressive or tensile strength is affected by many factors. However, there is still little research on red-bed mudstone. This paper carried out radial, axial and irregular rock sample point loading tests, uniaxial compression tests, and Brazilian splitting on four typical red-bed mudstones in southwest China. The effects of water content, clay mineral content, and point loading test method on the conversion accuracy were explored. A formula for converting the point loading strength of red-bed mudstone in southwest China into uniaxial compressive and tensile strength was established. Based on this formula, the saturated uniaxial compressive and tensile strength of red-bed mudstone in southwest China were estimated. The results can provide a reference for practical projects such as roadbeds, tunnels, and slopes.

2 EXPERIMENTAL EQUIPMENT AND SCHEME

2.1 *Testing material*

The red-bed mudstone samples used in the test were collected from construction sites in southwest China. The physical parameters of the four mudstones are shown in Table 1. The cores drilled on-site were processed into $\varnothing 50$ mm $\times 100$ mm and $\varnothing 50$ mm $\times 25$ cylindrical standard specimens according to the requirements of relevant regulations [9]. It is extremely difficult to prepare the red-bed mudstone to be the red-bed mudstone standard specimen in the saturated state; therefore, in the uniaxial compression test and the Brazilian splitting test,

Table 1. Basic physical parameters of red-bed mudstone (natural).

The type of mudstone	Mineral content /%				Density /g/cm³	Water content /%
	Clay minerals	Quartz	Feldspar	Calcite		
mudstone 1	41.6	39.6	14.5	3.1	2.39	5.20
mudstone 2	34.4	41.5	16.1	6.6	2.55	5.48
mudstone 3	27.1	57.8	6.9	7.4	2.67	1.46
mudstone 4	21.9	52.6	17.3	5.9	2.56	1.12

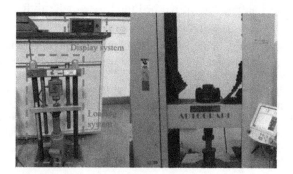

Figure 1. Instruments and equipment used in the test.

only mudstone specimens in dry and natural states were prepared. In the point loading test, mudstone specimens in dry, natural, and saturated states were prepared [13].

2.2 Experimental equipment

In the point loading test, the point loading tester (STDZ) was used to test the point loading strength of four kinds of red-bed mudstone, as shown in Figure 1 (a). The electronic precision material testing machine (Ag-250kn IS) was used for the uniaxial compression test and Brazilian splitting test, and the specific equipment is shown in Figure 1 (b).

2.3 Experimental scheme

In the point loading test, radial, axial and irregular rock sample tests of red-bed mudstones were carried out respectively according to the shape of mudstone specimens. The loading methods and size requirements of different test methods are shown in Figure 2. For each type

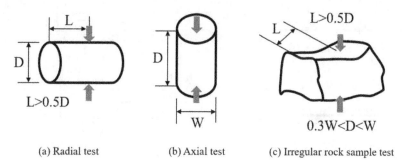

(a) Radial test (b) Axial test (c) Irregular rock sample test

Figure 2. Point load test classification and specimen size requirements [9].

of mudstone, 10 groups of radial tests, 10 groups of axial tests, and 10 groups of irregular rock sample tests were carried out in dry and natural states, while 30 groups of irregular rock sample tests were carried out in a saturated state.

3 TEST RESULTS AND DATA ANALYSIS

3.1 *The results and analysis of the point loading strength test*

The data of each type of red-bed mudstone in the dry and natural state can be divided into three groups, as shown in Figure 3. By comparing the dispersion degree, mean value and changing rule of point loading data of red-bed mudstone under different test methods, we can know that:

1. The point loading strength index of mudstone measured by different test methods is slightly different. According to the mean value of the point loading strength index, the point loading strength index of the axial test is slightly larger than that of others. This shows that the shape of the rock specimen can have a certain influence on the point loading strength index in the point loading test. The more irregular the rock shape is, the more discrete the data and the lower the point loading strength index is. It is difficult to determine the position of the loading point, and the size of the section after failure is different in the irregular rock sample test.

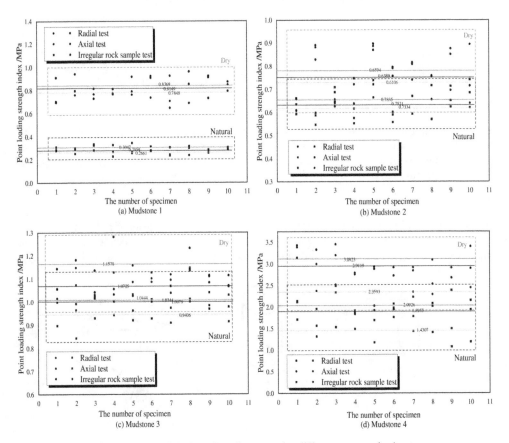

Figure 3. Point loading strength index of mudstone under different test methods.

2. The higher the clay mineral content is, the lower the dispersion degree of the point loading strength index is. It can be seen from Figure 3 that the maximum difference in the point loading strength index of mudstone 1, with the highest clay mineral content in the dry state is only 0.26 Mpa. However, the maximum difference in the point loading strength index of mudstone 4 with the lowest clay mineral content reached 1.6 MPa in the dry state. This indicates that the higher the content of clay minerals, the more obvious the plastic deformation of mudstone in the process of compression, the longer the time to fail, and the more uniform the change of load.

The point loading strength indices of four mudstones in a saturated state are shown in Figure 4. It can be seen that for the irregular rock sample test, the higher the clay mineral content is, the lower the degree of data dispersion is. It can be seen by comparing Figures 3 and 4 that the higher the clay minerals content is, the higher the degree of attenuation of point loading strength with the increase of water content, and the lower the point loading strength index is.

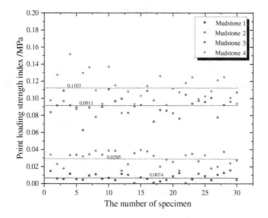

Figure 4. Loading intensity index of red-bed mudstone point in saturated state.

3.2 *Relationship between point loading strength index and uniaxial compressive strength*

According to relevant regulations [9], the conversion formula of the point loading strength index of rock to uniaxial compressive strength and uniaxial tensile strength is as follows:

$$R = 22.82 \cdot I_{s(50)}^{0.75}$$

$$\sigma_t = 0.9599 \cdot I_{s(50)}^{0.8562} \tag{1}$$

where R is the uniaxial compressive strength (MPa) of red-bed mudstone, σ_t is uniaxial tensile strength (MPa), and $I_{s(50)}$ is the point loading strength index.

The converted values and measured values are shown in Figures 5 (a) and (b). The water content has almost no effect on the conversion of uniaxial compressive strength from point loading strength, and the relative errors between the converted values and the measured values of uniaxial compressive strength in a dry state are basically the same as that in the natural state. However, the clay mineral content and the test method have a great influence on the relative error, and the results are shown in Figure 4 (c). Under the same test method, the higher the clay mineral content is, the closer the converted uniaxial compressive strength

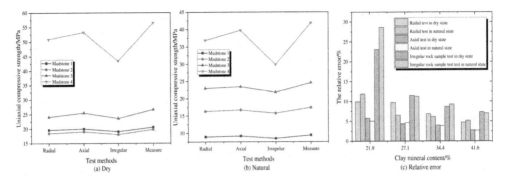

Figure 5. The converted values and measured values.

is to the measured uniaxial compressive strength. For the same mudstone, the relative error of uniaxial compressive strength obtained by the axial test is the smallest, and it is within 6%. The relative error of the irregular rock sample test is the largest, and it can reach 28.62%.

Because the test methods have a great influence on the conversion accuracy, Equation (1) cannot be used to convert the uniaxial compressive strength of rock under different test methods. Therefore, it has its own conversion formulas for different test methods. The water content does not greatly influence the conversion of uniaxial compressive strength, and the data in dry and natural states are analyzed together. Each type of point loading test method has a total of 8 sets of data for four types of mudstone, and the relationship between point loading strength index and uniaxial compressive strength under different test methods is shown in Figure 6. The new conversion formula of uniaxial compressive strength for different test methods is as follows:

$$R = \begin{cases} 24.78 \cdot I_{s(50)}^{0.78}, R^2 = 0.9985 & \text{Radial test} \\ 23.77 \cdot I_{s(50)}^{0.77}, R^2 = 0.9999 & \text{Axial test} \\ 27.01 \cdot I_{s(50)}^{0.89}, R^2 = 0.9777 & \text{Irregular rock sample test} \end{cases} \quad (2)$$

It can be seen that the accuracy of the new conversion formula is very high, and the goodness of fit is above 0.97. Therefore, Equation (2) can be used to accurately convert the uniaxial compressive strength of red-bed mudstone in southwest China. The saturated uniaxial compressive strength of the four types of mudstone is shown in Table 2 based on Equation (2).

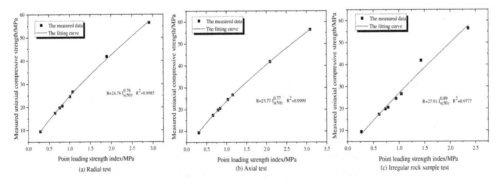

Figure 6. Relationship between point load strength and uniaxial compressive strength.

Table 2. Conversion of saturated uniaxial compressive strength of red-bed mudstone.

The type of mudstone	Mudstone 1	Mudstone 2	Mudstone 3	Mudstone 4
Converted value /MPa	0.3429	1.1740	3.2026	3.7968

3.3 Relationship between point loading strength index and uniaxial tensile strength

The converted values and measured values of uniaxial tensile strength are shown in Figure 7 (a) and (b). Water content has little influence on the conversion of uniaxial tensile strength from point loading strength, but clay mineral content and test methods greatly influence them. In addition, the relative error of uniaxial tensile strength is much lower than that of uniaxial compressive strength; most of them are above 50%, and the highest can reach 64.77%. The uniaxial tensile strength converted by the original formula has been seriously distorted and cannot accurately reflect the real uniaxial tensile strength of red-bed mudstone.

The conversion accuracy of red-bed mudstone is shown in Figure 7 (c). Under the same test method, the higher the clay mineral content, the more inaccurate the conversion of uniaxial tensile strength and the greater the relative error, which shows the opposite law to the uniaxial compressive strength. For the same mudstone, the relative error of uniaxial compressive strength obtained by the axial test is also the smallest.

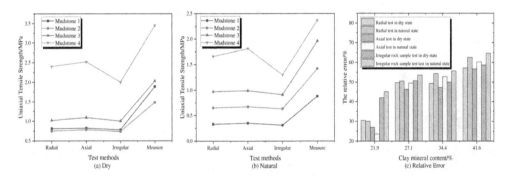

Figure 7. Influence of clay mineral content and test method on relative error.

The converted values of uniaxial tensile strength of red-bed mudstone are far less than its measured value, so Equation (1) must be modified. The relationship between point loading strength index and uniaxial tensile strength under different test methods is shown in Figure 8. The new conversion formula of uniaxial tensile strength for different test methods is as follows:

$$\sigma_t = \begin{cases} 1.8668 \cdot I_{s(50)}^{0.5417}, R^2 = 0.9516 \text{ Radial test} \\ 1.8161 \cdot I_{s(50)}^{0.5284}, R^2 = 0.9387 \text{ Axial test} \\ 1.9497 \cdot I_{s(50)}^{0.6285}, R^2 = 0.9787 \text{ Irregular rock sample test} \end{cases} \quad (3)$$

It can be seen from Figure 8 that the fitting effect of the new conversion formula is very good. It indicates that the saturated uniaxial tensile strength of red-bed mudstone calculated by Equation (3) is very close to the measured value. The saturated uniaxial tensile strength of the four mudstones is shown in Table 3 based on Equation (3). Equation (2) and Equation (3) are applicable to convert the mechanical strength of red-bed mudstone, which cannot be obtained by conventional experiments. In actual engineering, point loading tests which are

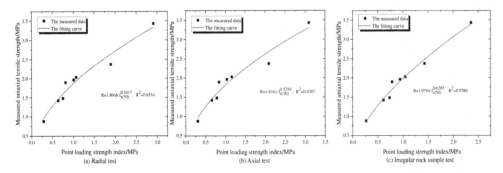

Figure 8. Relationship between point load strength and uniaxial tensile strength.

Table 3. Conversion of saturated uniaxial tensile strength of red-bed mudstone.

The type of mudstone	Mudstone 1	Mudstone 2	Mudstone 3	Mudstone 4
Converted value /MPa	0.0893	0.2129	0.4325	0.4878

convenient and fast can be directly carried out on the construction site. Then more accurate uniaxial compressive strength and uniaxial tensile strength of red-bed mudstone can be obtained through the new formulas.

4 CONCLUSION

In this study, the effects of water content, clay mineral content, and point loading test method on the conversion accuracy were explored. The following conclusions are obtained:

(1) In the point loading test, the point loading strength values obtained by different test methods are slightly different, where the values from large to small are the axial test, radial test, and irregular rock sample test. In addition, the data obtained from the axial test has the lowest dispersion, while the data obtained from the irregular rock sample test has the highest dispersion. The higher the water content or the lower the clay mineral content is, the greater the dispersion of the data is.
(2) By comparing the converted values and measured values of uniaxial compressive strength, it is found that the higher the content of clay minerals is, the closer the conversion value of uniaxial compressive strength is to the measured value. The conversion value of uniaxial compressive strength obtained from the axial test is the most accurate, while the relative error of the irregular rock sample test is the largest.
(3) By comparing the converted values and measured values of uniaxial tensile strength, the results show that the test method has the same effect on the conversion accuracy as the uniaxial compressive strength. In addition, the effect of clay mineral content on the conversion accuracy of uniaxial tensile strength is opposite to that of uniaxial compressive strength. The higher the clay mineral content, the worse the conversion accuracy.
(4) The conversion formulas of uniaxial compressive strength and uniaxial tensile strength were modified. According to different test methods, new conversion formulas with higher accuracy were obtained.

ACKNOWLEDGMENTS

This work was financially supported by the National Natural Science Foundation of China (No. 52074048, No.51774057).

REFERENCES

[1] Han L. (2019) *Chemical Intervention Study on Disintegration Process of Strongly Weathered Purple-red Mudstone in Badong Formation of Three Gorges Reservoir Area.* Hefei: Hefei University of Technology. Pp. 1–8.
[2] Li A.R., Deng H., Wang X.X., *et al.* (2021) Research on Creep Characteristics and Constitutive Model on Red-bed Mudstone Under Saturated-dehydrated Cycle. *Journal of Engineering Geology.* 29(03): 843–850.
[3] Dai Z.J., Guo J.H., Zhou Z., *et al.* (2020) Inversion and Prediction of Long-term Uplift Deformation of High-speed Railway Subgrade in Central Sichuan red-bed. *Chinese Journal of Rock Mechanics and Engineering.* 39(S2): 3538–3548.
[4] Wang X.Q., Yao H.Y., Dai L., *et al.* (2021) Experimental Study on Slaking Characteristics of Red-bed Soft Rock in Southern Anhui Province. *Chinese Journal of Underground Space and Engineering.* 17(3): 683–691.
[5] Guo Y., Chen Q., Zhou Z., *et al.* (2020) Quantitative Research and Microcosmic Mechanism Discussion on Red-bed Argillaceous Rock. *Electric Power Survey & Design.* 135(1): 39–43.
[6] Guo Y.H., Hou K.P., Jiang J., *et al.* (2019) Study on the Relationship Between Point Load Strength and Uniaxial Compressive Strength of Several Rocks. *China Tungsten Industry.* 34(05): 13–17.
[7] Yao Jiali, Yao Huayan, Dai Ling, *et al.* (2021) Study on the Mechanical Characteristics of Anisotropic Gneiss under Point Load and Uniaxial Compression. *Chinese Journal of Underground Space and Engineering.* 17(4): 1038–1044.
[8] Broch E. and Franklin J.A. (1972) The Point-load Strength Test. *International Journal of Rock Mechanics & Mining Sciences & Geomechanics Abstracts.* 9(6): 669–676.
[9] National Railway Administration. (2014) *Code for Rock Test of Railway Engineering: TB 10115-2014 [S].* Beijing: China Railway Publishing House. pp. 67–72.
[10] Sabatakakis N., Koukis G., Tsiambaos G., *et al.* (2008) Index Properties and Strength Variation Controlled by Microstructure for Sedimentary Rocks. Engineering Geology. 97(1–2): 80–90.
[11] Zhang Y.Y. and Li K.G. (2017) The Correlation Between the Point Load Strength and Uniaxal Compression Strength of Several Kinds of rocks. *Metal Mine.* 2: 19–23.
[12] Chen J.Q. and Wei Z.A. (2018) Comparison of Rock Strength from Different Point Load Tests and the Uniaxial Compressive Strength. *The Chinese Journal of Geological Hazard and Control.* 29(5): 72–77.
[13] Mo K. (2020) *Study on Disintegration, Strength, and Deformation Characteristics of Middle Weathered Mudstone in the Red Bed Area of Southern Sichuan.* Chengdu: Xihua university. pp. 55–56.
[14] Wu B.J., Xu G.L. and Liu W. (2020) Disintegration and Strength Weakening Characteristics of Red-Bed Mudstone in Badong Formation in the Three Gorges Reservoir Region. *Safety and Environmental Engineering.* 27(02): 50–57.

Civil Engineering and Energy-Environment – Gao & Duan (Eds)
© 2023 the Author(s), ISBN 978-1-032-56057-1

Numerical analysis of beach sediment dredging under different artificial sand laying schemes

Xiaodong An*
Shandong Ocean Culture Tourism Development Group Co. LTD, Rizhao, China

Bin Zhou*
Guocheng Group Co. LTD, China

Tao Gao* & Haiwen Fan*
Shandong Provincial Communications Planning and Design Institute Group Co. LTD, Jinan, China

Hongchang Hua* & Tingting Cui*
College of Energy and Electrical Engineering, Hohai University, Nanjing, China

ABSTRACT: By investigating the erosion caused by waves in different sections in artificial beaches of coastal restoration and remediation process and then revealing the general law of 2-dimensional sand transportation, this paper establishes a hydro-sand dynamic geomorphological model of the sea area where the shore beach of a coastal zone protection and restoration project is located, and adopts the wave-flow coupling method to numerically solve the wave-sediment dynamic evolution of regional erosion and siltation under three different artificial beach laying schemes. It is found that Option 1 has both an appropriate wave attenuation rate and sediment retention rate, and it also has the most outstanding overall performance among the three options. The sediment flushing and siltation in the first year is the largest, accounting for about 20%-30% of the total sediment transport, and the sediment flushing and siltation from the second year to the fifth year shows a yearly decrease. The sediment transport in the south side of the lower and middle part of the beach in the third area of the sand paving site is serious under the action of coastal flow, so that part of the beach should be maintained by sand replenishment.

1 INTRODUCTION

The aggravation of coastal erosion has seriously affected the survival and development of coastal countries and regions, especially sandy beaches with economic and ecological value. This is mainly due to global warming, increased marine development activities, extensive construction of coastal engineering facilities, and other factors [1] [2] [3]. Under the action of waves and nearshore hydrodynamic factors, sediment movement on the coast continuously causes changes in the coastline. There is a long history of studying the variation of coastal scour and silting and predicting its evolution trend, to which has been paid more and more attention. At present, many scholars have simulated the evolution of terrain erosion based on empirical formulas or mathematical models, explored the sediment movement characteristics of beaches, and proposed conservation and restoration measures [4] [5].

*Corresponding Author: cuitt061@163.com

Han Xuejian et al. [6] established a model of sediment transport and seabed evolution based on the hydrodynamic model and simulated and analyzed the sediment transportation and seabed evolution law of the beach from Xinkaihekou to Nanshan after the implementation of the remediation and restoration project. It was found that under the coupling effect of the wave current, the revetment effect of the artificial headland was limited when it existed alone; the sand dam eroded, the cover area behind the sand dam was silted up, and the sand dam played an effective role in maintaining the beach. Zhang Daheng et al. [7] analyzed the effect of the combined action of winter waves and artificial islands on the change of beach erosion in Riyue Bay, explored the mechanism of alluvial beach change, and found that the changes in beach landform morphology were affected by the construction of artificial islands, and the beach showed significant characteristics of siltation and erosion on both sides. Through research, Li Shan [8] proposed measures that could effectively slow down the erosion intensity of the offshore side of the Houridao Project and protect the underwater reef platform. That is, the engineering measures to optimize the structure of the northeast embankment and improve the top elevation and slope of the torsional block of the east sea seawall.

The coastal zone protection and restoration project of Sun Bay in Rizhao City starts from the north side of Liujiawan Ganhai Park and ends at the north side of Fuxin Fishing Port and carries out protection and restoration work within a total of 6.9 kilometers of shoreline. The construction scale is as follows: 3791 m of sandy coast restoration, 570,500 m^2 of restoration area, 1138.43 m of new ecological seawall, 236,400 m^2 of a coastal shelterbelt, and 450,700 m^3 of dredging of estuaries. The dynamic characteristics of wave and sediment and the law of sediment transport on coastal beaches should be studied in depth, and it is essential to protect the coast and strengthen the restoration and maintenance of the beach. A hydrostatic geomorphology model of the coastal beach of the Sun Bay Coastal Zone Protection and Restoration Project in Rizhao City is established in this paper. According to the water depth, terrain conditions, and sand plating particle size, the wave and sediment dynamics numerical solution is solved by using the wave coupling method in the Delft3D-FLOW module to solve the regional silt evolution under three different artificial beach laying schemes. The purpose of this paper is to study the erosion and brushing phenomenon caused by the wave action of different sections of artificial beaches in coastal restoration and remediation projects, to reveal the law of sand transport at the beach level, and to provide a basis for artificial sand laying schemes to determine the maintenance cycle of the beach.

2 CALCULATION MODELS AND METHODS

2.1 Numerical methods and calculation models

Delft3D-FLOW module is a sub-module of Delft3D, a comprehensive system of hydraulic environmental motion and sediment transportation developed by the WL Delft Hydraulics Research Institution in the Netherlands, which has the function of simulating hydrodynamics, waves, flow, morphology, etc. Delft3D-FLOW has been widely used worldwide to deal with problems such as large-scale water dynamics and sediment transport in estuaries, lakes, oceans, etc., high-dimensional hydrodynamic fields, and sediment transport.

The area of this numerical simulation is the near-shore sea area covering the engineering area, with an east-west distance of about 6328 m and a north-south distance of about 7980 m. The FLOW model adopts variable cells to partially encrypt the project area; the minimum grid size is about 5 m × 7 m, and the maximum grid size is 23 m × 45 m. Since the spatial accuracy of the WAVE module calculation result is insensitive compared to the FLOW module calculation result in the same area, the WAVE cell is 2 times the FLOW cell, and the cell nesting mode is adopted.

2.2 Research scheme and parameter setting

In the natural process, the dynamic and geomorphology are coupled interaction. A certain geomorphology shapes a certain hydrodynamic field, water movement carries sediment transport and thus induces geomorphological adjustments, and the geomorphological changes in turn feed back to the hydrodynamic field, constituting a coupled dynamic geomorphological system; this is the basic idea of the dynamic geomorphological model. In this paper, a hydrostatic geomorphological model of the coastal zone protection and restoration project of Sun Bay in Rizhao City was established; the sediment porosity of the sediment power module was set to 0.4 during the modeling process, the median particle size of the sediment under the natural ground type was set to 0.1 mm, the grading coefficient was selected to be 1.1, and the sand was laid on the beach (the laying elevation was + 1.5 m, and the initial slope was 1/ 34). The selected sediment median particle size is set to 0.3 mm, the gradation coefficient is selected to be 1.1, and the sediment power module adopts zero-flux zero-gradient boundary; the hydrodynamic field module propagates from the outer sea to the shore beach by means of E-directional standing waves (wave height 1.45 m, period 9.0 s) set at a boundary at a water depth of approximately 8 m.

According to the water depth, terrain conditions, and sand laying particle size, the wave sediment dynamic value solution was solved by means of wave sediment dynamics under three different artificial beach laying schemes by means of the wave coupling method in the delft3D-FLOW module. In the digital-analog simulation process, the damping characteristics of the seabed surface of the WAVE module are calculated using the Johnson equation of the module, and the damping coefficient is selected to be 0.067. The FLOW module adopts the Manning equation, and the Manning coefficients of the plane coordinates in both U and V directions are taken as 0.0263, and the Van Rijn formula is selected by the wave-induced shear solution. At the wall boundary, the flux of matter, momentum, heat, and turbulence are zero. In offshore boundary, the wave module of this calculation uses the wave spectrum defined by the parameter as the open boundary type, and the water flow module uses the tide level boundary and the Riemann boundary defined by the time strand.

3 RESULTS AND ANALYSIS

3.1 Numerical simulation of flushing under the action of constant waves

Three manual beach laying schemes are used: (a) scheme 1: the sand is laid at an initial shoreline elevation of + 1.5 m seaward, with the beach shoulder spanning 60 m laterally and sloping to the initial mudline in accordance with 1:34. (b) scheme 2: the sand is laid at an initial shoreline elevation of + 1.0 m seaward, with the beach shoulder spanning 60 m laterally and sloping down to the initial mudline in accordance with 1:34; (c) scheme 3: sand laying takes the initial shoreline to a seaward elevation of + 2.0 m, the lateral span of the beach shoulder is 40 m, and the slope is released to the initial mud line according to 1:34. The siltation distribution of the three schemes after 1-5 years under the action of constant waves is shown in Figures 1–3.

The profile sediment loss induced by sand spreading scheme 2 follows approximately the same pattern as that caused by sand spreading scheme 1, but the magnitude of sediment flushing is slightly different due to the different spreading elevations, i.e., sand spreading scheme 2 has a slightly higher sediment retention rate compared to sand spreading scheme 1. Specifically, Constant waves affected the lowest sand loss rate at site 1, with a loss rate of 3.8% in the first year, a loss rate of 1.6% in the second year, and a stable ground type of siltation in the next three years, so that the five-year sand loss rate of this site was about 5.4%. The sand laying loss rate of Constant waves in the second year of the second site was 4.8%, 2.6% in the second year, 1.4% in the third year, 0.6% in the fourth year, and roughly maintained the constant siltation of the ground type in the next year, so the five-year sand

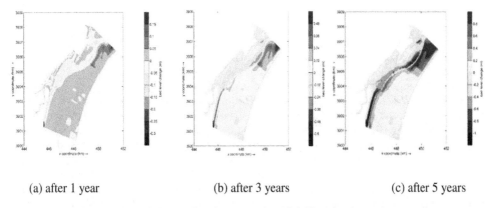

(a) after 1 year (b) after 3 years (c) after 5 years

Figure 1. The distribution of silting after 1-5 years of artificial beach scheme 1.

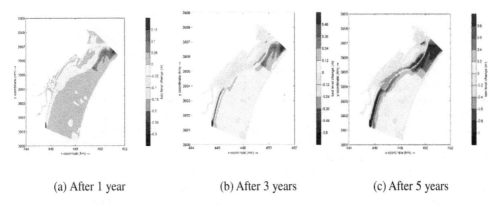

(a) After 1 year (b) After 3 years (c) After 5 years

Figure 2. The distribution of silting after 1-5 years under the artificial beach scheme 2.

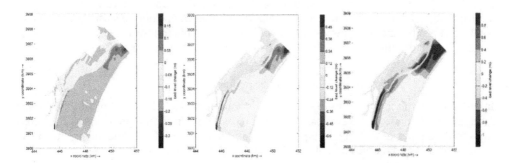

Figure 3. The distribution map of silting after 1-5 years of artificial beach scheme 3.

laying loss rate of this site was about 9.4%. Constant waves action site of three ground types in 4#, 5#, 6#, and 7# sections overall showed a scouring trend, of which the 7# section was most seriously washed; under the action of changing sea conditions, the loss rate in 7# section was 11.5% in the first year, 6.2% in the second year, 3.6% in the third year, 3.2% in the fourth year, 3.2% in the fifth year, and the total sand loss rate in the fifth year was 27.7%. The remaining three profiles were slightly increased by the sediment silt accumulation compared with the amount of hedging due to the impact of estuarine dynamic conditions, but the profile terrain still showed an overall erosion. Specifically, the total sand loss rate of the 4#, 5#, and 6# profiles in five years is about 20.4%, and compared with the sand laying scheme 1, the sediment loss rate caused by the sand laying scheme 2 is about 25%.

From the above results, it can be seen that the sediment loss induced by the sand laying scheme 3 is roughly similar to the law of the profile sediment loss caused by the sand laying scheme 1, but due to the different laying elevations, the sediment flushing range is slightly different, that is, the sediment retention rate of the sand laying scheme3, compared with the sand laying scheme 1, is clearly declining. Specifically, the sand loss rate of constant waves effect was the smallest, with a loss rate of 8.5% in the first year, 3.8% in the second year, and 1.2% in the third year (basically no sediment loss under the sand laying scheme 1 and in the third year), and the last two years basically maintained the stability of the ground type of silting, so the five-year sand laying loss rate of this site was about 13.5%. The sand laying loss rate of Constant waves in the second year of the second site was 11.4%, 6.9% in the second year, 3.4% in the third year, 1.4% in the fourth year, and roughly maintained constant siltation in the next year, so that the five-year sand laying loss rate of this site was about 23.1%. Constant waves action site of three ground types in 4#, 5#, 6#, and 7# sections generally showed a scouring trend, of which the 7# section was most seriously washed; under the action of Constant waves conditions, the loss rate in 7# section was 22.6% in the first year, 12.7% in the second year, 6.9% in the third year, 5.1% in the fourth year, 4.2% in the fifth year, and there is a five-year total sand laying loss rate of 51.5%. The total sand loss rate of the remaining three profiles 4#, 5#, 6# section in five years was about 43.5%; compared with the sand laying scheme 1, the sediment loss rate caused by the sand laying scheme 3 increased by as much as 34%.

In terms of sediment loss rate indicators alone, the sand paving profile of scheme 2 has the best sand retention effect, the sand laying profile of scheme 3 is the most severe under the coupling of waves and tides, the sediment loss volume of the sand paving section under the coupling action of scheme 3 is the most serious, and the sediment washing situation of the sand paving type of scheme 1 is in the middle. Comprehensive wave loss rate and sediment loss rate are the two indicators to consider. Although the second plan can achieve a high sediment retention rate, its reduction efficiency of the hydrodynamic field is low; the third plan has a better resistance against the wave, the tidal coupling effect, but inevitably there is a problem of poor sediment erosion rate. Therefore, the first plan can have both the appropriate wave attenuation rate and sediment retention rate. Comprehensive performance is the most prominent in the three comparison schemes, so the following recurrence period of wave action under the action of the silt numerical simulation was for scheme 1.

3.2 *Numerical simulation of sludge under the action of waves*

In order to determine the results of sediment transport and ground type erosion at the coastal sand laying site under the wave load in the reproduction period, the process and characteristics of the change of the ground type on the three south sides of the sand laying site in five years were explored on the basis of the above wave test combined with the E-wave direction, as shown in Figure 4.

Under the wave load conditions of the two-year recurrence period, due to the little difference between the wave height, the cycle, and the normal wave, the ground type of the sand laying site three continues to maintain the characteristics of the constant wave profile, showing the upward and downward silt. The sediment transport leads to the beach from the upper part of the erosion, and the erosion sediment falls on the downward side; that is, the maximum silt appears at the foot of the slope, and the largest erosion appears in the middle of the beach. Specifically, in the range of about 80-120 m, the junction zone between the front and back of the shore beach is the beach surface erosion area, and the maximum erosion type change is about 1.42 m. In addition, affected by the strength of the transport,

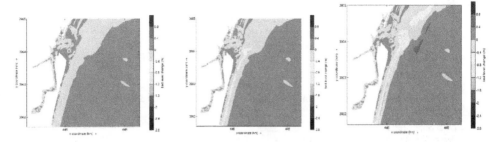

Figure 4. E-wave and 2-year recurrence period underground type siltation changes.

the sediment washed by the slope falls downward, and the silt falling area mainly occurs in the range of 120-160 m. The maximum silt depth is about 0.54 m, and the shore beach between the two areas shows micro-erosion or micro-siltation traits with different tide levels, but the amount of change is not high, and the maximum value is about 0.28 m.

Under the wave action of the ten-year and fifty-year recurrence periods, the ground type change of sand laying site 3 generally showed a trend consistent with the wave action of the two-year recurrence period, but the magnitude of the change of ground type erosion and the elevation change of ground type was higher, which was the reason for the continuous increase in the load wave height. Among them, the horizontal distance of the silt range is 120-170 m in the range of about 70-120 m in the range of wave erosion in ten years, and the horizontal distance of the silt range is 120-185 m in the range of about 55-110 m in the range of wave erosion in 50 years. As far as a certain wave condition is concerned, the sediment in the first year has the largest amount of sediment, accounting for about 20 to 30% of the total sediment transport, and the amount of sediment in the second year to the fifth year has decreased year by year, which is consistent with the change of the ground type under the action of the Constant wave. It should be noted that in the three areas of the sand laying site, the erosion range of the south side of the middle and lower part of the beach under the action of coastal flow is larger than that of the north side, and the sediment transport in this area is serious, making it the key area for sand replenishment and maintenance.

4 CONCLUSION

The wave-flow coupling method is used to numerically solve the regional sediment erosion and deposition evolution under three different artificial beach paving schemes. In terms of sediment loss rate indicators alone, the sand-laying section of scheme 2 has the best sand retention performance, scheme 3 has the highest volume of sediment loss in the sand-laying profile due to coupled wave and tidal action, and the sediment loss of the sand paving type of scheme 1 is in the middle. However, scheme 1 can have both an appropriate wave attenuation rate and a sediment retention rate, and the comprehensive performance of the three comparison schemes is the most prominent. As far as the E-wave conditions are concerned, the sediment flushing in the first year is the largest, accounting for about 20% to 30% of the total sediment transport volume, and the sediment flushing volume from the second year to the fifth year is decreasing year by year, which is consistent with the change of the ground type under the action of the constant wave. It should be noted that in the three areas of the sand laying site, the erosion range of the south side of the middle and lower part of the beach under the action of the coastal flow is larger than that of the north side, and the sediment transport in this area is serious, making it the key area for sand replenishment maintenance. In the future, it is necessary to improve the accuracy of the prediction model and optimize the artificial beach paving scheme.

REFERENCES

[1] Feng C., Su X.Z., Liu J.H., Li B., Lei G. Coastal Erosion in China and Countermeasures against Global Climate Change. *Progress in Natural Science*, 2008 (10): 1093–1103.

[2] Michalis I., Vousdoukas R.R., Lorenzo M., *et al.* Sandy Coastlines Under Threat of Erosion. *Nature Climate Change*, 2020, 10(3): 260–263.

[3] Joanne M., Raphael A.J., Wüst Paul J.H. Sediment Transport Along an Artificial Shoreline: "The Strand", Townsville, NE-Queensland, Australia. *Estuarine, Coastal and Shelf Science*, 2005, 66(1): 204–210.

[4] Ying X.M. *Study on the Impact of Yangshan Port Construction on the Evolution of Seabed Erosion and Deposition and Its Mechanism.* East China Normal University, 2011.

[5] Alex A., Bruce J., Guy G. Wave Characteristic and Morphologic Effects on the Onshore Hydrodynamic Response of Tsunamis. *Coastal Engineering*, 2011, 58(11):1034–1048.

[6] Han X.J., Kuang C.P., Gong L.X., Li W.B. Sediment Transport and Seabed Evolution Under Artificial Cape and Beach Conservation. *Oceans and Lakes*, 2022, 53 (04): 917–932.

[7] Zhang D.H., Shi L.Q., Gong Z.H., Guo J.L. Evolution Characteristics of Riyue Bay Beach Erosion and Deposition Under the Combined Action of Wave and Artificial Island in Winter. *Journal of Tropical Oceanography*, 2022, 41 (04): 71–81.

[8] Li S. *Study on Erosion and Deposition Characteristics of Artificial Island in Riyue Bay, Wanning, Hainan.* Ocean University of China, 2015.

Preparation and evaluation of gels for conformance control of high temperature and high salinity reservoirs

Hongbin Guo, Jijiang Ge* & Longjie Li
School of Petroleum Engineering, China University of Petroleum (East China), China

ABSTRACT: The gel is one of the most commonly used materials for reservoir conformance control and enhanced oil recovery in water flooding development reservoirs. However, harsh reservoir conditions such as high temperature and high salinity impose stringent requirements on the performance of the gel. In this study, acrylamide (AM)/ 2-acrylamide-2-methylpropanesulfonic acid (AMPS)/N-Vinylpyrrolidone (NVP) terpolymer and AM/AMPS copolymer were selected to prepare temperature and salinity resistant gels by crosslinking with hydroquinone (HQ) and hexamethylenetetramine (HMTA), respectively. A comparison of the stability of the gels prepared from the two polymers at 155°C in 25×10^4 mg/L salinity water revealed that the AM/AMPS copolymer was more suitable for the preparation of long-term stable temperature and salinity-resistant gel. Then, the gels suitable for application in a brine of 25×10^4 mg/L salinity at different temperatures were prepared using AM/AMPS polymers and evaluated. Finally, the plugging ability of AM/AMPS gel was evaluated by water flooding experiments. The results show that AM/AMPS gels have excellent plugging ability in porous media. The results of the study provide guidance for the design and application of gels in high-temperature and high-salinity reservoirs.

1 INTRODUCTION

Oil fields located in western China, such as the Xinjiang oil field, Tarim oil field and Tahe oil field, have large reservoir depths and high temperatures and salinity. After years of water flooding development in these fields, the problem of excessive water production has become increasingly serious, while the non-homogeneity of the formation has severely restricted further improvement of oil recovery. To control water production and enhance oil recovery, some measures are usually taken for reservoir conformance control to expand the swept area of water flooding. One of the widely used materials at present is polymer gel [1] [2] [3].

However, the harsh environment of the reservoir sets higher requirements for the performance of the gels. Most of the reservoirs in western China have temperatures above 110°C and formation water salinity above 20×10^4 mg/L. For example, some of the reservoirs in the Tarim oil field have temperatures up to 155°C and formation water salinity up to 25×10^4 mg/L. Gels prepared from conventional polymers, such as partially hydrolyzed polyacrylamide (HPAM) will degrade and precipitate very quickly under such conditions [4] [5] [6]. To improve the temperature and salinity resistance of gels, more stable temperature and salinity-resistant monomers have been introduced into the polymers [7] [8] [9]. Copolymers such as AM/AMPS, AM/AMPS/NVP, and PAtBA have been prepared for gel preparation by polymerizing acrylamide (AM) with monomers such as 2-acrylamide 2-methylpropanesulfonic acid (AMPS), N-vinylpyrrolidone (NVP), tert-Butyl acrylate (tBA),

---

*Corresponding Author: gejijiang@163.com

DOI: 10.1201/9781003433644-52

etc. [10] [11] [12]. In addition, it is necessary to use organic-type crosslinkers that crosslink polymers through covalent bonds, such as phenol, formaldehyde, hydroquinone (HQ), hexamethylenetetramine (HMTA), polyethyleneimine, etc. [2] [3] [9]. Because covalent bonds react more slowly than ionic bonds at high temperatures and have better temperature resistance, they can improve the practicality of the gel.

The development of temperature-and-salinity-resistant gels has been more fully developed, but few have evaluated the performance of gels in water with a salinity of 25×10^4 mg/L at 155°C. In this study, we selected two polymers, AM/AMPS, and AM/AMPS/NVP, as the main agents, and HQ and HMTA as crosslinkers to prepare the gels. The stability of the gels prepared from the two polymers was compared in a brine of 25×10^4 mg/L salinity at 155°C. The screened polymers were then used to develop temperature-and-salinity-resistant gels adapted to different temperatures in a brine of 25×10^4 mg/L salinity. Finally, the plugging ability of the gel in porous media was evaluated by water flooding experiments. The results of the study have implications for gel preparation and application in high-temperature and high-salinity reservoirs.

2 MATERIALS AND METHODS

2.1 Materials

In the study, the polymers used were AM/AMPS/NVP terpolymer (TP) and AM/AMPS copolymer (CP) provided by Qingdao Qucheng Technology Co. The average molecular weight of both polymers is around $6-8 \times 10^6$ g/mol. The molar ratio of AM: AM: NVP in TP is about 2:1:1. The molar ratio of AM: AMPS in CP is about 2:3. The crosslinker was analytically pure HQ and HMTA, purchased from Aladdin. Thiourea (TH) from Sinopharm Chemical Reagent Co., Ltd. was used as a deaerator. In addition, analytically pure inorganic salts, including sodium chloride, anhydrous calcium chloride, magnesium chloride hexahydrate, sodium sulfate, and sodium bicarbonate provided by Sinopharm Chemical Reagent Co. were used to prepare the simulated formation water.

In this study, the gelants of the gels were all prepared using simulated formation water with a total salinity of 25×10^4 mg/L. The composition of the simulated formation water is shown in Table 1.

Table 1. Composition of synthetic brine.

		Ions content (mg/L)				Total dissolved solids (mg/L)
Cl$^-$	SO$_4^{2-}$	HCO$_3^-$	Na$^+$	Ca^{2+}	Mg^{2+}	
153 642	500	43	79 129	14 756	2 028	250 098

2.2 Methods

2.2.1 Preparation of gel

All gels are composed of different concentrations of polymers, HQ, HTAM, and TH. Firstly, HQ, HMTA, and TH were dissolved into the simulated brine according to the gel composition. Subsequently, the polymer was slowly added while the solution was stirred. Finally, the mixture was stirred at 120 r/min for 2 hours using a stirrer to obtain a homogeneous gelant. In addition, we refer to HQ and HMTA collectively as crosslinkers, and the crosslinker concentrations below are their respective concentrations. For example, a 0.1% crosslinker concentration means that this gel contains 0.1% HQ and 0.1% HMTA.

The prepared gelant was dispensed into ampoules using a syringe, and each ampoule contained 20 g of gelant. Then, the ampoules were sealed with an alcoholic blowtorch and sealed in steel tanks containing an appropriate amount of water. Finally, they were placed in an oven at a certain temperature for heat treatment, and the properties of the gels, such as gelation time, strength, and thermal stability, were evaluated.

2.2.2 Evaluation of gel
In this study, the performance of the gels was evaluated mainly by gelation time, strength, and thermal stability.

The gelation time of the gels was measured by Sydansk's gel strength code [13]. In this study, we defined the time taken for the strength of the gel to reach the F level as its gelation time.

The strength of the gel was characterized by the storage modulus of the gel measured by an Anton Paar rheometer (MCR92) with parallel plate (25 mm) geometry at 25°C. The gel was cut into 1 mm thick cylindrical slices and placed in the middle of a parallel plate during the test. Then a strain amplitude oscillation scan test with a shear strain range of 1%-1000% and a shear frequency of 10 rad/s was performed. We considered the gel storage modulus within the linear viscoelastic region of the gel as the gel strength.

The thermal stability of the gels was characterized by the dehydration ratio of the gels after different times of heat treatment. The dehydration ratio of a gel was defined as the ratio of the mass of water removed from the gel to the initial mass of the gel. In this study, we considered gels with a dehydration ratio of less than 20% as stable gels.

2.2.3 Water flooding experiment
The plugging ability of the gels in the reservoir is characterized by the breakthrough pressure (P_b) and a residual resistance factor (F_{RR}) measured by water flooding experiments. The experiment was performed as follows: 1) a core of 21 cm in length and 2.5 cm in diameter was saturated with simulated brine by evacuation; 2) then, the brine was injected from one end of the core, and the pressure difference between the two ends of the core at different injection rates was recorded to calculate the permeability (k_{wi}) of the core; 3) next, a gelant of 1 pore volume (PV) was injected into the core; 4) The cores were then sealed in a gripper and aged in a high-temperature oven, waiting for the gelant to form a gel; 5) after the gel was formed, the excess gel was cleaned from both ends of the gel and the pipeline; 6) finally, brine was injected at a rate of 0.5 ml/min from one end of the core, and the pressure difference between the two ends of the core was recorded. We considered the maximum pressure difference that could be generated by gel plugging as the breakthrough pressure of the gel. We took the pressure difference between the two ends of the gel at 7.5 PV of water flooding to calculate the permeability (k_{wa}) of the core after gel plugging. The residual resistance factor was defined as the ratio of the permeability of the core before and after gel plugging (i.e., k_{wi}/k_{wa}). The test system was set at a pressure of 0.5 MPa to keep the water in a liquid state at high temperatures during the entire experiment, which was carried out at the temperature of 110°C.

3 RESULTS AND DISCUSSION

In this study, AM/AMPS/NVP terpolymer (TP) and AM/AMPS copolymer (CP) were selected as gel main agents, and HQ and HMTA were selected as crosslinkers to prepare gels that could adapt to high temperature and high salinity conditions. The structures of the gels prepared by crosslinking these two polymers with HQ and HMTA are shown in Figure 1.

To compare the temperature and salinity resistance of the gels prepared from the two polymers, we evaluated their stability in water with a salinity of 25×10^4 mg/L at 155°C.

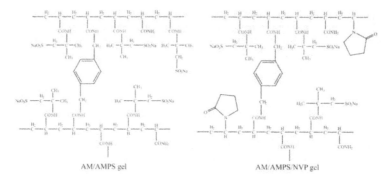

Figure 1. Schematic molecular structures of AM/AMPS gels and AM/AMPS/NVP gels.

3.1 *Evaluation of gel temperature and salinity resistance*

We prepared gels using 1% CP or TP crosslinked with 0.1%, 0.2%, 0.3%, and 0.4% crosslinkers, respectively, and placed them at 155°C for aging. The temperature and salinity resistance were compared by observing their dehydration after aging at different time. Figure 2 gives the states of the two gels after aging at 155°C at different time.

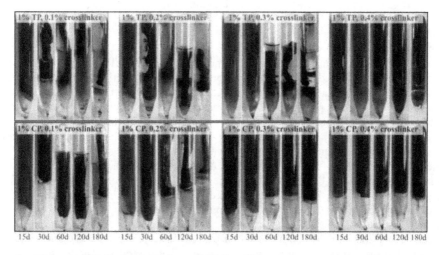

Figure 2. The state of the gels after aging at 155°C at different time.

The results showed that AM/AMPS/NVP gels with different crosslinker concentrations all exhibited different degrees of dehydration after aging for a certain period of time. AM/AMPS gels with crosslinker concentrations of 0.1% and 0.2% exhibited significant dehydration after aging up to 60 days, while AM/AMPS gels with crosslinker concentrations of 0.3% and 0.4% could stay stable for more than 180 days. Furthermore, the AM/AMPS gels were more stable at 155°C than AM/AMPS/NVP gels for both gels with the same polymer and crosslinker concentrations.

Both AMPS and NVP in the polymer are temperature-and-salinity-resistant monomers, and the higher their proportion in the polymer, the more stable the polymer [7] [9] [14] [15]. NVP is a non-ionic group with strong hydrogen bonding ability, providing better temperature-and-salinity resistance. Therefore, the stability of AM/AMPS/NVP gels is better than that of AM/AMPS gels in low-salinity water [11] [16]. However, the results of this study showed that the stability performance of AM/AMPS gels was superior in high-salinity water. This may be due to the effect of inorganic salts on the ability of NVP to stabilize the gel. Alternatively, this may be because the AM content in TP is 10% higher than that in CP.

3.2 *Preparation and evaluation of gels for different temperatures*

The above results indicate that AM/AMPS polymers are more suitable for preparing gels for use in high temperatures and high salinity reservoirs. Therefore, we used AM/AMPS gels crosslinked with HQ and HMTA to prepare temperature-and-salinity-resistant gels suitable for reservoirs with formation water salinity of 25×10^4 mg/L and temperatures of 110°C, 130°C, and 150°C, respectively. Then we evaluated their gelation properties at different temperatures.

Under the condition of 110°C, a polymer concentration of >0.5% and a crosslinker concentration of >0.1% in the gel are required. The gelation time of the gel is between 3-50 h, the gel modulus is between 3-5 Pa, and it can be stable for more than six months at 110°C as shown in Figure 3. Under the condition of 130°C, the gels with polymer concentration greater than 0.7% and crosslinker concentration greater than 0.1% can be stable for more than 180 days as shown in Figure 4c. The gelation time of the gel is between 2-50 h, and the storage modulus of the gel is between 5-11 Pa as shown in Figure 4. Furthermore, the temperature and salinity resistant gels demand higher polymer and crosslinker concentration at 150°C. The gels with a polymer concentration of 1.0% and crosslinker concentration of 0.1% and 0.2%, respectively, were severely dehydrated after aging at 150°C for 60 days, but the gel storage modulus would have a significant increase and still have high strength as shown in Figure 5b. Gels with a polymer concentration of 1.0% and crosslinker concentration $\geq 0.3\%$ can be stable for more than 180 days with a gelation time of less than 5 h, as shown in Figure 5.

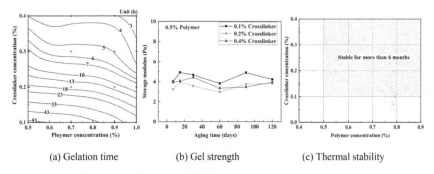

(a) Gelation time   (b) Gel strength   (c) Thermal stability

Figure 3. Performance of temperature-and-salinity-resistant gel at 110°C.

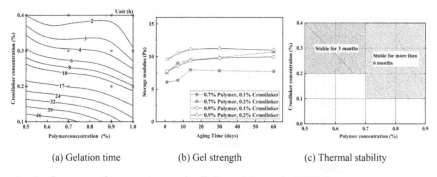

(a) Gelation time   (b) Gel strength   (c) Thermal stability

Figure 4. Performance of temperature-and-salinity-resistant gel at 130°C.

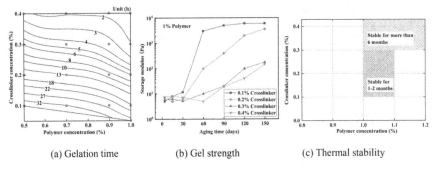

(a) Gelation time (b) Gel strength (c) Thermal stability

Figure 5. Performance of temperature-and-salinity-resistant gel at 150°C.

3.3 *Evaluation of the plugging ability of gels*

The plugging ability of gels in reservoirs is also of attention to researchers. It is a key parameter for good results when using gels for reservoir conformance control. The effect of porous media on gel properties is complex, resulting in some differences between the properties of bulk gels and the properties of gels in porous media [17] [18]. Although the evaluation of bulk gels can provide guidance for the application of gels, it does not directly reflect the plugging ability of gels in porous media.

In this study, we selected two well-adapted gels with different components for the water flooding experiments to evaluate the plugging ability of the gels in porous media. The permeability of the cores used in the experiments was about 2.5 μm². The relevant parameters and results of the experiments are shown in Table 2 and Figure 6.

Table 2. Experimental parameters and results of water flooding.

Gel composition	k_{wi} (10^{-3}μm²)	k_{wa} (10^{-3}μm²)	F_{RR}	P_b (MPa)
1% CP, 0.4% crosslinker	2812.8	2.0	1406.4	13.476
1% CP, 0.2% crosslinker	2563.6	8.0	320.45	6.895

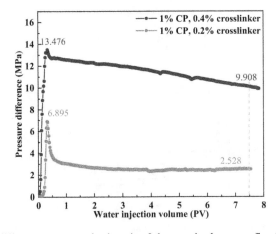

Figure 6. Pressure difference curves at both ends of the core in the water flooding experiment.

The results show that the gel can generate high plugging pressure in the core. The maximum plugging pressures generated by the gels with a polymer concentration of 1% and crosslinker concentrations of 0.2% and 0.4% were 13.476 MPa and 6.895 MPa, respectively. Such high blocking pressure allows subsequent injection water to enter the lower permeability zone, thereby increasing oil recovery. The F_{RR}s of 1406.4 and 320.45 for the two gels at the water injection volume of 7.5 PV were also excellent. The high F_{RR} indicated that the gel was able to keep the reservoir at a low permeability even after a large amount of formation water flushing. In summary, the gel prepared by crosslinking AM/AMPS copolymer with HQ and HMTA can provide excellent effects in the coherence control of the reservoir.

4 CONCLUSION

Based on the above results and discussions, the following conclusions were obtained:

(1) Temperature-and-salinity-resistant gels can be prepared by crosslinking AM/AMPS or AM/AMPS/NVP polymers with HQ and HMTA. In comparison, the stability of the gels prepared from AM/AMPS polymers was found to be superior in water with a salinity of 25×10^4 mg/L at 155°C.
(2) By adjusting the concentration of polymer and crosslinker, it is possible to prepare temperature-and-salinity-resistant gels that can be stable for more than 180 days at 110°C, 130°C and 150°C in brine with a salinity of 25×10^4 mg/L.
(3) Water flooding experiments show that the gel prepared by crosslinking AM/AMPS with HQ and HMTA has excellent plugging pressure and residual resistance factor, which can play a good role in reservoir conformance control.

ACKNOWLEDGMENTS

This work was financially supported by the China National Petroleum Corporation (grant number ZD2019-183-007).

REFERENCES

[1] El-Karsani K.S.; Al-Muntasheri G.A. and Hussein I.A. Polymer Systems for Water Shutoff and Profile Modification: A Review Over the Last Decade. *SPE Journal* 2014, 19, 135–149.
[2] Zhu D.; Bai B.; Hou J. Polymer Gel Systems for Water Management in High-temperature Petroleum Reservoirs: A Chemical Review. *Energy & Fuels* 2017, 31, 13063–13087.
[3] Bai B.; Zhou J. and Yin M. A Comprehensive Review of Polyacrylamide Polymer Gels for Conformance Control. *Petroleum Exploration and Development* 2015, 42, 525–532.
[4] Ryles R.G. Chemical Stability Limits of Water-Soluble Polymers Used in Oil Recovery Processes. *SPE Reservoir Engineering* 1988, 3, 23–34, doi:10.2118/13585-pa.
[5] Seright R.S.S. and Skjevrak I. Effect of Dissolved Iron and Oxygen on Stability of Hydrolyzed Polyacrylamide Polymers. *SPE Journal* 2015, 20, 433–441, doi:10.2118/169030-pa.
[6] Jouenne S.; Klimenko A. and Levitt D. Polymer Flooding: Establishing Specifications for Dissolved Oxygen and Iron in Injection Water. *SPE Journal* 2016, 22, 438–446, doi:10.2118/179614-pa.
[7] Dupuis G.; Antignard S.; Giovannetti B.; Gaillard N.; Jouenne S.; Bourdarot G.; Morel D. and Zaitoun A. A New Thermally Stable Synthetic Polymer for Harsh Conditions of Middle East Reservoirs. Part I. Thermal Stability and Injection in Carbonate Cores. *In Proceedings of the Abu Dhabi International Petroleum Exhibition & Conference*, 2017.
[8] Gaillard N.; Giovannetti B. and Favero C. Improved Oil Recovery using Thermally and Chemically Protected Compositions Based on co- and terpolymers Containing Acrylamide. *In Proceedings of the SPE Improved Oil Recovery Symposium*, 2010.

[9] Gaillard N.; Giovannetti B.; Leblanc T.; Thomas A.; Braun O. and Favero C. Selection of Customized Polymers to Enhance Oil Recovery from High Temperature Reservoirs. *In Proceedings of the SPE Latin American and Caribbean Petroleum Engineering Conference*, 2015.

[10] Sandengen K.; Meldahl M.M.; Gjersvold B.; Molesworth P.; Gaillard N.; Braun O. and Antignard S. Long-term Stability of ATBS type Polymers for Enhanced Oil Recovery. *Journal of Petroleum Science and Engineering* 2018, 169, 532–545, doi:https://doi.org/10.1016/j.petrol.2018.06.001.

[11] Zhu D.; Hou J.; Wei Q.; Wu X.; Bai B. Terpolymer Gel System Formed by Resorcinol–Hexamethylenetetramine for Water Management in Extremely High-Temperature Reservoirs. *Energy & Fuels* 2017, 31, 1519–1528, doi:10.1021/acs.energyfuels.6b03188.

[12] Guo H.; Ge J.; Zhao S.; Xu Y.; Zhou D.; Tao Z. Performance Evaluation of High-Strength Polyethyleneimine Gels and Syneresis Mechanism under High-Temperature and High-Salinity Conditions. *SPE Journal* 2022, 1–13, doi:10.2118/210593-pa.

[13] Sydansk R.D. A Newly Developed Chromium (III) Gel Technology. *SPE Reservoir Engineering* 1990, 5, 346–352.

[14] Gaillard N.; Giovannetti B.; Favero C.; Caritey J.-P.-P.; Dupuis G.; Zaitoun A. New Water Soluble Anionic NVP Acrylamide Terpolymers for Use in Harsh EOR Conditions. *In Proceedings of the SPE Improved Oil Recovery Symposium*, 2014.

[15] Vermolen E.C.; van Haasterecht M.J.; Masalmeh S.K.; Faber M.J.; Boersma D.M.; Gruenenfelder M. Pushing the Envelope for Polymer Flooding Towards High-temperature and High-salinity Reservoirs with Polyacrylamide Based Ter-polymers. *In Proceedings of the SPE Middle East Oil and Gas Show and Conference*, 2011.

[16] Juárez J.L.; Rodriguez M.R.; Montes J.; Trujillo F.D.; Monzòn J.; Dupuis G.; Gaillard N. Conformance Gel Design for High Temperature Reservoirs. *In Proceedings of the SPE Europec*, 2020.

[17] Seright R.S.S.; Fan T.; Wavrik K.; de Carvalho Balaban R. New Insights Into Polymer Rheology in Porous Media. *SPE Journal* 2010, 16, 35–42, doi:10.2118/129200-pa.

[18] Lai N.; Chen S.; Tang L.; Huang Y.; Xu H. Migration Characteristics and Profile Control Capabilities of Preformed Particle Gel in Porous Media. *Petroleum* 2021.

Application research and technology development of cryogenic energy storage materials

Fan Yang*, Chao Zhang, Bochao Zhang, Xi Zhong & Cong Zhen
CNOOC Gas & Power Group Co., Ltd., Beijing China

ABSTRACT: In recent years, the application of new technologies and materials has developed rapidly in cryogenic energy storage. To better grasp the development and application status of material technology in this field, the current situation of material selection, material technology, and standards of liquid ammonia, cryogenic hydrocarbon, and liquid hydrogen (LH_2) are summarized. The application of new or efficient alternative materials such as metal, thermal insulation, and concrete is studied. The research conclusion shows that low-temperature energy storage materials will be developed in the direction of low carbon, energy saving, standardization, and substitutability to meet the development needs of dual carbon energy transformation in the future.

1 INTRODUCTION

With the promotion of the shale gas revolution and the demand for new raw materials in the energy and chemical industry, the demand for ethane, ethylene, propane, and other energy has been growing in recent years. At the same time, with the need for global low-carbon development, the demand for gas energy consumption, such as natural gas, hydrogen, and ammonia (the carrier of hydrogen energy), is growing rapidly. These above gases can be stored and transported at cryogenic in the industrial way of freezing or semi-freezing after cryogenic liquefaction, which can effectively improve the efficiency of long-distance transportation such as ocean transportation. Take LNG, for example; its volume can be reduced by about 625 times at cryogenic, which can greatly improve ocean transportation efficiency and reduce costs. With the promotion of industrial development, the application of new technologies and materials in cryogenic energy storage has developed rapidly in recent years.

In terms of technology and application status, due to regional development and policy differences, such cryogenic energy storage materials are more or less different in material selection, standards, and other aspects. Take 9% Ni steel and austenitic stainless steel as examples; there are subtle differences and differences in the control of C, P, S, and other elements, as well as mechanical performance indicators worldwide. Many efficient alternative metal materials, efficient thermal insulation materials, low-carbon concrete, and other new materials have been rapidly applied.

To meet the needs of large-scale storage, transportation, and consumption of cryogenic fields such as LNG and LH2 in recent years,

This paper investigates the selection rules, new technology development, and application of energy storage materials such as liquid ammonia and cryogenic hydrocarbon. Moreover,

*Corresponding Author: yangfan5@cnooc.com.cn

it investigates LH$_2$ to master the development and application trend of material technology in this field and put forward suggestions and prospects for the future development of materials in this field in combination with the development requirements of the current international low-carbon and energy-saving situation. Finally, the future direction of materials in this field prospects and some suggestions for future materials development in the cryogenic energy storage industry are put forward.

2 CURRENT SITUATION OF MATERIAL SELECTION IN THE CRYOGENIC ENERGY STORAGE FIELD

As the core equipment of cryogenic energy projects, cryogenic storage tanks store frozen or semi-frozen cryogenic liquid gas energy. The materials of cryogenic storage tanks are generally divided into primary container material, secondary container materials, and thermal insulation materials according to the functional structure.

The main vessel materials are generally cryogenic-resistant metal materials, including ferritic cryogenic steel (cryogenic C-Mn steel, low nickel alloy steel, 9% Ni steel, etc.), austenitic cryogenic steel (generally 304 or 316 stainless steel), aluminum alloy, titanium alloy, etc. Since the material of the main container is in direct contact with the cryogenic medium, the material shall have sufficient strength and toughness at cryogenic and have good process performance, processing performance, and corrosion resistance. The secondary containers generally have low-carbon steel, reinforced concrete, and other materials. In addition, if the tank is a bimetallic full-capacity tank structure, the outer tank metal must be loaded with cryogenic medium leaked under extreme working conditions, so the same materials as the main container can be used generally. Thermal insulation materials generally include rock wool materials such as foam glass brick, expanded perlite, elastic felt or glass wool, polyurethane (PUR), polyisocyanurate (PIR) aeronenenebb gel felt, etc. It isn't easy to realize the thermal insulation effect for small-volume cryogenic and LH$_2$ storage tanks. Therefore, vacuum winding insulation or vacuum perlite insulation is generally selected. Materials are usually selected, as shown in Table 1 below.

Table 1. Typical materials selection of the cryogenic energy storage tanks (typical storage under normal pressure).

Numble	Cryogenic storage medium	Storage temperature (°C)	Primary container material	Secondary container material	Thermal insulation material
1	NH$_3$	−33.4	A537, S355, 16MnDR.	A516, S 355, 16MnDR	Cellular glass block, perlite, glass wool, resilient blanket
2	C$_3$H$_8$ (propane)	−42.2	A537, 16MnDR, 15MnNiNbDR	A516, S 355, 16MnDR, reinforced concrete	Cellular glass block, perlite, glass wool, resilient blanket
3	C$_2$H$_6$ (ethane)	−88.6	304 stainless steel, 9% Ni steel	304, 9% Ni steel, reinforced concrete	Cellular glass block, perlite, glass wool, resilient blanket
4	C$_2$H$_4$ (ethylene)	−103.9			
5	LNG	−162.2		reinforced concrete	
6	LH$_2$	−252.8	aluminum alloy, 304 or 316, titanium alloy	304, A516 or 16MnDR (cofferdam considered)	Vacuum multi-layer insulation, vacuum perlite

In terms of construction standards, cryogenic hydrocarbon storage standards are relatively mature, mainly including EN standards, GB standards, API standards, Japanese standards, etc. As for the storage standard of liquid ammonia, there is no special standard at present. At present, API 620-2018 (API 2018), EN14620-2006 (EN 2006), GB/T 26978-2021 (GB/T 2021), and other standards are mainly applied in the design and construction. It is understood that the European standard EN 14620, which is currently being revised, will supplement the relevant requirements for the construction of liquid ammonia. In terms of LH_2 storage standards, the international standards mainly include the small and medium volume LH_2 storage tank standard CGA-H-3-2019, Standard for Cryogenic Hydrogen Storage (CGA 2019), T/CATSI 05006-2021, Special Technical Requirements for Stationary Vacuum Cold Insulated LH_2 Pressure Vessels (T CATSI 2021), and the construction standard system for larger volume LH_2 storage tanks is lacking. It is believed that with the future hydrogen energy industry's rapid development, the standards for large-volume LH_2 storage tanks will soon be improved.

3 APPLICATION OF NEW MATERIALS AND DEVELOPMENT TRENDS OF TECHNOLOGY

In recent years, with the progress of industry and the low-carbon transformation and development of the energy industry, the field of cryogenic storage materials has made significant progress in low-carbon new materials, efficient alternative materials, etc., which has greatly promoted the overall technological progress of the cryogenic industry. China and other countries have recently begun to implement the policy support of "replacing steel with plastic," encouraged various industries to develop lightweight technology, and gradually expanded the application of plastic products in the industrial field to achieve the purpose of energy conservation and emission reduction. The demand for composite structures used in the cryogenic refrigeration industry is growing. Carbon fiber-reinforced epoxy composites, glass fiber-reinforced resin matrix composites, etc., have been used in cryogenic thruster tanks in China's aerospace field. In terms of concrete, metal materials, and cold insulation materials, there is also a trend of high-efficiency substitution, low carbonization, and standardized production.

3.1 *Metallic material*

With the upgrading of consumption demand for low-carbon clean energy, the construction of LNG storage facilities in the Asia Pacific and other regions, especially in China and other countries, has accelerated. And the LNG tank construction is showing super large-scale and large-scale construction. For example, as shown in Figure 1, CNOOC Yancheng "Green Energy Port" LNG Phase I Project, located in Jiangsu Province, China, has built four

Figure 1. CNOOC Yancheng "Green energy port" LNG phase I expansion project.

220,000 m³ storage tanks and is building six 270,000 m³ storage tanks (with a gross volume of 290,000 m³, which are the largest tank in the world at present).

Taking China as an example, it is predicted that the demand for 9% Ni steel in the next five years will be more than 200,000 tons. Standardized design and manufacturing in terms of material specifications and models are pursued to minimize excess materials and losses and improve materials' interoperability before the project.

In addition, Japan, China, and other regions have started to use improved 7% Ni steel and high manganese steel to replace 9% Ni steel, and the cost can be reduced by more than 10%, according to the assessment.

3.1.1 Modified 7% Ni steel

The improved 7% Ni steel adopts the new "TEMP" smelting process in recent years to improve the mechanical and mechanical properties of the steel plate itself. From the comparison of mechanical properties in Table 2, the improved 7% Ni steel can completely replace the 9% Ni steel.

Table 2. Performance comparison between modified 7% Ni steel and 9% Ni steel of typical manufacturers.

Heat treatment process	Rel/MPa	Rm/MPa	A/%	Z/%	(−196°C) Akv/J
7% Ni Steel(hot rolled)	675	895	15	72.5	9,9,8
9% Ni Steel(hot rolled)	660	850	18.5	72.0	15,17,18
7% Ni Steel(Heat treated)	675	730	25.0	75.5	235,246,238
9% Ni Steel(Heat treated)	681	726	25.0	77.5	234,236,231
EN10028-4 requirements (EN 2007)	≥ 585	680~820	≥ 18.0	–	≥ 80

In terms of engineering application, 7% Ni steel improved by Nippon Steel Corporation of Japan was successfully applied in a 230,000 m³ gas storage tank in Osaka, Japan, in 2013. It has been listed in Japanese industrial JIS and American ASME standards in the following years (Chen et al. 2021). China's Nanjing Iron and Steel Company and other manufacturers have also started developing 7% Ni steel and successfully applied it in a 50,000 m³ ethylene cryogenic tank in Guangxi Province in 2019.

3.1.2 The high manganese steel

In terms of high manganese steel, Daewoo Shipbuilding&Marine Engineering Company (DSME) and POSCO Iron&Steel Company of South Korea realized the application of high manganese steel developed in LNG fuel tanks on VLCC in June 2022. Chinese enterprises, China Shipbuilding Corporation, and CIMC have also completed the development of high-manganese steel. With the maturity of technology, it is expected to be used in onshore LNG tanks (Du et al. 2021).

3.1.3 Austenitic stainless steel for an LH_2 storage tank

Research at home and abroad has shown that austenitic stainless steel has good stability and is not prone to hydrogen embrittlement in a high hydrogen environment. For example, 304 and 316 stainless steel materials are not sensitive to hydrogen embrittlement in low-temperature LH_2 environments. It is understood that there are no technical problems caused by hydrogen permeation for the LH_2 storage tanks below 10,000 m³ that have been in service internationally. There is a lack of research data for larger volume LH2 storage tanks. In future research and development of larger volume LH$_2$ storage tanks, it is suggested that low-temperature hydrogen embrittlement resistance tests. Material pretreatment should still be carried out for materials to improve the hydrogen embrittlement resistance of materials further to prevent the occurrence of hydrogen embrittlement and ensure that materials can truly meet the safety requirements (Yang et al. 2022).

In terms of storage materials used for LH$_2$, steel enterprises in China and South Korea are developing the next to apply to larger volume LH$_2$ storage tanks and further solve the hydrogen embrittlement problem in the production of LH$_2$ storage containers generation of efficient austenitic stainless steel for LH$_2$ storage. Companies such as KRISO, POSCO, and KSOE in South Korea completed the research and development of 316HN stainless steel at the beginning of 2022. It is believed that the stainless steel materials used for LH$_2$ storage will achieve greater technological breakthroughs and applications in the future.

3.2 Thermal insulation material

Higher thermal insulation performance is required with energy storage in lower-temperature areas, such as LH$_2$. It is generally preferred to use vacuum multi-layer winding insulation with a better insulation effect. If possible, the gas evaporation rate can be further reduced according to the active insulation device in the tank. Some projects use the experience of the air separation industry, such as liquid oxygen, and adopt the thermal insulation method of multi-layer winding and perlite powder in a vacuum environment to solve the problem of difficult on-site installation of large-volume cryogenic storage tanks.

3.2.1 Vacuum Insulation Panel(VIP)insulation

VIP materials have been widely used in refrigerators and refrigeration industries in the early days. In recent years, it has begun to be used in cryogenic ships or storage equipment. Compared with other thermal insulation materials, it can be industrialized in cryogenic storage of cryogenic energy at a low thermal conductivity (Zhengzhou Shengshi Jinding Thermal Insulation Refractory Co., Ltd 2019) (generally 0.001~0.01 W/m.K).

3.2.2 Fiberglass Fiber Reinforced Plastic(GFRP)

In the field of cryogenic ships, higher performance requirements are put forward for the supporting structure due to reducing the heat leakage of the cold bridge as much as possible. In addition to the relatively low thermal conductivity, it is also required to have relatively strong bearing strength at low temperatures. This material is applied to the 2500m^3 LH$_2$ ship (already in service in 2022) and will also be expected to be used in subsequent LH$_2$ ships (as shown in Figure 2, C-Job Naval Architects of the Netherlands is building a 37500 m^3 LH2 ship).

Figure 2. Netherlands' C-Job Naval Architects is building 37500m^3 LH$_2$ ships (to be completed in 2027).

3.3 Concrete materials

Concrete is widely used as the outer tank material of large cryogenic hydrocarbon storage tanks (LNG, ethylene, ethane, etc.). Cement accounts for 7% of global carbon emissions. In general construction projects, the carbon content of concrete accounts for 50-85% of the total carbon content of buildings, so it is necessary to reduce the carbon content of reinforced concrete materials (Luo 2022). At the same time, with the development of prefabricated technology, more energy-saving concrete technology has begun to be used in low-temperature storage facilities.

3.3.1 Low-carbon concrete

With the development of dual carbon, low-carbon concrete materials have also begun to be used in the energy industry. By reducing the amount of cement in concrete, giving full play to the role of mineral additives such as fly ash and slag, and optimizing the mix ratio to achieve long service life and high durability of concrete, the current laboratory data can reduce carbon emissions by about 50% at most.

3.3.2 Fabricated concrete materials

Fabricated construction technology can complete prefabrication in the prefabrication yard and on-site assembly. It has the characteristics of low carbon, energy conservation, and environmental protection, reducing on-site workforce and machine investment, and can effectively save the construction period and reduce installation costs. It is widely used in the industrial field. In recent years, it has also begun to be widely used in low-temperature storage tanks. Figure 3 below shows the fabricated concrete pile cap of 220,000 m^3 LNG storage tank installation in progress, located in Jiangsu Province, China.

Figure 3. Fabricated concrete pile cap of the 220,000 m^3 LNG storage tank is an installation in progress.

4 CONCLUSION

Through the research on the current situation and trend of the selection of cryogenic energy storage materials such as liquid ammonia, cryogenic hydrocarbon, and LH$_2$, the following conclusions are drawn:

(1) With the strong demand for low-carbon energy in the future, the cryogenic energy industry will greatly develop, promoting the rapid development of new materials and technologies in cryogenic energy storage.
(2) With the progress of industrial development and the need for low-carbon construction, the concrete materials and thermal insulation materials used for cryogenic storage will show low-carbon production and efficient development in the future.

(3) The core materials of main containers for cryogenic storage, with the large-scale development and the need for energy conservation, carbon reduction, and cost reduction. "Plastic instead of steel" and improved low nickel steel will gradually replace the traditional high nickel steel materials, further reducing the industrial cost.

ACKNOWLEDGMENTS

This work was financially supported by a scientific research project of China National Offshore Oil Corporation (BZ-2022-04).

REFERENCES

API 620-2018, *Design and Construction of Large, Welded, Low-pressure Storage Tanks.*
CGA H-3-2019, *Standard for Cryogenic Hydrogen Storage.*
Chen Kaili, Xi Lianyun, Xie Zhanglong, *et al.* Development of New 7% Ni Steel for LNG Storage Tank, *Oil&Gas Storage and Transportation.* 2021,40 (10), 1181–1186.
Du Qinglin, Kang Shumei, Li Shuntao, Development of Ultra-cryogenic High Manganese Steel Welding Technology and its Application in LNG Tanks, *Technology Innovation, and Application*, 2021,(11) P40–43.
EN 10028-2007, *Part 4, Nickel Alloy Steels with Specified Low-temperature Properties.*
EN 14620-2006, *Design and Manufacture Site-built, Vertical, Cylindrical, Flat-bottomed Steel Tanks to Store Refrigerated, Liquefied Gases.*
GB/T 26978-2021, *Design and Construction of Vertical Cylindrical Flat Bottom Steel Cryogenic Liquefied Gas Storage Tanks Assembled on Site.*
Information on http://www.zzjdbw.cn/industrytrends/330.html
Information on https://doi.org/10.19912/j.0254-0096.tynxb.2022-0930.
Information on https://new.qq.com/rain/a/20220508A080NE00
Luo Xiaodong, Calculating Carbon Emissions of Ready Mixed Concrete and Analysis and Research on Low-carbon Technology *Path,* New Building Materials, 2022,49 (08) 160–166.
T CATSI 05006-2021, *Special Technical Requirements for Stationary Vacuum Insulated LH_2 Pressure Vessels.*

Multi-layered micro/nano filters for efficient air filtration

Wenhua Ma
Institute of Smart & Ecological Textile, Quanzhou Normal University, Fujian, China
College of Textile and Apparel, Xinjiang University, Urumqi, Xinjiang, China

Huan Qi*
Institute of Smart & Ecological Textile, Quanzhou Normal University, Fujian, China
College of Textile and Apparel, Quanzhou Normal University, Fujian, China

Yongmeng Zhang & Minggang Lin
Institute of Smart & Ecological Textile, Quanzhou Normal University, Fujian, China
College of Textile and Apparel, Xinjiang University, Urumqi, Xinjiang, China

Chuyang Zhang
Institute of Smart & Ecological Textile, Quanzhou Normal University, Fujian, China
College of Textile and Apparel, Xinjiang University, Urumqi, Xinjiang, China
College of Textile and Apparel, Quanzhou Normal University, Fujian, China

ABSTRACT: Inhalable particulate matter and the COVID-19 coronavirus threaten human health. Existing meltdown and electro spun air filters have more or less some shortcomings. This work proposed a novel methodology to fabricate high-performance air filters by combining meltdown and electro spun techniques. The structure and layers quantity of micro/nanofiber webs were adjusted to optimize filtration performance. The influence of laminated layers and pore size on the filtration performance of composite filters was thoroughly investigated. The loading test was also included for the filtration property. The increasing layers and thinning fiber web can improve the filtration efficiency and lower the pressure drop of the composite filter. The micro/nano filter (18.5gsm) fabricated by ten layers presented a high filtration efficiency of 97.94%, a low-pressure drop of 53.2 Pa, and a high-quality factor (QF) of 0.073 Pa^{-1} for NaCl aerosol particles. The laminated micro/nano filters developed here would be promising in the air filtration field.

1 INTRODUCTION

Particulate matter (PM) is one of the most important sources of air pollution (Grobety et al. 2010). Tiny airborne particles generally exist in solid dust, liquid droplets, aerogels, etc., and their chemical composition is extremely complex (Song et al. 2020). COVID-19 coronavirus is also airborne in the form of aerogel particles. It seriously threatens human health and life and greatly impacts the global economy (Tisdell 2020). Meltblown nonwovens are currently the most used commercial filters. After corona charging treatment, they have a satisfactory particle capture capacity (Zhang et al. 2020). However, the electret charge decays easily in practical environments, especially at high temperatures and high humidity, resulting in a dramatic drop in filtration efficiency (Campos et al. 2020). The electrets incorporation

---

*Corresponding Author: hwnqi@qztc.edu.cn

enhances the stability of charge storage in melt-blown fibers. It slows down the decay rate of filtration efficiency (Han et al. 2022; Kilic et al. 2015; Liu et al. 2019). Still, to a certain extent, it affects the polymer spinnability. Electrospun membranes have been investigated intensively in recent years due to their small fiber fineness and high filtration efficiency. However, there are many defects with pure electrospun membrane for air filtration, such as poor mechanical strength, high-pressure drop, and low-quality factors (Chen et al. 2020). To overcome these drawbacks, a lot of research has been done, such as surface structure design (Lou et al. 2016), fiber and pore size optimization (Liu et al. 2020; Xu et al. 2022), fiber surface modification (Yao et al. 2022). In the existing studies, electrospun membranes usually need to be stacked to a certain thickness to achieve high filtration efficiency. But the rise in membrane thickness can cause a sharp increase in filtration resistance, which limits their quality factor. The combination of ultrathin melt-blown nonwoven and ultrathin nanomembrane by laminated structure design to produce high efficiency and low resistance composite filters has not been reported.

In this work, micro/nanocomposite filters were prepared by laminating meltdown and electrospun nonwovens and applied for particle removal. The content of nano and microfibers was kept the same by controlling the spinning time and the number of layers. An automated filter tester evaluated the filtration performance. The surface morphology and pore size distribution were investigated to analyze the filtration mechanism. Excellent filtration performance and lower base weight endow micro/nano filters with an advantage in air filtration. The results provided a versatile strategy for further designing and developing air filters with excellent filtration.

2 MATERIALS AND METHODS

2.1 *Materials*

Polyvinylidene fluoride (PDVF, M_w = 1,000,000) was purchased from Huachuang Chemical Co., Ltd. (Foshan, China). N, N-dimethylformamide (DMF) was supplied by Yien Chemical Technology Co., Ltd. (Shanghai, China). Polypropylene (PP) pellets (MFI 1500) were supplied by China-Base Petrochemical Co. (Ningbo, China). All chemicals were used without further purification.

2.2 *Sample preparation*

Three kinds of PP melt blown (M_1, M_2, M_3) with different base weights were fabricated on the Spunbond-Meltblown-spun-bond (SMS) pilot line in the laboratory. The spinning temperature and drawing air temperature were 260°C and 270°C, respectively. The pressure of drawing air was 0.1 MPa. PVDF powder was dissolved in DMF by stirring for 10 h at room temperature. The meltdown was wound on the roller as the substrate for nanofibers. After receiving the nanofibers for a certain period, another piece of meltblown with equal base weight was overlaid to receive nanofibers for the equal time. This way, desired layer-by-layer micro/nano filters with homogeneous structures can be obtained. The injection speed, collecting distance, and applied voltage were 1.0 ml/h, 15 cm, and 25kv, respectively.

2.3 *Structure design of micro/nano filters*

Three kinds of micro/nano filters contained equal weight (18.50 g/m^2) of microfibers (16.50 g/m^2) and nanofibers (2.00 g/m^2) were fabricated and marked as M_1E_1*1, M_2E_2*3, M_3E_3*5. Detailed parameters of these samples are listed in Table 1.

Table 1. Parameters of laminated samples.

Sample	Number of layers	Base weight (g/m^2) (Meltblown)	(Nanofilm)	Total base weight (g/m^2)
M$_1$E$_1$*1	2	16.50	2.00	18.50
M$_2$E$_2$*3	6	5.50	0.67	18.50
M$_3$E$_3$*5	10	3.30	0.40	18.50

2.4 *Characterization*

The surface morphology of micro/nano filters was investigated by scanning electron microscope (TESAN MIRA LMS, Tescan China Ltd., China). The pore size distribution was measured by a capillary flow parameter (CFP-1500-AEXL, Porous Materials Inc, Ithaca, NY, USA). The filtration performance was evaluated on an automated filter tester (DR251XL, Wenzhou Darong Textile Instrument Co., Ltd., China). Moreover, a filtration loading test was performed according to GB 2626-2019. The concentration of NaCl aerosol was at 20 mg/m^3 with an airflow of 85 L/min.

3 RESULTS AND DISCUSSION

3.1 *Morphology of laminated micro/nano filter*

The bottom surface morphology of meltblown after filtration is shown in Figure 1a. Due to the poor interception capacity, sodium chloride particles were rarely observed on melt-blown

Figure 1. SEM images after filtration test. (a) Bottom of pure meltblown M$_1$, (b)-(d) Bottom layers of micro/nano filter M$_1$E$_1$*1, M$_2$E$_2$*3, M$_3$E$_3$*5, respectively.

fibers. While in Figure 1**b**, a large number of particles can be observed on the bottom nanofibers, indicating that the introduction of nanofibers significantly enhanced the interception capacity for particles. In Figure 1**c**, it can be found that there were fewer particles on the bottom nanofibers of M_2E_2*3 compared to M_1E_1*1. It may be due to the alternating arrangement of multilayer nanofibers and microfibers forming a multistage retention effect. Most of the particles were already captured before reaching the bottom layer. As shown in Figure 1**d**, M_3E_3*5 had the least number of particles on the bottom layer, further confirming this inference. Besides, the apparent hierarchical structure of random microfibers and nanofibers can be observed in M_1E_1*1 due to the alternating arrangement of different layers. However, in M_2E_2*3 and M_3E_3*5, the hierarchical structure gradually became less obvious and mixed with each layer. This blended structure will facilitate the synergistic effect of microns and nanofibers and improve the filtration performance. The combination of melt-blown and electrospun technologies endows micro/nano filters with versatile fiber diameters, which is conducive to the formation of complex and variable pore structures and increases the tortuosity of the pores.

3.2 *Pore size distribution*

The pore size distributions of micro/nano filters are shown in Figure 2. The pore sizes of M_1E_1*1, M_2E_2*3, and M_3E_3*5 were mainly concentrated in 5-7 μm. The peak value increased from 4.98 μm to 6.42 μm, reflecting that the content of larger pores had increased because the filter became fluffier with the increasing layers. The multilayer structure in the filter facilitates the formation of contact interfaces, which is conducive to improving pore size. In general, micro/nano filters have multi-scale pore sizes, which is essential to achieve high efficiency and low resistance.

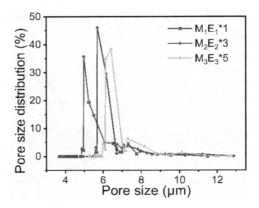

Figure 2. Pore size distributions of micro/nano filters.

3.3 *Filtration performance*

As shown in Figure 3**a**, the filtration efficiencies of M_1E_1*1, M_2E_2*3, and M_3E_3*5 were 95.60%, 97.99%, and 97.94%, respectively. The overall filtration efficiency tended to increase as the number of layers increased and the fiber webs became thinner. Meanwhile, their pressure drops were 58.6, 53.9, and 53.2 Pa, which showed a downward trend. The changes in filtration efficiencies and pressure drops were reflected in Figure 3**b** as a gradual increase in the quality factors (QFs). The QF increased from 0.052 to 0.073 Pa^{-1} when the number of layers increased to 10. The layer-by-layer micro/nanostructure enhanced the tortuosity of pores and endowed the sample with multi-scale pore sizes and diameters, thus improving the

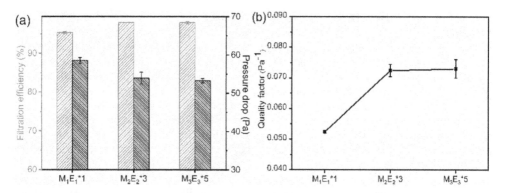

Figure 3. (a) Filtration efficiencies and pressure drops and (b) quality factors of laminated micro/nano filters.

ability to capture particles. In addition, the larger pore size resulted in a lower pressure drop compared to M_1E_1*1 and M_2E_2*3. These two factors gave M_3E_3*5 a satisfactory quality factor.

3.4 *Loading performance*

In the filtration process (Figure 4a), surface meltblown suffers the impact of airflow to maintain structural stability. Meltblown is a coarse filter to capture large particles (Figure 4b). Nanofibers will mainly capture the fine particles passing through the surface layer, as shown in the cross-section SEM image (Figure 4d). The captured particles can also agglomerate on the nanofibers to form larger granules (Figure 4c). In the multilayer structure, microfibers act as skeletons to provide enough strength and improve porosity.

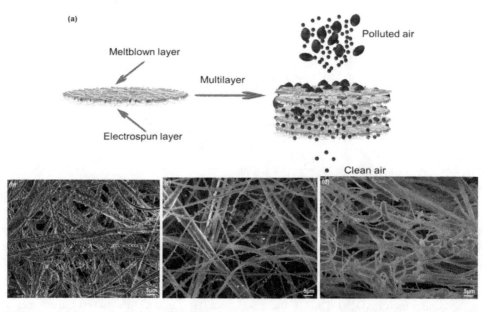

Figure 4. (a) Schematic diagram of the filtration process. SEM image of M_3E_3*5 after loading test (b) surface melt-blown layer, (c) bottom nanofilm layer, and (d) the cross-section.

Moreover, microfibers can capture large particles by inertial impaction and interception. The nanofibers play a role in capturing fine particles. The synergistic reaction mechanism of microfibers and nanofibers is the key to excellent filtration performance.

4 CONCLUSIONS

In this paper, micro/nano filters were prepared layer by layer via meltblown and electrospun technology. The filtration performance was evaluated, and the filtration mechanism was analyzed. The main conclusions can be summarized as follows:

(1) The construction of multi-scale fiber diameters and pore sizes facilitates the capture of particles.
(2) The alternating arrangement of ultrathin micro/nanofiber webs can integrate the advantages of microfibers and nanofibers and enhance their synergistic effect.
(3) The increasing layers and thinning fiber webs can improve the filtration efficiency and lower the drop pressure of micro/nano filters.
(4) The micro/nanomaterials (only 18.5gsm) fabricated by ten layers present a high filtration efficiency of 97.94%, a low-pressure drop of 53.2 Pa, and a high-quality factor (QF) of 0.073 Pa^{-1} for NaCl aerosol particles.

In future work, an efficient and controlled mixture of micro/nanofibers should be carried out to enhance the comprehensive filtration performance.

ACKNOWLEDGMENTS

The authors thank the College of Textiles and Apparel, the Smart & Ecological Textile Institute, and QNU for providing lab facilities. Fujian Province Nonwoven New Materials Innovation Laboratory Platform Project (No.2021FX08) funded this research.

REFERENCES

Campos R.K., Jin J., Rafael GH., et al. (2020) Decontamination of SARS-CoV-2 and Other RNA Viruses from N95 Level Meltblown Polypropylene Fabric Using Heat under Different Humidities. *Acs Nano*; 14: 14017–14025.

Chen R., Zhang H., Wang M., et al. (2020) Thermoplastic Polyurethane Nanofiber Membrane Based Air Filters for Efficient Removal of Ultrafine Particulate Matter PM0.1. *ACS Applied Nano Materials*; 4: 182–189.

Grobety B., Giere R., Dietze V., et al. (2010) Airborne Particles in the Urban Environment. *Elements*; 6: 229–234.

Han M.C., He H.W., Kong W.K., et al. (2022) High-performance Electret and Antibacterial Polypropylene Meltblown Nonwoven Materials Doped with Boehmite and ZnO Nanoparticles for Air Filtration. *Fibers and Polymers*; 23: 1947–1955.

Kilic A., Shim E. and Pourdeyhimi B. (2015) Electrostatic Capture Efficiency Enhancement of Polypropylene Electret Filters with Barium Titanate. *Aerosol Science and Technology*; 49: 666–673.

Liu J., Zhang H., Gong H., et al. (2019) Polyethylene/Polypropylene Bicomponent Spunbond Air Filtration Materials Containing Magnesium Stearate for Efficient Fine Particle Capture. *Acs Applied Materials & Interfaces*; 11: 40592–40601.

Liu Y., Qian X., Zhang H., et al. (2020) Preparing Micro/nanofibrous Filters for Effective PM 2.5 Under Low Filtration Resistance. *Chemical Engineering Science*; 217:115523.

Lou L.H., Qin X.H. and Zhang H. (2016) Preparation and Study of Low-resistance Polyacrylonitrile Nanomembranes for Gas Filtration. *Textile Research Journal*; 87: 208–215.

Song J., Liu Z., Li Z., et al. (2020) Continuous Production and Properties of Multi-level Nanofiber Air Filters by Blow Spinning. *RSC Adv*; 10: 19615–19620.

Tisdell C.A. (2020). Economic, Social, and Political Issues Raised by the COVID-19 Pandemic. *Economic Analysis and Policy*, 68: 17–28.

Xu Y,. Zhang X., Teng D, et al. (2022) Multi-layered Micro/nanofibrous Nonwovens for Functional Face Mask Filter. *Nano Research*; 15: 7549–7558.

Yao Z., Xia M., Xiong Z., et al. (2022) A Hierarchical Structure of Flower-Like Zinc Oxide and Poly(Vinyl Alcohol-co-Ethylene) Nanofiber Hybrid Membranes for High-Performance Air Filters. *ACS Omega*; 7: 3030–3036.

Zhang H., Liu N., Zeng Q., et al. (2020) Design of Polypropylene Electret Melt Blown Nonwovens with Superior Filtration Efficiency Stability through Thermally Stimulated Charging. *Polymers*; 12: 2341.

Is the NOx tax optimal? – Evidence from Inner Mongolia

Xinjiletu Yang, Zijie Qu*, Weihong Han & Yanli Yang
Inner Mongolia University of Technology, Hohhot, Inner Mongolia, China

ABSTRACT: Nitrogen oxide (NOx) emissions in Inner Mongolia have been high, and the setting of NOx taxes needs to be optimized. To this end, the article considers the atmosphere's self-cleaning capacity, and since the atmosphere has a certain self-cleaning capacity, making full use of this capacity may lead to a more optimal tax setting. Therefore, the article incorporates the atmosphere's self-cleaning capacity into the standard CGE model, constructs a dynamic model for tax optimization, and simulates the optimization of NOx taxation under different atmospheric self-cleaning capacities. The results show that (1) when NOx emissions exceed the atmospheric self-purifying capacity, the ratio of the decrease in NOx emissions to the increase in NOx taxes is 23.05/100. (2) when NOx emissions are below the atmospheric self-purifying capacity, the ratio of the increase in NOx emissions to the decrease in NOx taxes is 23.68/100.

1 INTRODUCTION

Within the last few decades, the rapid population growth and industrial economy in China have led to the overuse of fossil fuels, which has resulted in the emission of large amounts of harmful gases and pollutants (Peng et al. 2021; Sun et al. 2019; Wesseh et al. 2016). Among them, nitrogen oxides (NOx) have been one of the fastest-growing air pollutants in China in the last 20 years, and China is also one of the largest emitters of NOx in the world (Ronald et al. 2017). NOx not only causes many diseases but also causes smog, acid rain, and other pollution problems. Therefore, the reduction of nitrogen oxide emissions has attracted great attention, and it is clearly stated in the "13th Five-Year Plan" that by the end of 2020, the national total nitrogen oxide emissions should be reduced by 15% compared to 2015. Although China has achieved certain results in the treatment of NOx emissions in recent years from a national perspective, the task of emission reduction is still heavy. The regions with high NOx emissions in China are concentrated in northern China, among which Inner Mongolia has the highest per capita NOx emissions (Jiang et al. 2020), which shows that NOx emission reduction in Inner Mongolia has become an urgent problem to be solved.

How to reduce the environmental damage caused by NOx has become an urgent problem. Many scholars have made useful attempts, among which environmental taxes are considered more effective because market-based economic instruments usually make policies more powerful (Fang et al. 2022). NOx tax is a pollution tax on the emission of nitrogen oxides and is a type of environmental tax. China also started implementing the environmental protection tax law in 2018, including the sulfur dioxide tax, nitrogen oxide tax, and soot tax. However, the current tax rate of nitrogen oxides in China is too low and has not been able to achieve satisfactory emission reduction (Xue et al. 2022).

---

*Corresponding Author: qzj1470852@163.com

Moreover, according to the current Environmental Protection Tax Law of the People's Republic of China, the taxable air pollutants are determined according to the equivalent number of pollution equivalents converted from pollutant emissions. Although the pollution equivalent value has shown the different degrees of environmental hazards of each pollutant and the different costs of environmental treatment, this pollution equivalent value reflects the national average. It is not enough to reflect the individual regional environmental conditions with different environmental carrying capacities and the individual requirements of pollution treatment, so it is of great practical importance to study the optimization of the specific nitrogen oxide tax in Inner Mongolia.

However, fewer articles have been written on the optimization of NOx taxes, and most studies have focused on carbon taxes. The current studies on carbon taxes are broadly divided into two categories: the first group of scholars advocates a dynamic and uniform carbon tax rate (Fan *et al*. 2016; Zhang *et al*. 2020). They argue that the optimal carbon tax should increase with the GDP growth rate. The second group of scholars believes that a dynamic differentiated carbon tax rate is suitable for addressing diversity across regions and sectors. Zhang *et al*. (2019) proposed that China's optimal carbon tax model is a dynamic differentiated carbon tax model that follows the principle of gradually increasing the low initial tax rate (Zhang *et al*. 2019). Li *et al*. (2012) pointed out that a differentiated carbon tax is better than a uniform carbon tax because of its lower abatement cost (Li *et al*. 2012). In general, few studies on differentiated regional taxes exist in the existing literature.

Moreover, none have addressed the impact of atmospheric self-purification capacity on tax optimization. Considering the heterogeneity of major pollutants across regions in China, there will also be regional differences in optimal environmental protection tax rates. Therefore, to make the tax rate of NOx in Inner Mongolia more reasonable, we study the optimization of the NOx tax rate based on the perspective of atmospheric self-purification capacity (for atmospheric pollutants, it mainly refers to the ability of atmospheric self-purification: the ability to remove or reduce the concentration of atmospheric pollutants through the physical and chemical effects of atmospheric dilution and diffusion, dry and wet deposition, and chemical oxidation (Jiang *et al*. 2020)), and re-evaluate the tax rate of NOx in Inner Mongolia. The tax amount of nitrogen oxides in Inner Mongolia is set again.

Therefore, the next part of the paper is organized as follows: firstly, we quantify the atmospheric self-purification capacity of nitrogen oxides in Inner Mongolia. Secondly, we construct a CGE model for tax optimization under the limitation of atmospheric self-purification capacity. Finally, we determine the influence of atmospheric self-purification capacity on the setting of nitrogen oxides tax and provide corresponding conclusions and outlook.

2 ATMOSPHERIC SELF-PURIFICATION CAPACITY MEASUREMENT IN INNER MONGOLIA

To quantify the atmospheric self-purification capacity of Inner Mongolia and the atmospheric self-purification capacity module setting, the article was conducted through the self-purification capacity of water bodies (Zhang *et al*. 2021), and a study by Lei *et al*. (2022) concluded that the atmospheric self-purification capacity was determined by subtracting the fraction of NOx converted to from the atmospheric ambient capacity of NOx.

2.1 *Inner Mongolia nitrogen oxides atmospheric environment capacity measurement*

The A-value method has the characteristics of simplicity, convenience, and practicality, so it is widely used in the atmospheric capacity accounting of different types of regions (Gao *et al*.

2021). In this paper, we refer to the calculation method of Wang Hongchaoto to measure the atmospheric capacity of nitrogen oxides in Inner Mongolia (Wang 2017).

The A-value method of accounting for atmospheric environmental capacity is specified as follows.

① Determine the A-value of the accounting area.
② Determine the annual average concentration limits of NOx emissions Cki for different areas of the accounting region.
③ Determine the Aki values for each region.

$$A_{ki} = A * C_{ki} \tag{1}$$

In the above equation, A - is the geographically regional total control factor, 104 km²/a; k - the number of the control unit; i - the number of each functional partition in the control unit.

④ Determine the environmental capacity of different functional areas within each control unit.

$$Q_{ki} = A_{ki} * \frac{S_{ki}}{\sqrt{S_k}} \tag{2}$$

In the above equation: S_{ki} - the area of the ith functional area within a control unit, km²; S_k - the area of the kth control unit, km²;

⑤ Calculate the environmental capacity of each control unit Q_k.

$$Q_k = \sum_{i=1}^{n} Q_{ki} \tag{3}$$

⑥ The environmental capacity of the Inner Mongolia Autonomous Region is as follows:

$$Q = \sum_{1}^{n} Q_k \tag{4}$$

In the above equation: Q - Atmospheric capacity of Inner Mongolia Autonomous Region, 104t/a.

The A-values are based on those recommended in the Technical Methodology for Setting Air Pollutant Emission Standards. The range of A-values in Inner Mongolia (north of the Yinshan Mountains) is 5.6-7.0; the range of A-values in Inner Mongolia (south of the Yinshan Mountains) is 3.5-4.9. Based on the geographical location of the Yinshan Mountains, this paper assumes that the north of the Yinshan Mountains contains five administrative regions, namely Hulunbeier City, Xing'an Meng, Tongliao City, Chifeng City, and Xilingol Meng. The other seven administrative regions belong to the area south of Yinshan Mountain. According to the A-value determination method recommended by the Technical Guide for Total Air Capacity Control in Urban Areas, the difference is increased by 10% based on the minimum value. Therefore, the A-value of the Inner Mongolia (north of Yinshan) region is 5.74, and the A-value of the Inner Mongolia (south of Yinshan) region is 3.64.

Based on the 2020 construction land use data in the land use plans of 12 administrative regions in the Inner Mongolia Autonomous Region, this paper predicts the environmental capacity of atmospheric nitrogen oxides in Inner Mongolia from 2020 to 2030. The environmental capacity of atmospheric NOx from 2013 to 2020 is also projected backward based on the 2020 data, as shown in Table 1 below.

Table 1. Environmental capacity of nitrogen oxides in the Inner Mongolia Unit: is 10,000 tons.

Year	The area south of Yinshan Mountain	The area north of Yinshan Mountain	Total
2013	28.56861578	54.50396866	83.07258444
2014	28.66886515	54.69522708	83.36409223
2015	28.7694663	54.88715665	83.65662294
2016	28.87042047	55.0797597	83.95018017
2017	28.97172889	55.27303862	84.2447675
2018	29.07339281	55.46699576	84.54038857
2019	29.17541347	55.66163352	84.83704699
2020	29.27779214	55.85695427	85.13474641
2021	29.38053006	56.05296042	85.43349047
2022	29.48362849	56.24965436	85.73328285
2023	29.58708871	56.44703852	86.03412723
2024	29.69091197	56.64511532	86.33602729
2025	29.79509956	56.84388718	86.63898674
2026	29.89965274	57.04335655	86.94300929
2027	30.00457282	57.24352587	87.24809869
2028	30.10986106	57.4443976	87.55425866
2029	30.21551877	57.6459742	87.86149297
2030	30.32154724	57.84825815	88.16980539

Data source: A-value method calculation results.

2.2 Determination of nitrogen oxidation rate in Inner Mongolia

By referring to Wu Yangyang et al. (2020) and Wang Nianfei et al. (2016), nitrogen oxidation rate (NOR) is proposed, which is the transformation degree of NOx in the atmosphere and the formula of the related NOR. By referring to the method of Ding Shaobo et al. (2019), which calculated the nitrogen oxidation rate of Shijiazhuang in the winter of 2017, this paper calculated the NOR of Inner Mongolia based on the NOR of Suzhou (Wang et al. 2016). It determined that the nitrogen oxidation rate of Inner Mongolia was 0.1379.

2.3 Results of atmospheric self-purification capacity in Inner Mongolia

According to the design of the atmospheric self-purifying capacity measurement scheme, the atmospheric self-purifying capacity is measured as the following Table 2.

Table 2. Atmospheric self-purification capacity of Inner Mongolia Unit: 10,000 tons.

Year	Atmospheric capacity of nitrogen oxides	NOx conversion capacity	Atmospheric self-purification capacity
2013	83.07258444	11.45570939	71.61687505
2014	83.36409223	11.49590832	71.86818391
2015	83.65662294	11.5362483	72.12037464
2016	83.95018017	11.57672985	72.37345032
2017	84.2447675	11.61735344	72.62741407
2018	84.54038857	11.65811958	72.88226899
2019	84.83704699	11.69902878	73.13801821
2020	85.13474641	11.74008153	73.39466488
2021	85.43349047	11.78127834	73.65221214

(*continued*)

Table 2. Continued

Year	Atmospheric capacity of nitrogen oxides	NOx conversion capacity	Atmospheric self-purification capacity
2022	85.73328285	11.82261971	73.91066315
2023	86.03412723	11.86410614	74.17002108
2024	86.33602729	11.90573816	74.43028913
2025	86.63898674	11.94751627	74.69147047
2026	86.94300929	11.98944098	74.95356831
2027	87.24809869	12.03151281	75.21658588
2028	87.55425866	12.07373227	75.48052639
2029	87.86149297	12.11609988	75.74539309
2030	88.16980539	12.15861616	76.01118923

Data source: Formula accounting results.

3 CONSTRUCTION OF CGE MODEL FOR TAX OPTIMIZATION UNDER THE LIMITATION OF ATMOSPHERIC SELF-PURIFICATION CAPACITY

3.1 *Department division*

In order to explore the optimization of NOx taxation, the sectors with higher NOx emissions have to be separated first, and the 42 sectors in the input-output table are reorganized into 13 sectors based on the input-output table of the Inner Mongolia region in 2017. Referring to the study by Wang Junxia (2020), the three sectors with the highest NOx emissions are the non-metallic mineral products industry, the metal smelting, and rolling processing industry, and the electricity and heat production and supply industry, in that order (Wang *et al.* 2020). Next, the financial, construction, transportation, and chemical industries were separated. Finally, other sectors are integrated, including agriculture, light industry, manufacturing, energy industry, and services.

The article extends the CGE model's research in the optimization of atmospheric self-purifying capacity and NOx taxation by adding the indicators of atmospheric self-purifying capacity and NOx taxation to the standard CGE model. Due to the space limitation, only the module of atmospheric self-purifying capacity is introduced in the following.

3.2 *Atmospheric self-purification capacity module setting*

In order to introduce atmospheric self-purifying capacity into the CGE model, the quantified atmospheric self-purifying capacity is introduced into the model to establish a link with the whole economic system. The following introduces the "self-cleaning capacity of the atmosphere" into the model. Since the module of atmospheric self-cleaning capacity involves the adjustment of the tax amount, the module of NOx tax amount is set here first.

NOx tax module
Referring to the Air Pollutant Equivalent Value Table, the NOx pollution equivalent value is 0.95. Emissions are calculated in terms of emission factors, and the correlation equation between atmospheric self-purification capacity and NOx tax optimization is as follows.

$$EM_{no} = \eta_{no} \cdot QA_i \tag{5}$$

$$TEM_{no} = \sum EM_{no} \tag{6}$$

$$NOTAX = tauwp \cdot TEM_{no}/0.95 \tag{7}$$

Equation (5) represents NOx emissions from a given industry; equation (6) represents total NOx emissions; and Equation (7) represents the equation for NOx taxation.

EM_{no} and TEM_{no} in Equations (5) and (6) represent NOx emissions and total NOx emissions, respectively, while η_{no} and QA_i are NOx emission factors and provincial sectoral production, respectively; NOTAX in Equation (7) represents the NOx tax, and tauwp is the NOx tax amount.

Atmospheric self-purification capacity module
According to the article set environmental target requirements, when the atmospheric self-purification capacity is higher than the NOx emissions and the difference is within 0.05 million tons, the NOx tax at this time is considered to meet the environmental target requirements. The difference equation between atmospheric self-purification capacity and NOx emissions is as follows.

$$DVNO = spwno - TEM_{no} \qquad (8)$$

(8) where DVNO represents the difference between atmospheric self-purification capacity and NOx emissions as atmospheric self-purification capacity.

If the difference DVNO < 0 means that the NOx emissions exceed the atmosphere's self-cleaning capacity, then the NOx tax needs to be increased, and the equation is set as follows.

$$tno = tauwp * (1 + x\%) \qquad (9)$$

$$tauwp = tno \qquad (10)$$

Equation (9)(10) represents the increase in the NOx tax, tno is the NOx tax.

If the difference DVNO > 0.05, it means that the atmosphere's self-cleaning capacity is not fully utilized at this time, and it is necessary to increase the appropriate reduction of NOx tax to utilize the atmosphere's self-cleaning capacity fully. The equation is set as follows.

$$tno = tauwp * (1 - x\%) \qquad (11)$$

$$tauwp = tno \qquad (12)$$

Equations (11) and (12) indicates an appropriate reduction of the NOx tax.

3.3 Calibration of model data and parameters

The data basis for the operation of the CGE model is the social accounting matrix (SAM). The article is based on the 2017 input-output table of the Inner Mongolia region for the SAM table. The regional input-output table is divided into 42 sectors, while the article reorganizes the sectors into 13 based on the research needs. The data are mainly from the China Regional Input-Output Table (2017), Inner Mongolia Statistical Yearbook (2018), China Statistical Yearbook (2018), and tax data are mainly from the Inner Mongolia Tax Yearbook (2018), China Financial Yearbook (2018) and related calculations.

The endogenous parameters in the CGE model were solved based on the SAM table data using the inverse GAMS procedure. For the exogenous parameters, reference was made to the studies of Juhuang He (2002) and Lin (Lin & Jia 2017), and the corresponding corrections were made by combining the characteristics of this model and the actual conditions of the region. The model passed the consistency test, the Walrasian test, and the sensitivity test. The test results consistently indicated that the model was stable, which will not be repeated due to space limitations.

4 INNER MONGOLIA NOX TAX OPTIMIZATION SCHEME DESIGN

Theoretically, making full use of the atmosphere's self-purifying capacity means maintaining the atmosphere equal to the NOx emissions, but this exists only in an ideal state and is not easy to achieve. Therefore, the paper assumes that when NOx emissions are lower than the self-purifying capacity of the atmosphere and the difference is within 0.05 million tons, the NOx tax is considered to meet the environmental objectives, and the self-purifying capacity of the atmosphere is fully utilized. In order to find the optimal NOx tax optimization, the article sets up two optimization experiments. Experiment 1 investigates the quantitative relationship between the amount of change in NOx tax and the amount of change in NOx emissions in the process of reducing NOx emissions to below the self-purifying capacity of the atmosphere when NOx emissions are above the self-purifying capacity of the atmosphere. Experiment 2 investigates the quantitative relationship between the amount of change in NOx tax and the amount of change in NOx emissions when NOx emissions are below the self-purifying capacity of the atmosphere. The difference is greater than 0.05 million tons, reducing this difference to within 0.05 million tons. The quantitative relationship between the amount of change in NOx tax and the amount of change in NOx emissions.

4.1 Baseline scenario

In the baseline scenario, the model uses the current government environmental tax policy as the baseline scenario. The additional raw parameters for the NOx tax, with values shown in Table 3 below, and other variables remain unchanged.

Table 3. Table captions should be placed above the tables.

Year	The atmospheric capacity of nitrogen oxides
2017	1.2
2018	1.2
2019	1.8
2020-2030	2.4

4.2 Experiment 1: Static design of tax credits for NOx emissions exceeding the self-purifying capacity of the atmosphere

Experiment 1 is to simulate the effect of three levels of NOx taxes on the change of NOx emissions in a static scenario and then to obtain which level of NOx taxes can reduce NOx emissions to below their atmospheric self-purification capacity. Finally, measure the quantitative relationship between the change in NOx taxes and the change in NOx emissions. The relationship between the change in NOx tax and NOx emissions is finally measured, which provides the basis for the later experimental design of NOx tax.

Scenario SIM1 sets the NOx tax concerning the measurement results of Tang, Ming (2018), which is 3.29 RMB/pollution equivalent; Scenario SIM2 tax design refers to the data of NOx tax in other Chinese provinces. According to the relevant documents, the average value of Shanghai (8.55 RMB/pollution equivalent), Tianjin (8 RMB/pollution equivalent), Shandong (6 RMB/pollution equivalent), and Hubei (2.4 RMB/pollution equivalent) is 6.24 RMB/pollution equivalent. The scenario SIM3 tax design refers to Norway (21.94 kroner/

kg) (Weng 2018), Sweden (50 SEK/kg) (Coria 2021), France, Italy, and Spain (about $150/ton) (Liu 2014). Based on the current exchange rate, the average value of the three is taken as 16.72 RMB/pollution equivalent, as the current Chinese environmental protection tax provides a maximum air emission tax of 12 RMB/pollution equivalent. Therefore, in this scenario, half of the average value of the three will be used as the tax amount in 2021. The summary is shown in Table 4 below.

Table 4. Experiment 1 NOx tax design.

Scenario	NOx tax parameters
Sim1	3.29
Sim2	6.24
Sim3	8.36

4.3 *Experiment 2: Static design of tax credits for NOx emissions below the self-purifying capacity of the atmosphere*

Experiment 2 is based on Experiment 1 to investigate how to adjust the NOx tax to make full use of the self-cleaning capacity of the atmosphere when the NOx emissions fall below the self-cleaning capacity after the NOx tax is increased in a static scenario to achieve the environmental objectives while minimizing the impact on the economy. The relationship between the change in NOx tax and NOx emissions is finally measured, providing a basis for the subsequent experimental design of NOx taxes.

This experiment assumes that the self-purifying capacity of the atmosphere is 75.00 million tons in 2020 and 75.20 million tons in 2021, which is higher than the NOx emissions of 746.27 million tons in 2020. The atmospheric self-purification capacity is not fully utilized, and NOx tax adjustment is required.

Experiment 2 NOx tax design is based on the results of Experiment 1. From the relationship between the increase in NOx tax and the change in NOx emissions in Experiment 1, it is deduced that to make NOx emissions rose by 0.323 million tons. The NOx tax parameter needs to change by 1.4, which means a 58.3% reduction in the base of NOx tax in 2020. As the country's economy develops, NOx emissions should also be on a slow growth trend, and the actual NOx tax change should be less than 58.3%. Experiment 2 sets the percentage of NOx tax reduction to 50%. Then, based on 50%, increase and decrease 20% for a comparison experiment. The NOx tax parameters are set in the following Table 5.

Table 5. Experiment 2 NOx tax design.

Scenario	NOx tax parameters
Sim1	2.4*(1-30%)
Sim2	2.4*(1-30%)
Sim3	2.4*(1-70%)

5 EXPERIMENTAL RESULTS

5.1 Analysis of simulation results of experiment 1

Experiment 1 is based on a realistic scenario to study the design of the tax when NOx emissions are higher than the atmosphere's self-cleaning capacity. The main research objective is the quantitative relationship between the change in NOx taxes and the change in NOx emissions. The NOx emissions of the three scenarios are simulated separately in 2021. The results are shown in Figure 1 below.

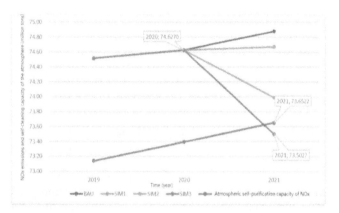

Figure 1. Relationship between nitrogen oxide emissions and its atmospheric self-purification capacity.

As seen in Figure 1, in 2020, NOx emissions exceeded the atmosphere's self-cleaning capacity. bAU is the baseline scenario and the simulation result of the current tax policy. It can be found that the NOx emissions in 2021 under the current policy also far exceed the atmosphere's self-cleaning capacity. By simulating the three scenarios, it can be seen that only the SIM3 scenario will bring the NOx emissions below the atmosphere's self-cleaning capacity. It means that NOx emissions fall below the atmosphere's self-cleaning capacity when the NOx tax is increased from $2.4 to $8.36 per pollution equivalent in 2021. Since NOx emissions are 748,766 tons in 2021 under the baseline scenario, they fall to 735,027 tons when the NOx tax is increased to $8.36/pollution equivalent. In other words, the NOx tax is raised by 5.96 Yuan/pollution equivalent, and NOx emissions are reduced by 137.39 thousand tons. Therefore, the study of Experiment 1 concludes that the ratio between the reduction of NOx emissions and the increase of NOx tax amount when NOx emissions exceed the self-purifying capacity of the atmosphere is 23.05/100.

5.2 Analysis of simulation results of optimization experiment II

Experiment 2 is based on a hypothetical scenario. The study investigates how to adjust the NOx tax so that the atmosphere's self-cleaning capacity can be fully utilized when the NOx emissions are lower than the atmosphere's self-cleaning capacity. Based on the baseline scenario, three levels of NOx taxes are set up for the simulation experiment to investigate the quantitative relationship between the change in NOx taxes and NOx emissions. The results are shown in the following Figure 2.

The BAU is the baseline scenario and is the simulation result of the current tax policy. It can be found that the NOx emissions in 2021 under the current policy are also far below the atmosphere's self-cleaning capacity. The simulation of the three scenarios shows that the

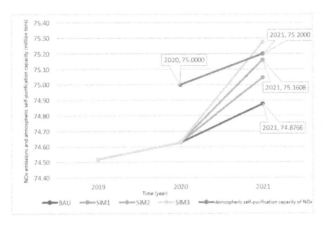

Figure 2. Relationship between nitrogen oxide emissions and its atmospheric self-purification capacity.

NOx emissions of the SIM3 scenario exceed the atmosphere's self-cleaning capacity in 2021. In other words, the NOx tax amount in scenario SIM3 is reduced too much, which leads to an excessive increase in NOx emissions.

For scenario SIM1, although its emissions have increased compared to the baseline scenario, the difference between its 2021 NOx emissions and the atmosphere's self-cleaning capacity is 0.1532 million tons, which exceeds 0.05 million tons, and therefore is not an optimized tax amount.

Moreover, only in scenario SIM2, when the NOx tax will be $1.2/pollution equivalent, the atmosphere's self-cleaning capacity is greater than the NOx emissions, and the difference is 0.0392 million tons, which satisfies the reasonable difference set in the article. That is to say, under the scenario that the NOx tax was 2.4 yuan/pollution equivalent in 2020, the experiment II study objective was satisfied when the NOx tax was reduced to 1.2 yuan/pollution equivalent in 2021. Since the NOx emissions are 748,766 thousand tons in 2021 under the baseline scenario, the NOx emissions rise to 751,608 thousand tons after the NOx tax is reduced to $1.2/pollution equivalent. In other words, NOx emissions rise by 0.2842 million tons when the NOx tax is reduced by 1.2 yuan/pollution equivalent. Therefore, the study of Experiment 2 concludes that the ratio between the increase in NOx emissions and the decrease in NOx tax is 23.68/100 when NOx emissions are below the self-purifying capacity of the atmosphere.

6 CONCLUSIONS

The article uses the A-value and nitrogen oxidation rate methods to quantify the atmospheric self-purification capacity. On this basis, the CGE model for tax optimization is constructed by incorporating the indicators of atmospheric self-purification capacity and NOx tax amount into the standard CGE model. It sets up an experimental scheme for tax optimization based on atmospheric self-purification capacity and studies the proportional relationship between the amount of change in NOx tax amount and the amount of change in NOx emissions.

The results show that the atmosphere's self-cleaning capacity plays an important role in optimizing the NOx tax amount, and the atmosphere's self-cleaning capacity should be considered when setting the tax amount. When NOx emissions exceed the atmosphere's self-cleaning capacity, the government needs to increase the tax, and the ratio between the reduction of NOx emissions and the increase of NOx tax is 23.05/10. Suppose NOx emissions are reduced too much, and the atmosphere's self-cleaning capacity is not fully utilized.

In that case, the ratio between the increase of NOx emissions and the reduction of NOx tax should be reduced at this time is 23.68/100.

In further studies, technological advances should be taken into account, and experimental simulations using the latest input-output tables would be more relevant and flexible. Secondly, the economic impact of dynamic adjustment of NOx taxes in a dynamic situation can be studied, which can be analyzed and assessed from a macroeconomic perspective, industrial structure, and intermediate input-output perspective. Finally, the huge regional heterogeneity of China should be noted, and the specific environmental tax rate should be best adapted to local conditions.

ACKNOWLEDGMENTS

This work was financially supported by the National Natural Science Foundation of China Project: Research on Randomized Improvement of CGE Model Based on Water Environmental Carrying Capacity Perspective and Its Optimization of Applicable Tax Amount for Water Pollutants (71864027); Research on the Impact Path of Carbon Trading Mechanism on Eco-efficiency of High Energy-Consuming Industries and Spatial and Temporal Simulation Evaluation (72263025); Humanities and Social Science Research Planning Project of the Ministry of Education Grant: Optimization Mechanism of Regional Fixed Tax Rate for Environmental Protection Tax Research: General equilibrium analysis based on environmental self-purification capacity and economic activities (19YJA790023); Inner Mongolia Natural Science Foundation Project: Research on the evaluation mechanism and uncertainty of economic loss of sand and dust disaster based on stochastic CGE model (2020LH07001).

REFERENCES

Coria Jessica, Magnus Hennlock and Thomas Sterner. Interjurisdictional Externalities, Overlapping Policies and NOx Pollution Control in Sweden. *Journal of Environmental Economics and Management* 107, 102444 (2021).

Ding Shao-bo, Lang Xing-Hua, Zhang Nan, et al. Characteristics and Pollution Source of Ambient PM2.5 in Shijiazhuang in Winter. *Journal of Environment and Health* 36(10), 894–897 (2019).

Fan Q, Zhou X and Zhang T. Externalities of Dynamic Environmental Taxation, Paths of Accumulative Pollution and Long-term Economic Growth. *Economic Research Journal* 51(08), 116–128 (2016).

Fang Guochang, Yang Kun, Tian Lixin and Ma Yuting. Can Environmental Tax Promote Renewable Energy Consumption? — An Empirical Study of the Typical Countries Along the Belt and Road. *Energy*. 260,125193 (2022).

Gao Chanjuan, Zhou Yingran and Zhang Chao, et al. TI Study on the Estimation of the Atmospheric Environmental Capacity in Jilin Urban based on Amending A-value Method. *Journal of Safety and Environment* 21(03), 1292–1299 (2021).

He J.H., Shen K.T. and Xu S.L. CGE Model of Carbon Tax and Carbon Dioxide Emission Reduction. *The Journal of Quantitative & Technical Economics* 19, 39–47 (2002).

Jiang L., He S. and Cui Y. Analysis of Driving Factors of Nitrogen Oxides Emissions in China Based on Spatial Econometric Models: Data from Satellite Observations. *Scientia Geographica Sinica* 40(3),364–373 (2020).

Jiang L., He S. and Cui Y. Analysis of Driving Factors of Nitrogen Oxides Emissions in China Based on Spatial Econometric Models: Data from Satellite Observations. *Scientia Geographica Sinica*. 40(3), 364–73 (2020).

Lei Peiyu, Zheng Jingli, Jia Ru and Meng Zhaowei. Pollution Characteristics of 4 Water-soluble Ions in PM2. 5 in Xi' a City Districts From 2017 to 2020. *Journal of Hygiene Research* 51(02), 233–238 (2022).

Li C., Fan Y. and Zhu L. The Study of the Iron and Steel Industry's Carbon Dioxide Emission Intensity Abatement Mechanism is based on a Two-stage Game Model. *Chin J of Manag Sci* 20(02), 93–101(2012).

Lin B. and Jia Z. The Impact of Emission Trading Scheme (ETS) and the Choice of Coverage Industry in ETS: A Case Study in China. *Applied Energy*. 205, 1512–1527 (2017).

Liu Ying. The Swedish NOx Emission Tax Collection Experience and Insights. *China State Finance*. (22), 74–75 (2014).

Peng H.R., Qi S.Z. and Zhang Y.J. Does Trade Promote Energy Efficiency Convergence in the Belt and Road Initiative countries? *Journal of Cleaner Production* 322,129063 (2021).

Ronald J.v.d.A., Mijling B., Ding J., Koukouli M.E., Liu F., Li Q., et al. Cleaning Up the Air: Effectiveness of Air Quality Policy for SO2 and NOx Emissions in China. *Atmospheric Chemistry and Physics* 17 (3),1775–1789 (2017).

Sun C., Ding D., Fang X., Zhang H. and Li J. How do fossil Energy Prices Affect the Stock Prices of New Energy Companies? Evidence from Divisia Energy Price Index in China's Market. *Energy* 169,637–645 (2019).

Tang Ming and Ming Hairong. Analysis of the Effects of Environmental Protection Tax on Pollution Control under the Perspective of Optimal Tax Rate: Calculation Based on the Practice of Environmental Protection Tax Levy. *Finance and Trade Research* 29(08), 83–93 (2018).

Wang Hongchao and Wang Xiaohui. Study on Regional Atmospheric Environmental Capacity based on a Value Method—Taking Ningguo Industrial Zone as an Example. *Guangdong Chemical Industry* 44(24), 76–77+83 (2017).

Wang Junxia, Li Man, Jing Hong, et al. Analysis and Suggestions on Nitrogen Oxide Emission Control in China. *Environmental Protection*. 48(18), 24–27(2020).

Wang N-F, Chen Y, Hao Q-J, Wang H-B, Yang F-M, Zhao Q, et al. Seasonal Variation and Source Analysis of the Water-soluble Inorganic Ions in Fine Particulate Matter in Suzhou. *Environmental Science*. 37(12), 4482–4489(2016).

Weng Yubo. The operation of the Norwegian NOX Fund and its Inspiration. *China Ship Survey* (12), 69–73+114–115 (2018).

Wesseh Jr. P.K., Lin B. and Atsagli P. Environmental and Welfare Assessment of Fossil-fuels Subsidies Removal: A Computable General Equilibrium Analysis for Ghana. *Energy* 116(1),1172–1179 (2016).

Wu Yangyang, Zhou Bianhong, Zhao Aling, et al. Size Distribution and Diurnal Variations of Water-soluble Ions in Water in Urban and Suburbs of Baoji City, *China. Environmental Pollution & Control* 42(09), 1085–1089 (2020).

Xue Jian, Zhu Di, Zhao Laijun and Li Lei. Designing Tax Levy Scenarios for Environmental Taxes in China. *Journal of Cleaner Production* 332,130036 (2022).

Zhang J., Ding L. and Sun L. Research on Enterprise Carbon Emission Decision Considering the Substitution Effect of the Stepped Carbon Tax and Carbon Trading. *China Popul, Resour and Environ*. 29(11), 41–48 (2019).

Zhang X., Huang T., Gan D. and Ye Z. Carbon Emission Reduction Investment for Coal-fired Power Plants and Policy Analysis Considering Carbon Price Floor. *Chin J of Manag Sci* 28(11), 167–174(2020).

Zhang Y., Li A.D., Tian Y., Zhou B., Chai M., Li H., et al. Influence of Sedimentation Rate on the Environmental Capacity of Total Nitrogen in Bohai Bay, China. *Journal of Soils and Sediments*. 21(10), 3225–33 (2021).

Study on strain characteristics of Zhoushan marine soft clay under continuous variable frequency cyclic loading

Jiajie Chen*, Feng Xiong* & Jinbao Wang
Department of Marine Engineering Equipment, Zhejiang Ocean University, Zhoushan, China

ABSTRACT: The traffic load given by traditional experiments often uses the form of cyclic load with a single frequency. However, the frequency of real traffic load is complicated. For example, the speed of public transportation will change during entering and leaving the station, resulting in different frequency combinations of cyclic load forms for foundation soil. Considering this engineering background, a series of tests on Zhoushan marine soft clay under cyclic loading with different combined frequencies were carried out using German WILLE dynamic triaxial apparatus to study the strain variation of Zhoushan marine soft clay under cyclic loading with variable frequencies. The research results show that the strain characteristics of soft clay under combined frequency cyclic loading are quite different from those under single frequency cyclic loading. The strain characteristics of soil under variable frequency cyclic loading have obvious frequency conversion nodes, and the final strain will be greater than that under single frequency cyclic loading. Therefore, the variable frequency cyclic load loading method can more accurately simulate the actual traffic load and obtain more practical test results. The experimental study can provide a reference for the engineering application of soft marine clay in Zhoushan.

1 INTRODUCTION

In recent years, the geotechnical engineering problems induced by traffic loads have received increasing attention (Cai et al. 2018; Gu et al. 2016; Lei et al. 2020; Qian et al. 2019). In particular, the roadbed settlement problem affects the safety of traffic travel. The soft clay road subgrade is directly subjected to the dynamic train loads transmitted by the superstructure, whose stiffness may deteriorate, and the accumulation of permanent deformation seriously affects the stability and safety of train operation. With the rapid development of the coastal economy and the establishment of Zhoushan New Area, according to the "Fourteenth Five-Year Plan" for the construction of the Yi-Ningbo-Zhou Open Corridor in Zhejiang Province. It is expected that by the end of the "Fourteenth Five-Year Plan," the area will form the overall pattern of "two nuclei, one belt, and two radiations" is expected to be formed by the end of the "14th Five-Year Plan." A strategic open channel with smooth domestic and international double circulation and land and sea integration will be built. However, the marine soft clay soil in this area is affected by unfavorable seismic and geological conditions, which often leads to a decline in the stability of the foundation soil, resulting in a series of problems such as the excessive settlement of engineering structures and the rupture of underground pipelines. The later maintenance and repair costs are high, which can easily cause large economic losses and even threaten the safety of people's lives.

---

*Corresponding Authors: 942180642@qq.com and 1418775104@163.com

Soft clays from different regions exhibit different kinetic properties. At present, the types of foreign research on soft clay are mainly concentrated in: Boston blue clay in the United States, Drammen clay in Norway, Ariake clay in Japan, and Mexico City soft clay. The domestic soft clay research mainly focuses on Tianjin Binhai soft clay, Shanghai soft clay, and Wenzhou soft clay. The same belongs to the typical soft clay in China. Still, the dynamic characteristics shown in different regions often differ greatly, not only related to their physical properties but also closely related to their stress history, stress path, strength, and the structure of the soft clay. It explains that the soft clay of a certain region When engineering design is carried out, it is necessary to combine the actual engineering background and not to copy the dynamic properties law of other regions in China.

In the past, scholars have conducted a lot of cyclic load tests based on the physical properties of the soil itself (particle gradation curve, pore ratio, liquid-plastic limit, compression coefficient, sensitivity, water content, liquid plasticity index, density), the initial stress conditions of the soil, and the loading conditions (Lei et al. 2020; Sakai et al. 2003; Seed et al. 1956; Wang J et al. 2013; Yasuhara et al. 1982).

Previously, scholars have studied soils using dynamic triaxial apparatus, mostly cyclic loading at a single frequency. Matisui et al. (1992) conducted stress-controlled triaxial cyclic shear tests using frequencies of 0.02-0.50 Hz on Senri clay with a plasticity index Ip of 0.55. They showed that for a given number of cycles, low-frequency loading produced higher pore water Wang (2019) studied soft clay soils and found that the pore water pressure was decreasing while the loading frequency was increasing. Yasuhara (1982) concluded that vibration frequency is a major influence on the dynamic properties of soils.

However, in the actual traffic loading, the dynamic load will form different frequency combinations due to the change in vehicle speed. Thus the test under the form of cyclic loading using a single frequency is not close to reality. Based on this paper, for the marine soft clay soil in the Zhoushan area, the combined frequency cyclic loading form is used by Wille dynamic triaxial instrument to investigate the influence law of different frequency combinations on the strain of soft clay soil. By comparing with the single frequency test, the effect of combined frequency cyclic loading on soft soil's dynamic properties is analyzed to provide a reference basis for the engineering application of soft marine clay found in the Zhoushan area.

2 METHODS AND MATERIALS

2.1 *Test apparatus and parameters*

The Wille dynamic triaxial apparatus imported from Germany is used in this experiment, as shown in Figure 1. The instrument adopts high-precision motor servo closed-loop control, which can accurately perform various dynamic and static tests while applying dynamic cyclic

Figure 1. Dynamic triaxial apparatus and schematic diagram.

loads in axial pressure and circumferential pressure simultaneously. The main components of the instrument include the dynamic triaxial instrument mainframe, circumferential pressure/volume controller, counterpressure/volume controller, dynamic pressure controller, various sensors, signal conditioning device, and control system and software. The instrument is equipped with GEOsys test control software, which can control the application of various waveforms, including sine, square, triangle, half-sine, or custom waveforms. The instrument can withstand a maximum axial load of 100kN, a maximum perimeter pressure of 2Mpa, and a maximum loading frequency of 0-5 Hz, which can simulate various complex working conditions such as seismic load, traffic load, engineering construction, and pit excavation.

2.2 Test soil sample

The soil samples used in the test were taken from the petrochemical base of Zhoushan Yushan Island and excavated to a certain depth in the pit (the soil taken was -12.25 to -18.74 m). The basic physical properties of the soft clay used in the test are shown in Table 1, and the particle size distribution curve is shown in Figure 3. During the test, to ensure the uniformity of the prepared specimens, the specimens were prepared by the layered pounding method, with a total of five layers and four pounds. The specimen size was 39.1 mm in diameter and 80 mm in height. After the specimen was successfully loaded into the dynamic triaxial pressure chamber, a circumferential pressure of 50 kPa was applied for pre-pressure to ensure stable molding. All specimens were saturated at 300 kPa peritectic pressure and 300 kPa counterpressure, and the next consolidation test was performed when the B-value was detected to be greater than 0.95. Soil specimens were isotropically consolidated under 100kPa pressure during consolidation, and the consolidation was completed when the change of drainage body was stable, and then dynamic load loading was carried out.

Table 1. Basic physical parameters of soil samples in Zhou Shan areas.

Void ratio e_0	Moisture content ω/%	Liquid limit w_l/%	Plastic limit w_p/%	Density ρ/g/cm^3	Liquidity index I_l	Coefficient of compressibility a_v/MPa^{-1}	Sensitivity S_t
1.114	45.25	45.83	23.34	1.835	0.9740	0.7800	7.500

2.3 Test protocol and operation procedure

The purpose of the test is to compare the difference between the cyclic load at a single frequency and the cyclic load at a combined frequency and to compare the effect of the cyclic load at different combined frequencies on the strain of the specimens.

The specific test procedure: Group A is a single frequency cyclic loading mode, the specimen is loaded with 2000 vibrations the whole time without drainage, the frequency is 1 Hz; Group B is a combined frequency cyclic loading mode, the specimen is loaded with 2000 vibrations, in which the loading is carried out at 0.5 Hz, after the end of 1000 vibrations, the specimen is loaded with 1000 vibrations using 1HZ, after the end of the two loading processes, the test is finished. The operation process of the group C specimen is the process of group B, and only the frequency order is changed. Specific test operations are shown in Table 2. During the cyclic loading period, the effective surrounding pressure is kept at a certain value, i.e., 100 kpa. The test termination condition adopts the double control index of strain and vibration: for the undamaged specimen, the test is terminated after 2000 total vibrations; for the damaged specimen, the strain reaches 20% as the test termination standard. The specific test parameters are listed below.

Table 2. Test loading scheme.

Test number	σ_3/kPa	q^{cyc}/kPa	CSR = $(q_{cyc}/2\sigma_3)$	f/Hz	N
A	100	60	0.3	1	2000
B	100	60	0.3	1 + 0.5	1000 + 1000
C	100	60	0.3	0.5 + 1	1000 + 1000

3 TEST RESULTS AND DISCUSSIONS

Figure 2(a) shows the variation curves of axial strain with vibration times under continuous loading at a single frequency (1 Hz), and Figure 2(b) shows the axial strain of the specimen for the first 20 s. The axial strain of the specimen under the cyclic dynamic loading mainly consists of recoverable elastic and non-recoverable plastic strain. The lowest point of the axial strain curve is the accumulated plastic strain of the specimen, and the strain difference between the highest point and the lowest point is the elastic strain. From Figure 2(a), it is known that the strain of the soil specimen is 3.93% when the number of cycles reaches 2000.

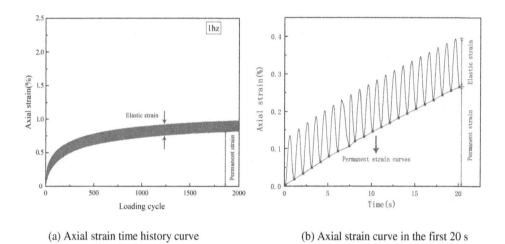

(a) Axial strain time history curve   (b) Axial strain curve in the first 20 s

Figure 2. Variation curve of axial strain with time under continuous loading.

Figure 3(a) shows the variation curve of axial strain with the number of vibrations under cyclic loading with combined frequency (1 Hz+0.5 Hz), which shows that the axial strain value is 0.75% at 1000 vibrations. Then the strain rate increases at the next stage due to the obvious frequency change node, and the final strain value is 1.49%. Figure 3(b) shows the variation curve of axial strain with the number of vibrations under cyclic loading at variable frequencies (0.5 Hz+1 Hz) by changing the frequency sequence. In the first stage, the axial strain of the specimen increased steeply, and after increasing the frequency, the strain of the specimen slowed down and finally was in a stable state, and the final strain value was 11.85%.

The deformation under the dynamic load of 0.5 Hz+1 Hz is greater than that under the dynamic load of 1 Hz and 0.5 Hz, and the deformation under the dynamic load of 1 Hz is smaller than that under the dynamic load of 1 Hz and 0.5 Hz. The deformation of the axial

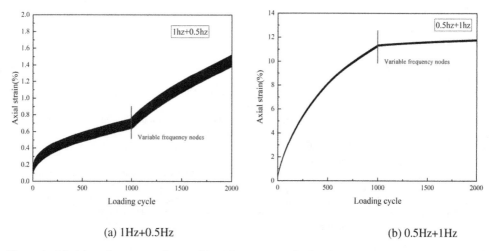

(a) 1Hz+0.5Hz   (b) 0.5Hz+1Hz

Figure 3. Axial strain curve under combined frequency cyclic loading.

strain under the three different loading methods is 0.5 Hz+1 Hz, 1 Hz+0.5 Hz, and 0.5 Hz. In summary, in the variable frequency mode, the axial strain change curve of the specimen showed the law of "jitter first and then slow" or "slow and then jitter."

This phenomenon is because the soil remains dense under the dynamic load of high-frequency 1 Hz, and the energy required to produce unit deformation is greater than that of the cab body under the dynamic load of low-frequency 0.5 Hz, which means that it is more difficult to deform. Moreover, in the lower frequency 0.5 Hz cyclic dynamic load, so that the super pore water pressure has a longer time to dissipate, the soil is compacted, the effective strength increases, the deformation increases, its deformation is greater than the deformation of the Shi body under the frequency of 1 Hz. So the soil deformation under the dynamic load of 1 Hz+0.5 Hz variable frequency is smaller than that under the dynamic load of 0.5 Hz+1 Hz variable frequency.

4 CONCLUSION

This paper carried out a series of cyclic triaxial tests under multi-frequency cyclic loading conditions for saturated clay soils in the Zhoushan area. The effects of different frequency combinations on the development pattern of axial strain in soft clay soils were analyzed, with the following main conclusions:

1. If the action of the dynamic train load on the specimen is considered as a single frequency of continuous loading, it will cause errors in judging the accumulated axial strain generated in the roadbed. Therefore, when studying the action of the dynamic train load, considering the continuous loading with variable frequency can reveal the dynamic effect of the dynamic train load on the roadbed more accurately and obtain more practically meaningful test results.
2. A big difference exists between the axial strain curve of a single frequency specimen and the axial strain curve of combined frequency. The soil specimen curve has obvious frequency conversion nodes under combined frequency.
3. Under the variable frequency, the deformation of the specimen is related to the order of the selected high and low frequency, and the deformation of the combination of high frequency + low frequency is significantly smaller than that of low frequency + high frequency.

REFERENCES

Akira Sakai, Lawalenna Samang, Norihiko Miura. *Partially-Drained Cyclic Behavior and its Application to the Settlement of a Low Embankment Road on Silty-Clay*. 2003, 43(1):33–46.

Cai Y., Chen Y., Cao Z., Ren C. A Combined Method to Predict the Long-term Settlements of Roads on Soft Soil Under Cyclic Traffic Loadings. *Acta Geotech* 2018.

Chuan Gu *et al.* Deformation Characteristics of Overconsolidated Clay Sheared Under Constant and Variable Confining Pressure[J]. *Soils and Foundations*, 2016, 56(3): 427–439.

Huayang Lei *et al.* Cyclic Behavior of Tianjin Soft Clay under Intermittent Combined-Frequency Cyclic Loading[J]. *International Journal of Geomechanics*, 2020, 20(10)

Huayang Lei, Yinggang Xu, Mingjing Jiang, *et al.* Deformation and Fabric of Soft Marine Clay at Various Cyclic Load Stages. *Ocean Engineering*. 2020, 195

Jiangu Qian *et al.* Effects of OCR on Monotonic and Cyclic Behavior of Reconstituted Shanghai Silty Clay. *Soil Dynamics and Earthquake Engineering*, 2019, 118: 111–119.

Matsui T., Bahr M.A., Abe N. Estimating Shear Characteristics Degradation and Stress-strain Relationship of Saturated Clays After Cyclic Loading. *Soils and Foundations*, 1992, 32(1): 161–172.

Seed H.B., McNeill R.L. Soil Deformation in Normal Compression and Repeated Loading Test. *Highway Research Board*. 1956, 141, 44–53

Wang J., Guo L., Cai Y.Q., Xu C.J. and Gu C. Strain and Pore Pressure Development on Soft Marine Clay in Triaxial Tests with Many Cycles. *Ocean Engineering*. 2013,74, 125–132

Wang J., Zhou Z., Hu X., *et al.* Effects of Principal Stress Rotation and Cyclic Confining Pressure on the Behavior of Soft Clay with Different Frequencies. *Soil Dynamics and Earthquake Engineering*, 2019, 118: 75–85.

Yasuhara K., Yamanouchi T. and Hirao K. Cyclic Strength and Deformation of Normally Consolidated Clay. *Soils and Foundations*. 1982, 22 (3), 77–91

Research on method for establishing standard system on green production and consumption in China

Yanxin Gao, Shuang Ding*, Dongfeng Gao, Yi Zhu & Rui Zhang
China National Institute of Standardization, Beijing, China

ABSTRACT: China pays great attention to ecological civilization construction and sustainable development, in which promoting green production and consumption are important to realize high-quality development. We will speed up the establishment of regulations, standards, and policies for green production and consumption, focusing on production, consumption, distribution, recycling, and other aspects. This paper summarized the development status of green production and consumption at home and abroad. It established a framework for a green production and consumption standard system in China by process methodology. This paper gave several recommendations for developing standardization on green production and consumption in China, which could provide scientific support for China's green, circular and low-carbon development.

1 INTRODUCTION

China always pays great attention to environmental protection and green development. Green production and consumption are important in building ecological civilization and achieving high-quality development. China has introduced a series of regulations and policy measures for green production and consumption, gradually forming a resource-saving and environmentally friendly production and lifestyle, and has given positive feedback. However, laws and policies of green production and consumption are imperfect, and there are still problems, such as insufficient incentives, constraints, and weak operability. In the future, we will accelerate the establishment of laws, regulations, standards, and policies related to green production and consumption. Its focus is on promoting green development in key aspects such as production, consumption, distribution, and recycling, which will formulate green production and consumption patterns.

2 RESEARCH PROGRESS

2.1 *Research status of green production at home and abroad*

The thought of green production points out the mode, goal, and requirement of economic development and plays an important role in guiding the policy of economic activity development. In the early 17th century, the British economist William PeIDI, considering the relationship between production and environment, proposed that "natural conditions restrict the ability of labor to create wealth." That is, the changes in the natural environment can even determine the development of production (PeIDI. 1981). In the 1960s, Rachel Carson

---

*Corresponding Author: dings@cnis.ac.cn

from the United States played an important role in forming ecological thought and environmental protection. Her book "Silent Spring" broke the silent night sky, gave birth to the development strategy of environmental protection, and attracted the wide attention of the world (Yang 2016). The initiative "Global Green New Deal," first proposed by the United Nations Environment Programme (UNEP) in 2008, seeks to foster a new industrial revolution by strengthening green investment by governments (Yu 2018). The green industry in China started late. Learning from the experienced of foreign green production on global economic and social development, China's green industry policy has been divided into three stages: The stage of emphasizing development over environmental protection (1978-1999), the embryonic stage of green industrial policy (2000-2011), and the initial development stage of green industrial policy (2012 to present) (Li et al. 2019). Nowadays, green issues have gradually attracted people's attention, promoting research, policy formulation, and implementation of green production in various countries.

2.2 Research status of green consumption at home and abroad

In the late 1980s, the "green consumer movement" began in Britain and then spread across countries from Europe and North America. The movement essentially called on consumers to buy environment-friendly products, encouraging producers to switch to producing environment-friendly products. In June 2008, the EU launched the "Sustainable Consumption and Production/Sustainable Industrial Policy Action Plan," an umbrella plan to guide the extension and improvement of other green consumption-related laws and regulations. In order to ensure the promotion and circulation of green products, the United States and Canada have formulated relatively complete enterprise-enterprise and enterprise-public institution green procurement plans. They also opened up the circulation channels of green products based on the North American Free Trade Agreement so that consumers can know, purchase, and use green products in a wider range.

The seventh chapter of China's Agenda 21, reviewed and adopted by the Chinese government in 1994, clearly stated the objectives of guiding sustainable consumption patterns. After that, the relevant content of green consumption gradually appears in the energy saving law, environmental protection, and circular economy. Besides, there are relevant articles in China's Constitution and Law of the People's Republic of China on the Protection of Consumers' Rights and Interests. In March 2020, the National Development and Reform Commission and the Ministry of Justice jointly issued "Opinions on Accelerating the Establishment of a Legal and Policy System for Green Production and Consumption," which put forward an overall plan for strengthening standard formulation. Moreover, to strengthen the construction of the standard green system, expand the coverage of standards, and accelerate the development and revision of standards in key areas. The implementation of this policy has clarified the reform direction of green production and consumption law and policy system, which will provide an important system guarantee for the green transition of economic and social development in China.

2.3 Research status of green production and consumption standardization

China pays great attention to ecological civilization construction and green sustainable development. The Chinese government has enacted a series of regulations and policy measures for green production and consumption through a standardization approach, supported by policy implementation, which vigorously increased green, circular and low carbon development. Besides, a green technology innovation system has been constructed.

2.3.1 Standardization lays the foundation for scientific management

Green production standardization provides technical support for enterprises' production, service, and operational processes while using procedures, standardization, and digital information technology to achieve the goal of standardized enterprise management. It promotes the quality of green products, provides consumers with higher quality products and services, and facilitates the formation of green consumption patterns. Green production and consumption standardization practices support implementing policies in energy conservation, water conservation, environmental protection, recycling, reclamation, low carbon, clean production, and green manufacturing. It gradually formed a more comprehensive and concrete roadmap for action, accelerated the development of energy conservation, clean production, and clean energy industries, and promoted ecological civilization construction.

2.3.2 Standardization can regulate and guide the market order

Through the standardization of green production and consumption and the implementation of policy systems, social resources can be integrated and guided, promoting innovation in enterprise development, forming a high-standard market system, and promoting green consumption transformation in society. For example, the Energy Efficiency Standard Label, as an important energy-saving management system in the field of end-use energy, provides product energy efficiency level labels through the publication of product catalogs of energy efficiency labels for household appliances, electronics, lighting, industry, and other fields to provide consumers with references for purchasing products and thus regulate and guide the market order.

2.3.3 Standardization practices are extensive

Green production and consumption standardization practice is based on the goal of energy saving, reduction of energy consumption and pollution by enterprises, providing green products and services, and advocating green consumption in society. Through standardization practices, the application of product energy efficiency labeling, demonstration of national energy saving standardization, circular economy standardization, green product standards, certification, and labeling system construction. Green financial innovation practices are widely carried out while promoting green transformation and high-quality development of the social economy according to the economic development level of regions. In the future, standardized practices for green production and consumption will promote energy saving and carbon reduction in industry and raise public awareness of green consumption.

3 PROCESS RESEARCH METHOD FOR STANDARD SYSTEM

Standards are documents developed by consensus through standardized activities and prescribed procedures that provide rules, guidelines, or characteristics for common and repeated use of various activities or their results. The construction of a standard system uses system theory to guide standardization work (GB/T 2018). This paper adopts Process Research Method to study and analyze the standard system. Any activity or group that uses resources to transform input into the output can be regarded as a process (GB/T 2016). In order to run an organization effectively, it is necessary to identify and manage the processes when it applies. Firstly, it is required to determine the various basic processes of management activities by the common characteristics of business management activities under market economy conditions. Then, starting from the basic connotation of standards and standardization concepts, their approaches, steps, procedures, methods, resources, conditions, and other factors are summarized to extract specific standards. Finally, the framework diagram and detailed table of the standard system are constructed.

4 FRAMEWORK DIAGRAM OF A STANDARD SYSTEM FOR GREEN PRODUCTION AND CONSUMPTION IN CHINA

This paper adopts a Process Research Method to build a systematic, comprehensive, scientifically feasible, clear, and logical system of green production and consumption standards, considering the green approaches of resource utilization, waste discharge, and recovery along the lifecycle stages of production, distribution, and consumption. The framework diagram of the standard system consists of seven sub-systems: green design standards, energy-saving standards, clean energy standards, standards for recycling, cleaner production standards, green consumption and living standards, and green financial service standards. The framework diagram of the standard system for green production and consumption is shown in Figure 1.

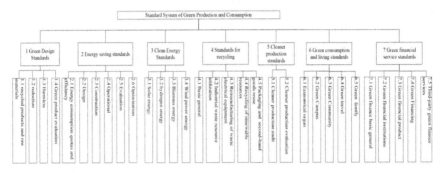

Figure 1. Framework diagram of a standard system for green production and consumption.

The green design standards sub-system consists of four main elements: standards for recycled products and raw materials, reduction, harmlessness, and evaluation of green products. Green design is an important pathway to realizing the goal of green production and life. The key point is to apply product design schemes that make the product easy to be disassembled, classify, and recycle in green manufacturing and improve the proportion of alternative use of recycled raw materials by formulating evaluation standards for green design products.

The energy saving standards sub-system comprises six main elements, including standards for energy consumption allowance and energy efficiency, design, construction, operation, evaluation, and optimization. In energy conservation and environmental protection, the key point will be to implement standards including ultra-low emissions of air pollutants, energy consumption allowance, and water intake for the steel and building materials industries. It will result in phasing out backward production capacity, gradually reducing excess capacity, and winning the battle against air pollution. Actively promote third-party evaluation of standards focusing on evaluating energy consumption allowance for key industry sectors such as steel, coking, ceramics, nonferrous metals, and flat glass.

The clean energy standards sub-system consists of four main elements: standards for solar energy, hydrogen energy, biomass energy, and wind power energy. Develop key standards for innovative technological achievements and demonstration projects of new energy and clean & efficient use of energy. It improves carbon dioxide utilization and storage standards, efficient gas turbines, large-scale wind energy, efficient solar energy, hydrogen energy, fuel cells, biomass, electric vehicles, and charging facilities.

The sub-system of standards for recycling consists of five main elements, including standards for basic, utilization of industrial waste, remanufacturing of electrical waste equipment, recycling of renewable resources and packaging, and second-hand goods reuse. Standards on resource conservation and recycling should be accelerated. Reuse and recycling standards should be developed for waste classification, comprehensive utilization of bulk industrial solid waste, express packaging, plastic waste, and textile waste. Besides, controlling hazardous substances in recycled raw materials and waste resource-based products and implementing the circulation transformation of industrial parks.

The cleaner production standards sub-system consists of two main elements: standards for cleaner production audit and evaluation. The standard system for improving cleaner production technology, the transformation of achievements, and construction will be developed. Besides, standards for cleaner production technology, the substitution of toxic and harmful substances, and the audit and evaluation of cleaner production should be developed. Dissemination and implementation of cleaner production standards and international standardization cooperation in cleaner production should be strengthened.

The green consumption and living standards sub-system consists of five main elements, including standards for resource-saving government, green campus, green community, green commuting, and green family. Revising green consumption and living standards should focus on green catering services, resource-saving government, schools, communities, and hospitals evaluation technical requirements.

The green finance service standards sub-system comprises five main elements, including standards for green finance basic, green finance institutions, green finance products, green financing, and third-party green finance services. The working pattern of green financial standardization should be innovated using the leading function of the standards, improving the operation and management of green finance and enhancing the innovative development of green finance products.

The quantity distribution of green production and consumption standards according to national, industry, and local standards is shown in Figure 2.

Figure 2. Quantity distribution of green production and consumption standards.

5 CONCLUSION AND SUGGESTION

This paper summarized the development status of green production and consumption at home and abroad. It established a framework for a green production and consumption standard system in China by process methodology. The framework diagram of the standard system consists of seven sub-systems: green design standards, energy-saving standards, clean energy standards, standards for recycling, cleaner production standards, green consumption and living standards, and green financial service standards. The distribution of the number of national standards, industry standards, and local standards in each standard sub-system is also analyzed. This research gradually improved the green production and consumption standard system and put forward the following suggestions for green production and consumption standardization:

5.1 Strengthen the construction of top-level technical standardization organization

Standardization management institutions should establish a general group of green development standardization to better play the basic, strategic and leading role in green standardization development at the top level. The key areas include green design, energy saving, clean energy, recycling, clean production, green consumption, and green finance. Associations related to green development should establish standardization technology alliances, promote the joint efforts of enterprises, universities, and research institutes., jointly develop leading alliance standards, and realize the rapid response of alliance standards to market demand.

5.2 Strengthen the implementation, supervision, and management of standards

Standardization Administration agencies will enhance the dissemination of green production and consumption by all kinds of media, including newspapers, television, and the internet. Advanced experience and model on green development will be summarized and promoted, resulting in good awareness of developing and utilizing standards. National and local administrative departments responsible for green development and standardization should strengthen standards implementation, supervision, and management. They also should actively conduct supervision, inspection, and evaluation of the implementation of standards in key industries and local areas through the comprehensive use of industry access, evaluation, assessment, government adoption, administrative law enforcement, supervision, and inspection.

5.3 Strengthen the construction of human resources on standardization

Give full play to the important role of experts in developing standards and policy-making. A database of standardization experts in the field of green production and consumption will be established, which will result in enhancing the soft power of standardization in green industries. Besides, it is necessary to promote the construction of human resources on international standardization in green development and train a group of international standardization talents familiar with green economy technology and international standardization rules. They also need to actively apply for the ISO technical committee or sub-technical committee, which will promote the internationalization of green production and consumption standards.

ACKNOWLEDGMENTS

Dean's Foundation Project financially supported this work "National Technical Committee for the Standardization of Product Recycling Basis and Management-Research on Standardization of Circular Carbon Reduction (2022)" (No. 542022Y-9375).

REFERENCES

GB/T 13016-2018 *Principles and Requirements for Constructing Standard System* [S].
GB/T 19000-2016 *Quality Management Systems-Fundamentals and Vocabulary* [S].
William PeIDI. *Selected Readings OF PEidi's Economic Works [M]*. Beijing: The Commercial Press,1981.
Xiaolin Yang. Review on the Concept of "Green Development" [J]. *Journal of Zhangjiakou Vocational and Technical College*, 2016,29 (4):16–18.
Xiaoping Li, Yijun Zhang and Feitao Jiang. Green Industrial Policy: Theoretical Evolution and Practice in China [J]. *Research of Finance and Economics*,2019(8):4–27.
Yin Yu and Yaobin Liu. Historical Context and Enlightenment of Green Development System Evolution at Home and Abroad [J]. *Resources and Environment in the Yangtze Basin*, 2018, 27 (7):1490–1500.

Study on grouting parameters and properties of grouting reinforced soil of ultra-fine Portland cement and normal Portland cement

Fan Chen, Wei Ouyang & Zhongmeng Guo
Powerchina Roadbridge Group Co., Ltd., Beijing, China

Yanhua Gao*
Urban Construction School, Beijing City University, Beijing, China

Haoran Pang, Yingxin Ma & Liangtao Zhu
Powerchina Roadbridge Group Co., Ltd., Beijing, China

Kun Wang & Liangcai Di
Sinohydro Engineering Bureau 4 Co., Ltd., Xining, China

Bangqing Xia
Zhejiang Wanning Technology Co., Ltd., Hangzhou, China

ABSTRACT: Ultra-fine Portland cement and normal Portland cement are widely used as grouting materials. Firstly, in this paper, these two grouting materials with the same water-cement ratio were used for grouting in the same stratum, and the ultra-fine Portland cement was grouted in several holes. And then, the moisture content, density, specific gravity, and straight shear tests of grouting reinforced soil were conducted at 7 days, 14 days, and 28 days after grouting, respectively. Finally, the grouting parameters of the two grouting materials and the basic physical properties and shear strength parameters of grouting reinforced soil were compared. The research results show that ultra-fine Portland cement has better injectivity than normal Portland cement. The physical properties of grouting reinforced soil of ultra-fine Portland cement are better than that of normal Portland cement. The density of grouting holes has a certain influence on the properties of grouting-reinforced soil. The research results provide a reference for selecting grouting material, the grouting construction, and the grouting effect of similar strata.

1 INTRODUCTION

Grouting reinforcement technology is widely used in foundation engineering, road engineering, tunnel engineering, water conservancy engineering, mining engineering, and other fields. Grouting has played a stabilizing and reinforcing role in the soil layers with unfavorable engineering geological conditions, such as weak, broken, and unstable strata and silty fine sand strata prone to water inrush and collapse. However, the grouting effect is related to the injectivity and permeability of the grouting material, the porosity, void size, and the heterogeneity of the rock and soil body, the grouting process, and other influencing factors (Liang 1999), which makes the research space of grouting reinforcement technology extensive. Under the same conditions as the geotechnical body and the grouting process, the choice of grouting material directly affects the grouting effect.

---

*Corresponding Author: gaoyanhua@bcu.edu.cn

DOI: 10.1201/9781003433644-58

In the soil layer grouting reinforcement engineering, appropriate grouting materials are selected according to the characteristics of the soil layer. Grouting materials are generally divided into organic grouting materials and inorganic grouting materials. Cement is a common inorganic grouting material with low cost, good durability, non-toxic and pollution-free, high strength and small permeability of stones, and is widely used at home and abroad. In addition, water glass is also an inorganic material with the characteristics of short gelling time, high early strength of grouting, low price, and non-toxic, so it is widely used. Water glass is used alone or to form double grout grouting with cement (Wang 2019; Ye 2013; Zhou et al. 2017). Guo J.Q. *et al.* (2019) use an ultra-fine cement slurry with a water-cement ratio of 1.5:1 to carry out indoor grouting and reinforcement experiments on silty sandy soil. Zou Z.S. *et al.* (1998) use ultra-fine cement to reinforce the water-rich fine sand layer with a thickness of 2~3 m on the roof of the tunnel of the Beijing Fuba Metro Line Project by the double row pipe method, which effectively controls the stability of the roof of the water-rich silty fine sand stratum. He B. *et al.* (2017) use water glass and calcium chloride with a volume ratio of 1:1 to inject into the silty fine sand stratum to solve the problem of roadway roof collapse. Zhou Y. (2012) uses normal Portland cement and water glass double slurry to carry out grouting reinforcement in the water-rich silty fine sand stratum of the Humaling Tunnel. Guo Y.W. (2016) uses 42.5# normal Portland cement and water glass double slurry for grouting in the sandy and silt-to-silty clay layers.

It can be seen from the above that normal Portland cement and ultra-fine cement are widely used as grouting materials. The comparative study on the slurry and stone body properties of the two grouting materials is in-depth (Zhou et al. 2017), and the properties of soil after grouting are also studied. Cheng P. *et al.* (2013) use pure cement slurry for grouting in the loose filling layer and test the soil's physical and mechanical properties before and after grouting. Compared with the soil before grouting, the density and cohesion of the soil after grouting are improved to a certain extent, the porosity is reduced to a certain extent, and the internal friction angle is unchanged, indicating that grouting effectively improves the mechanical properties of the loose fill. However, the comparative study on grouting parameters of ultra-fine Portland cement and normal Portland cement and the properties of soil after grouting is rare.

In summary, in this paper, ultra-fine Portland cement and normal Portland cement are used for grouting in the same formation with the same process, and the grouting parameters and the properties of the soil after grouting are studied, which provides data support for the selection of grouting materials and provides a reference for similar formation grouting.

2 GROUTING TEST AND VARIATION LAW OF GROUTING PARAMETERS OF DIFFERENT GROUTING MATERIALS

2.1 *On-site grouting test scheme*

The grouting site is located in Qiantang District, Hangzhou City. Grouting tests were carried out on the ground. In addition to the miscellaneous fill on the surface, the soil is mainly composed of fine silty sand mixed with sandy silt and locally contains clay lumps.

Grouting experiments were carried out on site using two materials, 42.5# normal Portland cement mortar, and ultra-fine Portland cement with a water-cement ratio of 1:1. The design idea of the test scheme is that a normal Portland cement grouting hole K1 is set to compare the difference grouting reinforcement between the two grouting materials. The K2, K3, and K4 grouting holes are enclosed into equilateral triangles with a side length of 0.8 m to simulate the grouting effect of actual engineering. The layout of the grouting hole is shown in Figure 1. The numbers 1, 2, 3, and 4 behind K indicate the order of grouting. Namely, grouting starts from hole K1, and then grouting is completed in sequence until hole K4. The depth of grouting is 3 meters from the surface to the underground. The grouting equipment is shown in Figure 2.

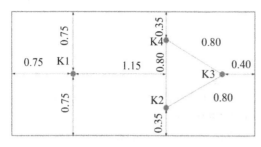
Figure 1. Location of grouting holes (unit: m).

Figure 2. Grouting equipment.

2.2 Grouting parameters

The regression method is adopted. In other words, the grouting tube is lifted upwards at a uniform speed while injecting. The average lifting speed is about 0.1 m/min. Grouting is carried out at a depth of 3-2 m below the surface, then at a depth of 2-1 m below the surface, and finally at a depth of 1-0 m below the surface.

The initial grouting pressure of the entire grouting process is below 0.5 MPa, the final pressure is above 3 MPa, and the final pressure is maintained during the grouting process. The grouting pressure of normal Portland cement and ultra-fine Portland cement is the same. The grouting time is 10~11 min/m, the total grouting amount of normal Portland cement is $0.8m^3$, and the average grouting amount of the three holes of ultra-fine Portland cement is 0.813 m^3. The grouting parameters are shown in Table 1.

2.3 Variation law of grouting parameters of different grouting materials

From the grouting scheme design and Table 1, it can be seen that:

Table 1. Grouting parameters statistics.

Grouting hole number	Grouting material (water-cement ratio 1:1)	Grouting hole depth(m)	Grouting pressure (MPa) Initial pressure	Grouting pressure (MPa) Final pressure	Grouting time (min) 3m-2m	Grouting time (min) 2m-1m	Grouting time (min) 1m-surface	Total grouting capacity (m^3)
K1	Normal Portland cement	3	0.12	3.2	10	11	11	0.80
K2	Ultra-fine Portland cement	3	0.13	3.1	10	10	11	0.83
K3	Ultra-fine Portland cement	3	0.35	3.3	11	10	11	0.82
K4	Ultra-fine Portland cement	3	0.12	3.2	11	11	11	0.79

2.3.1 Interference of the grouting sequence

K1 grouting hole is grouted first and is not affected by the grouting of other holes. Due to the long distance from K1, K2 grouting is less affected by K1 grouting. K3 and K4 are grouted successively after the front holes, and K2, K3, and K4 are relatively close, so they are affected by the grouting of adjacent holes.

2.3.2 *Comparison of grouting pressure between ultra-fine Portland cement and normal Portland cement*

Based on the analysis of section (1), the difference between normal Portland cement and ultra-fine Portland cement grouting can be illustrated by comparing K1 and K2 grouting holes. From the grouting pressure of the K1 hole and K2 hole, the grouting pressure of the ultra-fine Portland cement is 3.12% lower than that of normal Portland cement, which shows that for the same stratum. The grouting pressure of ultra-fine Portland cement is less than that of normal Portland cement, but the reduction ratio is small.

2.3.3 *Comparison of grouting amount between ultra-fine Portland cement and normal Portland cement*

In neglecting the influence of stratum inhomogeneity and other factors on grouting amount, during the grouting process, it was observed that the oozing slurry amount of ultra-fine Portland cement was significantly less. In contrast, the oozing slurry amount of ordinary cement grouting was serious, and the area and thickness of the oozing slurry were significantly larger than that of ultra-fine Portland cement. Moreover, it can be seen from Table 1 that the grouting amount of ultra-fine Portland cement is 3.75% higher than that of normal Portland cement (including the oozing slurry amount which has not been injected into the stratum during the grouting process). From the above two aspects, the grouting amount of ultra-fine Portland cement injected into the stratum is larger than that of normal Portland cement, which benefits grouting reinforcement.

2.3.4 *Comparison of grouting efficiency of ultra-fine Portland cement and normal Portland cement*

From the perspective of grouting time, the grouting time of ultra-fine Portland cement is 1 minute less than that of normal Portland cement. That is, the grouting efficiency of ultra-fine Portland cement is slightly higher than that of normal Portland cement.

2.3.5 *The variation law of grouting parameters for multi-hole grouting of ultra-fine Portland cement*

By comparing the grouting amount of the K2, K3, and K4 grouting holes, it can be concluded that the grouting amount gradually decreases. The grouting amount of the K3 hole was 1.2% lower than that of the K2 hole, and the grouting amount of the K4 hole was 3.65% lower than that of the K3 hole. The initial pressure of the K3 grouting hole is larger than that of other grouting holes, which the influence of stratum inhomogeneity may cause. From the perspective of grouting time, the grouting time of the K2, K3, and K4 grouting holes increases by 1 minute, in turn, indicating that the stratum is gradually consolidated, and the grouting time is gradually extended due to the influence of grouting in the first grouting hole.

3 INDOOR EXPERIMENT AND VARIATION LAW OF PHYSICAL AND MECHANICAL PROPERTIES OF GROUTING REINFORCED SOIL

3.1 *Indoor experiments of grouting reinforced soil*

In this paper, grouting-reinforced soil samples were taken from the site to carry out the indoor experiment of grouting-reinforced soil. The basic physical experiments of grouting reinforced soil were carried out 7 days, 14 days, and 28 days after the grouting was completed. A sand sampler or steel pipe was used for soil sampling, as shown in Figure 3(a). The sampling position is on the circumference with a radius of 25 cm and 50 cm from the grouting hole, and at the center of the K2, K3, and K4 grouting holes and the center of the triangle side (40 cm from the grouting hole). When grouting reinforced soil of ultra-fine Portland cement is taken from a circle with a radius of 25 cm and 50 cm, it is taken from the outside of the triangle to reduce the impact of multiple-hole grouting. The sampling number is formulated according to the grouting hole number-location-age period. The codes with two hole numbers behind K represent the sampling at the side center of the equilateral triangle. The codes with three-hole numbers behind K represent the sampling at the center of the equilateral triangle. A total of 13 numbered soil samples were taken.

According to the test standard in "Standard for Geotechnical Testing Method GB/T50123-2019"(GB/T50123-2019), the water content test, density test, and specific gravity test were carried out. The wet density of fine silty sand is measured by the ring knife method, and the pycnometer method completes the specific gravity test of soil particles. The main experimental equipment includes: KD-TEDD type electronic balance is used to weigh in moisture content, and density experiments, the maximum weighing of the balance is 2000g, and the sensitive quantity is 0.01 g; J300 type electronic balance is used in the specific gravity experiment, the maximum weighing of the balance is 200 g, and the sensitive quantity is 0.001 g; DJF-30/23-IIIA electric blast drying oven is used for drying soil samples; ZK-270 vacuum saturator, a thermometer with a scale of 0°C to 50 °C and a minimum resolution value of 0.5 °C, and pycnometer as shown in Figure 3(b) are used in specific gravity tests.

Similarly, according to literature (GB/T50123-2019), 100 N, 200 N, 300 N, and 400 N normal stress were applied sequentially, and direct shear tests were conducted on grouting reinforced soil sample of this project with unconsolidated and drained quick shear method. The loading rate is 0.8 mm/min. The experimental instrument is the ZJ strain-controlled direct shear apparatus, as shown in Figure 3(d). Direct shear test specimens after failure are shown in Figure 3(c).

(a) Samplers

(b) Specimen in specific gravity test

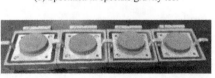

(c) Direct shear test specimen after failure

(d) ZJ strain-controlled direct shear apparatus

Figure 3. Indoor experiment of grouting reinforcement soil.

3.2 Basic physical properties of grouting reinforced soil

3.2.1 Data statistics of basic physical properties of grouting reinforced soil

The basic physical properties of grouting reinforced soil are shown in Table 2. Among them, dry density, porosity ratio, porosity, and saturation are calculated by formulas 1, 2, 3, and 4, respectively.

$$\rho_d = \frac{\rho_0}{1 + 0.01\omega_0} \quad (1)$$

$$e = \frac{\rho_w G_s}{\rho_d} - 1 \quad (2)$$

$$n = \frac{e}{1 + e} \quad (3)$$

$$S_r = \frac{\omega_0 G_s}{e} \quad (4)$$

Where, ρ_0 and ρ_d are wet soil density and dry density, respectively; ω_0 is the moisture content of soil samples; e is the porosity ratio of the specimen; ρ_w is the density of water in the soil; G_s is the specific gravity of pure water at T°C; n is for the porosity of the specimen; S_r is the saturation of the specimen.

Table 2. Statistical table of basic physical properties of grouting reinforced soil.

Sampling number	Water content (%)	Wet density (g/cm³)	Dry density (g/cm³)	Specific gravity	Porosity ratio	Porosity	Saturation (%)
K1-25-7	22.07	1.856	1.520	2.682	0.763	0.433	77.607
K1-50-7	21.239	1.974	1.628	2.675	0.641	0.391	88.568
K3-25-7	26.318	1.896	1.501	2.678	0.782	0.439	90.086
K3-50-7	23.456	–	–	–	–	–	–
K34-40-7	24.159	1.820	1.466	2.698	0.839	0.456	77.731
K234-46.19-7	24.469	1.902	1.528	2.655	0.736	0.424	88.289
K1-25-14	28.671	1.946	1.512	2.676	0.768	0.434	99.891
K1-50-14	24.761	1.817	1.456	2.716	0.864	0.463	77.880
K34-40-14	24.478	1.890	1.519	2.652	0.744	0.427	87.236
K234-46.19-14	25.031	1.932	1.545	2.716	0.756	0.431	89.906
K1-25-28	28.042	1.917	1.496	2.744	0.830	0.454	92.714
K1-50-28	27.255	1.976	1.553	2.726	0.754	0.430	98.595
K34-40-28	24.723	1.942	1.587	2.710	0.706	0.414	94.911
K234-46.19-28	26.314	1.979	1.537	2.715	0.765	0.433	93.430

3.2.2 The water content of grouting reinforced soil

The data on the moisture content in Table 2 are plotted in Figure 4. As can be seen in Figure 4:

(1) Judging from the moisture content curve of the reinforced soil of the two grouting materials for 7 days, the farther the grouting reinforced soil is from the grouting hole, the lower the water content is. At the same distance from the grouting holes, the moisture content of ultra-fine Portland cement grouting soil is higher than that of normal Portland cement grouting soil.

(2) The moisture content of grouting-reinforced soil for 14 days and 28 days is higher than that of grouting-reinforced soil for 7 days, mainly because the grouting is outdoor surface soil grouting and continuous rain after 7 days of grouting causes the increase of moisture content of sampling. In addition, the sampling depth increases gradually, and the 28 days sampling depth is the deepest, which also affects the change in water content.

(3) Ultra-fine Portland cement is used for grouting in grouting holes distributed in a triangle with a side length of 0.8. Compared to the triangular edge center (40 cm from the hole center) and the triangular center (46.19 cm from the hole center), due to the influence of grouting of the three grouting holes, the soil moisture content in the center is higher than that in the edge center. It indicates that the density of grouting holes impacts the water content of the soil layer after grouting.

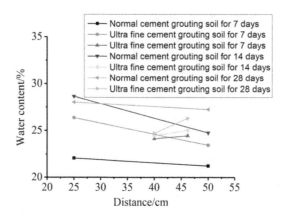

Figure 4. Water content change diagram of soil reinforced by two grouting materials separately.

3.2.3 Density and specific gravity of grouting reinforced soil

As can be seen in Table 2:

(1) The wet density value of grouting reinforced soil is concentrated between 1.82-1.98 g/cm^3. The average value is 1.91 g/cm^3. The dry density is between 1.82–1.98 g/cm^3, and the average value is 1.53 g/cm^3. The specific gravity value of grouting reinforced soil particles is between 2.65-2.75, and the average value is 2.696.

(2) The trend of change in density and specific gravity values is that the farther away from the grouting hole, the smaller the density and specific gravity. The density and specific gravity of ultra-fine Portland cement grouting soil are slightly greater than those of normal Portland cement grouting soil. The density and specific gravity of grouting reinforced soil in the triangle center are greater than in the triangle edge center. The density and specific gravity of grouting reinforced soil in the triangle edge center are greater than that of the triangle outer. That is, the density of the grouting hole has a certain influence on the density of the grouting-reinforced soil. Due to factors such as uneven soil quality (which may be caused by uneven soil or stone bodies formed by grouting slurry), the local data do not conform to this trend.

(3) In addition, the density tends to increase with age, which may be related to several factors, such as the hydration reaction of cement, and the grouting reinforced soil of the longer age is taken. The deeper the soil, there is a certain inhomogeneity of the formation itself and the difference in the grouting effect of deep and shallow layers.

3.2.4 *Porosity ratio, porosity, and saturation of grouting reinforced soil*
As can be seen in Table 2:

1. The pore ratio of grouting reinforced soil is concentrated between 0.64-0.87, the average value is 0.765, and the porosity is concentrated between 0.391-0.463, and the average value is 0.433. The saturation of grouting reinforced soil was concentrated between 77.60%-99.89%, with an average of 88.988%. High saturation is related to rainfall.
2. The relationship between porosity ratio, porosity and distance, grouting material, and grouting hole density in this paper is unclear. Some are positively correlated, others are negatively correlated, and the numerical difference is small. Similarly, the relationship between saturation and distance, grouting material, and grouting holes is unclear, but it is more affected by rainfall.

3.3 *Shear strength parameters of grouting reinforced soil*

3.3.1 *Data statistics of direct shear test results of grouting reinforced soil*
The material parameters of grouting reinforced soil are obtained by straight shear experiment, the cohesion is almost 0, and the friction angle statistics are shown in Table 3.

Table 3. Statistical table of friction angle of grouting reinforced soil.

Sampling number	Friction angle (°)	Sampling number	Friction angle (°)	Sampling number	Friction angle (°)
K1-25-7	32.843	K1-25-14	29.486	K1-25-28	30.560
K1-50-7	32.284	K1-50-14	31.314	K1-50-28	34.699
K34-40-7	31.520	K34-40-14	29.729	K34-40-28	33.124
K234-C-7	31.760	K234-C-14	30.630	K234-C-28	31.300

3.3.2 *Friction angle of grouting reinforced soil*
As can be seen from Table 3, the friction angle of grouting reinforced soil is mainly concentrated at 29.7°-34.7°, and the average value is 31.6°. The relationship between the friction angle, the distance from the grouting hole, and the relationship between the friction angle and the different grouting materials are unclear. However, due to rainfall, the friction angle of the grouting reinforced soil for 14 days is about 1° lower than that for seven days.

4 DISCUSSION

The grouting experiments are conducted in an outdoor stratum, and the stratum's inhomogeneity impacts the experimental results. This paper is unable to assess the impact of such uncertain factors. During grouting construction, where the stratum is not dense, and there are gaps, the grout will penetrate or split first, and there may be differences in the amount of grouting at different locations. The quantification of such differences needs to be further studied.

Grouting reinforced soil includes soil after grouting penetration and a stone body formed by cement slurry. This paper mainly studies the properties of the soil after grouting penetration. However, due to the uncertainty of the underground situation, there is occasionally stone mass formed by cement slurry in the soil sample, resulting in significant changes in the properties of grouting reinforced soil. The properties of the soil with stone body need to be further studied.

5 CONCLUSION

This paper used 42.5# normal Portland cement and ultra-fine Portland cement with the same 1:1 water-cement ratio for grouting in the ground depth of 0-3 meters in Hangzhou. Moreover, the grouting parameters of the two materials and the basic physical properties and shear strength parameters of the grouting reinforced soil are studied, respectively, and the following conclusions are drawn.

(1) The comparison of the grouting parameters of ultra-fine Portland cement and normal Portland cement is mainly reflected in the difference in the amount of grouting injected into the formation, and the amount of ultra-fine Portland cement injection is larger than that of normal Portland cement. In addition, the grouting pressure of ultra-fine Portland cement is slightly reduced compared with normal Portland cement grouting pressure, and the efficiency of ultra-fine Portland cement grouting is slightly higher than that of normal Portland cement grouting.

(2) When the ultra-fine Portland cement is injected into multiple holes under the grouting order of the equilateral triangle with a length of 0.8 m, the grouting volume is gradually reduced. As affected by the grouting of the first grouting hole, the stratum is gradually consolidated, and the grouting time is gradually extended.

(3) The water content is measured seven days after grouting, and the moisture content is lower with the increased distance from the grouting hole. The moisture content of ultra-fine Portland cement grouting is higher than that of normal Portland cement grouting at the same distance as the grouting hole. The water content of grouting-reinforced soil in the triangle center is higher than that in the side center, and the moisture content of grouting-reinforced soil in the side center of the triangle side is higher than that outside the triangle. It indicates that the tightness of the grouting hole impacts the water content of grouting reinforced soil.

(4) The farther away from the grouting hole, the smaller the density and specific gravity. The density and specific gravity of ultra-fine Portland cement grouting soil are slightly greater than those of normal Portland cement grouting soil, and the density and specific gravity of grouting reinforced soil in the triangle center of the grouting hole are greater than those in the triangle side center. The soil density and specific gravity of grouting reinforced soil in the side center of the triangle are greater than those outer soil of the triangle, which indicate that grouting material and the density of the grouting holes have a certain influence on the density of grouting reinforced soil. However, the relationship is unclear for porosity ratio, porosity, saturation, and the friction angle of the soil after grouting.

(5) Based on the comparison of the above parameters, the injectability of ultra-fine Portland cement in this test is better than that of normal Portland cement. The density and specific gravity of soil after ultra-fine Portland cement grouting are slightly larger than that after normal Portland cement grouting, indicating that the grouting effect of ultra-fine Portland cement is better.

ACKNOWLEDGMENTS

The authors acknowledge the fund for science and technology projects of Powerchina Roadbridge Group Co., Ltd. (LQKY2018-10) and the development fund of Beijing City University's scientific research fund project (KYF201902).

REFERENCES

Anchoring and Grouting Technology Professional Committee of Chinese Society of Rock Mechanics and Engineering, edited by Liang J.J. (1999) *Handbook of Anchoring and Grouting Technology*. China Electric Power Press, Beijing.

Cheng P., Zou J.F., Luo H., Luo W. and Zhao L.H. (2013). Experimental Research on Detection Method of Grouting Effect in Loose Filled Soil. *Journal of Central South University (Science and Technology)*, 44(09): 3800–3806.

Guo J.Q., Wang S., Meng C.J and Gao B.B. (2019). Experimental Study and Engineering Application of Grouting Model in the Silty Sand Stratum. *Science Technology and Engineering*, 19(24): 331–337.

Guo Y.W. (2016). *Mechanical Model of Grouting Reinforcement Soil and Application of Tunnel Engineering.* Beijing Jiaotong University, Beijing.

He B. and Zhao D. (2017) Application of Grouting Reinforcement Technique When the Roadway Crosses Through a Fine-sand Stratum. *Shaanxi Coal*, 36(04): 80–83.

National Standard of the People's Republic of China. (2021) *Standard for Geotechnical Testing Method GB/T50123-2019*. China Planning Press, Beijing.

Wang H.J. (2019). Study on Grouting Reinforcement Technology in Shield Tunnel in the Silty Fine Sand Stratum. *Sichuan Architecture*, 39(02): 173–175+178.

Ye Y. (2013). Silty-Fine Sand Stratum Shallow Mining Method Grouting Reinforcement Technique Guide. China Architecture and Building Press, Beijing.

Zhou M.R., Peng X.X., Su B.T. and Fan Y.T. (2017). Grouting Performance of Normal Portland Cement and Superfine Cement and Comparison of Grouting Effect in Loess. *Bulletin of the Chinese Ceramic Society*, 36 (05): 1673–1678.

Zhou Y. (2012). Application of Two-component Backward Split Grouting to the Humaling Tunnel in Water-rich Fine Sand. *Modern Tunneling Technology*, 49(04): 165–169.

Zou Z.S., Zhang Y.X., Guan J.F., Wang C.W., Huo H.S. and Wu A.F. (1998). Research on Silt and Fine Sand Roof Stabilization at Beijing Dabeiyao Metro by Grouting. *The Chinese Journal of Geological Hazards and Control*, 9(04): 66–70.

Research on the economic and environmental impacts of photovoltaic power generation systems in rural Tibet

Jiapeng Lu*

Beijing Luhe International Academy, Beijing, China

ABSTRACT: With global warming and energy security-related issues rising, countries are looking for clean, sustainable energy sources. What kind of clean energy is used depends a lot on geography. The average annual radiation intensity in Tibet, China, ranging from 6000 to 8000 MJ/m2, ranks second globally. So Tibet needs to develop the photovoltaic industry to use its solar energy better. This study analyzes and calculates the environmental and economic impacts of the poly-Si photovoltaic system in Tibet. The life cycle assessment and energy payback time are used to measure the two impacts of the photovoltaic system. Based on the main findings of this paper, it can be concluded that the poly-Si photovoltaic system has a huge advantage over traditional power generation methods because it has not only smaller environmental impacts but also greater economic benefits. Governments should focus on reducing the environmental impact of industrial silicon production to sustain the development of poly-Si photovoltaic systems.

1 INTRODUCTION

When the problems of energy security and global warming are becoming more and more severe, renewable energy is the need of the hour. Compared with non-renewable energies like coal, oil, and natural gas, renewable energies have numerous advantages. The top five are: 1. they do not emit GHGs in the use phase, which significantly mitigates climate change 2. they are inexhaustible 3. they can help reduce energy dependence 4. they are cheaper than conventional energies in much of the world 5. they have more regional policy supports. Therefore, renewables' clean and sustainable nature has compelled human beings to think seriously about it. (Umair Shahzad 2012); Governments around the world can accordingly give more support to the development of renewable energies, which will bring people more sustainable and safer energy systems; for example, R&D&D (research & development & demonstration), financial, incentive/subsidy, and public investment policies all require fiscal supports from governments (Tükenmez & Demireli 2012).

Among all the renewable energies like wind, solar, hydro, and geothermal energy, solar energy can be the best option for people in Tibet because it is the most abundant source of renewable energy there. The sun emits it at the rate of 3.8×10^{23} KW, out of which approximately 1.8×10^{14} KW is intercepted by the earth (Panwara et al. 2011). Tibet locates in southwestern China, where the average sunlight, ranging from 1600 to 3400 h (Wang et al. 2007), is the highest in China; the average annual radiation intensity, ranging from 6000 to 8000 MJ/m2, is the second worldwide because the transparency of Tibetan

---

*Corresponding Author: lujiapenghahaha@qq.com

atmosphere is high (Wang & Qiu 2009). Secondly, unlike hydro energy, which is seasonal energy due to the river's property of periodic drought and abundance, the solar energy output is more stable since the radiation intensity is relatively average throughout the year. Thirdly, large areas of desertified land in Tibet are conducive to centralized power generation. Suppose solar energy resources can be developed according to a 1% desert land utilization ratio. In that case, the installed scale of solar power generation in Tibet will be close to that of hydropower generation in Tibet (Wu 2021). Fourthly, because of the high dispersibility of the residents in Tibet, supplying power from a centralized grid is very difficult, so that the off-grid photovoltaic power generation system can meet the electricity demand of Tibet.

The rural population of Tibet is 2.32 million, accounting for 63.39% of the total population (Tibetan government 2021). Thus, the main part of electricity demand in Tibet comes from rural and suburban areas. Compared with urban areas, rural areas in Tibet are more dispersed, so off-grid photovoltaic power stations account for a large proportion of Tibet's photovoltaic power generation system. However, most of the current off-grid photovoltaic power stations in Tibet can only meet basic electricity demand in rural areas; with the improvement of farmers and herdsman's living standards and electricity demand, the design and capacity of the original off-grid photovoltaic power station can no longer meet the people's daily energy needs.

Moreover, the theoretical reserve of solar energy resources in the whole area is 6.86×10.5 billion kWh (Jiang 2019). However, according to a recent analysis, since the early 1990s, the total capacity of an installed photovoltaic system has been 20.77 MW (Wang 2021), so the solar resource in Tibet is far from being fully utilized. Plus, photovoltaic power stations' aging problems and lack of maintenance also severely influence the effect of power supply. Therefore, it is very important to comprehensively analyze the economic and environmental impacts of photovoltaic systems in rural areas of Tibet to call for more investment, development, and maintenance of photovoltaic systems there.

Many studies analyzed the photovoltaic system's economic and environmental benefits or costs. First, the photovoltaic system is affordable from both economic and environmental divisions. It is because the costs of avoiding GHG emissions using residential rooftop systems are 117–482 RMB/tCO2eq, which are distinctly lower than the 551 RMB/tCO2eq threshold for the cost of climate change impacts(Breyer et al. 2015). Besides, the energy payback time (EPBT) of different types of PV systems in Hong Kong ranged from 1.9 to 3.0, far less than the PV systems' lifespan of 30 years (Jin & Lin 2013). Second, there are numerous environmental benefits of the photovoltaic system: a case study reveals that according to the calculation of saving 0.34 kg of standard coal by 1 KW·h power, the photovoltaic power generation project in the research site saves 35 400 t of standard coal. It also reduces carbon dioxide emissions by 89 300 t per year, which can fully prove the effectiveness of the photovoltaic system in reducing carbon emissions(Shen et al. 2022). Furthermore, coal, animal manure, and firewood are the main energy sources in rural areas of the Qinghai-Tibet Plateau, accounting for 21.97%, 21.11%, and 16.7% of the energy sources used. They have generated many harmful substances to the environment, and solar energy can be a good replacement choice(Jiang et al. 2020).

However, few studies comprehensively analyze the economic and environmental impacts of the photovoltaic system in Tibet, one of the world's richest solar energy regions. Moreover, there are also few economic analyses based on the comparison between photovoltaic power and other renewable energies. Thus, this research uses life cycle analysis(LCA) and EPBT to analyze the economic and environmental impacts of the photovoltaic system in rural Tibet.

2 METHOD

2.1 The type of photovoltaic system in a study

This study focuses mainly on the off-grid photovoltaic system with poly-Si modules. There are three types of silicon solar cells: mono-silicon, poly-silicon, and amorphous silicon solar cells. Compared with mono-silicon and amorphous silicon solar cells, poly-silicon solar cells have many advantages. For example, 1. the photoelectric conversion efficiency of poly-Si solar cells is between 17%~18%, which is close to that of a mono-Si solar cell but much greater than that of an amorphous Si solar cell; 2. the manufacturing process of poly-Si solar cell is more convenient and simpler than that of the mono-Si solar cell; 3. the cost of poly-Si solar cell is lower than the cost of the mono-Si solar cell, and 4. the poly-Si solar cell does not have the obvious problem of efficiency decay. As a result, combined with residents' feature of dispersed distribution in Tibet, an off-grid photovoltaic system with poly-Si modules is used there (Wang 2021), so the study focuses mainly on this type of photovoltaic system.

The off-grid photovoltaic system mainly consists of a charging and discharging controller, inverter, solar cell, and accumulator, as shown in Figure 1. During the day, solar cells generate electricity when sunlight hits them; the controller will use part of the current to charge the battery, while another part will pass directly through the inverter from DC to AC to

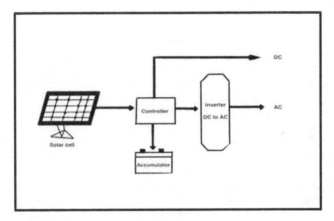

Figure 1. The components of an off-grid photovoltaic system.

power households. At night, the current in the accumulator is passed through the inverter from DC to AC to power the household. One of the main differences between an off-grid and grid-connected photovoltaic system is that an off-grid photovoltaic system includes an accumulator, but the grid-connected photovoltaic system does not. The accumulator can not only help the whole photovoltaic system to adjust the amount of electricity and stable output but can also ensure electricity supply in the absence of sunlight.

Different rural areas of Tibet have used different photovoltaic modules, so it is difficult to decide which photovoltaic module the study should base on. Under this circumstance, the study chooses the TSM-PE15M model of the poly-Si photovoltaic module from Trina Solar Energy Co., LTD. Trina Solar energy has built many different solar power stations in Tibet since 2002, and its photovoltaic module shipments ranked second globally in 2021. Therefore, the poly-Si photovoltaic modules from Trina Solar energy are very representative and reliable in Tibet. The characteristics of TSM-PE15M module are shown in Table 1. (Trina solar.com)

Table 1. Characteristics of the module in this study.

Item	Description
Module size	2015×996×35 mm
Mass	22.0 kg
Frame	Aluminium
Front glass	Tempered glass 3.2 mm
Type of cell	Poly-crystalline sillicon
Number of cells per module	144(6×24)
Efficiency of cells	17.90%
Operation life	25years
Open circuit voltage	46.7 V
Optimum operating voltage	37.9 V
Short circuit current	9.71 A
Optimum operating current	9.23 A
Maximum power at STC	350 Wp
Power tolerance	±3%

STC: irradiance 1000W/m², module temperature 25°C, AM=1.5

2.2 LCA (life cycle assessment)

2.2.1 System boundary and description

LCA is the systematic analysis of the potential environmental products or services during their entire life cycle(sphera.com 2020), which can bring strong insight into all processes, from the extraction of raw materials to recycling or disposal. Thus, LCA is used in this study. The typical life cycle of poly-Si modules includes quartz mining, industrial silicon production, poly-silicon production, poly-Si Ingot, poly-Si Wafer, poly-Si photovoltaic cell, poly-Si photovoltaic module, and recovery stage. Among them, poly-silicon production is responsible for the largest carbon emissions, accounting for about 84% of the industrial chain's main production line carbon emissions(Liu et al. 2020). The method of poly-Si production used in this study is modified Siemens because it is the most commonly used technique.

However, some parts of the photovoltaic module are not considered in the study: first, the balance of the system(BOS) is not considered since a previous study showed that BOS accounted only for an additional ∼0.2 years of EPBT of poly-Si photovoltaic system and ∼5g CO_2-eq/kWh of GHG emissions (Mariska & Eric 2005), so impacts of BOS on the environment are negligible; second, the use and maintenance of the photovoltaic system are not taken into account because related data is unavailable and these phases have very few environmental impacts (Dones & Frischknecht 1998); Third, Chinese photovoltaic market began to develop rapidly after 2002 (Sun et al. 2010), but the lifespan of a photovoltaic system is generally 25 years or so. Therefore, most data on photovoltaic system disposal is unavailable now, so the disposal phase of photovoltaic systems is not considered in this study. Fourth, different photovoltaic projects usually come with various transport methods and distances (Fu et al. 2014), which are extremely difficult to measure, so this study does not consider the transportation of photovoltaics too.

Taking what has been discussed into account, this study is based mainly on a photovoltaic system's production phase, and the study's system boundary is shown in Figure 2. The functional unit of this study was 1kWh based on a poly-Si PV module that could generate 23625kWh of electricity throughout its lifespan. It is assumed that the annual average sunshine is 3000 hours, and the lifespan of the PV system in this study is 25 years.

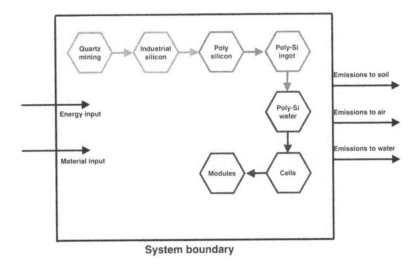

Figure 2. System boundary of photovoltaic system in this study.

2.3 *Energy payback time (EPBT)*

Energy payback time is the required period in which the photovoltaic system can produce the same amount of electricity with the energy consumed over its life cycle (Handbook of Energy Efficiency in Buildings 2019). EPBT is an excellent measurement of the cost of photovoltaic systems in the unit of electricity, so it is more convenient to compare the photovoltaic system with other renewable energy systems by using EPBT. Based on this method, the study can analyze a specific photovoltaic system's environmental and economic impacts more comprehensively.

(1) EPBT = W1/Ea
    W1 is the total primary energy demand in MJ, and Ea is the Annual power generation in MJ/year. (1)
(2) Annual power generation=A*H*PR*r
    Where A is the total solar panel area in m2, H is the annual average solar radiation on tilted panels in kWh/m2, PR is the performance ratio of the module in percentage, and r is the average solar panel efficiency in percentage. (2)

2.4 *Data source, emission factor, and characterization factor*

As shown in Table 2, data on each flow of photovoltaic production is collected from companies representing the current domain of photovoltaic technologies in China and other studies. The emission factor in this study was calculated using the module's weight in kilograms from a previous study (Fu *et al.* 2014) to divide the number of output substances. The characterization factor used in this study is global warming potential 100 (GWP100) from IPCC 2022. GWP100 refers to the greenhouse effect of each greenhouse gas corresponding to the mass of carbon dioxide that has the same effect in 100 years. It is a powerful index that can evaluate the environmental impacts of a product in terms of the greenhouse effect. Thus, the study chooses to use GWP100 as a characterization factor mainly.

Emission factor = Output substance amount[varied]/ Module weight[Kg]

Table 2. Inputs and emission factors of outputs in the module production process.

① Industrial silicon		② Poly-silicon	
Inputs		Inputs	
Quartz sand	26.82 kg	Metallurgical silicon (>99%)	7.96 kg
Standard coal	59.45 kg	Calcium oxide	8.54 kg
Emission factors of outputs		Hydrochloric acid (30%)	3.84 kg
Silicon (99%)	0.3618 kg/kg module	Hydrofluoric acid (20%)	0.08 kg
Carbon dioxide emissions to air	7.911 kg/kg module	Hydrogen (>99.8%)	0.65 kg
Carbon monoxide emissions to air	0.1014 kg/kg module	Nitric acid (35%)	0.29 kg
Slag from MG silicon production for disposal	0.2610 kg/kg module	Nitrogen gaseous	93.19 kg
Nitrogen oxides emissions to air	16.64 g/kg module	Silicon tetrachloride (>99%)	10.86 kg
Silicon dioxide emissions to air	0.1014 kg/kg module	Sodium hydroxide (20%)	6.30 kg
Sulfur dioxide emissions to air	0.0368 kg/kg module	Water	13,614.9 kg
③ Ingot		Electricity	2995.21 MJ
Inputs		Steam	504.19 kg
Solar grade multi-Si	7.22 kg	Emission factors of outputs	
Silicon carbide	81.09 g	Solar grade multi-Si	0.3286 kg/kg module
Quartz crucible	20.13 kg	COD emissions to water	4.895 g/kg module
Argon	13.8 kg	Chlorosilane emissions to air	1.7 g/kg module
Hydrofluoric acid (49%)	332.66 g	Hydrogen chloride emissions to air	2.157 g/kg module
Compressed air	24.57 m3	Hydrogen fluoride emissions to air	0.0132 g/kg module
Sodium hydroxide	61.39 g	Nitrogen dioxide emissions to air	0.1877 g/kg module
Water	644.90 kg	Silicon dust to air	0.4955 g/kg module
Electricity	206.30 MJ	Silicon dust (99%) for recovery	0.0495 kg/kg module
Steam	9.95 kg	Silicon tetrachloride emissions to air	0.55 g/kg module
Emission factors of outputs		Suspended solids to fresh water	3.263 g/kg module
Multi-Si ingot	0.3255 kg/kg module	Trichlorosilane emissions to air	1.865 g/kg module
Hydrogen fluoride emissions to air	0.0359 g/kg module	Water (evapotranspiration) emissions to air	356.7 kg/kg module
Silicon carbide	3.656 g/kg module	④ Wafer	
Waste acid	20.76 g/kg module	Inputs	
Waste quartz crucible for recovery	0.915 kg/kg module	Multi-Si ingot	7.16 kg

(continued)

Table 2. Continued

① Industrial silicon		② Poly-silicon	
Inputs		Inputs	
Water (evapotranspiration) to air	22.33 kg/kg module	Glass	3.23 kg
⑤ Cell		Silicon carbide	230.19 g
Inputs		Steel wire	22.41 kg
Multi-Si Wafer	4.37 kg	Acetic acid	0.79 kg
Ammonia	115.4 g	Detergent	2.92 kg
Ethanol (99.7%)	0.30 kg	Compressed air	38.04 m3
Hydrochloric acid (37%)	3.37 kg	Water	692.25 kg
Hydrofluoric acid	1.02 kg	Electricity	31.44 MJ
Nitric acid (70%)	1.87 kg	Emission factors of outputs	
Nitrogen	9.98 kg	Multi-Si Wafer	0.1986 kg/kg module
Phosphoric acid (85%)	12.2 g	Acetic acid	0.0359 kg/kg module
KOH (21%)	3.61 kg	Glass	0.1468 kg/kg module
Silver	88.92 g	Glue residues for disposal	14.48 g/kg module
Aluminum	0.50 kg	Silicon scrap for recovery	0.1232 kg/kg module
Water	1134.1 kg	Wastewater	20.06 kg/kg module
Natural gas	0.77 kg	**⑥ Module**	
Electricity	899.24 MJ	Inputs	
Steam	34.24 kg	Multi-Si solar cell	1.43 kW
Emission factors of outputs		Glass	82.84 kg
Multi-Si Solar cell	0.065 kW/kg module	Aluminum	15.41 kg
Ammonia emissions to air	0.4682 g/kg module	Polyethylene terephthalate part (PET)	4.28 kg
Hydrogen chloride emissions to air	0.2927 g/kg module	Polyvinyl fluoride film (PVF)	4.28 kg
Hydrogen fluoride emissions to air	0.2341 g/kg module	Ethanol	74.60 g
Nitrogen oxides emissions to air	3.631 g/kg module	Ethylene-vinyl acetate copolymer (EVA)	9.85 kg
NMVOC to air	2.062 g/kg module	Isopropanol	23.14 g
Water	52.865 kg/kg module	Water	154.58 kg
		Steam	21.24 kg
		Electricity	94.29 MJ
		Emission factors of outputs	
		Solar panels	0.0595 kW/kg module
		Activated carbon (charged) for recovery	3.638 g/kg module
		Water (evapotranspiration) emissions to air	5.610 kg/kg module
		Water emissions to freshwater	1.415 kg/kg module

3 RESULTS

3.1 *Environmental impacts of a photovoltaic system*

3.1.1 *Outputs in each phase of module production*

After calculating the emission factor of each output substance, the actual amount of outputs in each phase of module production can be calculated. It includes industrial silicon, poly-silicon, Ingot, Wafer, cell, and module phase outputs. Those outputs are calculated by using each output's emission factor to multiply the module's weight in this study, as shown in Table 3.

Table 3. Outputs in the module production process.

① Industrial silicon	
Outputs	
Silicon (99%)	7.96 kg
Carbon dioxide emissions to air	174.04 kg
Carbon monoxide emissions to air	2.23 kg
Slag from MG silicon production for disposal	5.74 kg
Nitrogen oxides emissions to air	366.08 g
Silicon dioxide emissions to air	2.23 kg
Sulfur dioxide emissions to air	1.03 kg
② Poly-silicon	
Outputs	
Solar grade multi-Si	7.23 kg
COD emissions to water	107.7 g
Chlorosilane emissions to air	37.4 g
Hydrogen chloride emissions to air	47.46 g
Hydrogen fluoride emissions to air	0.29 g
Nitrogen dioxide emissions to air	4.13 g
Silicon dust to air	10.9 g
Silicon dust (99%) for recovery	1.09 kg
Silicon tetrachloride emissions to air	12.1 g
Suspended solids to fresh water	71.78 g
Trichlorosilane emissions to air	41.02 g
Water (evapotranspiration) emissions to air	7846.35 kg
③ Ingot	
Outputs	
Multi-Si ingot	7.16 kg
Hydrogen fluoride emissions to air	0.79 g
Silicon carbide	80.44 g
Waste acid	456.66 g
Waste quartz crucible for recovery	20.13 kg
Water (evapotranspiration) to air	491.18 kg
④ Wafer	
Outputs	
Multi-Si Wafer	4.37 kg

(*continued*)

Table 3. Continued

① Industrial silicon	
Outputs	
Acetic acid	0.79 kg
Glass	3.23 kg
Glue residues for disposal	318.58 g
Silicon scrap for recovery	2.71 kg
Wastewater	441.23 kg
⑤ cell	
Outputs	
Multi-Si Solar cell	1.43 kW
Ammonia emissions to air	10.3 g
Hydrogen chloride emissions to air	6.44 g
Hydrogen fluoride emissions to air	5.15 g
Nitrogen oxides emissions to air	79.88 g
NMVOC to air	45.36 g
Water	1163.03 kg
⑥ module	
Outputs	
Solar panels	1.31 kW
Activated carbon (charged) for recovery	80.03 g
Water (evapotranspiration) emissions to air	123.43 kg
Water emissions to freshwater	31.14 kg

3.1.2 Carbon footprint analysis

The global warming potential of the photovoltaic module in this study is calculated through three steps. First, the electricity used in the module production process has global warming impacts. Therefore, calculating the greenhouse gases in the electricity generation process is very important. The methods of generating electricity in Tibet include thermal power generation, hydroelectric generation, and solar power generation. However, the hydroelectric and solar power generation process has no global warming effects, so thermal power generation is mainly considered in this study. Thermal power generation in Tibet accounts for 4.15% of total power generation (National Statistics Bureau 2021). China's national average grid emission factor is 0.813 kg CO2/kWh (Ke et al. 2012). The emission factor of natural gas is 29.8 (IPCC 2021).

Second, calculate the GWP of each module production phase. The GWP100 values used in this study are from IPCC Sixth Assessment Report. After calculation, the Industrial silicon phase accounts for174 Kg CO2-eq; the poly-silicon phase accounts for 28.3 Kg CO2-eq; the ingot phase accounts for 1.95 Kg CO2-eq; the wafer phase accounts for 0.297 Kg CO2-eq; cell phase accounts for 31 Kg CO2-eq; module phase accounts for 0.891 Kg CO2-eq. The total GWP of module production is 236 Kg CO2-eq. As shown in Figures 3 and 4, the industrial silicon phase of photovoltaic production accounts for the most carbon dioxide equivalent emission, 73.7%. Compared with the industrial silicon phase, other phases of photovoltaic production contribute very little, even negligible carbon dioxide equivalent to the total amount. Therefore, the environmental impacts of the photovoltaic system mainly come from industrial silicon production. To solve the problem of global warming by using a poly-Si photovoltaic system, it is very important to lower the carbon dioxide emission of industrial silicon production.

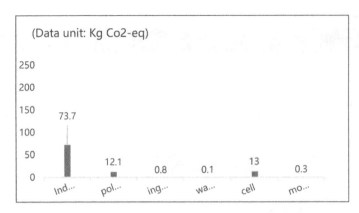

Figure 3. Carbon dioxide equivalent of each production phase.

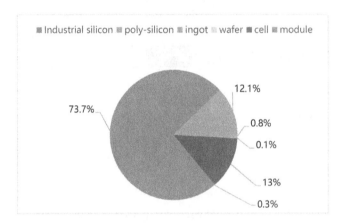

Figure 4. Percentage of carbon dioxide equivalent in each production phase.

Third, because the functional unit in this study is 1kwh, the calculated GWP has to be processed. Using the GWP of module production 236 Kg CO2-eq, divide the lifespan electricity generated 23625kWh. As a result, the GWP of module production in the functional unit is 0.01 Kg CO2-eq/kWh. When considered in a functional unit, it is obvious that the environmental impacts of the Poly-Si photovoltaic system are very small. Thus, a poly-Si photovoltaic system is a promising solution for carbon emission reduction.

3.1.3 *Energy payback time*

After calculation, the energy payback time of the module is 7.34 years. The annual average solar radiation on tilted panels in Tibet is 2192.35 kWh/m2. The total solar panel area in this study is 2.01m2. The performance ratio of poly-Si photovoltaic systems in China is usually 75% (Kawajiri et al. 2011). The average solar panel efficiency is 17.4%. Thus, the annual power generation of the module in this study can be calculated using 2192.35 kWh/m2 times 75% times 17.4% times 2.01m2 equals 575.1 MJ/ year. The total primary energy demand of the module in this study is 4224 MJ. Then, the energy payback time of the module can be calculated by using the total primary energy demand to divide annual power generation. The results show that the EPBT of the module in this study is far less than its lifespan of 25 years. After the energy payback time of the photovoltaic system, the energy generated by the system is accounted as a net gain. The poly-Si photovoltaic system in this study can continuously provide people with a net energy gain of about 17.7 years.

3.2 Economic impacts of the photovoltaic system

3.2.1 Cost of solar energy

The market price of the photovoltaic module in this study is between 62.6~76.5 $. To compare the price of electricity generated by a photovoltaic power station with that generated by a traditional thermal power station, we use the middle price of 70.1 $. The photovoltaic power station's average operation and maintenance cost are 0.007 $/W/yr (Wu 2021). Therefore, the operation and maintenance cost of the photovoltaic system of this study in its life span is 61.25 $. The photovoltaic system in this study can generate electricity of 23625 kWh in a lifespan of 25 years. Thus, this study's total cost of generating 23625 kWh is 131.35 $.

This study's total electricity generated by the photovoltaic system can be converted into 4063.5 kg standard coal. According to raw coal's conversion factor to standard coal of 0.714 3 kgce/kg, 4063.5 kg standard coal equals 5.689 tons of raw coal. Through October 14, 2022, the average price of raw coal is 110.3 $/ton. Generating electricity of 23625 kWh by the traditional thermal power station, the cost is 627.5 $. Therefore, to generate the same amount of power, the cost of using conventional thermal power is 4.8 times that of photovoltaic power, so photovoltaic power is also an excellent way of power generation financially.

3.2.3 Photovoltaic derived economy

In the place where the photovoltaic power station is built, many different industries are developing with the help of photovoltaics. With these industries combined with photovoltaic, the local economy in which photovoltaic power station is built is being positively influenced. For example: first, photovoltaic solving desertification. In many deserts where the climate is dry with very little rainfall and long hours of direct sunlight, the photovoltaic power station can effectively reduce surface water evaporation and wind speed, thus improving the living conditions of plants. Second, photovoltaic pluses agriculture. The construction of photovoltaic power stations can leave a large part of the land for developing agriculture, like plantation and fish breeding. Therefore, the photovoltaic power station provides people with enough electricity to use and maximizes the land utilization rate to boost the local economy further. Taking what has been discussed into account, the economic benefits of the photovoltaic system are abundant and far from being fully exploited, so continuously developing the photovoltaic industry will be an effective way to improve the economy of Tibet and, accordingly, China.

4 CONCLUSION

This study finished the carbon foot analysis of each phase of a poly-Si photovoltaic system, and the energy payback time was also calculated. Therefore, the environmental impacts of the poly-Si photovoltaic system were analyzed comprehensively. Moreover, this study also analyzed the economic impacts of the system. In conclusion, the poly-Si photovoltaic system has the largest environmental impact at the industrial silicon production phase of the whole production phase of the system. Thus, people need to make the environmental impacts of industrial silicon production as low as possible since solar energy is a key factor in achieving carbon neutrality and emission reduction. It is also very important to fully utilize photovoltaic systems' energy net gain period and lands where photovoltaic systems are built to boost the local economy.

However, there are some limitations to this study. First, this study's life cycle assessment of photovoltaic systems does not include the environmental impacts of BOS, system maintenance, transportation, and disposal. Hence, the environmental impacts of the photovoltaic system in this study are smaller than the actual impacts. Second, there are photovoltaic systems of different models in Tibet, so the results calculated in the study might be slightly different from that of some photovoltaic systems in Tibet, but the results of this study are still very representative.

Therefore, governments worldwide should invest more in the construction of databases, including data on BOS, maintenance, and transportation of photovoltaic systems, for future researchers to better analyze the environmental impacts of the system better. Furthermore, a well-developed disposal system for photovoltaic modules is also crucial to studies related to a photovoltaic system. It is because the disposal system of a photovoltaic module is still not mature in most countries.

REFERENCES

Alsema E. & De Wild M.J.(2005). Environmental Impact of Crystalline Silicon Photovoltaic Module Production. *MRS Online Proceedings Library (OPL)*, 895.

Breyer C., Koskinen O. & Blechinger P. (2015). Profitable Climate Change Mitigation: The Case of Greenhouse Gas Emission Reduction Benefits Enabled by Solar Photovoltaic Systems. *Renewable and Sustainable Energy Reviews*, 49, 610–628.

Dones R. & Frischknecht R. (1998). Life-cycle Assessment of Photovoltaic Systems: Results of Swiss Studies on Energy Chains. *Progress in Photovoltaics: Research and Applications*, 6(2), 117–125.

Fu Y., Liu X. & Yuan Z. (2015). Life-cycle Assessment of Multi-crystalline Photovoltaic (PV) Systems in China. *Journal of Cleaner Production*, 86, 180–190.

Jiang Jian Hong. (2019). Analysis of Solar Energy Resources Development in Tibet. *Power System Equipment*, 2019(24), 30–31.

Jiang L., Xue B., Xing R., Chen X., Song L., Wang Y. & Mi Z. (2020). Rural Household Energy Consumption of Farmers and Herders in the Qinghai-Tibet Plateau. Energy, 192, 116649.

Kawajiri K., Oozeki T. & Genchi Y. (2011). Effect of Temperature on PV Potential in the World. *Environmental Science & Technology*, 45(20), 9030–9035.

Ke J., McNeil M., Price L., Khanna N. Z. & Zhou N. (2013). Estimation of CO2 Emissions from China's Cement Production: *Methodologies and Uncertainties. Energy Policy*, pp. 57, 172–181.

Panwar N.L., Kaushik S.C. & Kothari S. (2011). Role of Renewable Energy Sources in Environmental Protection: A Review. *Renewable and Sustainable Energy Reviews*, 15(3), 1513–1524.

Peng J., & Lu L. (2013). Investigate the Development Potential of the Rooftop PV System in Hong Kong and its Environmental Benefits. *Renewable and Sustainable Energy Reviews*, 27, 149–162.

Ren F.R., Tian Z., Liu J. & Shen Y.T. (2020). Analysis of CO2 Emission Reduction Contribution and Efficiency of China's Solar Photovoltaic Industry: Based on Input-output Perspective. *Energy*, 199, 117493.

Shahzad U. (2012). The Need for Renewable Energy Sources. *Energy*, pp. 2, 16–18.

Shen Yi Zhou, Zhao Yan Ni & Qin Lei. (2022). Economic and Social Benefit Evaluation of Photovoltaic Power Generation Project Under the Background of Rural Revitalization: A Case Study of L County. *The Agricultural Economy of Shanxi* (13),133–137+141. doi:10.16675/j.cnki.cn14-1065/f.2022.13.043.

Sun Yu Xing, Yang Hong & Su Cheng Feng. (2010). Development of China's Photovoltaic Industry. *Semiconductor Technology* (02),101–104.

Tükenmez M., & Demireli E. (2012). Renewable Energy Policy in Turkey with the New Legal Regulations. *Renewable Energy*, 39(1), 1–9.

Wang Jun Le. (2021). Application Status and Suggestions of Off-grid Photovoltaic Power Stations in Areas Without Electricity in Xizang. *Tibet Science and Technology* (10),26–28+39.

Wang Q. & Qiu H.N. (2009). Situation and Outlook of Solar Energy Utilization in Tibet, China. *Renewable and Sustainable Energy Reviews*, 13(8), 2181–2186.

Wang Y.Q., Basang L. & Yang,Y.J. (2007). Thinking Over Adjustment of Energy Structure in Tibet. *Central South Forestry Inventory and planning*, 126(1), 60–3.

Wu Chang. (2021). Economic Benefit Analysis of Distributed Photovoltaic Power Generation. *Brand Research*, 2021(19):149–151. DOI:10.3969/j.issn.1671-1009.2021.19.048.

Wu Zhen Shuang. (2021). Discussion on the Development of the Solar Energy Industry in Xizang. *Tibet Science and Technology*.

Application of iron tailing waste rock aggregate to produce prefabricated laminated plate in construction engineering

Chi Zhang*
School of Civil and Environmental Engineering, Harbin Institute of Technology, Shenzhen, Guangdong China
China Construction Science & Technology Group Co., Ltd., Shenzhen, China

Binbin Li
Jianhua Building Materials (China) Co., Ltd, Zhenjiang, Jiangsu, China

Zhangmiao Li & Junqian Peng
China Construction Science & Technology Group Co., Ltd., Shenzhen, China

Tiejun Liu
School of Civil and Environmental Engineering, Harbin Institute of Technology, Shenzhen, Guangdong, China

ABSTRACT: This paper studied the basic morphology and structure of iron tailing waste rock from the Waitou mountain iron mine around Shenyang. The coarse and fine aggregate and prefabricated laminated plate were prepared from the iron tailing waste rock and successfully applied in construction engineering. According to the analysis of raw materials, the particle sizes of the iron tailing waste rock were about 0.1 mm-0.5 mm, and the main components were SiO_2, oxides of Fe, Mg, Ca, and other metallic elements. After making a suitable gradation through the sieve, they were used to prepare C30-grade concrete. In addition to iron tailing waste rock, fly ash as industrial solid waste was also used. The total content of industrial solid waste was 77.2% in concrete. Finally, the composite plate with a bulk density of 2480 kg/m^3, demolding strength of 28.3 MPa, and 7d compressive strength of 40.5 MPa was prepared. The laminated plates were successfully used in Building E of China Resources Ruifu in Shenyang (the office building of China Northeast Architecture Design and Research Institute).

1 INTRODUCTION

Iron tailing waste rock is a kind of typical industrial solid waste, which is stripped ore-free surrounding rock and rock in an iron mine and must be discharged to the waste rock field in time. It is the part of the surface of a large number of ore bodies produced by mining enterprises in the process of iron ore mining that cannot be used as ore [1]. With the rapid development of the iron and steel industry, the proportion of iron tailing waste rock in industrial solid waste is also increasing [2]. According to incomplete statistics, the annual increment of industrial solid waste in China is about 4 billion tons, and the comprehensive usage is only 60%. Among them, the comprehensive utilization rate of iron tailing waste rock is low, and the technological level of comprehensive utilization is far behind that of

---

*Corresponding Author: 13520735172@163.com

developed countries such as Japan and Germany [3]. The stockpiling of a large amount of iron tailing waste rock has brought many problems, such as land, environmental, and safety [4,5]. Currently, the treatment of iron tailing waste rock in China is still mainly landfill, which is a huge waste of resources. The current national environmental protection policies and construction industry policies constantly put forward the requirements of high-quality, high-level, and sustainable development to relevant enterprises, and under the background of the "30•60" carbon emission task proposed by the Chinese government, new platforms and industries that can absorb iron tailing waste rock in large quantities must be sought.

As iron tailing waste rock as a secondary resource has attracted increasing attention at home and abroad, recycling it in the building materials industry has become a good way to alleviate problems caused by its stockpiling. The biggest advantage of this approach is that iron tailing waste rock not only can be utilized in large quantities and with high added value but also can be introduced into the building materials industry as an excellent and ideal raw material to alleviate the problem of shortage of natural building materials. It realizes not only a circular economy but also energy-saving emission reduction, which is of great practical significance to the development of the industry and the promotion of national strategic policies [1].

As for iron tailing waste rock as a raw construction material, although there has been much previous research [6,7], China still has a weak influence on the resource reuse of iron tailing waste rock in the construction industry, with insufficient promotion. It is mainly considered a substitute for low-quality sand and stone, which has no competitive advantage over traditional building materials. In addition, due to the cost, it is difficult to prepare high-quality building materials products, which cannot be large-scale and industrialized, making it harder to be promoted [8,9]. The purpose of this study is to dredge a whole technical route from raw material source to component finished products and then to the engineering site, relying on the National Key Research and Development Plan "Solid Waste Resource Recovery" in the 13th Five-Year Plan to truly realize the large-scale practical application effect and as a demonstration, and a template to provide a reference for the entire industry. The implementation route is shown in Figure 1.

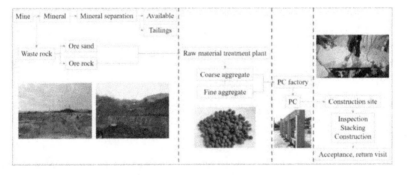

Figure 1. Schematic diagram of the technology roadmap.

2 METHODS AND MATERIALS

The iron tailing waste rock was taken from the Waitou mountain Iron Ore Plant. The cement was provided by the Liaoning Daying Cement Plant. The fly ash was provided by Fushun Liannianda Trading Co., Ltd. The water-reducing agent, slump retaining agent, water retaining agent, etc., were used as admixtures in the test. Ordinary tap water was used as mixing water.

Firstly, the basic composition and morphology of iron tailing waste aggregate and fly ash were characterized. It mainly included chemical composition characterization, mineral composition characterization, and SEM morphology characterization. Among them, the iron tailing waste rock raw materials were processed by the Liaoning Yilifang Sand Industry. The raw materials were broken by a jaw crusher, cone crusher, and sand-making machine for multistage crushing and then screened to get the aggregate with suitable gradation. The larger particle size would be returned to the sand-making machine to be broken again to prepare qualified concrete aggregate to supply the component factory.

Then, the iron tailing waste rock concrete laminated plates were prepared by the Shenyang Yatai factory. The preparation process was similar to that of a conventional laminated plate. However, due to the use of iron tailing waste rock, which was more difficult to process in aggregate, it is necessary to optimize gradation or use admixture to avoid possible problems such as stone settlement, segregation, and bleeding.

Finally, the laminated plates were transported to the engineering site of Building E of China Resources Ruifu (the office building of Northeast China Architecture Design and Research Institute) to hoist construction according to the drawing. To ensure an effective demonstration, a special design needs to be carried out for the iron tailings concrete laminated plate in the construction organization plan, which mainly included adding the subject of on-site inspection (such as the detection of special pollutants), the site for stockpiling the component, and the special identification of the component.

3 TEST RESULTS AND DISCUSSIONS

3.1 *Composition and structure of raw materials*

The basic composition of iron tailing waste rock, such as chemical components and mineral composition, had been analyzed. Its mineral composition is mainly quartz, as shown in Figure 2. The content of SiO_2, Al_2O_3, and Fe_xO_y in the waste rock of the Waitou mountain Iron Mine reaches 60.33%, 15.54%, 7.99%, and the rest mainly consists of metal oxides such as Na, Mg, K and Ca.

Round and smooth river sand are usually chosen as concrete sand, and its grain shape is conducive to the fluidity of concrete. Alternatively, machine-made sand with edges and corners can be used. Although its edges and corners may affect the fluidity of concrete and produce certain resistance during concrete pumping, it also has good cohesiveness [10]. In this paper, iron tailing waste rock was used as concrete aggregate after processing, and its particle morphology needs to be studied.

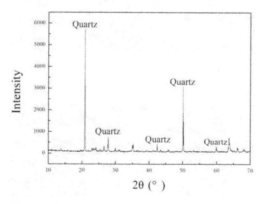

Figure 2. XRD image of iron tailings.

Iron tailings waste rock aggregate particles generally present fine sand or powder in a macroscopic state. As can be seen from Figures 3~6, the micro-morphological characteristics of iron tailing waste rock aggregate particles are as follows:

1. The particles were mostly irregular and sharp angular. The particles were mainly massive, needle-like, and flaky, with the surface more fluted;
2. The surface was rougher, which made its water absorption increase;
3. The irregular and sharp shape led to the increase of the friction between particles;
4. The irregular shape made its specific surface area larger; the water absorption rate increased; the viscosity and the consistency of concrete were higher.

The surface of the coarse aggregate of iron tailing waste rock had an obvious weathering effect and internal damage, as shown in Figures 3 and 4. Although it conforms to the corresponding specification requirements, the quality of concrete can be improved only by optimizing particle size. In general, if the strength of coarse aggregate was higher than that of concrete, concrete damage was caused by the bonding damage between aggregate and cement stone or cement stone itself. If the strength of the aggregate was lower, the aggregate damage was prior to that of cement stone, so the strength of the concrete was affected. Therefore, concrete made from rough and angular iron tailing waste rock had a higher strength than that made from smooth pebbles.

The fine aggregate of iron tailing waste rock contains more SiO_2, which is similar to natural sand in fact. Whereas, due to its rough surface and the shape with many sharp edges and corners, the friction between particles was large, as shown in Figures 5 and 6. With the

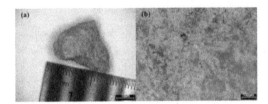

Figure 3. Macroscopic morphology of iron tailing coarse aggregate under optical microscope.

Figure 4. SEM images of iron tailing coarse aggregate.

Figure 5. Macroscopic morphology of iron tailing fine aggregate under an optical microscope.

Figure 6. SEM images of iron tailing coarse aggregate.

increase of its dosage in use, the fluidity of concrete is reduced, while water consumption is increased. However, due to the characteristics of iron tailing waste rock particles, the stress points in microstructure increased, and the volume stability of concrete would be inevitably enhanced. At the same time, according to literature reports, the active fine powder contained in iron tailing produced secondary hydration under alkaline conditions, and the C-S-H gel formed at the interface and its filling effect would form a "micro-aggregate effect" in the early strength of concrete.

The fly ash used in the test had a fineness modulus of 17% and a 28-day activity of 69%. In the actual test process, the fly ash collected from different areas was tested (Fly Ash Used in Cement and Concrete (GB/T 1596-2017)). The XRD results and SEM images of fly ash used in this study are shown in Figures 7 and 8. Its overall composition was similar to inorganic silicate, and its main components are SiO_2 and Al_2O_3, which significantly influence the activity and strength of fly ash. In fact, since the content index of such active substances was relatively stable, it can completely meet the use requirements. From SEM images of fly ash morphology, it can be seen that most particles were spherical, few were columnar, and the particles aggregated into vitreous bodies. Regardless of the size of the spherical particles, the

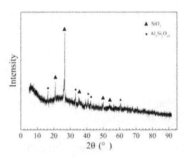

Figure 7. XRD image of fly ash.

Figure 8. SEM images of fly ash.

surface was uneven. The large and small particles were intertwined and attached, which makes fly ash have strong adsorption.

3.2 Preparation of iron tailing waste rock concrete laminated plate

The preparation of iron tailing waste rock concrete laminated plate required preliminary preparation and trial production. The specific steps were as follows: First, 2.4 t iron tailings and 1.6 t sand from Liaoning Yilifang Sand Industry were provided for two cubic meters of concrete. Then, it was necessary to prepare the admixture separately for the possible occurrence of concrete segregation and bleeding according to the gradation of the iron tailing waste rock aggregate. Next, the concrete mix proportion design and the trial match should be carried out to meet the workability and strength indexes. Finally, concrete trial production was carried out in the workshop.

Table 1. Gradation of iron tailings aggregate.

\multicolumn{3}{c	}{Coarse aggregate}	\multicolumn{3}{c}{Fine aggregate}
Sieve size (mm)	Grading sieve residue (%)	Accumulated sieve residue (%)	Sieve size (mm)	Grading sieve residue (%)	Accumulated sieve residue (%)
26.5	0.0	0	4.75	0	0
19.0	20.7	21	2.36	9.2	9.2
16.0	18.9	40	1.18	11.0	20.2
9.5	22.2	62	0.6	28.4	48.6
4.75	18.6	80	0.3	21.6	70.2
2.36	19.0	99	0.15	14.0	84.2
<2.36	0.7	100	<0.15	15.8	100

The aggregate gradation of iron tailings is shown in Table 1, while the raw material samples were inspected and retained according to relevant standards. It can be seen in Table 1 that the fineness modulus of iron tailing sand was small, while the powder content was relatively high. However, the grading of iron tailing rock with 5-20 particle size was relatively unreasonable, especially the 4.75 grade. Suitable water-reducing agents with low sensitivity and compound mixed with slump retaining agents were selected as the compound mother liquor to solve the problems above, ensuring the stable working of the mixing plant. Meanwhile, to avoid problems such as settlement, segregation, and bleeding due to the high density of iron tailings, a 2%~4% high-performance water retention agent was added to improve the cohesiveness of the concrete, ensuring the quality of concrete products.

According to the design experience of C30 laminated plate concrete, the mix proportion, as shown in Table 2, was used. The concrete that meets the requirements of workability and

Table 2. Mix proportion design of C30 iron tailings aggregate concrete.

\multicolumn{6}{c	}{Formula}	Admixture	Solid waste content (%)
Volume (L)	Bulk density (kg/m^3)	Cementing material content (kg/m^3)	Water binder ratio	Sand rate (%)	Water-reducing agent content (%)	Water-reducing agent + slump retaining agent + water retaining agent	77.2%
15	2400	420	0.4	48	0.19		

strength had been prepared by trial (see Figure 9). After a series of trials, the production of the C30 laminated plate was carried out in Shenyang, as shown in Figure 10.

Figure 9. Concrete samples to be tested.

Figure 10. Fabrication of concrete composite plates in the workshop.

3.3 *Application in construction engineering*

After the successful production of the laminated plates, they were applied in the super high-rise building of China Resources Ruifu Building-E in Shenyang on November 1, 2020, as shown in Figure 11. The building is the new office of Northeast China Architecture Design and Research Institute, with a total height of 129.9 m. The overall design service life of the building is 50 years, while the seismic fortification intensity is 7 degrees. Prefabricated

Figure 11. Images of the construction site.

laminated plate, prefabricated external wall (metal curtain wall), prefabricated internal partition wall, and prefabricated municipal components were adopted in the building. The assembly rate is 51.27% which meets the national assembly standard. The maximum size of the solid waste laminate plate is 2.6×3.47 m, while the maximum weight is 1.353 t. The demonstration is the first application of prefabricated concrete structural components with large content of solid waste on super high-rise buildings in China.

For the application of laminated plates based on solid waste, the construction plan should be improved as follows:

(1) The inspection of solid waste laminated plates when entering the site. In addition to the regular appearance and dimension inspection, the factory certificate of the solid waste component should be checked and retained. The following certificates should be checked: quality acceptance form of the prefabricated component, concrete sample inspection report, product certificate, and product manual;
(2) Storage of solid waste laminated plates. The storage positions should be specially set while the component of the same type should be stacked together;
(3) Acceptance process. The inspection of indoor radioactivity and air pollutants should be added;
(4) Pay a return visit. A special return visit mechanism for the solid waste components should be added, while a special follow-up record should be made. Focus on checking chromatic aberration, cracks, drumming, and other indicators.

4 CONCLUSION

Based on the results and discussions presented above, the conclusions are obtained as below:

1. After pretreatment, Iron tailing waste rock was successfully used as concrete aggregate to prepare prefabricated laminate plates. The total content of industrial solid waste reached 77.2%.
2. Most of the iron tailing waste rock particles were irregular and multi-angular, leading the strong friction between particles. The particles in the concrete were tightly combined and wrapped by the cementitious material. The microstructure was the basis for the good performance of iron tailing waste rock concrete.
3. Due to the physical and chemical characteristics of iron tailing waste rock, it was necessary to reasonably optimize the design of concrete mix proportion. Furthermore, concrete can obtain better quality through the use of admixtures.

ACKNOWLEDGMENTS

This work was financially supported by the National Key Research and Development Plan (2019YFC1907205).

REFERENCES

[1] Deng W., Jiang D., Yang B. and Lan Y. (2012) Comprehensive Utilization Status and Existing Problems of Iron Tailings in China. *Modern Mining*, 28(09): 1–3.
[2] Jingwu L. (2019) Comparative Analysis of Current Status and Disposal Technologies of Municipal Solid Waste. *China Resources Comprehensive Utilization*, 37(2): 107–109,138.
[3] Lei L., Zhou X., Li J., Cai X. and Guowen W. (2008) Status Quo and Pondering on Comprehensive Utilization of Mine Tailings Resources in China. *Express Information of Mining Industry*, 9: 5–8.

[4] Li D., Ni W. and Zheng Y. (2010) Experimental Research on High-strength Concrete Preparation with Large Content of Iron Tailings. *Metal Mine*, 2: 167–170.

[5] Liu R., Xu Z., Chang L. and Feng W. (2011) Current Status and Progress of Comprehensive Utilization of Tailings Resources. *Gold*, 11: 66–69.

[6] Xiao L.G., Jing-Hong Y.I. and Cui Z.X. (2010) Iron Tailings Comprehensive Utilization at Home and Abroad. *Journal of Jilin Institute of Architecture & Civil Engineering*, 4: 22–26.

[7] Yan M., Bai L., Zhang Y., and Zhang J. (2008) Current Situation, Problems and Countermeasures of Comprehensive Utilization of Iron Tailings in China. *Express Information of Mining Industry*, 7(7): 9–13.

[8] Yongliang C., Yimin Z. and Tiejun C. (2009) Progress in the Research of Using Iron Tailings as Building Material Resource. *Metal Mine*, 391: 162–165.

[9] Zhang S.H., Xue X.X. and Jin Z.F. (2004) Current Situation and Comprehensive Utilization of Iron ore Tailings Resources in our Country. *Journal of Materials and Metallurgy*, 3(4): 241–245.

[10] Zhang X., Baohua F.U., Liu J. and Zhou Z. (2014) Preparation and Properties of High Performance Concrete Based on the Iron Tailing Mixed Manufactured Sand. *Concrete*, 4: 116–118, 123.

Challenges and opportunities for recycling waste photovoltaic modules

Guochen Zhao*

Datang Northeast Electric Power Test & Research Institute, China Datang Corporation Science and Technology Research Institute, Changchun, P.R. China

ABSTRACT: China is a leading country in the photovoltaic market, and both new and cumulative installed capacities have ranked first in the world for many consecutive years. However, when the photovoltaic power station expires, the discarded photovoltaic modules will generate corresponding solid waste. We assume that the Chinese photovoltaic market began to develop in 2010, and the life of the modules is 20 years. By 2030, a large amount of solid waste will begin to be generated and increase yearly. Driven by the "dual carbon goal," photovoltaics will enter a new round of rapid development, and the resulting waste will also increase. Therefore, the recycling and harmless treatment of waste photovoltaic modules is an urgent problem that needs to be laid out in advance. In this work, we analyze the application prospects of waste photovoltaic module recycling. We further propose the challenges and opportunities currently facing the recycling of waste photovoltaic modules in China based on the necessity of recycling waste photovoltaic modules, the current situation of the photovoltaic recycling industry at home and abroad, and the overview of related recycling technologies. As the world leader of the photovoltaic industry in China, the development of the recycling industry will show the sunshine status of the photovoltaic industry. It is believed that the recycling of waste photovoltaic modules will have a good start.

1 INTRODUCTION

Photovoltaic power generation is a new energy technology that converts solar energy into electric energy. It has developed rapidly with the advantages of safety, reliability, cleanliness, high efficiency, and sustainability in recent years. It is expected to solve the current energy shortage and environmental protection problems. In 2021, the Chinese newly installed photovoltaic grid-connected capacity will be 54.88 GW, a year-on-year increase of 13.9%. The cumulative photovoltaic grid-connected installed capacity reached 308 GW, ranking first in the world in both new and cumulative installed capacity. The annual photovoltaic power generation was 325.9 billion kWh, a year-on-year increase of 25.1%, accounting for about 4.0% of the Chinese total annual power generation. It is estimated that the newly installed photovoltaic capacity will exceed 75 GW in 2022, and the cumulative installed capacity is expected to reach about 383 GW. In 2021, Chinese module output will reach 182 GW, a year-on-year increase of 46.1%, with mainly crystalline silicon modules. Among them, the output of the top five companies accounted for 63.4% of the Chinese total module output, of which the output of the top five companies exceeded 10 GW. Module production is expected to exceed 233 GW in 2022 (China Photovoltaic Industry Association 2021).

*Corresponding Author: 1257593514@qq.com

The life of photovoltaic modules can generally reach 25–30 years in an ideal environment. However, in practical applications, due to environmental erosion and ultraviolet radiation, problems such as line aging, sealant degradation, and electrochemical corrosion are prone to occur in the modules, resulting in practical problems. The service life is about 20 years, and a large number of distributed photovoltaics are scrapped early with the demolition of the buildings (Zhou et al. 2020). A set of forecast data from the International Energy Agency (IEA) shows that in 2030, global photovoltaic module recycling will reach about 8 million tons, ushering in a recycling tide. In 2050, nearly 80 million tons of photovoltaic modules worldwide will enter the recycling stage. China will face the need to recycle up to 1.5 million tons of photovoltaic modules in 2030 and about 20 million tons in 2050 (International Renewable Energy Agency 2016). Chinese photovoltaic market began to develop rapidly around 2010, and it is expected to usher in an "end of life" in 2030. Improper handling of waste photovoltaic modules will bring a heavy burden to the environment and society, and the recycling and reuse of photovoltaic modules are imminent.

2 RESEARCH STATUS

2.1 *Current status of foreign research*

Compared with the domestic photovoltaic industry, foreign developed countries entered the photovoltaic industry earlier and built photovoltaic power stations earlier. Therefore, they paid attention to the recycling of waste photovoltaic modules earlier.

On February 13, 2003, the European Parliament and the Council issued the "Waste Electrical and Electronic Equipment Directive" (the "WEEE Directive"), which was officially implemented on August 13, 2005. The Directive explicitly requires manufacturing practitioners to be responsible for recycling the products they produce that may pollute the environment, specifies, and sets requirements for the disposal of scrapped electrical and electronic equipment (Jiang 2021). On July 24, 2012, the European Parliament and the Council issued the 2.0 version of the WEEE Directive, clearly including photovoltaic modules in its scope of application and requiring that from 2014, all photovoltaic modules that want to enter the EU market must be affixed. The "wheelie bin" logo is uniformly designed by WEEE Directive 2.0.

In 2007, the EU established PV CYCLE, an agency that fully operates the recovery and recycling of crystalline silicon photovoltaic modules. According to the policies of different countries, PV CYCLE is committed to providing comprehensive waste crystalline silicon photovoltaic module recovery and recycling services for enterprises at all levels. It has established a recycling network with partners such as logistics and transportation companies. The agency has now set up hundreds of recycling points across Europe and has recovered over 10,000 tons of waste crystalline silicon photovoltaic modules. A similar organization to PV CYCLE is the Paris-based CERES CYCLE organization (Li et al. 2020).

In 2018, in the city of Rosset in southern France, PV CYCLE, Veolia Environnement, and the French Renewable Energy Union jointly built a recycling plant, using intelligent robots to separate, sort, process, and recycle waste crystalline silicon photovoltaic modules. Through the application of new processes and new technologies, at present, the recycling rate of waste crystalline silicon photovoltaic modules in the factory is as high as 95%, which is much higher than the standard of the photovoltaic module recycling industry and the WEEE Directive 2.0 (Sun 2021).

At the same time, PV CYCLE also developed the crystalline silicon photovoltaic module refurbishment business in 2017 and is committed to repairing, refurbishing, and reusing damaged crystalline silicon photovoltaic modules. Chinese companies have also begun to actively join PV CYCLE. Up to now, half of PV CYCLE's members are Chinese companies.

2.2 Current status of Chinese research

In the past few years, South Korea, Japan, and some countries from the European Union have made early arrangements for the industrialization of photovoltaic module recycling. Compared with the foreign photovoltaic industry, it is not too late to start the recycling market of retired photovoltaic modules in China.

During the "Twelfth Five-Year Plan" and "Thirteenth Five-Year Plan" period, China has supported the research and development of key processes and equipment for the treatment of waste crystalline silicon photovoltaic modules through the 863 projects and the National Key R&D Program on Renewable Energy and Hydrogen Energy Technology. Relying on these two topics, as well as the own investment of some enterprises, a number of 10 MW-30 MW demonstration lines of waste component treatment based on different treatment methods have been established. Nantong Riyixin has built a production line with a production capacity of 10,000 tons/year (equivalent to about 160 MW/year), realizing a breakthrough in the disassembly and processing of photovoltaic modules from laboratory to mass production. It is estimated that under the current technical level, if a high-capacity utilization rate is maintained, the investment recovery period of a physical recycling processing line with an annual processing capacity of 40,000 tons is about 8 years. This has certain economic benefits: the output of copper, silver, aluminum, and other bulk metals will increase in value in the future, and the yield is expected to increase further (Zhang & Wu 2022).

At the policy level, the "Carbon Peaking Action Plan before 2030" issued by the State Council clearly calls for "promoting the recycling of waste from emerging industries such as retired power batteries, photovoltaic modules, and wind turbine blades." The "Smart Photovoltaic Industry Innovation and Development Action Plan (2021–2025)" issued by five ministries and commissions, including the Ministry of Industry and Information Technology, also mentioned the need to "promote the research and development and industrial application of waste photovoltaic module recycling technology, and accelerate the comprehensive utilization of resources" (Don et al. 2022).

At the standard level, China issued the "General Technical Requirements for Recycling and Recycling of Thin-Film Solar Cell Modules for Buildings. (GB/T 38785-2020)" in 2020 and "General Technical Requirements for Recycling of Photovoltaic Modules (GB/T 39753-2021)" in 2021. However, both standards are recommended and not strictly binding. Other related supporting technical specifications and standards are missing and need to be continuously improved (Li et al. 2021).

At the enterprise level, under the pressure of carbon tariff barriers in international trade, and due to social responsibility and the need for enterprises to enhance their own brand competitiveness, enterprises have begun to actively invest in the recycling and disposal of waste photovoltaic modules, mainly including Ruisai Environmental Protection, Yingli Energy, Jingke Solar, Trina Solar, and many other companies.

3 RECYCLING PROCESS

At present, there are three mainstream solar cell technologies, namely crystalline silicon solar cells (polysilicon, monocrystalline silicon), thin film solar cells (cadmium telluride, copper indium gallium selenide, gallium arsenide), and new solar cells (such as perovskite). Crystalline silicon solar cells account for more than 95% of the solar cell market share. Solar cells are electrically interconnected in series and placed in weather-resistant packages called panels. Lead-tin solder is commonly used to connect tinned copper interconnects to silver-based metalized gridlines and tinned copper ribbons on the cell surface. A piece of tempered, rolled, low iron cover glass provides mechanical support and a moisture barrier. A layer of flexible polymer encapsulant, most commonly polyethylene-vinyl acetate (EVA), optically and mechanically couples the strings to the glass. Another layer of encapsulant and a flexible multilayer polymer backsheet (or another piece of glass) electrically insulate and protect the back of the cell. Polymer backsheets typically consist of polyethylene terephthalate (PET) for electrical insulation and a thin layer of fluoropolymer (e.g., polyvinylidene fluoride, PVF) to protect the outer surface from UV radiation. The junction box connects the solder ribbon inside the battery to the insulated copper wire outside the battery.

Manufacturers design PV modules to be generally reliable for 30 years or more to minimize uniform electricity costs and ensure expected conversion efficiencies for profitability. However, these robust designs make the separation and extraction of battery materials challenging. Based on extensive literature reports, we have identified three key steps in the recycling process: mechanical removal of bezels and junction boxes; separation of glass and silicon wafers by thermal, mechanical, or chemical process removal of encapsulant; subsequent separation and purification by chemical and electrolytic techniques of silicon wafers and specialty metals (e.g., silver, tin, lead, copper). The metal content in PV modules is typically less than 1%, including silver, copper that connects the cells, aluminum, lead, and tin. Recycling costs are high due to the high demands on energy, consumable materials, waste management, and labor, but they are a considerable source of income (Heath et al. 2020).

To our knowledge, none of the comprehensive recycling processes reported in the literature can fully recover all high-purity bulk and trace materials in crystalline silicon PV modules. In addition, the present lack of data characterizing process steps in terms of energy and material flow is a challenge for applying techno-economic analysis (TEA) and life cycle assessment (LCA) to identify economic and environmental hotspots and weigh virtually all proposed new processes for recycling crystalline silicon PV modules. We have only identified two technologies that integrate the recovery of several, but not all, trace materials that may be valuable or dangerous. We have comprehensive reports on these materials and energy flows. They are the "Full Recovery End of Life Photovoltaic (FRELP)" process and a process designed by "Arizona State University (ASU)."

The FRELP process is designed to maximize the recycling of used PV modules and minimize the waste of resources. Currently, a pilot-scale FRELP processing facility has been demonstrated, which is capable of processing approximately 1,300 photovoltaic panels per day. The process is capable of recovering large quantities of aluminum, glass, copper, and silver, but not lead and tin. First, the aluminum frame, cables, and junction boxes are disassembled and sold for further recycling. The glass and backsheet are heated in an infrared belt furnace to weaken their encapsulation, and hot knife cutting removes the glass from the remaining polymer and cell sheets. The separated glass is sieved and optically sorted into a clean glass for sale, and contaminated glass is to be treated (contains more than 2% impurities by mass). The encapsulant-coated battery strings are mechanically pulverized and incinerated at an off-site incinerator to remove organic compounds. Bottom ash remaining after incineration is treated by sieving, leaching, and filtration. Nitric acid is used to dissolve copper, silver, and other metals, leaving mostly silicon wafer fragments. Vacuum filtration was used to separate silicon from the leachate. The leaching solution is electrolyzed in three steps to extract the metal, and the spent electrolyte is neutralized and filtered before treatment, which is the most expensive step in the entire process (Latunussa et al. 2016a; 2016b).

The ASU process is designed to maximize the highest value of recycled material from used PV modules. The process primarily embodies the laboratory-scale recovery extraction of silver, lead, tin, and copper from exposed solar cells, including chemical processes such as leaching, electrolysis, and etching. The researchers propose a conceptualized process incorporating pyrolytic separation techniques to complete the separation of crystalline silicon wafers from glass and backsheets, enabling the complete recycling of used PV modules. First, after dismantling the PV panel frame and junction box, organic compounds such as EVA, PET, and PVF layers are burned off in a furnace, leaving behind glass, silicon wafers, and other residues. The silicon is then recovered by nitric acid leaching to produce soluble metal salts. The leaching solution is processed through a two-step electrolytic deposition technique to recover silver, copper, and lead oxide. The remaining silicon wafers are sequentially etched with hydrofluoric acid and sodium hydroxide to remove contact metal layers and passivation layers, thereby recovering usable silicon. The completed silicon wafers and glass can be recycled through the ASU process, and the recycled silicon can meet the extremely high purity levels of solar-grade silicon. However, with stricter purity requirements and the fragility of thinner cells, we believe this ideal is difficult to achieve (Cui et al. 2022; Huang et al. 2017).

4 APPLICATION PROSPECTS

Promoting and standardizing the recycling of waste photovoltaic modules can save resources, reduce the exploitation of primary resources, and reduce the energy consumption of resource extraction. At present, photovoltaic modules are mainly crystalline silicon photovoltaic modules. The components include glass, packaging materials, silicon wafers, backplanes, and metal frames. Among them, glass (about 70%), aluminum (about 10%), silicon (about 5%), silver, gallium, indium, and other rare metals (about 1%) have the possibility of recycling. Through the recycling and reuse of waste photovoltaic modules, the recycling of rare metals, glass, aluminum, and semiconductors can be realized to reduce the exploitation of primary resources, reduce the energy consumption of resource extraction, and achieve the purpose of low-carbon development.

Promoting and standardizing the recycling of waste photovoltaic modules is conducive to alleviating the pressure on the ecological environment. At present, most of the waste photovoltaic modules in China are not recycled and are usually landfilled directly or after being crushed. With the rapid development of the Chinese photovoltaic industry, if the construction of the photovoltaic module recycling and processing system stagnates, it will directly affect the development and reuse of land resources. In addition, metals such as lead and tin in crystalline silicon photovoltaic modules have high leaching toxicity, which can lead to soil and water pollution.

Promoting and standardizing the recycling and disposal of waste photovoltaic modules is conducive to the development of the circular economy. On the one hand, photovoltaic power generation generates a large amount of solid waste, leading to huge future disposal pressure. Especially in the central and eastern regions, the space for the disposal of solid waste is limited, and the environmental problems faced are more serious. Promoting the recycling of photovoltaic modules can effectively reduce the application of photovoltaics. On the other hand, recycling photovoltaic modules has good economic value. Most of the materials of waste photovoltaic modules can be recycled. Although the content of silver, aluminum, tin, and other metals contained in them is small, the recycling value is large.

Promoting and standardizing the recycling of waste photovoltaic modules is conducive to strengthening the green characteristics of the full life cycle of photovoltaic modules and promoting the green development of the photovoltaic industry. Recycling photovoltaic modules can improve the resource utilization efficiency of photovoltaic products and reduce carbon emissions in the manufacturing process. It realizes the green characteristics of the whole life cycle of production, use, and recycling of photovoltaic modules. It can also promote the development of the photovoltaic industry in accordance with the requirements of green and high quality. Using recycled glass to regenerate glass can save coal and electricity energy by 10–30%, reduce air pollution by 20%, and reduce mining exhaust emissions by 80%. Compared with the production of the same amount of primary aluminum, the energy consumption in the production of recycled aluminum is only 3%–5% of the former, and the carbon emission is only 0.23 tons, which is 2.1% of the carbon emission caused by electrolytic aluminum production. The production of 1 ton of recycled aluminum can save 3.4 tons of standard coal and 14 tons of water and reduce solid waste discharge by 20 tons. The energy consumption of silicon wafer production accounts for more than 50% of the energy consumption of module production, and more than 50% of the carbon footprint and climate impact comes from the production of silicon materials. The use of recycled silicon materials can greatly reduce carbon emissions (Liu & Yan 2021).

5 CHALLENGES

5.1 *Mistakenly believe that the large-scale decommissioning of components will take time, and the industry is not very enthusiastic*

If the decommissioning period is simply calculated based on the 20-year lifespan of components, it will not start to have large-scale component scrapping until 2030, that is, eight years later, and the scrapping amount is not high. Because of this, the industry has not paid enough attention to it. However, it should be taken into account that the photovoltaic power plants built in China in the early days, especially distributed power plants, are likely to be eliminated before retirement due to low product technology maturity and uneven product quality. Second, early subsidized power stations may also replace high-power components in advance due to higher investment returns, resulting in obsolete components. Therefore, the large-scale decommissioning period of photovoltaic modules may be significantly advanced. It is necessary to scientifically and reasonably calculate the growth trend of the photovoltaic module recycling and processing market to build consensus in the industry and promote the government and enterprises to advance policy formulation, commercialization, and other related work.

5.2 *The policy system has not yet been established, and the industry lacks effective support in the initial stage of development*

Although the disposal of waste modules is economically feasible, if the recycling and transportation of waste modules are considered, it is not yet economical. Special departments and funds are required to support the recovery of modules, especially for small and scattered distributed photovoltaics. In power stations, the recycling cost of discarded components is higher. In addition, in the early stage of development, due to the insufficient supply of discarded components, the waste component treatment cannot exert the scale effect. Certain subsidies are also required to promote industrialization. The European Union includes the recycling of photovoltaic modules into the "Waste Electrical and Electronic Equipment Directive" (i.e., "WEEE") for management. It stipulates the specific subject of recycling responsibility, recovery, and recycling rate. It requires each manufacturer to be responsible for providing funds for the recycling and disposal of waste of its products. To match it, PV CYCLE, an industry organization, was established to accept applications from institutions, organizations, and enterprises from all over the world to become members and to charge membership fees according to their market share. These costs are used for the recycling and centralized processing of photovoltaic modules, thus helping these companies to meet the EU's mandatory requirements for the disposal of waste photovoltaic modules with minimal investment. In contrast to China, although it has already implemented the "Regulations on the Management of the Recycling and Disposal of Waste Electrical and Electronic Products", it does not cover photovoltaic module products, nor does it have a special management policy for recycling and disposal of waste photovoltaic modules.

5.3 *The acquisition of waste components faces institutional and mechanism obstacles, and commercialization exploration could be smoother*

Professional enterprises involved in component recycling and processing earlier are faced with problems such as insufficient receipt of waste components in actual operations, resulting in insufficient equipment operating rate, inability to rapidly advance equipment and process optimization, and the inability to enter benign operations. The main reasons for the difficulty in obtaining discarded components are as follows: First, most of the existing power plants in China are owned by central state-owned enterprises. The recycling of waste components is accompanied by the risk of loss of state-owned assets. It is difficult to hand over to a third party without a compliant processing process. Second, the waste module processing companies are mixed, and the recycling and processing of photovoltaic modules should be paid by the module companies to deal with a certain fee. However, some small workshops do not need to pay or even pay the module companies for recycling because they have no follow-up environmental protection costs. After simple dismantling, the available materials, such as frames and glass, are sold, and those without corresponding processing capacity are simply landfilled or incinerated. It not only causes great pollution to the environment but also causes bad money to drive out good money, which significantly affects the healthy competition of the industry. Third, it is difficult to transfer waste components across provinces. According to the Law of the "People's Republic of China on the Prevention and Control of Environmental Pollution by Solid Waste," the transfer of solid waste out of the administrative areas of provinces, autonomous regions, and municipalities directly under the Central Government for storage and disposal shall be subject to the approval of the place of removal and the place of acceptance. However, companies responded that the current approval of cross-provincial transfer of discarded photovoltaic modules faces many obstacles in practice.

6 RECOMMENDATIONS AND ACTIONS

6.1 *Continue to increase the research and development and industrialization of component recycling technology*

The first is to strengthen the research on the recycling and processing technology of waste photovoltaic modules. It is needed to increase the research on the recycling and utilization technology of new components, such as flexible components, MWT components (recycling of non-strip components), and heterojunction components (recycling of indium compounds). The second is to strengthen the research on recycling and processing technology of production raw materials. In addition to recycling waste components, a certain proportion of materials, such as film, backplane, frame, glass, etc., will also be scrapped in the production process of photovoltaic products. The third is to improve the green development level of recycling and disposal work. Promoting energy saving and green emission reduction in the industrialized treatment of waste components would achieve harmless treatment. The fourth is to strengthen the green design of photovoltaic products. From the perspective of material selection and product design, follow-up recycling and processing issues are considered, such as developing packaging materials that are more conducive to the separation of film, backplane, glass, etc., and developing and promoting flexible component products (there is no problem of glass and frame recycling).

6.2 *Establish a component recycling system and mechanism*

The first is to cooperate with relevant ministries and commissions to research, formulate and publish the "Administrative Measures for the Recycling and Disposal of Waste Photovoltaic Modules." The responsible entities for recycling waste photovoltaic modules, the qualification certification of processing enterprises, and the recycling and processing procedures should be clearly stipulated. Industrial difficulties need to be solved, such as the recycling of distributed photovoltaic modules, as well as policy obstacles, such as power state-owned enterprises not providing waste modules due to concerns about the loss of state-owned assets and provincial-level circulation of waste modules. The second is to learn from the European model of promoting module recycling and processing through the waste photovoltaic recycling and processing organization PV CYCLE. The Photovoltaic Association takes the lead in setting up a special committee for the recycling and processing of photovoltaic modules. It collects membership fees, which are specially used to set recycling points and entrusted processing.

6.3 *Improve the development environment of component recycling*

The first is to scientifically and reasonably calculate the large-scale abandonment of photovoltaic modules for reference by industry practitioners and policymakers. The second is to sort out further and improve the technical standard system and certification rules for component recycling, do a good job in the top-level design of standards, and speed up the formulation and revision of standards. The third is to standardize the development order of the module recycling industry, and it is strictly forbidden to incinerate or landfill waste photovoltaic modules directly. Enterprises that cause further pollution and emissions to the environment in the process of disposing of waste components should be banned, and industry supervision needs to be increased to maintain a good environment for industrial development.

7 CONCLUSIONS

Since the 21st century, China has promoted the photovoltaic industry to leap forward through a series of measures such as subsidy incentives and become a global leader. By the end of 2021, the cumulative installed capacity of photovoltaic power generation in China was 306 million kilowatts (306 GW), ranking first in the world for many consecutive years. That year, the output value of the Chinese photovoltaic manufacturing industry exceeded 750 billion yuan, and the export volume reached a record high. After the "carbon neutrality goal" was put forward, photovoltaics ushered in a golden period of development and became an important force in promoting industrial economic growth. This paper analyzes the application prospects of recycling in the photovoltaic industry and proposes the challenges and opportunities currently facing the recycling and disposal of waste photovoltaic modules in China. At present, China mistakenly believes that the large-scale decommissioning of components will take time, and the enthusiasm for the industry is not high. Second, the policy system has not yet been established, and the industry lacks effective support in the initial stage of development. Third, the acquisition of discarded components faces institutional and mechanism obstacles, and commercialization exploration is not smooth. Therefore, in the future, China should continue to increase the research and development and industrialization of component recycling technology. At the same time, China should establish a system and mechanism for component recycling and improve the development environment for component recycling. It is also necessary to build a complete industrial chain of photovoltaic module recycling and reuse and open up the "last mile" of green development of the photovoltaic industry.

ACKNOWLEDGMENTS

This work was financially supported by the "Recycling and Reuse of Crystalline Silicon Photovoltaic Modules" project of Datang Northeast Electric Power Test & Research Institute.

REFERENCES

China Photovoltaic Industry Association. (2021) *China PV Industry Development Roadmap (2021)*. China Photovoltaic Industry Association, 2021.

Cui H., Heath G., Remo T., *et al.* (2022) Techno-economic Analysis of High-Value, Crystalline Silicon Photovoltaic Module Recycling Processes. *Solar Energy Materials and Solar Cells*, 238: 111592.

Dong Z.T., Li L.W., Yao M.J. (2022) Comprehensive Utilization of New Energy Solid Waste Ushered in a "Window Period." *China Energy News*, (001).

End-of-Life Management:Solar Photovoltaic Panels IEA-PVPS Task 12, Report #T12–06:2016 (International Renewable Energy Agency, International Energy Agency Photovoltaics Power Systems Technology Collaboration Programm 2016).

Heath G.A., Silverman T.J., Kempe M., *et al.* (2020) Research and Development Priorities for Silicon Photovoltaic Module Recycling to Support a Circular Economy. *Nature Energy*, 5(7): 502–510.

Huang W.H., Shin W.J., Wang L., *et al.* (2017) Strategy and Technology to Recycle Wafer-Silicon Solar Modules. *Solar Energy*, 144: 22–31.

Jiang H. (2021) Research on the Policy of Recycling and Treatment of Waste Photovoltaic Modules. *Solar Energy*, (3):9–13.

Latunussa C.E.L., Ardente F., Blengini G.A., *et al.* (2016a) Life Cycle Assessment of an Innovative Recycling Process for Crystalline Silicon Photovoltaic Panels. *Solar Energy Materials and Solar Cells*, 156: 101–111.

Latunussa C., Mancini L., Blengini G., *et al.* (2016b) *Analysis of Material Recovery from Silicon Photovoltaic Panels EUR 27797*(Publications Office of the European Union).

Li C.W., Hu L., Fan Y.B., *et al.* (2020) Current Situation Research and Standard Discussion of Recycling and Utilization of Photovoltaic Modules. *China Standardization*, (S1).

Li Y.W., Deng X., Luo D., *et al.* (2021) Research on the Current Situation of Photovoltaic Module Recycling at Home and Abroad. *Green Building*, 13(06).

Liu J.J. and Yan J.G. (2021) Strengthen the Recycling of Waste Photovoltaic Modules and Open Up the "Last Mile" of Green Development of the Photovoltaic Industry. *China Economic & Trade Herald*, (23).

Sun Z.Y. (2021) Analysis on Recycling Method of Waste Crystalline Silicon Photovoltaic Modules. *Solar Energy*, (09).

Zhang Y.Y. and Wu K.Z. (2022) The "Last Mile" of the Photovoltaic Green Chain: The Photovoltaic Module Recycling Industry Has Entered the Eve of the Outbreak. *China Business Journal*, (C06).

Zhou Z., Sun K.W., Jiang L. *et al.* (2020) Research Progress on Recycling Technology of Waste Photovoltaic Modules. *Journal of Central South University (Science and Technology)*, 51(12).

Reconstruction method of vertical seawall based on ecological engineering concept

Biao Zhou, Zijian Guo, Qi Hang & Ying Jiang*
State Key Laboratory of Coastal and Offshore Engineering, Dalian University of Technology, Dalian, China

ABSTRACT: Traditional vertical seawalls have been recognized with poor wave-absorbing performance and serious damage to the local natural environment. Under the influence of the 'green development and ecologicalization' concept in China, the importance of the ecological construction of seawalls has also been emphasized. However, limited research has focused on the reconstruction method of the vertical seawall from the perspective of ecological engineering. To deal with this, this paper made an effort by broadly investigating existing ecological transformation measures of vertical seawalls, scrutinizing the present situation of vertical seawalls in China, and discussing the potential development prospect from an ecological engineering perspective. Three types of ecological transformation measures, physical, biological, and mixing measures, have been investigated. Moreover, it is identified that, in general, the ecological transformation of vertical seawalls should adhere to the basic concept of ecological priority and adopt natural restoration as the main method, supplemented by artificial restoration, to achieve the purpose of realizing the coordination and unity of the protection function and ecological construction of the seawall and the harmonious coexistence of human and nature.

1 INTRODUCTION

The seawall is an artificial structure used to protect coastline erosion and the stability of ships in the harbor. As part of a largely coastal defense system, seawalls play an important role in preventing storm surges and shoreline retreats. Before 2017, China's seawall protection construction mainly adopted traditional physical protection, with reinforced concrete or riprap method for hard protection. Traditional physical protection mainly considers the effect of disaster prevention and mitigation of embankment engineering but lacks consideration of ecological impact.

With more than 40% of the global population (about 2.4 billion) currently living within 100 kilometers of the coast, the increase in the size of global seawalls has led to a massive loss of natural habitats on a large spatial scale (Bradford *et al.* 2020). Most hard seawalls destroy the balance between marine and terrestrial ecosystems and negatively impact the water quality and living environment of the sea (Zhang *et al.* 2020). Compared to natural shorelines, empirical data show that there are reductions of 23% biodiversity and 45% abundance under seawall conditions (Gittman *et al.* 2016). This destroys the local ecology, which in turn leads to the loss of habitat for some local species and/or the advantage of invasive species, affecting the ecological stability of this area.

*Corresponding Author: yingjiang@dlut.edu.cn

Leading by the 'National Seawall Construction Plan' and the 'Technical Guide for Ecological Construction of Reclamation Projects (Trial)', it is proposed to combine the 'Seawall Construction' with the 'Green Development and Ecologicalization' concepts together and to enforce the ecological construction of seawalls in China from the perspective of ecological engineering concept (Xu et al. 2021). Ecological engineering is the design of sustainable ecosystems, with the objectives of restoring ecosystems severely disturbed by human activities and developing new sustainable ecosystems with social and ecological values. The materials and design methods used in the vertical seawall are relatively simple; therefore, it is particularly important to investigate the transformation and repairment of the traditional vertical seawalls that have been built. In line with this consideration, by focusing on the reconstruction measures of vertical seawalls on low-lying coasts based on ecological engineering, this paper summarizes the ecological reconstruction methods and application scope of the vertical seawalls. Meanwhile, potential issues and prospects of ecological reconstructions of vertical seawalls in China have been discussed to further support the green and ecological development of China.

The main content of this paper is organized as follows: Section 1 is a background introduction, and Sections 2 to 4 is the detailed inspection of three types of transportation measures, e.g., the physical, biological, and biological barrier mixed transformation measures of vertical seawalls. Section 5 discussed the present efforts, effects, potential applications, and development prospects of ecological seawall construction in China. Finally, the conclusion and suggestions are given in Section 6.

2 PHYSICAL TRANSFORMATION MEASURES

In most cases, hard structures are ecologically inferior substitutes for natural coasts, and the spatial range and complexity of artificial habitats are generally much smaller than those of natural habitats. Existing studies have shown that the reduction of environmental heterogeneity in artificial environments is one of the reasons for the low biodiversity in artificial structures. Most organisms cannot survive on vertical surfaces; therefore, the steep intertidal zones also negatively influence the quality of habitats (Firth et al. 2014).

2.1 Artificial habitat

Compared with the natural coastal zone, the species richness of the tide level in the artificial structure is significantly higher than that of the upper tide level, and the species richness supported by the rocky beach is higher than that of the lower exposed rock. The main reason for this phenomenon is the lack of diversity in intertidal habitats and reduced prey refuges. Biodiversity supported by artificial structures is lower than that in natural habitats. Artificial habitats can effectively improve the biodiversity of vertical seawalls. Part of the newly constructed seawall creates a tidal pool by omitting large sandstone blocks on the embankment surface (Chapman & Blockley 2009), replacing riprap structures with biological blocks (Firth et al. 2014), or adding prefabricated reinforced concrete pools around the seawall (Perkol-Finkel & Sella 2015). Other artificial habitats add concrete flowerpots to the surface of vertical seawalls (Browne & Chapman 2014; Hall et al. 2019). These tidal pools support species that can be found in natural rock pools and missing in seawalls or species in seawalls by increasing the complexity of habitats.

2.2 Marine environmental heterogeneity

Changes in artificial habitats can also be used to maintain protected or commercially valuable species. Increasing the complexity of the surface of vertical seawalls is a very effective method. On a small scale, the composition and surface roughness of building materials have a significant effect on the structure and function of the colonial assemblage. Cracks and pits provide important shelter for many species, but the surface of most coastal defensive buildings lacks this microhabitat. Panels with high surface complexity often have high biodiversity. Therefore, in order to improve the overall complexity of the vertical seawall, some experiments use a manual operation to increase the seawall surface cracks, holes, and grooves (Firth *et al.* 2014; Martins *et al.* 2016; Strain *et al.* 2018). The holes on the surface of the vertical seawall reduced the mortality of juvenile oysters (Strain *et al.* 2018), and increased the number of commercially valuable cap scallop patellas (Martins *et al.* 2016). The tiles on the surface of the seawall not only protect the seawall from erosion but also provide shelter for the native bivalves (Bradford *et al.* 2020). With the increase in the roughness of the seawall surface, the proportion of vertical seawalls covered by waves decreased by 100% (Salauddin *et al.* 2021). Most of the cracks, holes, and grooves are carried out on the new structure or protection measures on the surface of the seawall. The cracks, holes, and grooves can increase the structure's aesthetics and strengthen the seawall's structure.

Physical transformation measures can improve the species diversity and richness of organisms within a certain range, protect and proliferate the characteristics of certain commercial species, and require lower costs. However, limited by the relatively small scale of physical measures, the spatial scope of their beneficial effects is also limited.

3 BIOLOGICAL TRANSFORMATION MEASURES

Biological transformation measures aim to increase the diversity and abundance of important species in local sea areas by introducing native or exotic species that contribute to the stability of ecosystem structure. Biological transformation measures can also strengthen the competitiveness of local dominant species to inhibit harmful alien species. By planting native Saccostrea cuccullata oysters, Bradford *et al.* (2020) promoted the natural recruitment of a species and enhanced marine biodiversity in the intertidal zone of the seawall. Perkol-Finkel *et al.* (2012) attempted to transplant C. barbata juveniles from habitats lost to seawalls on the Adriatic coast, where C. barbata juveniles had higher survival rates than their original habitats. The construction of coastal defense structures affects coastal ecosystems, altering the combination of native species in the area, removing regional barriers, facilitating the dispersal of non-native species, and increasing habitat heterogeneity. Alien species may increase the complexity of local ecosystems and impose a negative impact on the environment. Therefore, a certain amount of biological and environmental basic research work is needed before conducting experiments. Biological transformation measures are good methods to optimize the community composition and structural stability of biologically damaged areas. However, due to the limitation of test time duration, changes caused by new species in the structure of the ecosystem could be well investigated. The long-term effects of the biological transformation measures remain to be verified.

Since the environment and species in different regions are different, it takes great numbers of time and energy to investigate the characteristics of beneficial species and the adaptability of the designated environment. Meanwhile, the tolerance of foreign organisms in most regions is relatively low, further increasing the cost and difficulty of implementing biological transformation measures.

4 BIOLOGICAL BARRIER MIXED TRANSFORMATION MEASURES

Marine vegetation canopy dissipates wave energy, which is an important solution for coastal protection ecological engineering (Duarte *et al.* 2013). Ecosystem-based biological barrier utilization is effective for long-term coastal protection (Veettil *et al.* 2021).

4.1 Coastal protection forest

The design and construction schemes of some built seawalls have not fully considered the environmental coordination, ecology, and other aspects. They have also not fully considered the coordination with the local ecosystem. The engineering construction has even caused adverse effects on the protection of wetlands, beaches, and mangroves. For example, nearly 76% of the disappearance of native mangroves in Guangxi is related to the construction of seawalls (Fan & Li 1997). The coastal protection forest system is an important ecological protection barrier in coastal areas of China, the effect of which has been fully reflected. By 2020, China has completed the construction of 8,515,200 hectares of coastal protection forest. The total annual comprehensive benefit value of the coastal protection forest project is estimated to be nearly 1.26 trillion RMB, of which the ecological benefit value is 8,185 billion RMB, the economic benefit value is 449.2 billion RMB, and the social benefit value is 2 billion RMB (World Famous Ecological Engineering 2022). Selecting suitable vegetation according to geographical location and climatic conditions is an important factor in ensuring the benefits of the seawall and coastal protection forest system.

Mangroves grow in the upper intertidal zone of tropical and subtropical low-energy coasts and play an important role in wind and wave protection and biodiversity conservation. The use of mangroves as potential coastal biological barriers has been studied and tested in-depth (Ghazali et al. 2016). South China area adopts the mangroves as part of the coastal shelter forest system. Meanwhile, mangroves are planted on the seaside of seawalls to protect beaches in parts of southern China (Zhang et al. 2015). Moreover, the coastal defense system composed of mangroves and vertical seawalls can effectively prevent the occurrence of wave overtopping and reduce economic losses (Iryanto et al. 2020). The comparative analysis highlights that about 70% of successful mixed infrastructure cases are based on an understanding of the ecological and hydrological changes caused by infrastructure, and mixed infrastructure is more cost-effective than separate hard structures (Waryszak et al. 2021).

4.2 Reef

Creating conditions to enable the wetland ecosystem around the seawall to survive and absorb wave energy simultaneously are the two fundamental requirements for the green ecological seawall. Coral reefs are often distributed on tropical coasts, with low suspended sediment concentration and strong wave action required (Gao et al. 2022). Studies have shown that coral reefs can reduce 97% of wave energy, and reef ridges alone dissipate 86% of wave energy, which can effectively resist typhoon disasters (Ferrario et al. 2014). A large-scale coral reef experiment in the Gulf of Mexico has promoted the expansion of wetlands. The results show that mixed restoration techniques have a good effect on mitigating erosion, expanding adjacent wetlands, and creating habitats (Sharma et al. 2016). Oyster reefs are widely distributed in tidal flats and are suitable for growth in temperate regions. Oyster reef breakwater system can greatly reduce the negative ecological effects of wave energy and seawall.

The mixed transformation measures have strengthened the function of the vertical seawall and greatly improved the stability and complexity of the ecosystem. However, these types of measures need to be completed in large quantities, including a larger scope of implementation, a longer time span, relatively higher costs, etc.

5 PRESENT SITUATION AND DEVELOPMENT PROSPECT OF ECOLOGICAL SEAWALL CONSTRUCTION IN CHINA

5.1 Present situation of ecological seawall construction in China

Since 2006, the water conservancy industry has completed the compilation of 'Seawall Engineering Design Specification' and improved the construction standards of traditional seawalls in China. However, there are still some problems that exist in the construction of seawalls, such as the lack of landscape, the destruction of the natural form of the coast, the destruction of the wetland system, the lack of coastal shelter forest system construction, and the lack of green space system planning (Liu *et al.* 2006). Historically, the construction of ecological seawalls in China began with the adoption of biological measures to protect beaches. Since 1978, Spartina alterniflora has been planted in the intertidal zone in front of seawalls in Guanyun County, Jiangsu Province, which promoted the siltation of beaches in front of seawalls and ensured the stability of seawalls (Zhao *et al.* 2019). Spartina alterniflora has a good wave-dissipation effect, but it is a typical invasive species that can occupy the living space of the local marsh vegetation and cause serious ecological problems. Li *et al.* (2019) studied the landscape structure relationship between seawall and mangrove in Beihai Coastal National Wetland Park and proposed a 'seawall-mangrove beach' model for rational planning of mangrove in front of the seawall. In summary, the existing research mainly focuses on combining the seawall and swamp or the coastal shelter forest ecosystem. Although this type of system can effectively restore the vegetation ecological buffer zone of the coastal zone, research on the modification of smooth seawall surfaces to increase complexity is insufficient.

At present, there are three successful cases of ecological seawall construction in China. The representative ecological cases are as follows: (1) By combining seawall and mangrove ecosystems, Hongshahuan of Fangchenggang West Bay in Guangxi improves landscape effect and protection ability effectively (Fan *et al.* 2017). (2) Shanghai Wusong Paotaiwan Wetland Park makes full use of the beach resources in front of the dike to create a large area of wetland landscape to reduce the waves in front of the seawall and provides basic conditions for the ecological construction of the seawall (Tian *et al.* 2020). (3) In Chongming Island ecological seawall in Shanghai, by planting beach vegetation, the effect of wave dissipation and siltation is realized, and the habitat for marine organisms is provided (Xu *et al.* 2019). Based on the aforementioned targeted engineering planning and design, the interaction of different ecological units, such as mangroves and reefs, has been fully utilized to resist marine disasters like storm surges caused by sea level rise and extreme climate. Meanwhile, ecological benefits of pollution control and habitat improvement have also been achieved.

5.2 *Main challenges and constraints*

Most of the ecological technology has been recognized with pertinent and sound effects, but there are still some problems that existed such as poor portability and incomplete consideration of restrictive factors. In the selection of ecological engineering interventions, the most critical issue is to consider the effects of various physical factors (e.g., wave action, sediment load), chemical factors (e.g., salinity, pollution load), and biological factors (e.g., larval supply, close to the introduction point of invasive species) on the transformation effect. Existing studies have shown that the growth of salt marsh vegetation and mangroves will be severely limited under frequent tidal inundation. Therefore, it is recommended that relatively high ground and infrequent inundation sites should be selected for wetland restoration. A reasonable consultation with local ecologists, oceanographers, and other experts to discuss and cooperate is critical to maximizing the effect of ecological engineering devices (O'Shaughnessy *et al.* 2020).

5.3 *Application potential and development prospect in China*

The ecological transformation of seawalls and the construction of new seawalls need to add the concept of ecological civilization construction into consideration, which will become the future development trend of seawall construction in China. The traditional vertical seawall will be gradually replaced by the ecological seawall, which is conducive to protecting the ecological environment. The ecological construction of the seawall should consider the terrestrial and marine ecosystems from a holistic perspective, which means building a complex ecosystem structure, and providing good living environments for organisms. To achieve the acceleration of the ecological seawall development, the following three points should be considered first:

1. Interdisciplinary development and cooperation with relevant departments should be strengthened. The construction of an ecological seawall needs to integrate the knowledge of ecology, oceanography, geography, and sociology (Xu et al. 2019). However, until now, it is still common to find seawall engineers and technicians without sufficient background knowledge of ecology and ecological researchers without sufficient experience in developing and applying seawall protection engineering technology. Therefore, it is very important to strengthen further the development of interdisciplinary subjects and the cooperation of relevant departments to promote seawall ecological engineering.
2. Constructing the coastal defensive system based on ecological engineering. To effectively improve the protection and adaptability of the coastal zone to sea level rise, ecological engineering should be regarded as the basic concept of the coastal defensive system. It is critical to adjust measures to local conditions and transform from simple defensive engineering to a comprehensive system of ecological engineering. Experiments have shown that adding ecological engineering interventions to existing seawalls can reduce wave height and energy, wave overflow, and flood risk behind seawalls (Salauddin et al. 2021).
3. Developing and improving the seawall ecological construction and evaluation criteria. For some projects with poor ecological construction of seawalls, the basic performance requirement of the seawall has not been achieved, and the ecological, social, and economic benefits are far below the target value. Therefore, it is necessary to carry out the technical standards of ecological seawall construction as soon as possible, and standardize the technical system of ecological seawall construction, to scientifically guide the full implementation of seawall ecological engineering (Zhang et al. 2020).

6 CONCLUSION AND SUGGESTIONS

In general, foreign experiments on physical transformation measures for the ecological transformation of vertical seawalls are relatively abundant, while domestic experiments mainly adopt biological barrier measures for the ecological transformation of vertical seawalls. For the ecological transformation of domestic vertical seawalls, the mixed transformation measures are time-consuming and of high costs, but they have ecological and economic benefits are good. The ecological benefits of physical transformation measures are limited, but the time is short, the cost is low, and the scope of application is wide. Biological measures have a high cost, difficult implementation, and limited scope of application, but they are highly targeted and have clear objectives. Considering the ecological effect and economic cost-effectiveness, this paper recommends using biological barriers, supplemented by physical transformation measures, for the specific marine environment and biological species.

The ecological transformation of vertical seawalls should adhere to the basic concept of ecological priority and adopt the method of natural and artificial restoration. The cost and benefit of ecological restoration of vertical seawalls are comprehensively analyzed from the perspectives of economy, society, and culture. The ecological transformation of the seawall needs to consider the natural conditions, such as the current situation of local natural resources, hydrological dynamics, topography, and marine disasters, and give priority to the tidal wave protection function of the seawall. Appropriate intervention measures should be taken to form a coastal defense system of ecological engineering with practical significance so as to realize the coordination and unity of protection function and ecological construction of a seawall and the harmonious coexistence between humans and nature.

ACKNOWLEDGMENT

This research is supported by grants from the National Key R&D Program of China (2021YFB2600200), Fundamental Research Funds for the Central Universities (DUT20GJ202 and DUT20RC (3)010), and the State Key Laboratory of Coastal and Offshore Engineering (LY2101) at Dalian University of Technology through partial funding and the use of equipment.

REFERENCES

Bradford T.E., Astudillo J.C., Lau E.T.C. et al. Provision of Refugia and Seeding With Native Bivalves Can Enhance Biodiversity on Vertical Seawalls. *Marine Pollution Bulletin*. 2020, 160(111578).

Browne M.A. and Chapman M.G. Mitigating Against the Loss of Species by Adding Artificial Intertidal Pools to Existing Seawalls. *Marine Ecology Progress Series*. 2014, 497: 119–129.

Chapman M.G., Blockley D.J. Engineering Novel Habitats on Urban Infrastructure to Increase Intertidal Biodiversity. *Oecologia*. 2009, 161(3): 625–635.

Duarte C.M. Losada I.J., Hendriks I.E. et al. The Role of Coastal Plant Communities for Climate Change Mitigation and Adaptation. *Nature Climate Change*. 2013, 3(11): 961–968.

Fan H., HE B., Wang X., et al. The Conception and Practices of Ecological Sea Dyke. *Guangxi Sciences*. 2017, 24(05): 427–434.

Fan H. & Li G. Effect of Sea Dike on the Quantity, Community Characteristics and Restoration of Mangrove Forest Along Guangxi Coast. *Chinese Journal of Applied Ecology*. 1997(03): 240–244.

Ferrario F., Beck M.W., Storlazzi C.D., et al. The Effectiveness of Coral Reefs for Coastal Hazard Risk Reduction and Adaptation. *Nature Communications*. 2014, 5(3794).

Firth L.B., Thompson R.C., Bohn K., et al. Between a Rock and a Hard Place: Environmental and Engineering Considerations when Designing Coastal Defence Structures. *Coastal Engineering*. 2014, 87 (SI): 122–135.

Gao S., Jia J. and Yu Q. Green Sea Dykes: An Overview of Their Principles of Sediment, Geomorphology and Ecosystem Dynamics. *Journal of Tropical Oceanography*. 2022, (04):1–19.

Ghazali N., Zainuddin K., Zainal M.Z., et al. The Potential of Mangrove Forest as a Bioshield in Malaysia. *2016 IEEE 12th International Colloquium on Signal Processing & Its Applications (CSPA)*. 2016: 322–327.

Gittman R.K., Scyphers S.B., Smith C.S., et al. Ecological Consequences of Shoreline Hardening: A Meta-Analysis. *Bioscience*. 2016, 66(9): 763–773.

Hall A.E., Herbert R.J.H., Britton J.R., et al. Shelving the Coast with Vertipools: Retrofitting Artificial Rock Pools on Coastal Structures as Mitigation for Coastal Squeeze. *Frontiers in Marine Science*. 2019, 6(456).

Iryanto, Bunga M.S., Mustamiin M., et al. Numerical Modelling of Mangrove Merged with Seawall for Investigating Wave Mitigation Over Flat Topography. *Journal of Physics: Conference Series*. 2020, 1581: 12001–12006.

Li L., Liu W., Cai S., et al. Models of Ecological Seawall Construction in Beihai Coastal National Wetland Park in Guangxi. *Wetland Science*. 2019, 17(03): 277–285.

Liu Q., Chen W., Hu M., et al. Seawall Construction and Landscape Ecological Problems in China. *Yangtze River*. 2006(11): 93–94.

Martins G.M., Jenkins S.R., Neto A.I., et al. Long-term Modifications of Coastal Defences Enhance Marine Biodiversity. *Environmental Conservation*. 2016, 43(2): 109–116.

O'Shaughnessy K.A., Hawkins S.J., Evans A.J., et al. Design Catalogue for Eco-engineering of Coastal Artificial Structures: A Multifunctional Approach for Stakeholders and End-users. *Urban Ecosystems*. 2020, 23(2): 431–443.

Perkol-Finkel S., Ferrario F., Nicotera V., et al. Conservation Challenges in Urban Seascapes: Promoting the Growth of Threatened Species on Coastal Infrastructures. *Journal of Applied Ecology*. 2012, 49(6): 1457–1466.

Perkol-Finkel S., Sella I. Harnessing Urban Coastal Infrastructure for Ecological Enhancement. *Proceedings of the Institution of Civil Engineers-Maritime Engineering*. 2015, 168(3): 102–110.

Salauddin M., O'Sullivan J.J., Abolfathi S., et al. Eco-Engineering of Seawalls-An Opportunity for Enhanced Climate Resilience from Increased Topographic *Complexity. Frontiers in Marine Science*. 2021, 8(674630).

Salauddin M., O'Sullivan J.J., Abolfathi S., et al. Eco-Engineering of Seawalls—An Opportunity for Enhanced Climate Resilience From Increased Topographic Complexity. *Frontiers in Marine Science*, 2021, 8.

Sharma S., Goff J., Cebrian J., et al. A Hybrid Shoreline Stabilization Technique: Impact of Modified Intertidal Reefs on Marsh Expansion and Nekton Habitat in the Northern Gulf of Mexico. *Ecological Engineering*. 2016, 90: 352–360.

Strain E.M.A., Morris R.L., Coleman R.A., et al. Increasing Microhabitat Complexity on Seawalls Can Reduce Fish Predation on Native Oysters. *Ecological Engineering*. 2018, 120: 637–644.

Tian P., Sui W., Sun P., et al. Application of Ecological Dike in Coastal Protection of Hangzhou Bay. *China Harbour Engineering*. 2020, 40(10): 40–44.

Veettil B.K., Ward R.D., Nguyen T.K.D, et al. The Use of Bioshields for Coastal Protection in Vietnam: Current Status and Potential. *Regional Studies in Marine Science*. 2021, 47(101945).

Waryszak P., Gavoille A., Whitt A.A., et al. Combining Gray and Green Infrastructure to Improve Coastal Resilience: Lessons Learnt from Hybrid Flood Defenses. *Coastal Engineering Journal*. 2021, 63(3SI): 335–350.

World Famous Ecological Engineering [EB].http://lyj.zj.gov.cn/art/2022/4/19/art_1277845_59029758.html, 2022(04)/2022(08).

Xu W., Chen C., Liu J. et al. Study and Application of the Assessment on Ecological Seawall Construction Suitability. *Journal of Applied Oceanography*. 2021, 40(04): 659–668.

Xu W., Tao A., Liu J., et al. The Enlightenment of International Coastal Zone Ecological Protection for China's Ecological Sea Dike Construction. *Ocean Development and Management*. 2019, 36(10): 12–15.

Zhang C., Jia H., Wu L. et al. Research Progress of Ecological Construction Technology of Ssawall and Suggestions on Promoting the Ecological Construction of Seawall in China. *Ocean Development and Management*. 2020, 37(09): 57–61.

Zhang C., Jia H., Wu L., et al. Research Progress of Ecological Construction Technology of Seawall and Suggestion of Seawall in China. *Ocean Development and Management*. 2020, 37(09): 57–61.

Zhang H., Han G., Wang D., et al. Ecological Engineering Based Adaptive Coastal Defense Strategy to Global Change. *Advances in Earth Science*. 2015, 30(09): 996–1005.

Zhao P., Zhu Z., Jiang H., et al. The Development and Outlooks of the Ecological Seawall. *Marine Science Bulletin*. 2019, 38(05): 481–490.

Application of time series augmented reality model to underwater topographic change of riprap

Ya Wen*

Wanjiang Institute of Technology, Ma'anshan Anhui, China

ABSTRACT: Aiming at the prominent problems of underwater terrain change monitoring of ripraps, such as limited monitoring period, low accuracy of underwater terrain elevation data acquisition, low acquisition efficiency, and insufficient coverage of scanning range, a prediction method of underwater terrain change of riprap based on autoregressive AR model is proposed. The method constructs the experimental data set and determines the order according to the FPE criterion, calculates the estimated parameters of the autoregressive AR model by the least square estimation method, and obtains the models of each order on this basis, thus completing the construction of the autoregressive AR model. In the case application analysis experiment, the experimental data set is obtained after gross error elimination and error correction of the previous eight periods of measurement data in a riprap area. The model order is determined according to the FPE order determination criteria. The AR model parameters are solved based on the experimental data set to establish the time series AR model. Based on the same data set, the bathymetric survey is conducted for three groups of data of random fixed points, random sections, and random areas. The fitting and prediction analysis are conducted for the water depth data of the next five periods.

1 INTRODUCTION

The underwater terrain elevation data is the database for a series of underwater projects, such as the determination of riprap construction location, underwater riprap thickness detection, and riprap completion survey (Cheng et al. 2022; Patrick et al. 2016). The traditional single-beam bathymetry system has low accuracy of line scan data, low acquisition efficiency, and it is difficult to achieve full coverage scanning. Therefore, the system has great applications in the field of seabed topography measurement and marine resource development.

Time series analysis is a dynamic analysis method based on time series data. Through the correlation between existing time series data, a mathematical model is established, and the model is used to predict the data at the next moment (Qin et al. 2021; Winters et al. 2020). The data obtained by the underwater observation using the multi-beam bathymetric technology in the riprap revetment project are observed in different time periods, and the information and laws contained in these bathymetric data are also different. In order to explore the laws between these water depth data, this paper uses the autoregressive AR model in the time series analysis method to predict and analyze the observation data of the rock riprap revetment project. Project quality assessment standards provide an objective basis (Zhang et al. 2021).

---

*Corresponding Author: wenya@hhuwtian.edu.cn

2 AUTOREGRESSIVE AR MODELS

2.1 *The principle of the least squares method to construct the model*

Currently, the widely used AR models are:

$$x_t = \varphi_1 x_{t-1} + \varphi_2 x_{t-2} + \varphi_3 x_{t-3} + \ldots\ldots + \varphi_p x_{t-p} + \varepsilon_t \tag{1}$$

Among them, x_i is the observation sequence, φ_i is the autoregressive coefficient, p is the order of the model, and ε_t is the random error of the model.

Error equation can be obtained for the time series: $x_1\ x_2\ x_3\ldots..x_n$

$$v_{p+1} = \hat{b}_1 x_p + \hat{b}_2 x_{p-1} + \hat{b}_3 x_{p-2} + \ldots\ldots + \hat{b}_p x_1 - x_{p+1}$$

$$v_{p+2} = \hat{b}_1 x_{p+1} + \hat{b}_2 x_p + \hat{b}_3 x_{p-1} + \ldots\ldots + \hat{b}_p x_2 - x_{p+2}$$

$$\ldots\ldots$$

$$v_n = \hat{b}_1 x_{n-1} + \hat{b}_2 x_{n-2} + \hat{b}_3 x_{n-3} + \ldots\ldots + \hat{b}_p x_{n-p} - x_n$$

which is:

$$V = A\hat{b} - L \tag{2}$$

Among them, the estimated parameters can be obtained by the least squares method:

$$V = \begin{pmatrix} v_{p+1} \\ v_{p+2} \\ \ldots \\ v_n \end{pmatrix},\ \hat{b} = \begin{pmatrix} \hat{b}_1 \\ \hat{b}_2 \\ \vdots \\ \hat{b}_p \end{pmatrix},\ L = \begin{pmatrix} x_{p+1} \\ x_{p+2} \\ \ldots \\ x_n \end{pmatrix},\ A = \begin{pmatrix} x_p & x_{p-1} & \ldots & x_1 \\ x_{p+1} & x_p & \ldots & x_2 \\ \ldots & \ldots & \ldots & \ldots \\ x_{n-1} & x_{n-2} & \ldots & x_{n-p} \end{pmatrix}.$$

$$\hat{b} = (A^T A)^{-1} A^T L \tag{3}$$

Accuracy evaluation:

$$\hat{\sigma}^2 = \sum \frac{\hat{\varepsilon}_t^2}{(n - 2p)} \tag{4}$$

2.2 *Order criteria for AR models*

Since the order of the model cannot be determined in advance, the order of the model should be determined in advance in the modeling process. Then the estimated parameters of the autoregressive AR model are calculated according to the least squares estimation method of Equation (3) to obtain models of each order.

In general, the more parameters in the model, the better the fit. However, as the parameters continue to increase, the required information also increases. Under the condition of certain information, the more parameters, the larger the estimation error of the parameters, and the less reliable the obtained model is. Therefore, when selecting the model, the parameters should be as few as possible. But the fewer parameters, the larger the fit residuals. Therefore, when determining the model order, it is necessary to take into account the relevant requirements of parameters and residuals. In autoregressive AR models, common order-setting criteria include the minimum final forecast error criterion (FPE), the linear assumption method, and the minimum information criterion (AIC). This paper is mainly based on the FPE criterion to determine the order.

When an autoregressive AR model is used to fit a certain observation process, there is always a model of a certain order, and the order at this time n_0 is the best. When the order of the model is lower than this optimal order ($n < n_0$, the fitting of parameters is missing), fitting a high-order curve with a low-order curve will result in an under-smooth phenomenon; when the model order is higher than this optimal order ($n > n_0$, hyperparameter fitting is used), if a high-order curve is used to fit a low-order curve, over-smoothing will occur. Whether it is the lack of parameters or the fitting of too many parameters, the variance of the prediction error of the AR model will increase. In order to determine a reasonable order of the AR model and balance the error caused by the fitting of hyperparameters or lack of parameters, the best method is to obtain the optimal order of the autoregressive AR model with a minimum variance of the one-step forecast error. This is the basic idea of the FPE order criterion. Therefore, the FPE criterion can also be called the minimum final prediction criterion, and the optimal order is the order in which the final prediction error is the smallest (Moretto et al. 2014).

Let the model suitable for random sequence $\{x_t, 1 \leq t \leq n\}$ be:

$$x_t = \varphi_1 x_{t-1} + \varphi_2 x_{t-2} + \varphi_3 x_{t-3} + \ldots + \varphi_p x_{t-p} + \varepsilon_t \tag{5}$$

Among them, $E(\varepsilon_t) = 0$, $E(\varepsilon_t \varepsilon_t) = \sigma \varepsilon^2$. Let the estimated value of φ_j be $\widehat{b}_j (1 \leq j \leq p)$ Use $\widehat{x}_t(1)$ to represent the one-step prediction value of time t representing the moment that is t, the forecast value for the moment, so we get:

$$\widehat{x}_t(1) = \widehat{b}_1 x_t + \ldots + \widehat{b}_p x_{t-p} \tag{6}$$

Then the variance of the one-step forecast error is:

$$E[x_{t-1} - \widehat{x}_t(1)]^2 \approx \left(1 + \frac{p}{n}\right) \sigma \varepsilon^2 \tag{7}$$

Where the expression in Equations (4)–(6) is the $\sigma \varepsilon^2$ residual variance of the fitted model of the parameter $\widehat{b}_j (1 \leq j \leq p)$.

When the total sample size n is large enough, there are:

$$E[\widehat{\sigma}\varepsilon^2] \approx \left(1 - \frac{p}{n}\right) \sigma \varepsilon^2 \tag{8}$$

The above formula indicates that $\widehat{\sigma}\varepsilon^2/(1 - \frac{p}{n})$ is an unbiased estimate of $\sigma \varepsilon^2$. In Equations (4)–(6), use unbiased estimation to replace $\sigma \varepsilon^2$, and we can get:

$$E[x_{t-1} - \widehat{x}_t(1)] \approx \left(1 + \frac{p}{n}\right)\left(1 - \frac{p}{n}\right) \sigma \varepsilon^2 \tag{9}$$

In summary, the calculation formula of FPE is:

$$\text{FPE}(p) = \frac{(n+p)}{(n-p)} \widehat{\sigma}_\varepsilon^2 \tag{10}$$

It can be seen that the coefficient $\frac{(n+p)}{(n-p)}$ increases with the increase of p, and the residual of the AR model $\widehat{\sigma}_\varepsilon^2$ begins to decrease with the increase of p, but when p exceeds the real model order p_0 of the sequence x_t, the residual does not decrease. At this time, $\frac{(n+p)}{(n-p)}$ plays a leading role. When the order increases from low order to high order, the residual begins to decrease with the increase of the order. When p exceeds p_0, it can be proved that the residual value no longer decreases in a sense. Therefore, the order p that makes FPE(p) reach the minimum value is the best order of the model.

3 CASE APPLICATION ANALYSIS

3.1 Water depth fitting and prediction analysis of random points

Through 8 months of field data collection work, gross errors were eliminated, and errors were corrected for the 8-phase multi-beam data. Three fixed points (named here DMD-1, DMD-2, DMD-3) are randomly sampled in the point cloud data, and the riprap before construction (Phase 1) and after the construction starts (Phase 2 ~ Phase 8) are randomly sampled. Data were analyzed using time series methods. The specific data of three random points are shown in Table 1.

Table 1 Random three-point water depth data table in the underwater riprap area of Laohaiba. (Unit: m)

Time Point number	Phase 1 2014-1	Phase 2 2014-2	Phase 3 2014-3	Phase 4 2014-4	Phase 5 2014-5	Phase 6 2014-6	Phase 7 2014-7	Phase 8 2014-8
DMD1	−36.904	−34.225	−34.624	−34.852	−34.965	−35.011	−35.104	−35.114
DMD2	−35.596	−32.977	−33.257	−33.496	−33.564	−33.657	−33.704	−33.714
DMD3	−33.615	−30.819	−31.117	−31.379	−31.599	−31.652	−31.679	−31.708

For the data of DMD-1, DMD-2 and DMD-3 in the first eight periods, the time series AR model is used to analyze and establish a mathematical model. The order of the model is determined to be 5 according to the FPE order determination criteria. Using the data of the first eight periods, the least quadratic method is used to solve the model parameters, and the data of the ninth to thirteenth periods are predicted. The predicted data for the ninth to thirteenth periods are shown in Table 2.

Table 2. Random three-point water depth data table in the underwater riprap area of Laohaiba. (Unit: m)

Time Point number	Predict 1	Predict 2	Predict 3	Predict 4	Predict 5
DMD1	−35.136	−35.144	−35.129	−35.123	−35.1003
DMD2	−33.756	−33.772	−33.784	−33.812	−33.825
DMD3	−31.705	−31.703	−31.693	−31.685	−31.674

Through the fitting and prediction of the water depth data, the thickening value of each measuring point in the project acceptance is now compared with the design thickening value, that is, the calculation of the thickening rate. This is shown in Table 3.

Table 3. Calculation table of random three-point thickening rate in underwater riprap area. (Unit: m)

Time Point number	Phase 1 2014-1	Phase 2 2014-2	Phase 3 2014-3	Phase 4 2014-4	Phase 5 2014-5	Phase 6 2014-6	Phase 7 2014-7	Phase 8 2014-8
DMD1	134%	114%	104%	97%	92%	90%	89.5%	89%
DMD2	131%	117%	105%	102%	97%	95%	94%	92%
DMD3	139%	125%	112%	101%	98%	96%	95%	95%

According to the calculation of the above water depth data, thickening value, and thickening rate, the specific analysis conclusions are as follows:

1. With the passage of time and the progress of the project, the water depth data in this area suddenly rose from the first phase (before throwing) to the second phase (the first phase after throwing) due to human interference and the accumulation of riprap, resulting in a sharp change in water depth. Judging from the thickening values (2.679, 2.619, 2.776), the riprap raised the riverbed, causing it to change sharply.
2. From the second period to the fifth period, the three water depths decreased. Similarly, from the thickening value, the three thickening values also decreased to the same degree (−0.74, −0.587, −0.76). In the four months after the completion of the riprap construction, as some small stones are washed by the water flow, the larger and more stable stones will sink and silt due to their own gravity and the softness of the bottom of the riverbed.
3. Looking at the measured water depth data from the fifth period to the eighth period, and the corresponding changes in the thickening value (−0.149, −0.151, −0.109) and the thickening rate (92%–89%, 97%–92%, 98%–95%), it can be seen that the water depth begins to balance, and the thickening value only decreases slightly.
4. The data of the last five periods predicted by the time series and the calculated thickening value are almost completely consistent with the aforementioned data of the fifth to eighth periods, indicating that the water depth data and thickening will not change greatly since then.

Therefore, under this hydrological condition, for the inspection and acceptance of riprap construction in this area, it is more appropriate to perform a multi-beam scan before construction and to perform an acceptance scan within the fourth month after the construction is completed. If it is too early, it may lead to a deviation in the thickening value. If it is too late, it will affect the construction acceptance of the construction party. If the monitoring is too frequent, it will inevitably increase the cost and cause economic losses.

For the above randomly selected points, all the water depth data in the small area are analyzed accordingly, and the multi-beam scanning data and the pre-construction data are thickened for the completion acceptance (the fifth monitoring after the end of rock dumping). The thickening value of most points in the fifth monitoring is between 1.6 m and 2.4 m. Compared with the design thickening value of 2 m, according to the "Jiangsu Province Yangtze River Underwater Smooth Ripple Revetment Project Quality Acceptance" Measures (for Trial Implementation) "(hereinafter referred to as "Measures"), Article 6 expresses the specific value in "the average thickening value of the section or the thickening value of each measuring point should be located at 65%~135% of the design thickening value." That is, the thickening value is 1.3 m~2.7 m, which has well completed the design indicators, and also shows that the selection of the acceptance time is also more appropriate.

3.2 *Water depth fitting and prediction analysis in a random area*

We, therefore, analyze the riprap area surface of a small area within the riprap area. Here, according to the water depth point cloud data in the area, the volume required for filling the area to the horizontal plane of 0 m in each phase is calculated. The plane area of the area (the plane area selected here is 3680.8 m^2) is used to calculate the thickening value of the area. Similarly, fill volume and thickening value are also fitted and predicted by using the time series AR model. Tables 4 and 5 show the filling data of Phase 8 and the filling forecast data of Phase 5, respectively.

Table 4. Data table of random filling of a certain area of underwater riprap. (Unit: m³)

Time	Filling volume
Phase 1	92170.6
Phase 1	82537.9
Phase 3	83874.1
Phase 4	85166.0
Phase 5	85313.3
Phase 6	85515.7
Phase 7	85559.9
Phase 8	85615.1

Table 5. Predicted fill data table for a random area of underwater riprap. (Unit: m³)

Time	Predict the ninth period	Predict the tenth period	Predict the eleventh period	Predict the twelfth period	Predict the thirteenth period
Filling volume	85756.07	85830.02	85928.36	86035.40	86123.07

4 CONCLUSION

Due to the interference of the accumulation of artificial riprap, the water depth data in the riprap area will rise sharply from before the riprap to one month after the riprap, and the water depth changes sharply, raising the riverbed. Because some of the small stones are washed by the water flow, the larger and more stable stones will sink and squeeze due to their own gravity and the softness of the bottom of the riverbed, so from the first month after throwing to the fourth month after throwing, the water depth decreased. At the same time, there was a corresponding reduction, reaching 119%, 107%, and 100% of the design value in the next three months. The water depth predicted by the time series and the corresponding thickening value tends to balance, which are 96%, 94%, 93%, and 93%, indicating that the riverbed after the riprap also begins to stabilize. Under the cost constraint, the time series AR model can better fit the real underwater terrain change data of riprap, and the appropriate time for monitoring underwater terrain change that can balance the economic cost and monitoring accuracy is to conduct monitoring before the construction and another monitoring within the fourth month after the construction. Compared with the traditional riprap underwater terrain change monitoring method, this method can better complete the riprap underwater terrain change monitoring task, obtain the most appropriate monitoring time, reduce economic costs, improve the efficiency of riprap construction inspection and acceptance, and effectively solve the project management and control problems of riprap construction inspection and acceptance.

ACKNOWLEDGMENTS

This work was supported by the Study on the three-dimensional variation law of underwater riprap revetment projects based on the time series AR model (KJ2021A1212).

REFERENCES

Cheng H., Ma P., Dong G., Zhang S., Wei J. and Qin Q. (2022). Characteristics of Carboniferous Volcanic Reservoirs in Beisantai Oilfield, Junggar Basin. *Mathematical Problems in Engineering*, 2022.

Moretto J., Rigon E., Mao L., Delai F., Picco L., and Lenzi M.A. (2014). Short-term Geomorphic Analysis in a Disturbed Fluvial Environment by Fusion of LiDAR, Colour Bathymetry and dGPS Surveys. *Catena*, 122, 180–195.

Patrick C.J., Weller D.E., and Ryder M. (2016). The Relationship Between Shoreline Armoring and Adjacent Submerged Aquatic Vegetation in Chesapeake Bay and Nearby Atlantic Coastal Bays. *Estuaries and Coasts*, 39(1), 158–170.

Qin Q., Cheng H., Wang M., Sun M., and Zhao L. (2021). "Analyzing the Wettability of Tight Sandstone of Taiyuan Formation in Shenfu Block, Eastern Margin of Ordos Basin," *IOP Conference Series: Earth and Environmental Science*, vol. 671, no. 1, Article ID 012022.

Winters M.A., Leslie B., Sloane E.B., and Gallien T.W. (2020). Observations and Preliminary Vulnerability Assessment of a Hybrid Dune-based Living Shoreline. *Journal of Marine Science and Engineering*, 8(11), 920.

Zhang W., Cheng Z., Cheng H., Qin Q., and Wang M. (2021, July). Research of Tight Gas Reservoir Simulation Technology. In *IOP Conference Series: Earth and Environmental Science* (Vol. 804, No. 2, p. 022046). IOP Publishing.

Preliminary analysis of Rectisol and Selexol (NHD) in pre-combustion carbon capture technology

Guochen Zhao*

Datang Northeast Electric Power Test & Research Institute, China Datang Corporation Science and Technology Research Institute, Changchun, P.R. China

ABSTRACT: In recent years, global warming has seriously threatened the development of human society, the living environment, and the economy. The issue of CO_2 emission reduction is urgent. China is one of the countries with the largest CO_2 emissions in the world. At present, the Chinese energy consumption structure is dominated by coal, supplemented by fossil fuels such as oil and natural gas. In order to effectively reduce the emission of CO_2 gas in the flue gas and slow down the intensification of the greenhouse effect, it is necessary to develop the capture and storage technology of flue gas CO_2 and realize the mature technological treatment as soon as possible. This work highlights pre-combustion carbon capture technologies, including low-temperature methanol washing (Rectisol) and polyethylene glycol dimethyl ether method (Selexol) or NHD. We outline the technical principle, process flow, and technical characteristics of the two technologies and put forward the prospect of the two technologies combined with the research status at home and abroad.

1 INTRODUCTION

Recently, with the continuous growth of the demand for non-renewable energy by related enterprises, all sectors of society have begun to pay attention to the consumption of coal-fired resources. The introduction of decarbonization technologies, such as low-temperature methanol washing technology in the coal chemical industry, is a feasible means to recycle and reuse limited resources. It can control the loss of the coal chemical industry in production. With the continuous expansion of the application scope of this technology, the pressure of shortage of natural gas and oil resources will be significantly eased. Therefore, enough attention should be paid to the application of low-temperature methanol washing technology in the coal chemical industry, and efforts should be made to promote and popularize it as soon as possible so as to realize environmental protection and low consumption production.

In terms of CO_2 capture, four decarbonization process routes, namely pre-combustion, post-combustion, oxyfuel combustion, and chemical chain combustion, have been developed mainly for fossil fuel thermal power plants. Considering that the outlet pressure of the water gas produced by the integrated coal gasification combined cycle (IGCC) power generation system is relatively high, generally, around 2.5-5 MPa, the CO_2 separation using the physical solvent absorption method with high technical maturity will be an ideal choice at this stage. The core of the CO_2 separation process in the IGCC power generation system and the CO_2 separation process used in industrial processes such as synthetic ammonia and natural gas purification is the same. However, the focus of solvent selection is different, and solvent selectivity needs to be comprehensively considered. The more classic physical absorption

---

*Corresponding Author: 1257593514@qq.com

process mainly includes low-temperature methanol washing (Rectisol), propylene carbonate method (Flour), polyethylene glycol dimethyl ether method (Selexol), N-Methylpyrrolidone process (Purisol), as well as the successful NHD decarbonization process developed by the Nanhua Company Research Institute in the early 1980s (Liu 2011; Zhang et al. 2010).

This work introduces two typical pre-combustion carbon capture technologies based on physical absorption methods. One is the low-temperature methanol washing (Rectisol), and the second is the polyethylene glycol dimethyl ether method (Selexol) or NHD. The technical principle, process flow, and technical characteristics of the two decarbonization technologies are mainly described. Combined with the research progress of related technologies at home and abroad, the future application prospects of the two decarbonization technologies are proposed.

2 RECTISOL CARBON REMOVAL TECHNOLOGY

2.1 *Technical introduction*

2.1.1 *Technical principle and process flow*

Low-temperature methanol washing technology (Rectisol) uses methanol organic solvent as an absorbent and utilizes the physical properties of methanol with high solubility for CO_2, H_2S, COS, and other acid gases under low-temperature conditions. It also simultaneously or in stages removes a part of acid gas from the raw gas. This technology has been widely used in acid gas removal in the petroleum industry, coal chemical industry, fertilizer industry, city gas industry, and other fields.

The low-temperature methanol purification process is mainly composed of gas absorption and solvent regeneration. The operating units include an absorption tower, medium-pressure flash tank, CO_2 desorption tower, H_2S enricher, thermal regeneration tower, methanol-water rectification tower, and CO_2 compressor. Two typical low-temperature methanol cleaning processes are one-step and two-step, the main difference being the gas absorption stage. If sulfide and CO_2 are absorbed at the same time, it is called a one-step process. The step-by-step absorption of CO_2 and sulfide is called a two-step process, and there are two solvent regeneration systems accordingly (see Figure 1) (Yang et al. 2016).

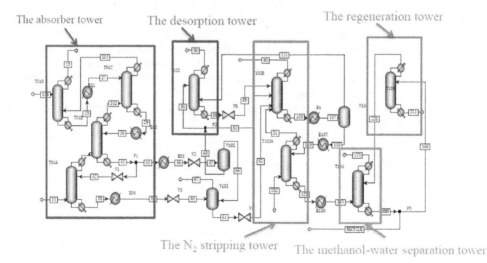

Figure 1. Rectisol wash process modeling (Yang et al. 2016).

2.1.2 Technical features

1. It has a strong absorption capacity for acid gas and a high purification degree. The total sulfur in the purified gas can be reduced to less than 1 ppm, and CO_2 can be removed to less than 10 ppm.
2. Methanol solvent has higher selectivity for the absorption of CO_2, H_2S, and COS, so the desulfurization and decarbonization of gas can be carried out in two or the same absorption towers in stages and selectively. The purity of the recovered CO_2 can meet the needs of urea production, and the sulfur can be directly recovered from the exhaust gas rich in H_2S by the Claus method.
3. With excellent chemical stability and thermal stability, the solvent does not foam during the absorption process, which is conducive to stable production.
4. Operating at low temperatures, the methanol solution regeneration energy consumption is small, the circulation amount of the solvent is saved, and the operating cost is low.
5. Methanol is less corrosive and does not require special anti-corrosion materials, which can save equipment costs.
6. Methanol solvent is cheap and easy to obtain and has a wide range of sources. However, the low-temperature methanol washing technology has shortcomings, such as a long process flow and a complex methanol regeneration process, which brings certain difficulties to operation and maintenance (Zhao et al. 2012).

2.2 Research status

2.2.1 Current status of foreign research

The emergence of low-temperature methanol washing technology can be traced back to the research work of Lurgi and Linde in the 1950s. In 1954, Luqi Company built the world's first industrial demonstration unit of low-temperature methanol washing in Sasol Company, South Africa, to purify the gas produced by the pressurized Luqi furnace. Linde is the first company to apply low-temperature methanol washing technology to purify sulfur-containing shift gas in a fertilizer plant, thus opening a new chapter in the application of low-temperature methanol washing technology (Stiegel & Maxwell 2001).

2.2.2 Current status of Chinese research

Domestic research on the low-temperature methanol washing process began in the 1970s. The Lanzhou Design Institute of Sinopec Group, the Nanhua Group Research Institute, Zhejiang University, the Shanghai Chemical Industry Research Institute, the Dalian University of Technology, the Beijing University of Chemical Technology, and other units were engaged in basic theoretical research, chemical process simulation calculation, thermodynamics and basic data measurement, and mathematical model of gas-liquid balance calculation. At present, many large-scale acid gas purification plants in China have adopted the low-temperature methanol washing process, some of which have been in operation for nearly 20 years and have accumulated rich experience in design, construction, installation, and operation (Wang 2013).

3 SELEXOL/NHD CARBON REMOVAL TECHNOLOGY

3.1 Technical introduction

3.1.1 Technical principle and process flow

The polyethylene glycol diether process, also known as Selexol or DEPG process, is a gas purification process using a mixture of polyethylene glycol dimethyl ether [$CH_3O(C_2H_4O)_nCH_3$, n=2~9] as an absorbent. It has a good separation effect in removing acid gases such as H_2S, CO_2, and mercaptan.

In a typical Selexol process, solvent regeneration can be achieved by stripping or heating. Polyethylene glycol dimethyl ether has a good separation effect on CO_2 and H_2S acid gas and is less corrosive to equipment, but the process is complicated, and the cost of solvent is relatively high. In addition, due to the high viscosity of polyethylene glycol dimethyl ether, when operating at a low temperature, the mass transfer rate and tray efficiency in the absorption process will be reduced. The amount of solvent circulation needs to be increased, resulting in high operating costs (see Figure 2) (Kapetaki et al. 2015).

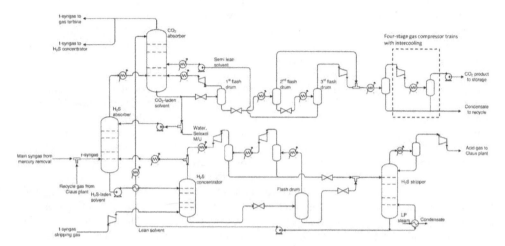

Figure 2. Schematic diagram of an integrated dual-stage Selexol process (Kapetaki et al. 2015).

3.1.2 Technical features

1. It has low total energy consumption, high gas cleanliness, less solvent loss, and less H_2 and N_2 dissolution loss.
2. It has the dual function of removing CO_2 and sulfide.
3. The solvent has good chemical stability, no foaming, no degradation, and no corrosion to carbon steel equipment (Liu et al. 2019).

3.2 Research status

3.2.1 Current status of foreign research

The polyethylene glycol dimethyl ether method, also known as the Selexol purification method, was invented by Frank Porter of Allied Chemical Company in 1958. Use low-temperature polyethylene glycol dimethyl ether (Selexol), a good solvent that can dissolve acid gases under high pressure. In 1965, the United Chemical Company of the United States developed a multi-component polyethylene glycol dimethyl ether mixed solvent for synthesis gas purification. In 1982, Norton Corporation acquired the technology. In 1989, United Carbon obtained the patent right. In 1993, UOP merged with Union Carbide and obtained the exclusive license for wholesale Selexol technology (Qin et al. 2007).

3.2.2 Current status of Chinese research

In the early 1980s, the China Southern Chemical Corporation Research Institute developed a decarburization and desulfurization process using polyethylene glycol dimethyl ether homologues as absorbents, referred to as the NHD process. The NHD process is similar to the foreign Selexol process and has a strong ability to dissolve H_2S and CO_2 in the mixed gas. Both techniques are physical purification processes, but the solvents used are different. At present, the NHD process has been widely used in the removal of acid gas in industrial processes such as natural gas and refinery gas (Gui et al. 2014).

4 FUTURE OUTLOOK

Compared with other purification methods, the two purification methods of low-temperature methanol washing and improved NHD have high purification degrees, low energy consumption, and low operating cost. They are both good methods for syngas purification. However, the two methods have their own characteristics. The selection must be comprehensively considered based on many factors, such as the overall process flow, the conditions of each cooperating unit device, the requirements for synthesis gas purification, and the economic strength of the project construction.

The absorption selectivity of low-temperature methanol to H_2S and CO_2 is poorer than that of improved NHD solvents. Therefore, for methanol projects, it is only required to remove sulfides from synthesis gas and to preserve CO_2 in it as much as possible. Low-temperature methanol solvents are not as good as improved solvents.

With the construction of large-scale coal-to-ammonia, coal-to-methanol, coal-to-dimethyl ether, coal-to-natural gas, and coal-to-hydrogen plants, the low-temperature methanol washing process, one of the pillar technologies of the new coal chemical industry, will have broad application prospects. At present, most of the low-temperature methanol washing processes used in China are imported technologies, and the investment cost is relatively high. In order to reduce costs, enhance market competitiveness and maximize benefits, domestic production plants and research institutes should strengthen research on this process. We should focus on independent innovation, integrated innovation, introduction, digestion, absorption, and re-innovation. It is also crucial to increase the research and development and technological transformation of the process and develop world-class large-scale low-temperature methanol washing proprietary technology and equipment with independent intellectual property rights. In order to reduce costs and enhance market competitiveness, the technical and economic level of the device and the low-temperature methanol washing device that has achieved localization in production practice need to be continuously improved.

5 CONCLUSION

The wide application of low-temperature methanol washing technology and polyethylene glycol diether process in the industrial field, especially the introduction into the coal chemical industry, has achieved extremely remarkable results. Recently, China has made breakthroughs in the application of low-temperature methanol washing technology and has gradually mastered the independent research and development capabilities of some equipment. Low-temperature methanol washing technology has strong absorption and selectivity to acid gas, and it has the characteristics of stable overall operation. In today's petrochemical industry, fertilizer industry, coal chemical industry, and other fields, low-temperature methanol washing technology is applied. Considering the economics of the decarbonization process and the limitations of the classical physical absorption process, it is necessary to strengthen the selection and application of "new-high-efficiency-green" absorbents, optimization and innovation of "absorption-regeneration" processes, desulfurization and decarbonization integration, and the coupling separation technology development.

ACKNOWLEDGMENTS

This work was financially supported by Datang Northeast Electric Power Test & Research Institute.

REFERENCES

Gui X., Wang C.W., Yun Z. et al. (2014) Research Progress of Pre-Combustion CO_2 Capture Technology. *Chemical Industry and Engineering Progress*, 33(7): 1895–1901.

Kapetaki Z., Brandani P., Brandani S. et al. (2015) Process Simulation of a Dual-Stage Selexol process for 95% Carbon Capture Efficiency at an Integrated Gasification Combined Cycle Power plant. *International Journal of Greenhouse Gas Control*, 39: 17–26.

Liu H., Wang X.L. and Yang X.S. (2019) Operation Summary and Comparison of Hot Potash Decarburization and NHD Decarburization Systems. *Nitrogenous Fertilizer Progress*, (2): 36–40.

Liu H.Z. (2011) Analysis of Energy Saving and Emission Reduction in Synthetic Ammonia Industry. *Chemical Industry and Engineering Progress*, 30(6): 1147–1157.

Qin X.D., Li Z.X., Song H.Q. et al. (2007) Talking about the Comparison of Technical and Economic Indicators of Low-Temperature Methanol Washing and NHD Process. *Technology & Development of Chemical Industry*, 36(4): 35–42.

Stiegel G.J. and Maxwell R.C. (2001) Gasification Technologies: the Path to Clean, Affordable Energy in the 21st Century. *Fuel Processing Technology*, 71(1-3): 79–97.

Wang J.M. (2013) Technical Advantages and Application Progress of Low-Temperature Methanol Washing Process. *Chemical Fertilizer Design*, 51(6): 1–6.

Yang S., Qian Y. and Yang S. (2016) Development of a Full CO_2 Capture Process Based on the Rectisol Wash Technology. *Industrial & Engineering Chemistry Research*, 55(21): 6186–6193.

Zhang G.M., Chu W.F. and Geng H.J. (2010) Research Progress and Application of Low-Temperature Methanol Washing Process. *Chemical Engineer*, 2010 (10): 31–33.

Zhao P.F., Li S.D. and Wang L.Z. (2012) Low-Temperature Methanol Washing Technology and its Application in Coal Chemical Industry. *Chemical Industry and Engineering Progress*, 31(11): 2442–2448.

Status and countermeasures of cadmium pollution in soil

Baodan Yang, Shuang Cui*, Xiuju Sun, Weijun Qi & Xinyue Liu
Key Laboratory of Wastewater Treatment Technology of Liaoning Province, College of Environmental and Chemical Engineering, Shenyang Ligong University, Shenyang, P.R. China

ABSTRACT: The pollution of heavy metal Cd in the soil environment has become increasingly serious, which has attracted the close attention of many countries. This paper summarized the sources of heavy metal cadmium pollution in soil, the harm of cadmium pollution to soil, plants, and human beings, and the forms of heavy metal cadmium in soil. Based on the cognition of the harm of heavy metals to food safety, it provides the basis for formulating the relevant standards of cadmium pollution in the soil in different environments.

1 INTRODUCTION

Soil is the basis of human survival, one of the important natural resources and the lifeline of the entire ecosystem. However, with the development of transportation and industrialization, heavy metal pollution in the soil is becoming increasingly serious.

Heavy metals usually refer to metals with an atomic density of elements (quasi metals and metals) greater than 6.0 g/cm^3, except arsenic (As), boron (B), and selenium (Se). They include elements necessary for biologies, such as cobalt (Co), copper (Cu), chromium (Cr), manganese (Mn), zinc (Zn), and nonessential elements, such as cadmium (Cd), lead (Pb), mercury (Hg). These essential basic elements are trace for animals, plants, and human life activities and are called essential "trace elements" or "micronutrients." Nonessential metals have plant and animal toxicity and are called toxic elements. They are harmful to animals, plants, and humans at high concentrations (Adriano 2001).

Soil heavy metal pollution means that the concentration of harmful elements in the soil exceeds the soil background value, and the concentration of heavy metals in the soil is too high due to excessive deposition of heavy metals caused by human activities. Research shows that heavy metals increase through human activities and usually have a high bioavailability (Lamb et al. 2009).

2 SOURCES OF HEAVY METAL CADMIUM POLLUTION IN SOIL

Heavy metals can enter the soil through different pollution channels, such as industrial "three wastes", domestic garbage, agricultural sewage irrigation, and traffic pollution. Industrial pollution is mostly caused by the discharge of untreated "three wastes", i.e., waste residue, wastewater, and waste gas, which leads to soil pollution. The solid wastes generated in the industrial production process are directly dumped into the soil without any treatment. Through the long-term effects of natural phenomena such as sunlight and rain washing, the

---

*Corresponding Author: ccshuang@163.com

mobility of heavy metals in the soil is enhanced, and they spread to the surrounding soil in a funnel shape or along the radial direction (Xiong 2010). The pollution scope is expanded. Domestic pollution mainly comes from the stacking of domestic garbage without classified treatment, and the content of heavy metals in some urban garbage exceeds the standard. This stacked garbage will release toxic elements into the soil under other functions, such as rainwater leaching, which are mainly released into the soil in an effective state, leading to the increase of the migration capacity of heavy metals in the soil and serious groundwater pollution (Cui et al. 2012).

Sewage irrigation is the main cause of agricultural pollution. In the past, due to China's weak economic strength, backward industrial technology, and equipment, a large number of urban and industrial sewage was directly discharged into farmland without treatment. Because it contains a large number of toxic and harmful substances that seriously exceed the standard, it will cause a series of problems to the environment. It is reported that 45% of the total area of sewage irrigation is polluted. The relatively serious pollution is mainly caused by heavy metal mercury and cadmium. Every year, due to sewage irrigation, 2.5 billion kg of grain is reduced, and more than 5 billion kg of grain is polluted (Chen et al. 1999). In addition, unreasonable long-term use of chemical fertilizers, pesticides, paints, etc., will also cause serious heavy metal pollution to the soil environment.

Automobile transportation will also cause serious pollution to the atmosphere and soil because the automobile engine, automobile gasoline, lubricating oil, tires, and gilded parts can release pollutants such as heavy metal Cd due to wear or combustion during use (Cui et al. 2012). For example, automobile exhaust emissions not only cause urban air pollution but also pollute the soil on both sides of the road.

3 HARM OF HEAVY METAL CADMIUM POLLUTION IN SOIL

Heavy metal pollution in soil has the characteristics of concealment, long-term, and irreversibility, so it poses a huge potential threat to soil, plants, and human systems. Microbes in the soil cannot decompose the heavy metal Cd deposited in it but will be absorbed by plants. This will not only harm the physiological process of plants but also pose a serious threat to human health indirectly through the role of the food chain due to the continuous accumulation of heavy metal Cd in the soil. The toxicity of heavy metals in the soil will affect the ecosystem for a long time (Oliveira & Pampulha 2006). At present, soil heavy metal pollution has become a hot topic (Jia 2007).

3.1 Hazards to soil

In the soil, most heavy metals remain relatively stable, but after entering the soil, they are not easy to be decomposed and difficult to migrate out of the soil. When the content of heavy metals in the soil exceeds the capacity of crops to absorb them, it will cause environmental problems such as soil fertility decline, hardening, and structural and functional imbalance, which will have a significant negative impact on the soil's biological characteristics, physical and chemical properties, and microbial community structure. For instance, the balance of the soil ecosystem is destroyed, the soil biological community structure shrinks, and the diversity decreases. As a result, soil ecological structure and functional stability are seriously affected (Yuan 2012).

Some scholars have conducted much research and proved that the biomass of microorganisms in the soil polluted by heavy metals is significantly lower than that in the soil using manure. The diversity of soil microbial communities is also significantly reduced (Wang & Ma 2005). Kuperman and Carreiro (1997) studied the impact of heavy metal pollution on soil microbial biomass and soil enzyme activity of the grassland ecosystem. They found that more than half of the soil microbial biomass indicators (such as number, diameter, length, etc.) decreased. Soil enzyme activity significantly decreased 10-50 times with the increase of soil heavy metal concentration.

3.2 Harm to plants

Excessive heavy metal content in the soil also has potential harm to plants. Heavy metals absorbed into plants can induce plants to produce certain substances, which have toxic effects or other adverse effects on enzymes and metabolic processes in plants, and indirectly cause damage to plants (Wang & Ma 2005). As we all know, the production of "cadmium rice" is caused by Cd pollution of soil crops. Similarly, cadmium is enriched in rice, potato, wheat, and other crops, which not only directly affects human health use, but also seriously affects local and international commodity markets (Roberts et al. 1994; Kirkham 2006; Mavropoulos et al. 2002).

3.3 Hazards to human beings

Heavy metals accumulated in the soil can affect human health in many ways. For example, plants absorb heavy metals in soil and then endanger human health through the circulation of the biological chain. Heavy metals in soil migrate to groundwater due to runoff or leaching, which pollutes water sources and affects human health (Zhang et al. 2006).

Cadmium mainly accumulates in the human liver, kidney, and testicular tissues. Male workers who have been engaged in cadmium work for a long time have low levels of androgen in their urine, resulting in a significant reduction or even lack of mature sperm and other serious symptoms. Because the use of "cadmium rice" will lead to an increase in the content of Cd in human urine, when the human body ingests or inhales excessive Cd, it will cause pathological changes in various organs of the human body. It can lead to anemia, hypertension, bone mineral density reduction, an increase in the probability of fracture, rheumatoid arthritis, nephritis, ulceration, etc. Its harm can reach several decades (Li et al. 2011; Wang & Ma 2005). In 1955-1972, a kind of soil pollution event caused by heavy metals was found in the Shentongchuan basin of Japan, namely the bone pain disease event. It is mainly due to the large area of pollution of water and food caused by heavy metal cadmium poisoning. Nerve pain, osteomalacia, bending of limbs, deformation of the spine, and brittle bone will occur in various parts of the body, resulting in difficulty in movement, inability to eat, and incomparable pain.

4 FORMS OF HEAVY METAL CADMIUM IN SOIL

The harm of heavy metal cadmium in soil depends not only on the content of heavy metal cadmium in soil but also on the existing forms of heavy metals and the proportion of each form (Li et al. 2011). The existing forms of cadmium in soil generally include water-soluble cadmium and water-insoluble cadmium (Chen 2007).

After heavy metals enter the soil, they form different forms through various physical and chemical reactions. The forms of heavy metals in the soil not only affect their environmental behavior but also seriously affect the activity of heavy metals and the bioavailability of plants.

Therefore, understanding the changes in the forms of heavy metals in soil is of great significance for analyzing and understanding their environmental behavior and environmental effects, predicting the effect of soil leaching on the remediation of contaminated soil, and determining the treatment plan (Liu 2012). The forms of heavy metals are classified as shown in Table 1.

Most domestic researchers are based on the Tessier method. Lena et al. (1997) showed that among all forms of heavy metals, the exchangeable state has the strongest biological

Table 1. Speciation classification of heavy metals.

Methods	Species of heavy metals
BCR method	Acid soluble (exchangeable and carbonate bound), reducible (oxide bound), oxidizable (organic and sulfide bound) and residue
Tessier (Tessier et al.,1979)	Exchangeable, carbonate, iron manganese oxide, organic matter and residue
Cambrell	Water soluble, exchangeable, inorganic compound precipitated, macromolecular humus bound, hydroxide precipitated and absorbed (or adsorbed), sulfide precipitated and residue
Shuman (Zhou et al., 2007)	Exchangeable, water-soluble, carbonate bound, loose bound organic, manganese oxide bound, tight bound organic, amorphous iron oxide bound and silicate mineral

activity, followed by the carbonate-bound state and iron manganese oxide bound state, while the organic bound state and residue state have the lowest biological activity.

Exchangeable state: Exchangeable heavy metals refer to metals adsorbed on clay, humus, or other components (Huang et al. 2012). Exchangeable heavy metals are the most active and toxic part of the soil. They are the most sensitive to soil environmental changes. They are the most easily released under neutral conditions, easily absorbed by plants, and most easily transformed into other forms of metals. They are the most mobile and bioavailable forms in soil, the main cause of soil heavy metal pollution, and the main source of harmful organisms (Zheng 2010). Its content can reflect the impact of human pollution discharge on the soil environment over a period of time.

Carbonate bound state: Carbonate bound state is a coprecipitation form of heavy metals formed on carbonate minerals (Wei et al. 1999). The pH value has an important influence on the change of carbonate heavy metals. It migrates and transforms under different pH values, which is potentially harmful. The increase in soil pH value is conducive to forming carbonate, while with the decrease in pH value, carbonate heavy metals are easily re-released into the soil environment, and mobility and biological activity are significantly improved (Zheng 2010).

Ferromanganese oxide bound state: Ferromanganese oxide bound state refers to that the heavy metals in the soil are contained outside the minerals or the powder particles exist in the soil. The main reason for its formation is that the specific surface area of active ferromanganese oxide is large, which affects the adsorption or precipitation of heavy metals on anions (Han et al. 2005). The existence of the bound state of iron and manganese oxides is related to the Eh value (redox potential, index of redox reaction intensity) and pH value in the soil. When the Eh value and pH value are high, iron and manganese oxides are easy to form; otherwise, iron and manganese oxides are difficult to form (Du 2011).

Organic binding state: Organic binding state refers to the metal formed by complexing heavy metals with animal and plant residues, humus, and other organic substances in the soil. The organic bound state can reflect the human emission of rich organic pollutants in water and soil (Du 2011).

Residual form: Residual heavy metals are the result of natural weathering, and most of them exist in the soil lattice of silicate and primary and secondary minerals (Li et al. 2004).

It is not easy to release and be absorbed by plants under normal natural conditions, and it can exist stably in soil sediments for a long time.

5 CONCLUSION AND OUTLOOK

In the middle and late 1970s, China began to investigate the heavy metal Cd pollution in farmland, but so far, there is no research report on the overall status of heavy metal Cd pollution in soil. In 1980, according to the report on China's agricultural environment, it was indicated that the area of heavy metal Cd pollution in farmland in China had reached 9333 hectares. Subsequently, it was proposed that the area of heavy metal Cd pollution was 13333 hm^2. This data is still the main basis for China's assessment of farmland heavy metal Cd pollution (Cui et al. 2006).

The current situation of soil pollution in China is as follows: the overall situation is severe, some areas are seriously polluted, and the quality and safety of agricultural and sideline products caused by soil pollution are increasing yearly (Chen 2013).

The pollution of heavy metal Cd in the soil environment is becoming increasingly serious, which has attracted the close attention of many countries. Based on the recognition of the harm of heavy metals to food safety, they have made a series of strict limit standards for farmland soil.

ACKNOWLEDGMENTS

The work was financially supported by the Shenyang Scientific Plan Project (21-109-3-06), the National Natural Science Foundation of China (41773093), Innovation and Entrepreneurship Training Program for College Students.

REFERENCES

Adriano D. *Trace Elements in Terrestrial Environments: Biogeochemistry, Bioavailability, and Risks of Metals*, Springer Verlag, New York, 2001.
Chen Huaiman, Zheng Chunrong, Tu Cong *et al.*, Current Situation of Heavy Metal Pollution in Soil in China and its Control Countermeasures. *Royal Swedish Academy of Sciences*, 1999, 28 (2): 130–135
Chen Senlin. A Brief Discussion on the Current Situation of soil Pollution in China and Research on Comprehensive Treatment. *Charming China*, 2013 (11): 297–297
Chen Yuan. Research Progress on Cadmium and its Occurrence form in soil. *Guangdong Science of Trace Elements*, 2007, 14 (7): 7–13
Cui Bin, Guo Yin, Sun Shiyou *et al.*, Research Progress on the Status Quo, Harm and Remediation Technology of Heavy Metal Pollution in Soil. *Anhui Agricultural Science*, 2012, 40 (1): 337–375, 347
Cui Lituo, Geng Shigang, Li Zhiwei. Current Situation of Cadmium Pollution in Farmland Soil in China and its Control Countermeasures. *Modern Agricultural Science and Technology*, 2006 (11S): 184–185
Du Pei. Remediation of Chromium Contaminated Soil by Organic Acid Leaching. *Shenyang University of Aeronautics and Astronautics*, 2011.
Han Chunmei, Wang Linshan, Gong Zongqiang *et al.*, Speciation Analysis of Heavy Metals in Soil and its Environmental Significance. *Journal of Ecology*, 2005, 24 (12): 1400–1502
Huang Siyu, Peng Xiaochun, Wu Yanyu *et al.*, Advances in Speciation Analysis of Heavy Metals in Soil. *Guangdong Chemical Industry*, 2012, 39 (2): 86–87
Jia Xueping. Source and Improvement Measures of Heavy Metal Pollution in Soil. *Modern Agricultural Science and Technology*, 2007, (9): 197–199
Kirkham M.B. Cadmium in Plants on Polluted Soils: Effects of Soil Factors, Hyperaccumulation, and Amendments, *Geoderma* 137 (2006) 19–32.
Kuperman R.G., Carreiro M.M. Soil Heavy Metal Concentrations, Microbial Biomass and Enzyme Activities in a Contaminated Grassland Ecosystem. *Soil Biology & Biochemistry*, 1997, 29 (2): 179–190.
Lamb D.T., Ming H., Megharaj M., Naidu R. Heavy Metal (Cu, Zn, Cd, and Pb) Partitioning and Bioaccessibility in Uncontaminated and Long-Term Contaminated Soils, *J. Hazard. Mater.* 171 (2009) 1150–1158.
Lena Q.M. and Gade N.R. Chemical Fractionation of Cadmium, Copper, Nickel, and Zinc in Contaminated Soils. *J. Environ. Qual*, 1997,26(2):259–264.
Li Guangyun, Cao Yongfu, Zhao Shumin *et al.*, Soil Heavy Metal Hazards and Remediation Measures. *Shandong Forestry Science and Technology*, 2011, (6): 96–101
Li Ziqing, Chen Ling, Qiu Yanling *et al.*, Speciation Analysis of Heavy Metals in Soil of Shanghai Chemical Industry Zone. *Ecological Environment*, 2004, 13 (2): 154–155

Liu Xia. Study on the Leaching Remediation of Cu and Pb in Contaminated Lou Soil by Chelating Agents and Surfactants. *Northwest Agricultural and Forestry University*, 2012

Mavropoulos E., Rossi A.M., Costa A.M., Perez C.A.C., Moreira J.C. and Saldanha M., Studies on the Mechanisms of Lead Immobilization by Hydroxyapatite, *Environ.Sci. Technol.* 36 (2002) 1625–1629.

Oliveira A. and Pampulha M.E., Effects of Long-Term Heavy Metal Contamination on soil Microbial Characteristics, *J. Biosci. Bioeng.* 102 (2006) 157–161.

Roberts A.H.C., Longhurst R.D., Brown M.W. Cadmium Status of Soils, Plants, and Grazing Animals in New Zealand, N, Z, J. *Agric. Res.* 37 (1994) 119–129.

Tessier A., Campbell P.G.C., Bisson M. Sequential Extraction Procedure for the Speciation of Particulate Trace Metals. *Anal Chem*, 1979, 51 (7): 844–851.

Wang Shuying and Ma Xiaohua, Harm and Remediation of Heavy Metal Pollution in Soil. *Journal of Shangqiu Normal University*, 2005, 21 (5): 122–124

Wei Junfeng, Da Qing, Jin Lian *et al.*, Study on the Speciation and Distribution of Heavy Metals in Urban Sediment of Guangzhou. *Soil and Environment*, 1999, 2 (1): 10–14

Xiong Yanjun, Current Situation of Soil Pollution and Control Measures in China. *Modern Agricultural Science and Technology*, 2010, (8): 294–297

Yuan Xin. Study on Distribution Characteristics of Heavy Metals in Kongjia sewage Irrigation Area of Tongliao City. *Beijing Jiaotong University*, 2012

Zhang Mingkui, Fang Liping, Zhou Cui. Bioavailability and Mobility Evaluation of Heavy Metals in Contaminated Soil: Comparison of Four Methods. *Journal of Applied Ecology*, 2006 (8): 1501–1504

Zheng Shun'an *Study on Transformation and Migration Characteristics of Heavy Metals in Typical Farmland Soils in China.* Ph.D. Thesis of Zhejiang University, 2010

Zhou Kangmin, Tang Zhiyun, Huang Guangming *et al.*, Study on Speciation Analysis Methods of Heavy Metals in Soil. *Jiangsu Geology*, 2007, 31 (3): 165–175

Research process on alkaline regulation and solidification regulation of red mud

Dongmei Yan
Guangxi Industry Research Institute Intelligent Agriculture Research Institute Co., Ltd., Nanning, China

Shuai Zou*
School of Mechanical Engineering, Guangxi University, Nanning, China
Guangxi Key Laboratory of Petrochemical Resource Processing and Process Intensification, Nanning, China

Maoli Yang
College of Physics and Electrical Engineering, Liupanshui Normal University, Guizhou, China

Jing Yang, Mingyuan Dou & Qing Feng
School of Mechanical Engineering, Guangxi University, Nanning, China
Guangxi Key Laboratory of Petrochemical Resource Processing and Process Intensification, Nanning, China

ABSTRACT: Red mud is a strong alkaline waste residue discharged from bauxite ore refining alumina, which is huge in quantity and has great environmental risks. This paper analyzes the related research on the research direction of alkaline regulation and solidification regulation in the process of red mud solidification disposal. It puts forward suggestions for the research direction of red mud solidification.

1 INTRODUCTION

Red mud, also known as bauxite residue, is a solid waste produced by the alumina production industry. According to statistics, for every 1 t of alumina produced, 1.5~2.5 t of red mud is produced (Samal et al. 2013). The worldwide stockpile of red mud is about 5.0×10^9 t and is still growing at an annual growth rate of 1.5×10^8 t. As a major producer of alumina, China currently has a red mud stockpile of more than 6×10^8 t, which is increasing at a rate of 7×10^7 t per year. Red mud has strong alkalinity, high salinity, and fine particle size, which makes its comprehensive utilization of resources face many problems. At the same time, the environmental safety problems caused by the massive accumulation of red mud not only seriously restrict the high-quality development of the alumina industry but also bring serious challenges to regional ecological protection.

In recent years, management strategies for tailings waste disposal and mine ecological disposal have received extensive attention (Carlo et al. 2019). Restoration is considered to be an effective strategy for dealing with bulk solid waste and reducing its environmental risks. However, due to some inherent physical and chemical characteristics of red mud, such as high alkalinity, high salinity, and poor physical structure, the restoration process of natural vegetation is limited and time-consuming. Red mud is highly alkaline, has the ability to

---
*Corresponding Author: zoushuai1218@st.gxu.edu.cn

release continuously, and has poor physical structure. Therefore, to realize the vegetation coverage of red mud yards, the problems of high alkalinity, poor physical structure, and nutrient shortage of red mud should be solved first to realize the soil remediation of red mud (Figure 1).

Under the action of natural long-term factors, the physical structure, chemical characteristics, and biodiversity of red mud have been basically improved (Li *et al.* 2021) and can support a small number of plant growth. However, the lack of available nutrients limits the sustainable growth and microbial colonization of plants. Appropriate human intervention is conducive to achieving the goal of reclamation and can greatly shorten the cycle of ecological reconstruction in the disposal area. Therefore, many studies have focused on improving the physicochemical and biological properties of red mud in a short time by adding various ameliorants (such as nitrogen fertilizer, compost, and sewage sludge).

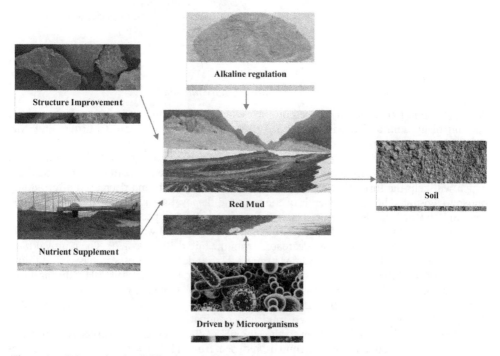

Figure 1. Schematic of solidification regulation of red mud.

2 ALKALINE REGULATION

Alkaline regulation is the key link to improving the physicochemical properties of red mud and promoting red mud solidification. Adding gypsum, organic matter modifier, microbial screening, and metabolic acid production can improve the physical and chemical properties of red mud and reduce its alkalinity. Since red mud soil alkaline regulation cannot cause damage to the alkaline mineral phase and introduce new harmful substances in the process of de-alkalization, the research on red mud soil alkalization regulation mainly focuses on adding gypsum, organic matter, and microbial screening. Table 1 summarizes the alkaline regulation of red mud by different treatment methods.

Table 1. Alkaline regulation of red mud with different treatments.

Method	Mechanism of action
Ammonia chloride	Ion exchange between ammonium and sodium ions
Carbon dioxide	Acid-base neutralization removes free base and tricalcium aluminate
Gypsum, phosphogypsum, sulfuric acid + calcium containing double salt CAM	Calcium and sodium ion exchange; Neutralization of residual acid
Acid waste liquid, acid waste residue	Neutralize with red mud free base and chemically bound base
citric acid	Alkaline OH^-, CO_3^{2-} and precipitated $Al(OH)_4^-$ were consumed
Humus, fulvic acid, organic matter	Neutralize with red mud free base and chemically bound base
microorganism	Metabolism produces acid, acid, and base neutralization

2.1 Alkaline regulation based on the addition of inorganic matter

Alkaline regulation is achieved based on the exchange of calcium and sodium ions, and the amount of gypsum added will affect the effect of alkaline regulation. Courtney and Xue (2019) found that gypsum can effectively reduce the alkalinity and exchangeable sodium content of red mud, which is beneficial to plant growth. When the amount of gypsum is 5%, the pH can be reduced to about 8.9 by replacing the exchangeable sodium in the red mud, which will help the formation of red mud soil. The pH of red mud decreased after adding phosphogypsum. The surface depth of the red mud disposal area was 0~20 cm and 40~60 cm, and the pH of red mud was 8.3~8.5 and 8.4~9.5, respectively (Xue et al. 2020). According to the research of Li et al. (2019), after adding 1.50 wt% phosphogypsum for 91 days, the pH value of bauxite slag decreased from the initial 10.83 to 8.70. The removal rates of free alkali and exchangeable sodium were 97.94% and 75.87%, respectively. In addition, the study showed that there was a significant positive correlation between pH value and free base and exchangeable sodium ($P < 0.05$). The effect of the free base composition is CO_3^{2-} > OH^- > AlO_2^- > HCO_3^-. In 2019, Zeng et al. (2019) used sulfuric acid + calcium-containing double salt CAM to de-alkalize red mud and conducted soil chemistry research on de-alkalized red mud. The results showed that the pH of the red mud decreased from 10.84 to 6.79. The sodium content of red mud is reduced from 11.709% to 0.302%, and its de-alkalization rate is as high as 97.42%.

2.2 Alkaline regulation based on the addition of organic matter

The alkalinity of red mud can be reduced under the action of organic matter such as peat soil, lignocellulosic waste residue, and humic and organic acid. The degradation of biomass provides abundant C, N, P, Ca, Mg, and other essential elements for the growth and metabolism of microorganisms, which stimulates the recovery of microbial activity. Then, the microorganisms can neutralize the alkaline substances in red mud by metabolizing acid, thereby reducing the Its salinity.

Zheng et al. (2012) mixed red mud and molasses alcohol waste liquid in different proportions to neutralize the acid and alkali in alkaline red mud and acid waste liquid, in m(red mud):m(waste liquid) = 4:6 When the temperature is lower than 60°C, the pH value of the mixed pile is reduced to 7.3~7.5, the fermentation degree of the pile is high, and the degree of loosening can be increased; when the control temperature is lower than 60°C, the covering film is beneficial to fermentation. In 2018, Zhang et al.'s (2018) research showed that the waste alcohol mash, a by-product of sugar production, can significantly reduce the pH value of red mud. The pH of red mud can be reduced to 6.5 at 1:3 and 6.5 at 1:6. Liao et al. (2019) found that mixing lignocellulosic acid waste residues and adding compound microbial inoculants can significantly reduce the alkalinity of red mud. 9.02, and it dropped to 8.35 after adding compound microbial inoculants.

Dong et al. (2020) studied the effect of calcium nitrate and humus on the formation of red mud aggregates. The results showed that the combined addition of calcium nitrate and humus had a more significant effect on the improvement of red mud. The combined addition of calcium nitrate and humus can reduce the pH of red mud to about 8, which accords with the local normal soil pH value. Through the improvement by adding fly ash, the salinity and alkalinity of the red mud matrix were controlled effectively, and its pH value decreased significantly. At 540 days, the pH value decreased to 8.49, close to the reference soil (8.51) (Dong et al. 2021). The study of Wan et al. (2022) showed that the pH value of red mud could be reduced from 11.08 to 9.00 by de-alkalization of phosphogypsum, and the pH value of red mud could be reduced to about 8.50 by using phosphogypsum and fulvic acid. Deciduous leaves, straws, and corn straws (Hu et al. 2022) can reduce the pH value of red mud but cannot play a decisive role in regulating the alkalinity of red mud. Additional gypsum or modifiers are needed to reduce the pH value to a level acceptable to ordinary plants (Sun et al. 2022).

Li et al. (2017) showed that citric acid could reduce the alkalinity of red mud and provide organic carbon to improve the physical and chemical properties of red mud, but this method is expensive. The study of Kong et al. (2017) also shows that citric acid is an important step in reducing alkalinity. By comparing the results of inorganic acid, a new type of citric acid and acid-gypsum mixed treatment combination in reducing the pH value and total alkalinity of residue. Transforming alkaline mineral phase citric acid can consume alkaline OH^-, CO_3^{2-} and precipitated $Al(OH)_4^-$ and increase the distribution of macro aggregates. It is a promising method for repairing bauxite slag disposal areas.

2.3 *Microbial-driven alkaline regulation*

Microbial-driven alkalinity regulation is a strategy to improve the environment by reducing the alkalinity of red mud by microbial metabolic acid production. The method is low in cost and has a good application prospect in the alkaline control of red mud yards. A fungus RM-28 was isolated from red mud that significantly reduced red mud pH from 11.8 to 8.2 and has the potential to be used alone or in combination with inorganic/organic amendments to facilitate reforestation and red mud restoration/red mud contaminated sites (Anam et al. 2019). Song et al. (2019) screened a saline-alkali-tolerant strain ZH-22 from the red mud yard. ZH-22 can produce organic acids (oxalic acid/tartaric acid) in the alkaline medium, thereby reducing the pH of red mud quickly to around 9.3 and keeping it longer. Furthermore, according to the alkalinity and aggregation of bauxite residues in response to Penicillium oxalicum colonization in the column, Pseudomonas oxalate lowered the pH of the residues to about 7 after 30 days of surface exposure to aerobic conditions, which was effective in reducing the alkalinity of bauxite residues (Liao et al. 2019).

3 SOLIDIFICATION REGULATION

Red mud is complex in composition but seriously lacks organic matter and nutrients. It has poor air permeability and is easy to harden. The particles cannot form reasonable agglomerates, and the ability to retain water and fertilizer is poor. Therefore, alkaline regulation of red mud and solidification regulation are required. Solidification regulation mainly focuses on gypsum, organic matter modifier, and microbial screening, which can improve the soil

Table 2. Solidification regulating of red mud with various ameliorant.

Soil amendment	Effect of amendment
Phosphogypsum, poultry manure	Increase aggregates, reduce fine particles, and improve porosity.
Sulphuric acid and double salt containing calcium	Promote the formation of particle aggregate and improve its porosity.
Lignocellulosic residue, compound microorganism	Increase organic matter content and available water capacity.
Gypsum, earthworm manure	Promote the agglomeration of red mud particles and increase the stability of microaggregates.
Sugar by-products	Reduce the bulk density.
Corn stover, bagasse	Decrease bulk density, increase porosity, and promote agglomeration.
Microorganism	Increase the content of large particles, promote the aggregation and stability of particles, and increase the number and diversity of microbial communities.

properties of red mud to a certain extent. Table 2 summarizes the study on the regulation and control of red mud matrix soil by using different soil ameliorants.

3.1 Soil regulation based on adding inorganic matter

Gypsum plays an important role in improving red mud and accelerating the solidification process. Gypsum exists stably in bauxite slag, continuously provides Ca^{2+}, and inhibits the dissolution of combined alkali. In addition, phosphogypsum can promote the formation of large aggregate structures (Li et al. 2019). The addition of phosphogypsum increases the Ca^{2+} on the surface of the bauxite slag and reduces the Na^+ and Al^{3+}. The bauxite slag, after phosphogypsum treatment, obtains greater aggregates and larger pore sizes (Tian et al. 2021). Finally, the aggregate stability of bauxite slag is improved, and the formation of soil in bauxite slag is promoted (Tian et al. 2019). The addition of phosphogypsum and poultry manure significantly increased the proportion of 1~2 mm in red mud agglomerates and increased the average weight diameter of red mud 0~20 cm and 20~40 cm layers (Xue et al. 2020). However, by using sulfuric acid and calcium-containing double salt to control the solidification of red mud, the content of soluble salt in red mud was significantly reduced. The particle size of red mud was increased from 1.25 μm to 17.5 μm, which promoted the formation of particle aggregates and increased its porosity (Zeng et al. 2019).

3.2 Soil regulation based on adding organic matter

Organic matter such as lignocellulosic waste residue, peat soil, humic acid, compost, and sludge can improve the red mud matrix by improving the effective water capacity, organic nutrients, and bulk density. In 2019, Liao et al. (2019) added lignocellulose waste residue and composite microbial inoculants to red mud to increase the organic matter content and effective water capacity. When compound microbial inoculants were added, and the mass ratio of red mud to lignocellulose residue was 7:3, the organic matter content of red mud increased from 6.13 g/kg to 24.92 g/kg, and the effective water capacity increased from 8.80% to 19.17%. Biomass has a loose texture, high porosity, and low bulk density. Physical mixing with red mud can mechanically improve the composition of red mud matrix particles, looseness, bulk density, and porosity. Ca^{2+} can weaken the dispersion effect of Na^+ on fine particles by replacing it with Na^+ in red mud. It can promote the agglomeration of fine particles in the red mud matrix and increase the stability of micro-aggregates. Jones et al. (2011) found that biomass can promote the agglomeration of red mud particles. Therefore, after adding vermicompost to red mud, it contains a large number of biologically active microorganisms. The metabolites of microorganisms can effectively promote the agglomeration of red mud particles, which greatly increases the content of macro aggregates. Adding 8 wt% vermicomposts and 2 wt% gypsum, the aggregates in red mud can increase from 60.24% to 75.34% after 60days and increase to 84.75% after 90 days (Wang et al. 2019). Both gypsum and vermicompost can promote the agglomeration of red mud particles. The promoting effect is gypsum + vermicompost > vermicompost > gypsum. In 2018, Zhang et al. (2018) added sugar by-products to red mud, reducing the bulk density of red mud from 0.994 to 0.368. In 2022, Hu et al. (2022) took the Bayer process red mud as the research object and chose corn stalk as biomass Amendment by analyzing the changes of basic physical and chemical indicators of soil, soil enzyme activities, and metabolic levels of microbial communities. With the addition of 10 wt% biomass, the bulk density of the red mud matrix decreased to 0.55 g·cm^{-3}, the porosity reached 71.2%, and the mean weight diameter (MWD) of the particles increased to 0.38 mm. After biomass improvement treatment, the growth and metabolism level and diversity of the microbial community in red mud and the activities of soil urease, phosphatase, and dehydrogenase were significantly increased.

3.3 Microbial-driven soil regulation

Screening of salinity-tolerant microorganisms from red mud yards can improve the physical and chemical properties of red mud through metabolism. A salt-tolerant bacterium ZH-22 found in red mud can increase the content of large particles and promote inter-particle agglomeration and its stability; this strain survives well in red mud and promotes the number and diversity of microbial communities (Song et al. 2019). RM-28 can significantly reduce the toxicity and conductivity of red mud, effectively promote the dissolution of tricalcium phosphate, and improve the bioavailability of phosphorus (Anam et al. 2019).

The organic acids produced by Pseudomonas oxalicum dissolve and radiate from the residue. Inoculation with Pseudomonas oxalate significantly increased the Ca^{2+} content in the bauxite residue while decreasing the Na^+ content. The Ca^{2+} content is beneficial to the stable aggregates in the bauxite slag (Liao et al. 2019). Meanwhile, Pseudomonas oxalate is a strong cellulolytic microorganism that can produce cellulase. Bagasse was added to the residue as a nutrient for Pseudomonas oxalate, thereby realizing the regulation of solidification of the bauxite residue.

4 CONCLUSION

1. Inorganic modifiers such as gypsum and organic matter can reduce the alkali value and high salinity of red mud, promote particle agglomeration, and improve the permeability coefficient.
2. Organic matter can also provide nutrients for plants, form stable complexes with metal cations, stabilize soil structure, and provide energy sources for microorganisms.
3. Salt-alkali-tolerant microorganisms have the potential to regulate solidification and can improve the red mud matrix to a certain extent.
4. After human intervention, the soil properties of red mud have been improved, but there is still a lack of systematic research on the evolution of red mud soil. Further studies on the interaction between soil property changes, organic matter accumulation, and decomposing soil microbial communities during the regulation of red mud solidification will contribute to our understanding of the regulation of red mud solidification.

REFERENCES

Anam G.B., Reddy M.S. and Ahn Y. (2019) Characterization of Trichoderma Asperellum RM-28 for its Sodic/Saline-Alkali Tolerance and Plant Growth Promoting Activities to Alleviate Toxicity of Red Mud. *Sci. Total Environ.* 662: 462–469.

Courtney R., Xue S.G. (2019) Rehabilitation of Bauxite Residue to Support Soil Development and Grassland Establishment. *Cent. South Univ.* 26(2): 353–360.

Di Carlo E., Boullemant A. and Courtney R. (2019) A Field Assessment of Bauxite Residue Rehabilitation Strategies. *Sci. Total Environ.* 663: 915–926.

Dong M.Y., Dong Y.P., Xu Z.W., Shao Y.F., Liu X.J., Hu X.X. and Liu A.J. (2021) Resilience of Soil Microbiome and Enzyme Activity with Soil Amelioration of Bayer Process Red Mud. *China Environ. Sci.* 41(02): 913–922.

Dong Y.P., Liu X.J., Dong M.Y., Xu Z.W., Liu A.J. and Hu X.X. (2020) Improvement Effect of Calcium Nitrate and Humus on the Aggregate Formation in Bauxite Residue. *Environ. Pollut. Control.* 42(10): 1205–1210.

Hu S.X., Lu S.Q., Wang X., Rong F.X., Dong M.Y., Xu Z.W. and Liu A.J. (2022) Amelioration Effect of Cornstalk Biomass on Soil Genesis of Red Mud. *Chin. J. Environ. Eng.* https://kns.cnki.net/kcms/detail/11.5591.X.20220725.1737.008.html

Jones B.E.H., Haynes R.J. and Phillips I. Influence of Organic Waste and Residue Mud Additions On Chemical, Physical and Microbial Properties of Bauxite Residue Sand. (2011) *Environ. Sci. Pollut. R.* 18(2): 199–211.

Kong X.F., Li M., Xue S.G., Hartley W., Chen C.R., Wu C., Li X.F. and Li Y.W. (2017) Acid Transformation of Bauxite Residue: Conversion of its Alkaline Characteristics. *J. Hazard. Mate.* 324(Pt B):382–390.

Li H., Qu Y., Yao M.J., Tian W.J., Wang X.Q., Shi B., Cao L.N., Yue L.F. and Cao K.Q. (2021) Natural Soil Genesis in Red Mud and Underlying Microbial Mechanism. *Chin. J. Appl. Ecol.* 32(04): 1452–1460.

Li W., Zhu X.B. and Tang S. (2017) Selective Separation of Sodium From Red Mud with Citric Acid Leaching. *Sep. Sci. Technol.* 52(11): 1876–1884.

Li Y.W., Luo X.H., Li C.X., Millar G.J., Jiang J. and Xue S.G. (2019) Variation of Alkaline Characteristics in Bauxite Residue Under Phosphogypsum Amendment. *Cent. South Univ.* 26(2): 361–372.

Liao J.X., Zhang Y.F., Cheng Q.Y., Wu H., Zhu F. and Xue S.G. Colonization of Penicillium Oxalicum Enhanced Neutralization Effects of Microbial Decomposition of Organic Matter in Bauxite Residue (2019) *J. Cent. South Univ.* 26(2): 331–342.

Liao J.X., Tang Q., Zhou L.W., Zhu S.X., Huang K.C. and Zeng D.J. (2019) Studies of Lignocellulose Waste Residue on Dealkalization and Amendment of Red Mud. *Environ. Sci. Technol.* 42(01): 31–36.

Samal S. and Ray A.K., Bandopadhyay (2013) Proposal for Resources, Utilization and Processes of Red Mud in India—a Review. *Int. J. Miner. Process.* 118: 43–55.

Song J., Wang D.W., Zhang X.J., Li Z.H., Yang Z.H., Qiu K.Y. and Wang Y.Y. (2019) Isolation of an Alkali-tolerant Bacteria and Its Improvement of Bauxite Residue. *J. Henan Univ. (Nat. Sci.)* 49(01): 26–35.

Sun Y.H., Zhang Y.H., Wang M.X. and Zhang N. (2022) Study on The Effect of Organic Materials on Red Mud Matrix Improvement. *Guangdong Canye* 56(07): 26–29.

Tian T., Ke W.S., Zhu F., Wang Q.L., Ye Y.Z., Guo Y. and Xue S.G., Effect of Substrate Amendment on Alkaline Minerals and Aggregate Stability in Bauxite Residue (2019) *J. Cent. South Univ.* 26(2): 393–403.

Tian T., Zhang C.L., Zhu F., Yuan S.X., Guo Y. and Xue S.G.Effect of Phosphogypsum On Saline-Alkalinity and Aggregate Stability of Bauxite Residue (2021) *T. Nonferr. Metal. Soc.* 31(5): 1484–1495.

Wang Q.L., Li Q., Pang Y., Zhao C., Huang T., Zhao R. and Peng D.P. (2022) Feasibility of Solidification of Phosphogypsum Dealkalized Red Mud by Applying Fulvic Acid. *Environ. Eng.* 40(07): 31–37.

Wang Q.L., Ye Y.Z., Xue S.G., Jiang J., Zhu F. and Tian T. (2019) Effects of Ameliorants on Aggregate Stability of Bauxite Residue. *J. Univ. Chin Acad. Sci.* 36(04): 530–536.

Xue S G., Ke W.S., Zhu F., Ye Y.Z., Liu Z., Fan J.R. and Hartley W. (2020) Effect of Phosphogypsum and Poultry Manure on Aggregate-Associated Alkaline Characteristics in Bauxite Residue. *Environ. Manage.* 256: 109981.

Zeng H., Lu F., Hu G.Y., Tang H.H., Wang L., Sun W. and Hu Y.H. (2019) Study on New Process of Removing Alkali from Red Mud by Bayer Process and Its Soil Formation. *Conservation and Utilization of Mineral Resources* 39(03): 1–7.

Zhang L.F., Ren L.H., He Y.T., Huang J.H., Hu X.W., Tian S.L., Ning P. and Qiu J.R. (2018) Effect of Soil-Conversion Red Mud by Using Sugar By-Products. *Chin. J. Environ. Eng.* 12(04): 1228–1236.

Zhen Y.P., Zhu W.F. and Guo W.M. (2012) Soil Preparation by Mixing and Fermenting Red Mud and Molasses Alcohol Wastewater. *J. Guilin Univ. of Technol.* 32(01): 109–114.

# Research progress in dispersion stability of nanolubricant additives

Ting Li*, Junmiao Wu, Zhipeng Zhang & Rui Wang
School of Mechanical Engineering, Shenyang Jianzhu University, Shenyang, Liaoning, China

Qianqian Zou
School of Material Science and Engineering, Shenyang Jianzhu University, Shenyang, Liaoning, China

Yulan Tang*
School of Municipal and Environmental Engineering, Shenyang Jianzhu University, Shenyang, Liaoning, China

ABSTRACT: Ultra-fine particle size and excellent physical properties of nanoparticles have attracted considerable attention. Despite adding lubricating additives into lubricating oil that can effectively reduce friction and wear, nanoparticles in lubricating oil are very easy to agglomerate and have poor dispersion, which leads to their limited application in engineering. With scientific and technological development, great advances have been made in nano-lubricating additives in scientific research and industrial applications. In the literature, a variety of nano-lubricating additives with good dispersibility have been used to improve the tribological properties of lubricating oils, which are widely used in various fields. This review summarizes the efforts and progress of dispersion methods of nano-lubricating additives in recent years, including physical treatment methods, surfactant methods, and surface modification methods.

1 INTRODUCTION

Due to the existence of friction, it would be inevitable to cause the wear of mechanical components in the mechanical system. Serious friction and wear in the system will lead to a series of adverse consequences, including engine failure, bearing failure, etc. These adverse consequences are difficult to ensure the smooth operation of mechanical systems in all industries (Shahnazar et al. 2016). It is generally perceived that nano-lubricating additives (also known as nanolubricants) have special structure composition and excellent performance, which can greatly reduce friction and wear; therefore, it has been used to solve the problem of friction and wear (Ba et al. 2018).

When the particle size of nanoparticles becomes smaller, the surface energy and specific surface area of nanomaterials themselves become larger, so the particles are easily agglomerated with each other. The aggregation behavior of nanoparticles limits their ability to lubricate the contact area so that the friction effect is weakened (Chen et al. 2019). Although nanoparticles have been widely used to improve the tribological properties of lubricating oils, there are also some known problems. At present, in order to deal with the dispersion stability problems in the development of nanolubricants, researchers have made great efforts in physical treatment (Mosleh et al. 2009), use of surfactants (Taha-Tijerina et al. 2013), and surface modification of nanoparticles (Yang et al. 2012). This paper offers a systematic summary of the research progress of dispersion methods of nanomaterials in lubricating oil and considers the future development trend of nano-lubricating additives.

---

*Corresponding Authors: liting@sjzu.edu.cn and tyl98037@163.com

DOI: 10.1201/9781003433644-67

2 SEVERAL METHODS TO IMPROVE THE DISPERSION STABILITY

2.1 Physical treatment method

The physical treatment method, also known as the mechanical dispersion method, is to use instruments or equipment to stir, grind, break, and other methods to change the surface activity of nanoparticles when nanolubricants are added. The physical treatment methods available for the dispersion of nanoparticles in the base oil include mechanical stirring, ultrasonication, ball milling, and homogenization under high pressure.

Al-Hamadani *et al.* (2015) used ultrasonic treatment to treat SWNTS, graphene, and fullerene particles, which significantly enhanced their dispersion stability. The research shows that ultrasonic treatment makes the particle surface produce reaction groups, which overcome the van der Waals force between particles and form a well-dispersed suspension. Maheswaran *et al.* (2018) found that ball milling and grinding had a significant effect on controlling particle size, thereby improving the dispersion stability of garnet nanoparticles in the base oil. In addition, high-pressure homogenization is also used to prepare nanolubricants. High-pressure homogenization is effective in enhancing dispersion stability, and the operation is simple. Wan *et al.* (2015) fully dispersed h-BN nanoparticles into SE15W-40 base oil with the help of a high-shear homogenizer. The results show that nano BN lubricating oil can keep stable for more than two weeks. Generally speaking, if the above physical methods can be used at the same time, the stability and uniformity of nanoparticles in the basic lubricant will be greatly improved.

2.2 Surfactants

Surfactant is an amphiphilic substance with polar and non-polar groups. The polar group at one end of its molecule and the surface of the nanoparticle absorb electrostatically, forming a protective film on the surface of the nanoparticle. The non-polar group at the other end is compatible with the organic solvent, which promotes the stable dispersion of nanoparticles in the solvent.

Sumdani *et al.* (2019) successfully dispersed multi-walled carbon nanotubes (MWCNTs) in epoxy resin using anionic surfactant linear alkyl benzene sulfonic acid (LABSA). They observed the dispersion of MWCNTs in a polymer matrix using the scanning electron microscope. The results showed that MWCNTs were well dispersed in epoxy resin, and the agglomeration was inhibited. All the properties of MWCNTs were significantly improved. Clark *et al.* (2011) studied the influence of different concentrations of NaDDBS and CTAB surfactants on the dispersion of carbon nanotubes, as shown in Figure 1. With the increase of molecular surfactant concentration, the adsorption force on the surface of carbon nanotubes

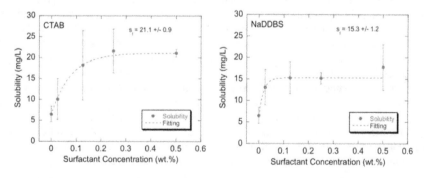

Figure 1. Dispersion of CTAB and NaDDBS Nanotubes at Different Surfactant Concentrations (Clark *et al.* 2011).

gradually increases, which enhances the interaction between nanoparticles and water, thus inhibiting the aggregation of nanoparticles and significantly improving the dispersion stability.

Ghasemi et al. (Musavi et al. 2019) dispersed titanium oxide nanoparticles into engine lubricating oil, in which oleic acid was used as a surfactant. According to the change of viscosity, the shear rate increases, and the viscosity decreases with the presence of surfactant, which means that the addition of surfactant helps eliminate agglomeration and enhance the stability of nanofluids. S. Another study by Musavi et al. (Ghasemi et al. 2018) is to use surfactants from the sodium dodecyl sulfate (SDS) group to enhance the stability of copper oxide and silicon oxide nanoparticles in the basic cutting fluid. The results show that the stability of nanoparticles with sodium dodecyl sulfate (SDS) is significantly improved, and the cutting surface can be improved compared with the fluid without SDS. The reason lies in the high ability of surfactant to disperse nanoparticles in the fluid medium and prevent the aggregation of nanoparticles. It can be seen from the current research that the commonly used surfactants are linear alkyl benzene sulfonic acid, oleic acid, sodium dodecyl sulfate, etc. Besides, dispersants can also be used as surfactants. The compatibility of the substance as a surfactant with the oil-based suspension is crucial because the choice of surfactant depends on the properties of particles and base oil.

2.3 *Surface modification of nanoparticles*

At present, the surface modification methods of nano-lubricating additive particles can be divided into the surface physical modification and surface chemical modification according to their modification principles, including surface coating modification, surface grafting modification, and coupling agent surface modification.

2.3.1 *Surface coating modification*

Surface coating modification is to change the surface state through surface adsorption or surface deposition of surface additives and nanoparticles, especially to improve the dispersion of nanoparticles. The surface coating is similar to the "core/shell" structure, in which the original particles are regarded as "cores" and the surface coating as "shells". The different types of coating layers can be divided into organic polymer coating, inorganic coating, biological macromolecule coating, and so on.

Xiong et al. (2012) used hydrazine hydrate as a reducing agent and tetradecyl hydroxamic acid (THA) as an organic polymer modifier to prepare oil-soluble copper nanoparticles without phosphorus and sulfur by in-situ surface modification technology. Copper nanoparticles coated on the surface can be well dispersed in some organic solvents, such as benzene, toluene, chloroform, and lubricating oil. The results show that the organic modifier can effectively prevent the agglomeration of nano copper powder and provide good dispersion ability. In addition, Ma et al. (2021) studied inorganic coating. Silica is used as the "core," and copper and molybdenum disulfide as the "shell," which core-shell structure silica-copper and silicon dioxide-molybdenum disulfide microspheres are formed after surface deposition and coating. Then, they are added to the poly (ethylene glycol) α—the olefin 40 (PAO 40) base oil and are uniformly mixed after ultrasonic treatment. Finally, the friction coefficient is measured with a ball plate friction and wear tester. The results show that compared with a pure base oil, the core-shell structure is added (SiO_2-Cu, SiO_2-MoS_2). The dispersion stability of the additive is better, and the friction coefficient is reduced by 32.47% and 30.98%, respectively.

2.3.2 *Surface graft modification*

The method of surface grafting modification is to achieve the purpose of modification by the chemical reaction between the modifier and the nanomaterial, and then joining the modifier group on the surface of the nanomaterial to some of its properties.

Zhang et al. (2010) used stearic acid (SA) to modify the surface of anatase (TiO$_2$) nanoparticles with an average particle size of 10 nm and used the modified SA-TiO$_2$ as an additive for liquid paraffin. The results showed that the liquid paraffin containing SA-TiO$_2$ had better dispersion than the unmodified liquid paraffin and showed good anti-wear and anti-friction properties under all loads. Fan et al. (2015) prepared ILs-modified graphene oxide (MGO) by grafting the epoxy group of graphene oxide with ILs. The results showed that the physical and chemical properties of GO, such as thermal and chemical stability, compatibility, and dispersion in MACs lubricants, were improved by the modification of ILs.

2.3.3 Coupling agent surface modification

A coupling agent is a kind of organosilicon compound with a special structure, and it is a kind of material with an amphiphilic structure. Some of the groups can react with the surface of the nanoparticles to form chemical bonds. Another part of the group can react with organic materials chemically or physically, effectively improving the dispersion of nanoparticles in lubricating oil.

Luo et al. (2014) modified nano Al$_2$O$_3$ particles prepared by hydrothermal method with silane coupling agent KH-560 and added them to lubricating oil. Through the four-ball and thrust-ring friction test, they studied the tribological properties of nano Al$_2$O$_3$ with different concentrations as lubricating oil additives. The wear scar diameter is shown in Table 1. The results show that the modified nano Al$_2$O$_3$ can effectively improve the lubricating performance of lubricating oil compared with the base oil. The reason is that the modified nano Al$_2$O$_3$ particles can be well dispersed in the lubricating oil, showing excellent dispersion stability.

Table 1. Average wear scar diameter of grinding balls under different Al$_2$O$_3$ additive concentrations. (Yang et al. 2016).

Concentration (wt%)	0	0.05	0.1	0.5	1.0
Average (μm)	597.58	433.21	348.09	441.43	581.76
Reduction (%)	0	27.51	41.75	26.13	2.65

Yang et al. (2016) successfully prepared oleic acid surface-modified lanthanum trifluoride graphene oxide (OA-laF$_3$-GO) nanohybrid material using surface modification technology. Their study then added it into liquid paraffin as a lubricating oil additive to study the tribological performance of OA-aF$_3$-GO hybrid material as liquid paraffin lubricating additive at different content. The research shows that the OA-laF$_3$-GO nanohybrid material is 0.5 wt %. The OA-laF$_3$-GO nano mixture can effectively improve the tribological properties of liquid paraffin compared with the single liquid paraffin.

3 CONCLUSION AND OUTLOOK

This paper presents several commonly used methods to improve the dispersion of nanomaterials as lubricating additives in detail. Among them, the mechanical dispersion method to prepare nanolubricants is the most widely used by previous researchers, but its effect is worse than that of surface modification of nanoparticles. The surface modification of nanoparticles can make full use of the respective excellent characteristics of nanomaterials and modifiers. Then the nano-lubricating material with new characteristics is prepared, which can greatly improve the dispersion in lubricating oil or other organic solvents.

The research on the dispersion of nano-lubricating additives should not be limited to the modification process and modifier. We should combine the structure and characteristics of the modified nanomaterials, tribological properties, and friction mechanism to improve the dispersion and stability of nano-lubricating additives in lubricating oil and to prepare a practical lubricating oil additive.

ACKNOWLEDGMENTS

The authors appreciate the financial support provided by the Key Research and Development Program of Liaoning Province (No. 2021JH2/10100003).

REFERENCES

Al-Hamadani Y.A.J. et al. (2015). "Stabilization and Dispersion of Carbon Nanomaterials in Aqueous Solutions: A Review." *Separation and Purification Technology* 156:861–874.
Ba Z. et al. (2018). "Composite Nanoparticles Based on Hydrotalcite as High Performance Lubricant Additives." *Industrial & Engineering Chemistry Research*.
Chen Y et al. (2019). "Dispersion of Nanoparticles in Lubricating Oil: A Critical Review." *Lubricants* 7(1).
Clark M.D et al. (2011). Understanding Surfactant Aided Aqueous Dispersion of Multi-Walled Carbon Nanotubes." *J Colloid Interface Sci* 354(1):144–151.
Fan X. and Wang L. (2015). "High-Performance Lubricant Additives Based on Modified Graphene Oxide by Ionic Liquids." *J Colloid Interface Sci* 452:98–108.
Ghasemi R. et al. (2018). "Effects of TiO_2 Nanoparticles and Oleic Acid Surfactant on the Rheological Behavior of Engine Lubricant Oil." *Journal of Molecular Liquids* 268:925–930.
Luo T. et al. (2014). "Tribological Properties of Al_2O_3 Nanoparticles as Lubricating Oil Additives." *Ceramics International* 40(5):7143–7149.
Ma X. et al. (2021). "Tribological Properties of SiO_2@Cu and SiO_2@MoS_2 Core–Shell Microspheres as Lubricant Additives." *Tribology Letters* 69(3).
Maheswaran R. and Sunil J. (2018). "Experimental Analysis of Tribological Properties of Ultrasonically Dispersed Garnet Nanoparticles in SN500 grade Lubricating Oil." *Industrial Lubrication and Tribology* 70 (2):250–255.
Mosleh M. et al. (2009). "Modification of Sheet Metal Forming Fluids with Dispersed Nanoparticles for Improved Lubrication." *Wear* 267(5–8): 1220–1225.
Musavi S.H. et al. (2019). "Effects of Reinforced Nanoparticles with Surfactant on Surface Quality and Chip Formation Morphology in MQL-Turning of Superalloys." *Journal of Manufacturing Processes* 40:128–139.
Shahnazar S. et al. (2016). "Enhancing Lubricant Properties by Nanoparticle Additives." *International Journal of Hydrogen Energy* 41(4):3153–3170.
Sumdani M.G. et al. (2019). "The Effects of Anionic Surfactant on the Mechanical, Thermal, Structure and Morphological Properties of Epoxy–MWCNT Composites." *Polymer Bulletin* 76(11):5919–5938.
Taha-Tijerina J. et al. (2013). "Multifunctional Nanofluids with 2D Nanosheets for Thermal and Tribological Management." *Wear* 302(1-2): 1241–1248.
Wan Q. et al. (2015). "Tribological Behaviour of a Lubricant Oil Containing Boron Nitride Nanoparticles." *Procedia Engineering* 102:1038–1045.
Xiong X. et al. (2012). "Preparation and Evaluation of Tribological Properties of Cu Nanoparticles Surface Modified by Tetradecyl Hydroxamic Acid." *Tribology Letters* 46(3):211–220.
Yang C. et al. (2016). "Preparation of Surface–Modified Lanthanum Fluoride–Graphene Oxide Nanohybrids and Evaluation of their Tribological Properties as Lubricant Additive in Liquid Paraffin." *Applied Surface Science* 388:497–502.
Yang G.B. et al. (2012). "Preparation and Tribological Properties of Surface Modified Cu Nanoparticles." *Transactions of Nonferrous Metals Society of China* 22(2): 366–372.
Zhang L. et al. (2010). "Synthesis and Tribological Properties of Stearic Acid-Modified Anatase (TiO_2) Nanoparticles." *Tribology Letters* 41(2):409–416.

Modeling rock deformation and breaking considering the initial compaction stage

Ben Wang*

State Key Laboratory of Geomechanics and Geotechnical Engineering, Institute of Rock and Soil Mechanics, Chinese Academy of Sciences, Wuhan, China
University of Chinese Academy of Sciences, Beijing, China

ABSTRACT: Rock is a material that is often encountered in oil and gas extraction, mining engineering, hydro, and nuclear power engineering. It is important to simulate the whole deformation and breaking process of rocks under external loads. To consider the initial compaction stage, a nonlinear elastic constitutive model is introduced into the combined finite-discrete element method. The uniaxial compression simulation of Transjurane Sandstone is carried out. Compared with the results of the traditional method, the stress-strain curve and failure pattern of the new method are closer to that of the experimental test.

1 INTRODUCTION

Rock is a material that is often encountered in oil and gas extraction (Yang & Zou 2019), mining engineering (Luo et al. 2021), hydropower engineering (Hu et al. 2018), and nuclear power engineering (Li et al. 2019). Due to complex geological processes and the influence of human factors (such as drilling and sampling, excavation disturbance and blasting vibration, etc.), there are always some micro-cracks in the rocks. The existence of these micro-cracks is closely related to the macro-mechanical behavior of rocks. As shown in Figure 1, the progressive failure process of rock can be divided into the following stages (Martin & Chandler 1994): I. Crack closure and compaction stage, II. Linear elastic region, III. Stable crack growth, IV. Unstable cracking, V. Post-peak stage.

Accurately simulating the whole process of rock deformation and failure under external load is of great significance for the study of rock mechanics. As a continuum-based method, it is difficult for the finite element method (FEM) to simulate the fracturing and breaking of rocks. The discrete element method (DEM) can simulate the fracturing of rocks, but it has difficulties in parameter calibration (Mishra & Murty 2001). The combined finite-discrete element method (FDEM) proposed by Munjiza (2004) integrates the advantages of FEM and DEM and is very suitable for simulating the progressive failure process of rocks (Wang et al. 2021). However, the traditional FDEM ignores the closure effect of micro-cracks, so it cannot simulate the nonlinear behavior of rocks under compression in the initial compaction stage.

This paper introduces a nonlinear constitutive model into FDEM to simulate rock deformation and breaking, including the initial compaction stage.

---

*Corresponding Author: wangben19@mails.ucas.ac.cn

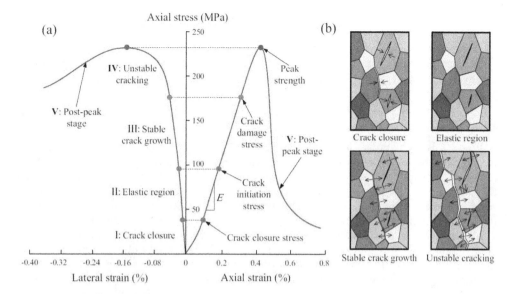

Figure 1. A diagram showing the stages of rock deformation in a uniaxial compression test (Martin & Chandler 1994): (a) several stress levels are determined from the stress-strain curve; (b) a schematic representation showing different crack behaviors including crack closure, crack initiation, crack propagation and coalescence.

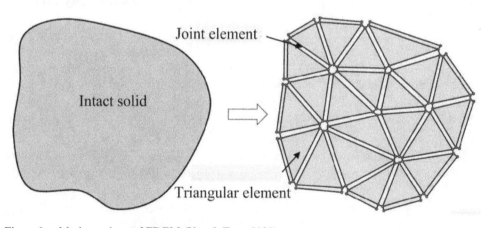

Figure 2. Mesh topology of FDEM (Yan & Tong 2020).

2 PRINCIPLES OF FDEM

The basic idea of FDEM is to separate a continuous body into a series of constant-strain triangular elements and insert non-thickness joint elements for bonding between adjacent triangular elements, as shown in Figure 2. The initiation, propagation, and intersection of cracks in the continuum are simulated by the damage and failure of joint elements.

FDEM is solved by an explicit algorithm. According to Newton's second law, the governing equation of the whole system is obtained as follows.

$$\mathbf{M}\ddot{\mathbf{x}} + \mathbf{C}\dot{\mathbf{x}} + \mathbf{F}_{int}(\mathbf{x}) - \mathbf{F}_{ext}(\mathbf{x}) - \mathbf{F}_c(\mathbf{x}) = \mathbf{0} \qquad (1)$$

Where **M** and **C** are the system mass and damping diagonal matrices, respectively; **x** is the vector of nodal displacements; $\mathbf{F}_{int}$, $\mathbf{F}_{ext}$, and $\mathbf{F}_c$ are the vectors of internal resisting forces, applied external loads, and contact forces, respectively.

The damping matrix **C** is introduced to the governing equation to dissipate the kinetic energy of the system or use dynamic relaxation to solve quasi-static problems. **C** is calculated as follows.

$$\mathbf{C} = \mu \mathbf{I} \tag{2}$$

Where μ is the damping coefficient, and **I** is the identity matrix. Contact forces, $\mathbf{F}_c$, are calculated between any two overlapping triangular elements according to a penalty method (Munjiza & Andrews 2000) in the normal direction and a Coulomb-type friction law (Mahabadi et al. 2012) in the tangential direction. Internal resisting forces, $\mathbf{F}_{int}$, include the resisting forces of triangular elements, $\mathbf{F}_e$, and of the joint elements, $\mathbf{F}_j$. The calculation of $\mathbf{F}_j$ (constitutive behavior of joint elements) in this paper is the same as that of (Lisjak et al. 2014), so it is not repeated. It should be noted that, for the consideration of the initial compaction stage in compression, the calculation of $\mathbf{F}_e$ is carried out according to a non-linear elastic constitutive model (Peng et al. 2015) instead of the traditional linear elastic constitutive model, which would be further explained in the next section.

3 CONSTITUTIVE MODEL OF TRIANGULAR ELEMENTS

As shown in Figure 1, the initial stage of the stress-strain curve of rocks under uniaxial compression is concave upward. The secant modulus can be expressed as follows (Peng et al. 2015).

$$E_c = E_0 + (E - E_0)C \tag{3}$$

Where E_0 is the initial modulus, E is the tangent modulus at a post-compaction stage, and C is the compaction coefficient that is calculated as follows.

$$C = 1 - \exp\left[-\left(\frac{\varepsilon}{f_0}\right)^m\right] \tag{4}$$

Where ε is the axial strain, m and f_0 are two material parameters. The stress tensor of triangular elements is calculated by replacing E with E_c in the linear elastic constitutive equation (Munjiza 2004):

$$\mathbf{T} = \left[\frac{E_c}{1+v}\mathbf{E}_d + \frac{E_c}{1-v}\mathbf{E}_s + 2\mu\mathbf{D}\right]/\sqrt{|\det\mathbf{F}|} \tag{5}$$

Where **T** is the stress tensor, and **F** is the deformation gradient. $\mathbf{E}_d$ and $\mathbf{E}_s$ are the shape change part and volume change part of Green-St. Venant strain tensor, respectively. v is Poisson's ratio, and **D** is the strain rate tensor.

4 NUMERICAL SIMULATION

The uniaxial compression numerical test of Transjurane Sandstone is carried out to verify the capacity of the improved FDEM to simulate the initial compaction stage and rock breaking. The physical and mechanical properties of Transjurane Sandstone are shown in Table 1 (Kazerani 2013).

Table 1. Physical and mechanical properties of transjurane sandstone.

Property	Value
Young's modulus, E (GPa)	12.5
Poisson's ratio, v	0.3
Internal cohesion, c(MPa)	8.5
Internal friction angle, $\phi(°)$	41.0
Brazilian tensile strength, BTS(MPa)	2.8
Uniaxial compressive strength, UCS(MPa)	40.0

4.1 *Numerical model and the input micro parameters*

The mesh of the numerical model is shown in Figure 3. The sample width is 50 mm, and the height is 100 mm. The sample is divided into triangular elements with an average side length

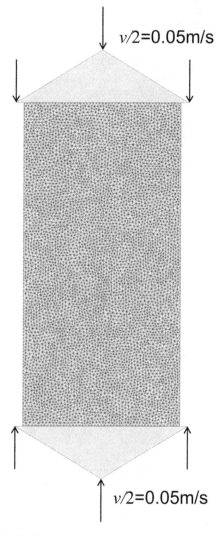

Figure 3. Numerical model of uniaxial compression.

of 1 mm. Two rigid loading plates move towards each other with a constant velocity at both ends of the sample. Since the loading speed can influence the macro-mechanical response of the sample, the velocity is taken as 0.05 m/s. Although this speed is much higher than the actual loading speed, the trial tests show that the simulation results no longer vary with the loading speed when the loading speed is less than or equal to this speed. The time step is taken as 1.2×10^{-9} s to ensure numerical stability.

The input micro parameters are listed in Table 2. The three parameters E_0, m, and f_0 are determined by trial and error, and the other input parameters are determined according to the calibration method explained in (Kazerani 2013).

Table 2. Input parameters in the simulation.

Parameter	Value
Density, ρ (kg/m^3)	2600
Initial modulus, E_0(GPa)	2.3
Tangent modulus at post-compaction stage, E (GPa)	12.5
Material compaction parameter, m	1.274
Material compaction parameter, $f_0(\times 10^{-3})$	2.845
Poisson's ratio, v	0.3
Damping coefficient, μ(kg/m·s)	11402
Normal penalty of joint elements, p_{fn} (GPa)	375
Tangential penalty of joint elements, p_{fs} (GPa)	375
Tensile strength, f_t (MPa)	1.7
Internal cohesion, c(MPa)	7.6
Internal friction angle, ϕ(°)	39.0
Mode I fracture energy, G_{fI} (J/m2)	40
Mode II fracture energy, G_{fII} (J/m2)	120
Contact penalty, p (GPa)	54.3
Sliding friction angle, ϕ_r (°)	39.0

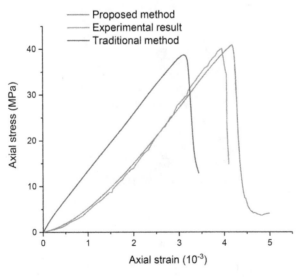

Figure 4. Comparison of stress-strain curves obtained from the proposed method, experimental result, and the traditional method.

4.2 *Simulation results*

The stress-strain curve of the proposed method is compared with that of the experimental test and the traditional method (Kazerani 2013), as shown in Figure 4. It can be seen that the curve of the proposed method is closer to that of the experimental result.

The comparison of failure patterns is shown in Figure 5. It can be seen that the numerical result from the proposed method is close to that of the experimental result.

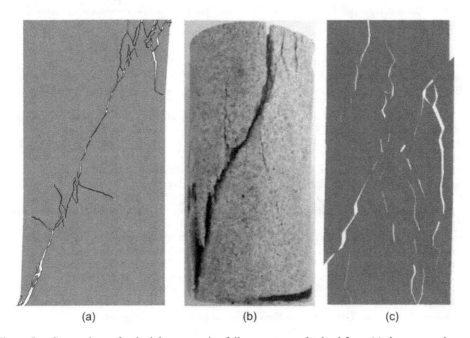

Figure 5. Comparison of uniaxial compressive failure patterns obtained from (a) the proposed numerical method, (b) the experimental result, and (c) the traditional numerical method.

5 CONCLUSION

To accurately simulate the whole process of rock deformation and breaking, a nonlinear elastic constitutive model considering the initial compaction stage is implemented into the combined finite-discrete element method. The uniaxial compression simulation of Transjurane Sandstone is carried out to verify the proposed method. The results indicated that, compared to the traditional method, the stress-strain curve and failure pattern of the proposed method are closer to that of the experimental test. The proposed method can provide a useful tool for future works about problems that are sensitive to the initial compaction stage of rocks.

ACKNOWLEDGMENT

We gratefully acknowledge financial support from the National Key R&D Program of China (2020YFA0711802).

REFERENCES

Hu Y.G., Liu M.S., Wu X.X., Zhao G. and Li P. (2018). Damage-Vibration Couple Control of rock Mass Blasting for High Rock Slopes. *International Journal of Rock Mechanics and Mining Sciences*.

Kazerani T. (2013). Effect of Micromechanical Parameters of Microstructure on Compressive and Tensile Failure Process of Rock. *International Journal of Rock Mechanics and Mining Sciences*, 64, 44–55.

Li X.F., Li H.B. and Zhang G.K. (2019). Damage Assessment and Blast Vibrations Controlling Considering Rock Properties of Underwater Blasting. *International Journal of Rock Mechanics and Mining Sciences*, 121.

Lisjak A., Grasselli G. and Vietor T. (2014). Continuum-Discontinuum Analysis of Failure Mechanisms Around Unsupported Circular Excavations in Anisotropic Clay Shales. *International Journal of Rock Mechanics and Mining Sciences*, 65, 96–115.

Luo Y., Xu K., Huang J., Li X., Liu T., Qu D. and Chen P. (2021). Impact Analysis of Pressure-Relief Blasting on Roadway Stability in a Deep Mining Area Under High Stress. *Tunneling and Underground Space Technology*, 110, 103781.

Mahabadi O.K., Lisjak A., Munjiza A. and Grasselli G. (2012). Y-Geo: New Combined Finite-Discrete Element Numerical Code for Geomechanical Applications. *International Journal of Geomechanics*, 12(6), 676–688.

Martin C.D. and Chandler N. A. (1994). The progressive Fracture of Lac du Bonnet Granite. *International Journal of Rock Mechanics and Mining Sciences & Geomechanics Abstracts*, 31(6), 643–659.

Mishra B.K. and Murty C.V.R. (2001). On the Determination of Contact Parameters for Realistic DEM Simulations of Ball Mills. *Powder Technology*.

Munjiza A.A. (2004). *The combined finite-discrete element method.* John Wiley & Sons.

Munjiza A. and Andrews K.R.F. (2000). Discretised Penalty Function Method in Combined Finite-Discrete Element Analysis. *International Journal for Numerical Methods in Engineering*, 49(11), 1495–1520.

Peng J., Rong G., Cai M. and Zhou C.B. (2015). A Model for Characterizing Crack Closure Effect of Rocks. *Engineering Geology*.

Wang B., Li H., Shao Z., Chen S. and Li X. (2021). Investigating the Mechanism of Rock Fracturing Induced by High-Pressure Gas Blasting With a Hybrid Continuum-Discontinuum Method. *Computers and Geotechnics*.

Yan C. and Tong Y. (2020). Calibration of Microscopic Penalty Parameters in the Combined Finite–Discrete-Element Method. *International Journal of Geomechanics*, 20(7), 4020092.

Zhi Y. and Caineng Z.O.U. (2019). "Exploring Petroleum Inside Source Kitchen": Connotation and Prospects of Source Rock Oil and Gas. *Petroleum Exploration and Development*, 46(1), 181–193.

Research on influencing factors of compressive strength of fly ash-based geopolymer mortar new building structure materials

Chao Li
Institute of Civil Engineering, Huzhou Vocational and Technical College, Huzhou Key Laboratory of Green Building Technology, Huzhou, China

Jianhua Li*
Jiyang College, Zhejiang A & F University, Hangzhou, China

Xueyong Xu & Lele Yu
Institute of Civil Engineering, Huzhou Vocational and Technical College, Huzhou Key Laboratory of Green Building Technology, Huzhou, China

ABSTRACT: To investigate the influencing factors of the compressive strength of fly ash-based geopolymer mortar, the Sand/FA ratio, the concentration of AS, the modulus of AS, liquid–solid ratio were studied by orthogonal test and single variable method, respectively. Results indicated that the Sand/FA ratio has little effect on the compressive strength of geopolymer mortar. The higher the concentration of AS and the greater the modulus of AS, the greater the compressive strength of geopolymer mortar. The liquid–solid ratio and compressive strength show the opposite trend. The higher the liquid–solid ratio, the lower the compressive strength of the geopolymer mortar. When the liquid–solid ratio is 0.65, the compressive strength of the geopolymer mortar reaches the maximum.

1 INTRODUCTION

In 2021, China's energy consumption was 5.24 billion tons of standard coal (China National Bureau of Statistics 2022). As a big producer and consumer of thermal power, which leads to approximately 1,148 million tons of carbon dioxide emissions, a large amount of solid waste—fly ash produced at the same time. The emission of fly ash is as high as 650 million tons, but the comprehensive utilization rate is only 70% (Li et al. 2022). Fly ash is one of the bulk industrial solid wastes in China that is produced in the production process of coal-fired industries such as thermal power generation. Untreated fly ash will not only cause environmental pollution but also enter the atmosphere, threatening public safety (Jiang & Huang 2015). Some achievements have been made in the reuse of fly ash cause of the attention of more and more scholars. At present, the construction industry is the main application field for the research of fly ash, including cement, concrete, engineering backfill, and road engineering (Geng et al. 2012).

Among which fly ash is one of the most widely studied and applied materials, geopolymer is the general term for high alumina silicate materials such as metakaolin, fly ash, and slag. It is the research direction of many scholars to study the mechanical properties, durability, high-temperature resistance, and material mix ratio of geopolymer mortar.

---

*Corresponding Author: 20759618@qq.com

Palomo et al. (Alonso & Palomo 2001) found that the higher the PH value of the solution, the longer the migration time of ions in the geopolymer and the longer the setting hardening time of the geopolymer, resulting in the decrease of the mechanical properties of the geopolymer. However, Hou et al. (2007) showed that when K_2SiO_3 was used as an activator, the compressive strength of fly ash-based polymers increased with the increase of activator concentration. The strength of the geopolymer reached the maximum when the concentration was 2 mol/L. Zheng et al. (2008) showed that the compressive strength of geopolymer was related to the modulus of sodium silicate. When the concentration was low, the strength of the geopolymer increased with the increase of the modulus of sodium silicate. As the modulus reached 1.4, the strength of the geopolymer reached the maximum, and then the strength of the geopolymer decreased with the increase in the modulus of sodium silicate. Ryu et al. (2013) also drew similar conclusions: the higher the alkali concentration was, the higher the splitting tensile strength and compressive strength of the geopolymer were. The hydration products of geopolymer were aluminates with an amorphous structure. Djobo et al. (2016) studied the effect of curing conditions on the strength of geopolymer. The results showed that the apparent density, porosity, and compressive strength of geopolymer mortar cured at 80°C were better, but the mechanical properties of geopolymer cured at high temperatures decreased slightly after 180 d. Elyamany et al. (Elyamany et al. 2018; Khalil, Elgabbas et al. 2020; Murthi et al. 2020; Rocha et al. 2018; Wetzel & Middendorf 2019; Zhu et al. 2020) also conducted a similar study. The results show that the mechanical properties of geopolymer mortar can be improved by increasing the curing temperature, increasing activator concentration, and decreasing the water-binder ratio. More and more construction projects adopt geopolymer, and the relevant research is increasingly urgent simultaneously (Aguirre-Guerrero et al. 2017; Ma et al. 2018).

The published research on the geopolymer mortar mainly focuses on the factors affecting the geopolymer mortar, such as the concentration of alkali activator, cement sand ratio, water glass modulus, and curing temperature.

The novelty of this study is that it refers to the strength of commonly used mortar in China, and with this strength range as a reference, a geopolymer mortar with corresponding strength is prepared. The geopolymer mortar is made by considering the factors such as the Sand/FA ratio (sand fly ash ratio), the concentration of AS (concentration of alkali solution), the modulus of AS (modulus of alkali solution), liquid–solid ratio, which can provide a reference for the design of fly ash base polymer mortar conforming to China's national standards. The main objective of the present study is to:

1. Fly ash base polymer mortar with common strength is prepared through the test;
2. The effects of the Sand/FA ratio, the concentration of AS, the modulus of AS, and the liquid–solid ratio on the compressive strength of geopolymer mortar were studied.

2 MATERIALS AND METHODS

2.1 Material

2.1.1 Sand

The sand shall be local river sand after cleaning and screening. The standard sieve (Highway Science Research Institute of the Ministry of Communications 2005) is adopted for screening, and the pore sizes are 4.75 mm, 2.36 mm, 1.18 mm, 0.6 mm, 0.3 mm, and 0.15 mm from large to small. The retained percentage of sand is shown in Table 1, and the sieve-analysis curve is shown in Figure 1. The fineness modulus of sand is 2.23, according to the calculation (Highway Science Research Institute of the Ministry of Communications 2005).

Table 1. Retained percentage of sand.

Sieve Aperture(mm)	Residue(g)	Grader Retained Percentage (%)	Cumulative Screening Percentage (%)
4.75	11.9	2.38	2.38
2.36	60.8	12.16	14.54
1.18	49.6	9.92	24.46
0.6	62.8	12.56	37.02
0.3	129.2	25.84	62.86
0.15	141.2	28.24	91.10
Bottom	44.7	8.94	100.04

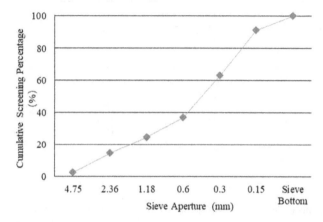

Figure 1. Cumulative sieve curve.

2.1.2 *Alkali activator solution*

The sodium silicate solution, sodium hydroxide, and distilled water were mixed to prepare the alkali activator solution needed in this experiment. The modulus of the original sodium silicate solution was 2.31, the concentration was 42%, the degree of Bomer was 50, and the purity of NaOH was 98%.

2.1.3 *Fly ash*

The main chemical composition of a low calcium fly ash is shown in Table 2, which was provided by a local construction material company used in this research.

Table 2. Chemical composition of Fly ash.

Material	Al_2O_3(%)	S_iO_2(%)	H_2O(%)	SO_3(%)	C_aO(%)	Alkali(%)	F_e(%)	Ignition Loss (%)
Fly ash	24.2	45.1	0.85	2.1	5.6	1.2	0.85	2.8

2.2 *Methods*

The fly ash in this test is a Grade I low calcium fly ash provided by a local building material company in Huzhou. Table 2 shows the main chemical composition.

First, mix sodium water glass, sodium hydroxide, and distilled water in a beaker to prepare the alkali activator solution required for the test. Then, add the fly ash and alkali activator solution into the mixing pot with the wall wet, and stir for half a minute; subsequently, sand was added while stirring. After stirring for 2 minutes, it was allowed to stand for 1 minute, and after stirring for another 2 minutes, it was loaded with a size of 70.7 mm × 70.7 mm × 70.7 mm cube test mold and each group had 3 test blocks. Tamp 25 times with a tamping rod and smooth the surface with a spatula. Table 3 shows the components of geopolymer mortar.

Table 3. Composition of geopolymer mortar.

Mix ID	Sand/ g	Fly Ash/ g	AS /g	Sand/ FA ratio	Concentration of AS	Modulus of AS	Liquid–Solid ratio
M1S35	1750	500	350.0	3.50	22%	1	0.7
M1S45	1750	389	272.2	4.50	22%	1	0.7
M1S40	1750	438	306.3	4.00	22%	1	0.7
M2N16	1750	438	306.3	4.00	16%	1	0.7
M2N18	1750	438	306.3	4.00	18%	1	0.7
M2N20	1750	438	306.3	4.00	20%	1	0.7
M3M09	1750	438	306.3	4.00	22%	0.9	0.7
M3M11	1750	438	306.3	4.00	22%	1.1	0.7
M3M12	1750	438	306.3	4.00	22%	1.2	0.7
M4G60	1750	438	262.5	4.00	22%	1	0.6
M4G65	1750	438	284.4	4.00	22%	1	0.65
M4G75	1750	438	328.1	4.00	22%	1	0.75

After the test piece is manufactured, the formwork shall be removed after curing at room temperature for one day, and the compressive strength test shall be conducted on 3/7/28 days, respectively. The compressive strength test complies with the Chinese national code "test code for cement and cement concrete of Highway Engineering" (Highway Science Research Institute of the Ministry of Communications 2020). Based on M1S40 samples (Sand/FA ratio 4.0, the concentration of AS 22%, modulus of AS 1, liquid–solid ratio 0.7), this paper adjusts four parameters to study the influence of these four parameters on the compressive strength of polymer mortar.

3 RESULTS AND DISCUSSION

Table 4 shows the compressive strength data of geopolymer mortar at different ages. The compressive test results of geopolymer mortar with different ratios are analyzed and discussed in detail in this section.

3.1 *Effect of sand/FA ratio*

Sand-cement ratio not only affects the working performance of geopolymer mortar but also affects the compressive strength of geopolymer mortar to a certain extent. Table 4 and Figure 2 showed the compressive strength of geopolymer mortar at different ages when the sand-cement ratio changed from 3.5 to 4.5. Compared with M1S35, M1S40, and M1S45, the greater the sand-cement ratio, the higher the strength of the geopolymer. However, the sand-cement ratio changes from 3.5 to 4.5, and the strength of geopolymer mortar increases by only 6% as the effect of the Sand/FA ratio on the strength of geopolymer mortar is very limited.

Table 4. Compressive strength of geopolymer mortar.

Mix ID	3-Day			7-Day			28-Day		
M1S35	1.8	1.8	1.8	4.3	4.6	4.7	7.6	7.6	7.9
M1S45	1.9	2.0	1.9	4.7	4.5	5.0	8.1	7.9	8.1
M1S40	1.8	2.1	2.1	4.9	4.7	5.0	8.3	8.3	7.9
M2N16	—	—	—	—	—	—	1.4	1.5	1.4
M2N18	—	—	—	—	—	—	3.2	3.3	3.1
M2N20	—	—	—	2.1	1.9	1.9	6.9	7.0	7.4
M3M09	1.9	2.0	1.9	4.7	4.5	5.0	8.1	7.9	8.1
M3M11	—	—	—	2.3	2.0	2.3	6.3	6.3	6.6
M3M12	1.91	1.98	1.87	4.68	4.54	5	8.13	7.87	8.07
M4G60	2.0	2.1	2.1	4.9	4.8	4.9	10.6	10.4	10.5
M4G65	2.2	2.2	2.3	5.1	5.0	5.1	12.3	12.3	11.6
M4G75	2.1	2.1	2.0	4.8	4.7	4.8	9.0	8.6	9.2

Note: The strength of the part of the test pieces is too low to be detected.

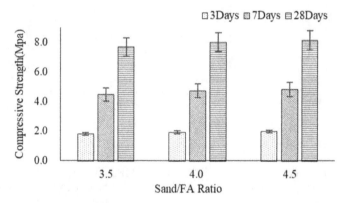

Figure 2. Compressive strength after 3/7/28 days.

3.2 Effect of concentration of AS

To study the effect of the concentration of AS on the compressive strength of geopolymer mortar, M2N16, M2N18, M2N20, and M1S40 were compared. Figure 3 shows that when the concentration of AS is increased from 16% to 22%, the 28-day compressive strength of geopolymer mortar is increased from 1.4 MPa to 8.1 MPa. This indicates that the higher the concentration of AS, the higher the water glass component participating in the chemical reaction, and the more hydrates formed, which leads to higher compressive strength. The early strength of the geopolymer mortar is formed slowly. When the solution concentration is low (16–20%), the 3-day and 7-day strengths of the mortar are too low to be measured.

3.3 Effect of modulus of AS

M3M09, M1S40, M3M11, and M3M12 were compared to study the effect of the modulus of AS on the compressive strength of geopolymer mortar. It can be seen from Figure 4 that the higher the modulus of AS, the higher the compressive strength of the geopolymer mortar. When the modulus of AS increases from 0.9 to 1.2, the 28-day compressive strength of

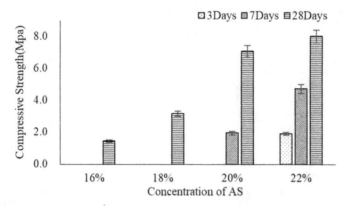

Figure 3. Compressive strength after 3/7/28 Days.

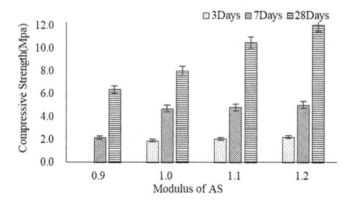

Figure 4. Compressive strength after 3/7/28 days.

geopolymer mortar increases from 6.4 MPa to 12.1 MPa. When the modulus is 0.9, the 3-day compressive strength of the geopolymer is too low to be detected.

3.4 *Effect of liquid–olid ratio*

M4G60, M4G65, M1S40, and M4G70 were compared to study the effect of the liquid–solid ratio on the compressive strength of geopolymer mortar. Figure 5 shows that when the

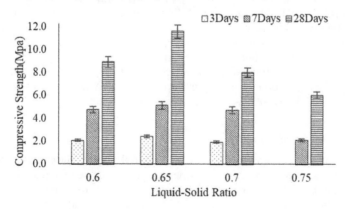

Figure 5. Compressive strength after 3/7/28 days.

liquid–solid ratio is lower than 0.65, the higher the liquid–solid ratio, the lower the compressive strength of the geopolymer mortar. A higher liquid–solid ratio means that less fly ash corresponds to the unit mass of the alkali solution, which will also lead to the reduction of the strength of the hydrate formed. When the liquid–solid ratio is 0.6, the fluidity of the geopolymer mortar decreases, resulting in an increase in internal voids, which leads to a decrease in strength.

4 CONCLUSIONS

Sand/FA ratio, concentrations of AS, modulus of AS, and liquid–solid ratio can all affect the compressive strength of geopolymer mortar. Orthogonal tests and single variable methods are used to study the influence of these factors on the compressive strength of geopolymer mortar.

The following conclusions are drawn:

1. The influence of the Sand/FA ratio on the strength of geopolymer mortar is weak and can be ignored;
2. The concentrations of AS and the modulus of AS will directly affect the amount of water glass participating in the chemical reaction, which has a great impact on the compressive strength of geopolymer mortar. The higher the concentrations of AS and the greater modulus of AS, the greater the compressive strength of geopolymer mortar;
3. When the liquid–solid ratio is 0.65, the compressive strength of geopolymer mortar reaches the maximum.

ACKNOWLEDGMENT

This research was supported by:

School Level Planning Project of Huzhou Vocational and Technical College No. 2022YB02.
Zhejiang basic public welfare research program, grant number LGF19E080014.
Research on The Application of Special Public Welfare Technology for High-level Talents of Huzhou Vocational and Technical College No. 2022GY05.
Huzhou Public Welfare Application Research Project No. 2021GZ59.

REFERENCES

Aguirre-Guerrero A.M., Robayo-Salazar R.A. and Gutiérrez R.M. (2017). A Novel Geopolymer Application: Coatings to Protect Reinforced Concrete Against Corrosion. *Applied Clay Science*, 135: 437–446.
Alonso S. and Palomo A. (2001) Calorimetric Study of Alkaline Activation of Calcium Hydroxide–Metakaolin Solid Mixtures. *Cement & Concrete Research*, 31(1): 25–30.
China National Bureau of Statistics. (2022) *Statistical Bulletin on the National Economic and Social Development of the People's Republic of China in 2021*, http://www.stats.gov.cn/tjsj/zxfb/202202/t20220227_1827960.html
Djobo J., Elimbi A., Tchakoute H.K. and Kumar S. (2016) Mechanical Properties and Durability of Volcanic Ash Based Geopolymer Mortars. *Construction & Building Materials*, 124 (OCT.15), 606–614.
Elyamany H.E., Elmoaty A.E.M.A. and Elshaboury A.M. (2018) Setting Time and 7-day Strength of Geopolymer Mortar with Various Binders. *Construction and Building Materials*, 187, 974–983.
Highway Science Research Institute of the Ministry of Communications. (2005) *Test Methods of Aggregate for Highway Engineering*, JTG E42-2005.

Highway Science Research Institute of the Ministry of Communications. (2020) *Test Methods of Cement and Concrete for Highway Engineering*, JTG 3420-2020.

Hou Y. F., Wang D.M. and Qiao L. (2007) Effects of Activator on Compressive Strength of Fly Ash-based Geopolymers. *Journal of Building Materials*, (02), 214–218 (in Chinese).

Khalil M.G., Elgabbas F., El-Feky M.S. and El-Shafie H. (2020) Performance of Geopolymer Mortar Cured Under Ambient Temperature. *Construction and Building Materials*, 242.

Lipin Jiang, Lei Huang. (2015) Present Situation and Development Trend of Comprehensive Utilization of Fly Ash. *Coal Chemical Industry*, 43(02): 64-68+63 (in Chinese).

Ma C.K., Awang A.Z. and Omar W. (2018) Structural and Material Performance of Geopolymer Concrete: A Review. *Construction and Building Materials*, 186 (OCT.20), 90–102.

Murthi P., Poongodi K., Saravanan R., Chary K.R. and Gobinath R. (2020). Effect of Ratio between Na_2SiO_3 and NaOH Solutions and Curing Temperature on The Early Age Properties of Geopolymer Mortar. *IOP Conference Series Materials Science and Engineering*, 981, 032060.

Pengfei Geng, Shuai Gao, Fengge Chu. (2012) Comprehensive Utilization of Fly Ash. *Clean Coal Technology*, 18(2):102–104 (in Chinese).

Qin Li, Yuebin Yang, Jun Liu, Hongjin Xin, Shu Xu, Jinxue Liu, Xiao Hou. (2022) Present Situation and Prospect of Utilization of Fly Ash in China. *Energy Research and Management*, (01):29–34 (in Chinese).

Rocha T.D.S., Dias D.P., Coelho Franca F.C., Rangel D.S.G.R. and da Costa de Oliveira Marques, Larissa Rodrigues. (2018) *Metakaolin-based Geopolymer Mortars with Different Alkaline Activators (Na+ and K+). Construction and Building Materials*, 178 (JUL.30), 453–461.

Ryu G.S., Lee Y.B., Koh K.T. and Chung Y.S. (2013) The Mechanical Properties of Fly Ash-based Geopolymer Concrete with Alkaline Activators. *Construction & Building Materials*, 47(oct.), 409–418.

Wetzel A. and Middendorf B. (2019) Influence of Silica Fume on Properties of Fresh and Hardened Ultra-high Performance Concrete based on Alkali-activated Slag. *Cement and Concrete Composites*, 100(2): 53–59.

Zheng J.R. and Liu L.N. (2008) Experimental Study on Formation Conditions of Metakaolinite-based Geopolymer. *Journal of Zhengzhou University (Engineering Science)*, 29(2): 44–47 (in Chinese).

Zhu P., Hua M., Liu H., Wang X. and Chen, C. (2020) Interfacial Evaluation of Geopolymer Mortar Prepared with Recycled Geopolymer Fine Aggregates. *Construction and Building Materials*, 259, 119849.

Civil Engineering and Energy-Environment – Gao & Duan (Eds)
© 2023 the Author(s), ISBN 978-1-032-56057-1

Description of strain softening curve by relative referring

Enyang Zhu*, Yinxi Ma, Jiaying Wang, Yangbo Li & Yuqi Zhang
School of Civil Engineering, North China University of Technology, Beijing, China

ABSTRACT: Strain softening is one of the fundamental behaviors of geotechnical materials, and strain-softening shape evolutions are widely exist. In this paper, by applying relative referring, a kind of total expression of strain softening shape evolution $y(x)$ is presented. With three parameters, respectively, reflecting the final y value, the peak y value, and the x value corresponding to peak y, the presented total expression $y(x)$ is qualified in describing the majority of kinds of strain-softening shape evolutions.

1 INTRODUCTION

Strain softening and strain softening shape evolutions widely exist in geotechnical engineering (Zhu 2015). These nonmonotonic evolutions can be reasonably described in elasto-plastic incremental constitutive models, such as the unified hardening model (UH model) and the structured unified hardening model. According to the UH model, taking the normal compression line (NCL) as the reference line, the isotropic compression line of the reconstituted soil finally converges to the NCL, and the magnitude of the tangent slope increases monotonically from a small value to the compression index λ. As shown in Figure 1, the tangent slope of one point on the isotropic compression line is determined by the relative position of the tangency point to the NCL (Zhu 2015). In the description of the over-consolidated soil under shearing, as the shear strain develops monotonically, the potential failure stress ratio M_f decreases monotonically and tends to the critical state stress ratio M (Hong et al. 2012; Yao 2015; Yao et al. 2012). Referring to this dynamic M_f, the stress ratio

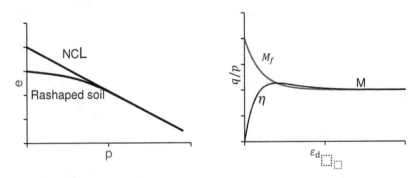

Figure 1. Descriptions of isotropic compression and shearing by the UH model.

---

*Corresponding Author: zhuenyang@ncut.edu.cn

η increases to a peak value and then decreases to tend to the critical state stress ratio M (Hong et al. 2012; Liu & Shen 2006; Yao et al. 2011, 2012). In this process, the strain-softening shape evolution of the stress ratio η is also determined by the relationship between the current η value and current M_f value (Liu et al. 2012; Wang et al. 2021; Yao et al. 2011, 2019; Yao & Kong 2012; Zhu & Yao 2013). Inspired by this internal variable referring method, a full quantity description of strain softening shape evolution is presented in this paper.

2 FULL QUANTITY DESCRIPTION OF STRAIN SOFTENING SHAPE EVOLUTION

2.1 Full quantity description of strain softening shape evolution

In Zhu's work (Zhu 2015), a relative referring method incrementally describing strain softening curves is presented. Let y_r be the reference variable in the rectangular coordinate system $x \sim y$, and the current variable y evolves with the reference variable y_r as the target, which would be expressed incrementally as:

$$\begin{cases} y_r = y_r(x) \\ dy = (y_r - y)dx \end{cases} \quad (1)$$

According to Equation (1), different reference variable functions $y_r(x)$ lead to different evolutions of the current variable y. This incremental description is qualified in reflecting different kinds of strain softening shape evolutions, but usually, the full quantity description cannot be obtained, which makes it difficult to be applied in practical engineering to reflect the overall evolution. Consequently, Equation (1) is developed to be the following form.

$$\begin{cases} y_r(x) = a + b \cdot e^{-cx} \\ dy = c(y_r - y)dx \end{cases} \quad (2)$$

In Equation (2), there are 3 model parameters: a, b, and c. With the boundary condition $y(0) = 0$ for simplicity, the differential equation in Equation (2) can be solved to be:

$$y(x) = a(1 - e^{-cx}) + cbxe^{-cx} \quad (3)$$

Considering both $y_r(x)$ and $y(x)$, the intersection point coordinate (x_i, y_i) is obtained as:

$$\begin{cases} x_i = (a+b)/(bc) \\ y_i = a + b \cdot e^{-\frac{a+b}{b}} \end{cases} \quad (4)$$

From Equation (3), as the independent variable x tends to be infinity, the limitation of the dependent variable $y(x)$ is $\lim_{x \to +\infty} y(x) = a$. Thus, parameter a reflects the final asymptotic value of the strain-softening shape evolution, which can also be applied to determine the value of parameter a. According to Equation (2), as $y_r = y$, $(dy/dx) = 0$, the dependent variable $y(x)$ reaches the maximum value of $y_{\max} = y_i = a + b \cdot e^{-\frac{a+b}{b}}$. After parameter a is determined, parameter b can be determined from the peak value of the strain-softening shape evolution. Then, according to coordinate x_i in Equation (4), parameter c is related to the x coordinate of the peak point. Therefore, after parameters a and b are determined, parameter c can be determined from the x value corresponding to the peak point of the strain-softening shape evolution.

2.2 Description of two typical evolutions

For the first typical evolution, the reference variable is constant $y_r(x) = a$. In this case, the parameters $a > 0$, $b = 0$, and $c > 0$, then Equation (2) degenerates to Equation (5).

$$\begin{cases} y_r(x) = a \\ dy = c(y_r - y)dx \end{cases} \quad (5)$$

Then, the full quantity description of the current variable $y(x)$ is written as follows:

$$y(x) = a(1 - e^{-cx}) \quad (6)$$

Both the reference variable $y_r(x)$ and the current variable $y(x)$ are illustrated in Figure 2.
When $a = 1$ and $c = 1, 2, 3$, the reference variable $y_r(x)$ and the current variable $y(x)$ are illustrated in Figure 3(a). When $c = 1$, and $a = 1, 2, 3$, the current variable $y(x)$ is illustrated in Figure 3(b).

Figure 2 can also be applied to encourage the students. Any target (the constant y_r) is to be determined to win through continuous hard work ($dy > 0$ just as $y < y_r$).

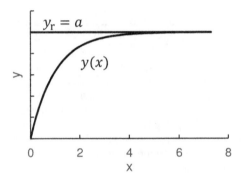

Figure 2. Current variable evolution referring a constant variable.

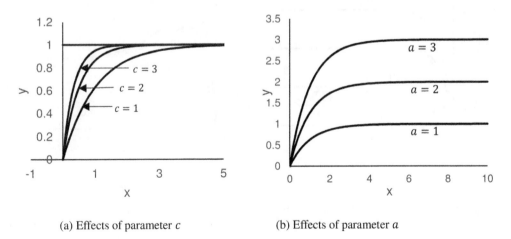

(a) Effects of parameter c (b) Effects of parameter a

Figure 3. The current variable $y(x)$ referring a constant variable with different parameters.

However, if the target is not kept to be constant, what will happen to the students? That is the second typical evolution. As the reference variable decreases to tend to a constant, in this case, the parameters $a > 0$, $b > 0$, and $c > 0$. Both the reference variable $y_r(x)$ and the current variable $y(x)$ are illustrated in Figure 4.

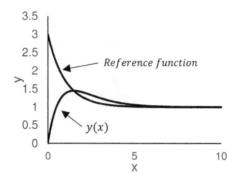

Figure 4. The current variable $y(x)$ referring a decreasing reference variable.

Initially, $y < y_r$, $(dy/dx) > 0$, and the function $y(x)$ increases. As $y(x)$ gradually increases, (dy/dx) gradually decreases until y meets y_r and (dy/dx) reaches 0, at which point $y(x)$ reaches its peak. Subsequently, the current point crosses above the reference line, then $y > y_r$ and (dy/dx) turns to be negative, the current variable $y(x)$ begins to decrease. Finally, both y and y_r tend to have an asymptotic value.

For different parameters a, b, c, the current variable $y(x)$ is illustrated in Figure 5. When $b = 1$, $c = 1$, and $a = 1, 2, 3$, the current variable $y(x)$ is illustrated in Figure 5(a). When $c = 1$, $a = 1$, and $b = 1, 2, 3$, the current variable $y(x)$ is illustrated in Figure 5(b). When $a = 1$, $b = 1$, and $c = 1, 2, 3$, the current variable $y(x)$ is illustrated in Figure 5(c).

As the reference variable increases to tend to a constant, in this case, the parameters $a > 0$, $b < 0$, and $c > 0$. The reference variables $y_r(x)$ and the current variable $y(x)$ are illustrated in Figure 6.

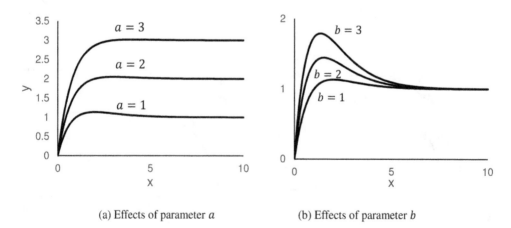

(a) Effects of parameter a (b) Effects of parameter b

Figure 5. The current $y(x)$ referring a decreasing $y(r)$ with different parameters.

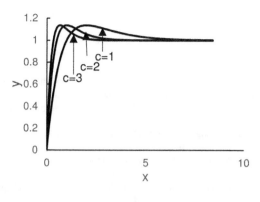

(c) Effects of parameter c

Figure 5. (Continued)

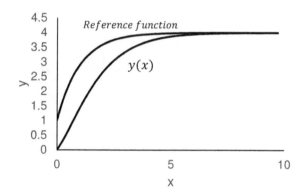

Figure 6. The current $y(x)$ referring an increasing y_r.

3 CONCLUSION

Based on the relative referring idea, a full quantity description of strain softening shape evolution with three parameters is formulated. For the three parameters a, b, and c, respectively control the final value, the peak value, and the x coordinate corresponding to the peak value, the presented full quantity description is qualified to simulate general strain softening shape evolutions.

REFERENCES

Hong Z.S., Zeng L.L., Cui Y.J. et al. (2012) Compression Behaviour of Natural and Reconstituted Clays. *Geotechnique*, 62(4): 291–301.

Liu E.L., Huang R.Q. and He S.M. (2012) Modeling the Deformation Properties of Rock Samples by Binary Medium Model. *Journal of Hydraulic Engineering*, 43(10):1237–1242.

Liu E.L., Shen Z.J. (2006) Modeling Compression of Structured Soils. *Rock and Soil Mechanics*,2006(04):615–620.

Wang W.H., Wang Y.Q. and Zhang H.G. (2021) Construction and Verification of Post-peak. Rock Strain Softening Model. *Chinese Journal of Underground Space and Engineering*, 17(s2):546–551+608.

Yao Y.P. (2015) Advanced UH Models for Soils. *Chinese Journal of Geotechnical Engineering*, 37(02):193–217.

Yao Y.P., Gao Z.W., Zhao J.D., Wan Z. (2012) Modified UH Model: Constitutive Modeling of Overconsolidated Clays Based on a Parabolic Hvorslev Envelope. *Journal of Geotechnical and Geoenvironmental Engineering*, 138(7): 860–868.

Yao Y.P. and Kong Y.X. (2012) Extended UH model: Three-dimensional Unified Hardening Model for Anisotropic Clays. *Journal of Engineering Mechanics*, 138(7):853–866.

Yao Y.P., Niu L., Cui W.J. et al. (2011) UH Model for Unsaturated Soils. *Chinese Journal of Geotechnical Engineering*, 33(6): 833–839.

Yao Y.P., Tian Y., Zhou A.N. and Sun D.A. (2019) Unified Hardening Law for Soils and its Construction. *Scientia Sinica (Technologica)*, 49(01):26–34.

Zhu E.Y. (2015) Constitutively Modeling the Compression Deformation of Structured Clay. *Rock and Soil Mechanics*, 36(07):1915–1922.

Zhu E.Y. (2015) Mathematic Expression Method of Strain Softening and its Application. *Journal of Hydraulic Engineering*, 46(S1):188–193.

Zhu E.Y. and Yao Y.P. (2013) A Structured UH Model Proceedings of Constitutive Modeling of Geomaterials, *Advances and New Applications*. Beijing: Springer, 675–689.

Author index

An, X. 424

Ba, Z. 3
Bai, S. 321
Bai, Y. 91
Bai, Z. 378

Cao, T. 197
Chen, F. 477
Chen, J. 465
Chen, Y. 33, 232
Cheng, X. 409
Cheng, Y. 39, 237
Cheng, Z. 169
Cui, C. 351
Cui, M. 364
Cui, S. 538
Cui, T. 424
Cui, Y. 415

Dang, Y. 237
Dao, J. 261
Deng, C. 297
Di, L. 477
Ding, S. 328, 471
Dong, L. 190
Dong, S. 393
Dou, M. 544
Du, C. 39

Fan, H. 424
Fan, W. 341
Fang, F. 141
Fang, S.-P. 134
Fang, X. 321
Fang, Z. 48
Feng, Q. 544
Feng, S. 9
Feng, Y. 415

Feng, Z. 364
Fu, J. 351
Fu, Q. 211, 378

Gan, T. 123
Gao, D. 328, 471
Gao, J. 409
Gao, S. 76
Gao, T. 403, 424
Gao, Y. 328, 471, 477
Ge, J. 431
Geng, F. 321
Guo, H. 431
Guo, Z. 477, 517

Han, W. 453
Hang, D. 33
Hang, Q. 517
Hou, Y. 218, 364
Hou, Z. 218
Hu, J. 277
Hu, K. 253
Hu, T. 108
Hu, X. 409
Hu, Y. 76, 190
Hu, Z. 146
Hua, H. 424
Huang, F. 134
Huang, F.Q. 176
Huang, J. 108
Huang, M. 378
Huang, M.T. 211
Huang, X. 364

Ji, Q. 403
Jiang, C. 18
Jiang, Y. 517
Jing, L. 269

Kuang, Z. 108

Leng, X. 211
Li, B. 141, 499
Li, C. 563
Li, D. 190, 203
Li, F. 33
Li, G. 357, 403
Li, H. 117, 285
Li, J. 563
Li, L. 431
Li, M. 100, 169, 253, 409
Li, S. 357
Li, T. 39, 551
Li, X. 232
Li, Y. 141, 146, 357, 571
Li, Z. 108, 499
Lin, M. 446
Liu, F. 9, 76, 269
Liu, J. 39, 190, 246
Liu, T. 197, 499
Liu, W. 370
Liu, X. 67, 538
Liu, Y. 117, 351
Lu, J. 487
Lu, Y. 33
Luo, J. 25
Lv, J. 176
Lyu, L. 39

Ma, W. 446
Ma, Y. 477, 571
Ma, Z. 386
Mao, H. 321
Ming, C. 108

Nie, X. 146

Ou, X. 91
Ouyang, W. 477
Ouyang, Z. 237

Pang, H. 477
Pang, J. 108
Pei, Z. 141
Peng, J. 499
Peng, Y. 146, 237

Qi, H. 446
Qi, J. 246
Qi, S. 415
Qi, W. 538
Qiao, M. 146
Qin, T. 321
Qin, Z. 123
Qiu, J.-L. 134
Qiu, Y. 162
Qu, Z. 453

Ren, Z. 409

Shang, X. 48
Shao, B. 321
Shi, X. 156
Song, Y. 3
Sun, X. 409, 538

Tan, H. 211, 378
Tan, W. 203, 253
Tan, Z. 162
Tang, J. 321
Tang, X. 123
Tang, Y. 551
Tang, Z. 176
Tao, C. 48
Tao, C. 48
Tian, Z. 335

Wang, B. 556
Wang, C. 117
Wang, D. 277
Wang, J. 277, 465, 571

Wang, K. 351, 477
Wang, L. 39
Wang, M. 386
Wang, R. 415
Wang, R. 551
Wang, S. 134, 141, 335
Wang, X. 357
Wang, Z. 100
Wen, Y. 525
Wu, B. 67, 91, 146, 237, 269, 386
Wu, J. 551
Wu, R. 108
Wu, W. 190

Xia, B. 477
Xiao, S. 108
Xie, Y. 277
Xiong, F. 465
Xiong, Z. 321
Xu, C. 232
Xu, H. 48
Xu, J. 409
Xu, T. 9
Xu, X. 563
Xu, Y. 335
Xu, Z. 341

Yan, D. 544
Yan, Y. 25
Yang, B. 538
Yang, F. 439
Yang, J. 364, 544
Yang, L. 357
Yang, M. 544
Yang, Q. 261
Yang, X. 453
Yang, Y. 9, 67, 341, 386, 453
Yao, G. 409
Ye, B. 67
Yin, C. 218
You, H. 123
Yu, L. 563

Yu, X. 393
Yu, Y. 225, 261

Zhang, B. 190, 439
Zhang, C. 439, 446, 499
Zhang, D. 108
Zhang, H. 341
Zhang, M. 117
Zhang, Q. 364
Zhang, R. 328, 471
Zhang, S. 176
Zhang, W. 108
Zhang, X. 39, 76, 225
Zhang, Y. 364, 446, 571
Zhang, Z. 91, 232, 551
Zhao, D. 409
Zhao, G. 508, 532
Zhao, J. 297
Zhao, W. 237, 364
Zhao, Y. 91, 386
Zhao, Z. 341, 364
Zhen, C. 439
Zheng, C. 409
Zheng, H. 409
Zheng, S. 351
Zheng, X. 246
Zheng, Y. 351
Zhong, G. 409
Zhong, W. 162
Zhong, X. 439
Zhou, B. 424, 517
Zhou, L. 393
Zhou, T. 203, 253
Zhu, D. 393
Zhu, E. 141, 232, 571
Zhu, L. 477
Zhu, P. 415
Zhu, X. 351, 403
Zhu, Y. 328, 471
Zhuang, H. 261
Zou, C. 67
Zou, Q. 551
Zou, S. 544
Zou, X. 190